D1158246

PREPARATIVE METHODS OF POLYMER CHEMISTRY

Preparative Methods of Polymer Chemistry

Second Edition

WAYNE R. SORENSON
Conoco Plastics
Division of Continental Oil Company
Wilton, Connecticut

TOD W. CAMPBELL
Department of Chemistry
University of Arizona
Tucson, Arizona

INTERSCIENCE PUBLISHERS
a division of John Wiley & Sons, New York · London · Sydney · Toronto

On May 9, 1968, when the writing of this second edition had been recently finished, my former co-worker, present co-author, and longtime good friend, Tod Campbell, met with an untimely death. His contributions to polymer research, many of them represented in this book, will be recognized by most readers. It is sad to think of the many research advances now lost that would have come from his recently begun career at the University of Arizona. The saddest thing of all is the personal loss that all who knew him will inevitably feel. The completion of this book was necessarily among the last of his activities. I personally hope that whatever good the book may have about it, and whatever useful service it may perform for polymer chemists, will serve in part as the kind of memorial that seems proper for Tod Campbell.

WAYNE R. SORENSON

May, 1968

Preface to the Second Edition

Since the first edition of this book appeared in 1961, polymer chemists have made major advances in many areas of new polymer chemistry, with a resultant increase in polymer types, polymer forming reactions, and catalytic techniques to polymerize species hitherto considered not polymerizable. This remarkable growth is indicated by the considerable growth in size of this second edition. Major advances have been made, particularly in the vinyl field, which have necessitated an almost complete revision of Chapter 4. Most of the other chapters have been markedly changed by addition of new material and deletion of that which is less appropriate. Noteworthy additions to Chapter 3 are an expanded section on Block Condensation Elastomers, and a section on High Temperature Polymers.

We have retained our original philosophy of keeping background discussion to a minimum. However, we have also attempted to provide a framework of commentary to highlight the significance of certain individual syntheses and place each section in the proper perspective. We have tried as before to give ample reference to the specific texts and articles that can supply detailed discussion on most polymer categories.

We again wish to thank our respective Managements for permission to write this second edition, and to our many friends throughout the world who provided advice, criticism, and encouragement. Among the latter, we wish especially to thank W. K. Wilkinson, E. J. Frazza, and J. Fath. A special group of our colleagues have gone so far as to provide us with entire preparations or supplementary detail which we have used. Our indebtedness to these individuals will be acknowledged at the appropriate place in the text.

Finally, for typing we wish to thank Virginia Mize, Dolores Cline, Suzeahn Massey, Rose Quincy, and Mary Pack.

WAYNE R. SORENSON
TOD W. CAMPBELL

January, 1968.

Preface to the First Edition

The purpose of this book is to provide a reference work containing detailed procedures for the synthesis and handling of a wide variety of polymer types. Although such information is readily available for most low-molecular-weight organic compounds, in the case of polymers it is scattered over a large number of more or less (usually less) accessible journals and patents. We have therefore assembled here the procedures involved in the laboratory preparation of most of the known classes of polymers. In cases where the original literature did not provide sufficient detail, supplementary information is given based on our own experience and that of our colleagues. In many instances this has involved a careful checking of the preparation and the procedures may therefore be used with confidence in their operability.

Since the preparation of useful high-molecular-weight polymers requires that considerable attention be paid to the purification of monomers, solvents, and other reaction intermediates, as well as the choice of suitable equipment and reaction conditions, such information is provided in the different procedures wherever necessary.

As indicated in Chapter 1 (Introduction) it is also our hope that the book might be of use as a supplementary text for a laboratory course in polymer chemistry or an advanced organic synthesis course.

As is always the case, we are indebted to our colleagues, without whose unselfish contribution of time and knowledge this book would not have been possible. We would like to offer special thanks to Professor C. S. Marvel of the University of Illinois and Professor H. Mark of Brooklyn Polytechnic Institute, for their unfailing enthusiasm and encouragement. We are also indebted to Warren Watanabe of Rohm and Haas, J. P. Schroeder, John Wynstra and R. K. Walton of the Union Carbide Plastics Company, and C. G. Overberger of Brooklyn Polytechnic Institute, for most helpful reviews of various portions of the book.

Of our colleagues at the du Pont Company, we would like to thank Fred Billmeyer, Roger A. Hines, Alfred C. Webber, and Neil Keiser, all of the Polychemicals Department, L. P. Hubbuch of the Fabrics and Finishes Department, and A. C. Stevenson and C. M. Barringer of the Elastomers Department for most helpful comments and suggestions.

We would like to thank the management of our own Textile Fibers Department for permission to write this book. To the following of our colleagues in the Textile Fibers Department, our gratitude for encouragement, technical assistance, and many trenchant comments: Jim Van Oot, Sid Maerov, Norton Higgins, Emerson Wittbecker, Fred Sweeny, John Schaefgen, Vic Shashoua, Bill Statton, Frank Moody, Tom Mackey, Helen Anderson, Fran Cramer, Bob Taylor, Al Goodman, Herman Marder, Wayne Hill, Paul Morgan, Ray Tietz, Lup Jung, Ralph Beaman, and Hal Bonner.

Thanks are due to Dan Sauers, Walt Brown, and Norm Van Hove for help in preparing the illustrations.

Finally, our special thanks to Tena Evlom, Mary Joan Reese, Hilda Smith, and Jean Iannarone, who waded through reams of illegible scribblings, stacks of incoherent records, and numerous revisions to produce the final manuscript.

Wayne R. Sorenson
Tod W. Campbell

Contents

CHAPTER 1

Introduction

The organic chemist today is fortunate in the abundance of literature available on the preparative methods for organic compounds. In any moderately well equipped library, it will not take long to locate a detailed laboratory procedure for preparing at least a prototype of a compound in question, if not the exact compound itself.

In polymer chemistry, on the other hand, the worker has been limited to the scattered original research and patent literature to find procedures for the synthesis of polymers. Detail is frequently lacking; laboratory directions are often dismissed in a sentence or two and are useful only to the skilled, experienced worker. The chemist in search of a good method for making a specific polymer, or detailed examples of a variety of polymer-forming reactions, has not had a single convenient reference source, let alone the many that the organic chemist can refer to for synthetic methods.

In the subsequent chapters of this work, the primary intention is to provide such a reference work, containing detailed procedures for the synthesis of a wide variety of polymer types. Most of the known classes of polymers are represented, as are most of the known organic polymer-forming reactions. These procedures were selected from the literature, and have been, in most instances, supplemented with the detail necessary to make them useful as relatively small-scale laboratory preparations.

Descriptions of equipment, purification and/or synthesis of intermediates, manipulative techniques, and typical physical properties of the products have been presented in the majority of the preparations. The organization of the syntheses that follow is necessarily arbitrary. We will not attempt to justify the order of presentation over the many other possible schemes. In most cases, the naming of polymers follows the standard organic practice of using either IUPAC or trivial nomenclature, depending on which provides the more handleable, descriptive name, from which the structure can be deduced.

The basis for selection of preparations has been the first-hand experience of the authors and of our associates, who have been consulted on each phase of the book. (We have endeavored to properly acknow-ledge this in the Preface and throughout the book.) This has been tantamount to a "checking" of a majority of the preparations, with a consequent high degree of operability attached to each experiment.

The term "polymer" means many things to many people. In its broadest sense, it includes the tars and resins left in still pots, and the brown, viscous results of unsuccessful syntheses. Again, the term may be applied to low molecular weight products containing more than two of the same repeat unit.

In this book, the term "polymer" is reserved exclusively for a sub-stance of sufficiently high molecular weight such that the properties have become reproducibly fixed. We have deviated from this high standard in only a very few instances, where a particularly interesting or novel principle is involved. It will be found that the preparation of polymers of high molecular weight requires much skill in purification of inter-mediates, and much attention to technique.

The usefulness of this work is intended to be two-fold. First, it should serve as a reference book for chemists who are involved in some phase of polymer synthesis and handling. Second, it should be a useful adjunct to a laboratory course on the preparation and handling of polymers, or an advanced organic synthesis course. A number of representative polymer-forming reactions are within the necessary time and equipment limitations of the usual organic laboratory course and could be included as examples of typical organic reactions applied to the synthesis of polymers. Other polymer-forming reactions offer unique opportunities for the demonstration of organic reactions having no parallel in the chemistry of simple molecules. The polymerization of monoisocyanates and of vinyl monomers are examples of such reactions.

Table 1.1 is a list of polymer preparations suggested as being par-ticularly suitable for inclusion in an advanced laboratory course. These are chosen as representative of significant polymers, polymer-forming reactions, and polymerization systems.

Table 1.1

Polymer Preparations

Polymer	Preparation number
6–6 Nylon	2
Partially N-isobutylated 6–6 nylon	8
Polynonamethylenepyromellitimide	18
6–10 Nylon	20
Polyethyleneterephthalamide	22
Poly(2,5-dimethylpiperazine terephthalamide)	23
Poly(hexamethylene m-benzenedisulfonamide)	30
Poly(decamethyleneurea)	45
A polythiosemicarbazide	55
Poly(ethylene N,N'-piperazinedicarboxylate)	59
Poly(tetramethylene hexamethylenedicarbamate)	62
Poly[ethylene methylene bis(4-phenylcarbamate)]	64
Poly(ethylene terephthalate)	68
Poly(1,4-phenylene adipate)	76
Poly[2,2-propanebis(4-phenylcarbonate)]	77
Poly(tetramethylene isophthalate)	80
A polysulfonate	84
Poly(m-phenylcarboxylate)	88
A polyurethane foam	99
A polyurethane elastomer	100
An ordered aromatic copolyamide	108
An all aromatic polypyromellitimide	110
Poly(1,4-xylylenyl)-2-methylpiperazine	121
A polysulfone	122
Poly(ethylene tetrasulfide)	126
Polystyrene	143,145
ABS polymer	147
Polystyrene foam	150
Polyacrylonitrile	163
Poly(vinyl acetate)	168
Poly(vinyl alcohol)	170, 171
Poly(methyl methacrylate)	190
Polyisobutylene	212
Polystyrene (anionic catalyst)	222
Polyacrylonitrile (anionic catalyst)	226
Polypropylene	236
cis-1,4-Polybutadiene	253
trans-1,4-Polybutadiene	255
Syndiotactic 1,2-polybutadiene	256

(continued)

Table 1.1 (*continued*)

Polymer	Preparation number
GR-S rubber	257
Polyisoprene	263,266
6-Nylon	281
4-Nylon	286
Poly-α-L-glutamic acid	302
Polyethylene oxide	318
Poly[3,3-bis(chloromethyl)trimethylene ether]	330
Poly(tetramethylene ether)	337
Polydimethylsiloxane	344
Phosphonitrilic chloride polymer	351
Polyformaldehyde	361,363
Poly-p-xylylene	391
A crosslinkable polyester resin	413
Phenol–formaldehyde resin	419

CHAPTER 2

Preparation, Fabrication, and Characterization of Polymers

Although the reactions used in the preparation of polymers are usually identical to those used in synthesis of small molecules, the high molecular weight of the polymeric products and the physical result of chain size and interactions give polymers the properties that set them apart. Consequently, they often require special methods of handling and characterization which are quite different from those used with small molecules.

I. Techniques for Preparing and Handling Polymers

In addition to the usual experimental methods, the following represent techniques of particularly wide application to the laboratory synthesis of polymers.

1. Use of Constant Temperature Baths

It is sometimes necessary to heat polymerization reactions for long periods of time at constant temperature. One of the most convenient ways to do this is by means of a vapor bath (Fig. 2.1). The large (2 × 15 in.) test tube is filled about one-fourth full, and is then heated to boiling. The vessel to be heated is suspended in the vapors and soon reaches a constant temperature.

Table 2.1 is a partial list of materials which may be used as vapor baths for temperature control. Although most of these have been used and found to be effective, stabilities for long use vary widely. Since some tend to superheat or change with use, it is recommended that the actual vapor temperature be checked routinely.

Conventional constant temperature baths, electrically heated and controlled, can be used for lower temperatures than those where vapor baths are particularly suited. Bottle tumblers and shakers are valuable for polymerization of rather large numbers of samples at the same temperature, as is often necessary in any extensive research program.

5

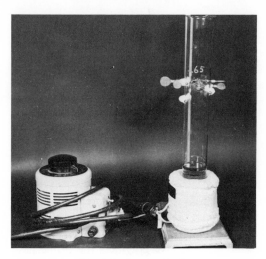

Fig. 2.1. A vapor bath.

Tumblers in which a dozen or more large or small soda bottles can be accommodated are available commercially. (Research Appliance Co., Allison Park, Pa., 15101.)

2. Purification of Reagents

Although purification of reagents is not peculiar to polymer chemistry alone, it is mentioned here since it is essential for the success of practically any polymerization. Solids should be recrystallized to a constant, and sharp, melting point, and liquids should be fractionated to give a product with a single gas chromatographic peak if possible. The ultimate proof of purity is, however, successful polymerization. Specialized techniques will be mentioned in the appropriate places.

It will be noted in the preparative examples that the use of an inert gas is almost routinely specified to initially purge a reactor vessel or to continuously cover or sweep a polymerization system. The reason is that oxygen may directly interfere in a polymerization reaction or cause degradation of polymer or reactant. It is necessary, therefore, that the inert gas used be low enough in oxygen content to actually prevent these problems. High purity argon has generally one of the lowest oxygen contents of any commercially available gas and is denser than air; it is an excellent choice for blanketing reactions and purging oxygen from a system. It is also quite expensive and is therefore not often selected for extensive routine use. "Lamp grade" nitrogen can be pur-

Table 2.1
Liquids for Vapor Baths

Compound	Boiling point, °C.	Compound	Boiling point, °C.
Water	100	Diethylene glycol	245
Toluene	111	Diphenyl	255
n-Butanol	117	Diphenyl ether	259
Perchloroethylene	121	Diphenylmethane	265
Methyl Cellosolve[a]	125	o-Chlorodiphenyl	268
Chlorobenzene	133	Diphenylmethane-	
Ethyl Cellosolve	135	o-hydroxydiphenyl (60/40)	270
m-Xylene	139	Methyl naphthyl ether	275
Anisole	152	Biphenyl/diphenylene	
Cyclohexanone	156	oxide (25/75)	275
Cyclohexanol	160	Acenaphthene	277
Phenetole	166	Triethylene glycol	282
Butyl Cellosolve	171	Dimethyl phthalate	283
p-Cymene	176	Diphenylethane	284
o-Dichlorobenzene	179	o-Hydroxydiphenyl	285
Phenol	181	Diphenylene oxide	288
Decahydronaphthalene	190	Fluorene	295
Ethylene glycol	197	Benzophenone	305
m-Cresol	202	p-Hydroxydiphenyl	308
Tetrahydronaphthalene	206	Hexachlorobenzene	310
Naphthalene	218	Arochlor 1242[b]	325
Methyl salicylate	222	o-Terphenyl	330
Butyl Carbitol[a]	231	Arochlor 1248	340
n-Decyl alcohol	231	Anthracene	340
Methylnaphthalene	242	Arochlor 1254	365
		Anthraquinone	380

[a] Trademarks for Union Carbide's ether solvents.
[b] Trademark for Monsanto's chlorinated aromatic hydrocarbon.

chased which is directly satisfactory for many uses where the residual oxygen (ca. $10^{-4}\%$) may have only a minor effect on the rate or some other aspect of polymerization. Where nitrogen is used to sweep a system for a long period at high temperature, even small amounts of oxygen may lead to degradation. To remove a large part of the oxygen remaining in commercial nitrogen, it is often satisfactory to pass it through a solution of an aluminum alkyl in a high boiling solvent, or to pass the nitrogen over copper turnings heated to 900° C. (1). In the former method, a relatively high molecular weight aluminum alkyl should be used because these are safer to handle; the best choice is the tri-alkylaluminum from the growth reaction of triethylaluminum and ethylene, which has an average alkyl length of 12 carbons in a Poisson distribution from 2 to over 18 (2).

Solid catalysts have also been described that remove oxygen from commercial nitrogen at room temperature (3). A basic aqueous solution of sodium hydrosulfite with sodium anthraquinone-β-sulfonate has also been described (4), but this requires drying the gas afterwards for many purposes. In most of the preparative examples of this book, nitrogen is often used to purge air from a system by simple displacement. While this is effective for many purposes, evacuation and refilling with nitrogen is undoubtedly better and should be considered whenever possible.

Instead of blanketing a reaction flask continuously with a flow of nitrogen, it is practical in some instances to blanket initially the flask and contents with nitrogen, then to attach a nitrogen-filled balloon to the sole gas outlet (e.g., to the top of a condenser) at the same time as the nitrogen flow to the flask is closed off. Thus, a slight positive pressure of nitrogen is maintained, and the balloon acts as a safety valve in the event of excessive pressure buildup from the polymerization itself. The technique (5) is applicable to polymerization of liquid monomers and is a useful way to reduce the consumption of inert gas.

When nitrogen or other cylinder gases are not available, it is possible to displace air by the addition of pieces of solid carbon dioxide (5a). This can work quite well in aqueous systems (e.g., free radical polymerization of unsaturated monomers), but would be unsuited in many ionic or coordinate polymerizations.

3. Sealed Tube Reactions

Sealed tubes are used quite frequently in the synthesis of polymers, probably more so than in conventional organic syntheses. They are used both for the preparation of condensation polymers by melt polymerization and for the polymerization at moderate temperatures of vinyl monomers. A typical tube is shown in Fig. 2.2, together with the long-stemmed funnel used to add either liquids or finely divided solids without contaminating the upper part of the tube where the final seal is to be made. These tubes are made of hard glass, either from standard wall, or extra heavy, glass tubing. Since these tubes must be completely strain-free to withstand high internal pressures, it is recommended that they be purchased commercially or fabricated by a competent glass blower.

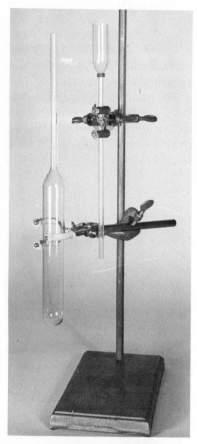

Fig. 2.2. Tube used for sealed tube reactions.

Fig. 2.3. Result of explosion of a sealed tube protected by a steel sleeve.

When sealed, the polymer tube represents a potential bomb which can do much damage if treated improperly. Figure 2.3 shows the appearance of a steel sleeve used to enclose the lower part of a polymer tube, after "something went wrong." Admittedly, Fig. 2.3 represents an extreme not often met. For most purposes, enclosing the tube in a sleeve of glass cloth (Fig. 2.4) will offer sufficient protection if the tube is enclosed completely and the ends of the sleeve are tied shut. Tubes shielded in this manner and shock-loaded at 2000 p.s.i. from a nitrogen cylinder have shattered, but were completely contained. Steel sleeves also may be used for protection.

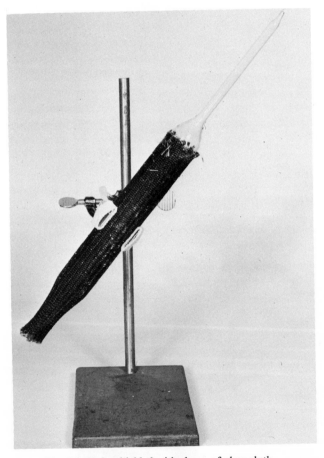

Fig. 2.4. Tube shielded with sleeve of glass cloth.

A. Vinyl Polymerization in Sealed Tubes and Bottles

Vinyl polymerizations may be adversely affected by oxygen, and many vinyl monomers are low boiling. To prevent access of oxygen and loss of monomer, it is convenient to seal the polymerization mixture in a glass polymer tube under nitrogen. The tube is then immersed in a constant temperature bath and mechanically shaken or tumbled during the course of the polymerization. For monomers which boil close to room temperature, commercially available pressure bottles, or carbonated beverage bottles, may be used in place of the sealed tube. Sealed tubes should not be used for large-scale preparations. Tubes should not exceed 250–300 ml. capacity and should not be filled more than one-half full.

When glass pressure tubes are sealed with an oxygen torch, care must be taken to build up a proper seal which maintains the thickness of the wall of the tube. All seals should be annealed, if possible. Furthermore, quantities of monomer larger than those recommended in the experiments should not be used since some of the polymerizations are exothermic. In the event of an exothermic polymerization, quite excessive pressures may be built up inside these tubes. For this reason, all pressure reactions should be routinely carried out behind adequate safety shielding, and tubes should be opened or vented cautiously behind a good barricade and with precooling.

Alternatively, the commercially available pressure bottles (Fig. 2.5a) or ordinary carbonated beverage bottles (Fig. 2.5b) with an appropriate closure may be used where the pressures dealt with are not excessive. For example, butadiene at temperatures up to 60°C. can be safely contained, but vinyl chloride (b.p. $-13°C.$) is marginal in safety at 40°C. It has been found (2) that a beverage bottle closed with a rubber septum and standard metal cap will withstand up to 200 p.s.i. at slow loading, at which point the cap will usually blow off. In few instances will the bottle itself shatter before the cap fails, but bottles should be handled in every case as if this were likely to happen; and, all the foregoing comments on safety, plus the usual commonsense warnings against the hazards incurred by haste in laboratory operations should be applied to work with sealed bottles. Sealed bottles are extremely convenient reaction vessels for many purposes, and one must guard against a cavalier attitude to their potential dangers. It should be recognized that any sealed glass vessel of this type constitutes a potential bomb and must be handled with extreme caution.

As is discussed in Chapter 4, it is sometimes necessary in vinyl copolymerization to add the more reactive monomer steadily or in

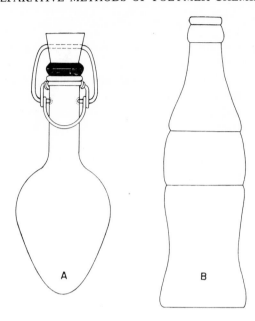

Fig. 2.5. Pressure vessels for polymerization.

distinct increments as polymerization proceeds in order to achieve a more uniform distribution of both monomers in each macromolecule. When the less reactive monomer is a gas and the more reactive a liquid, this can be done on a small scale with a beverage bottle as reaction vessel by the use of a pressure buret (5b) (Fig. 2.6). Sufficient nitrogen pressure is applied to the top of the buret to force monomer into the bottle. Liquid flow is regulated by a stainless steel valve (e.g., Whitey 2RS4). The buret is placed inside a sleeve of heavy-walled clear plastic tubing as an added safeguard, and is supported above the top and below the bottom fittings by mounting brackets that restrain the fittings when pressure is applied. Buret and bottle should be fully shielded in use.

B. Condensation Polymerization in a Sealed Tube

Most high-temperature polycondensation reactions are carried out in sealed tubes in the absence of air to minimize oxidative color formation and loss of materials. Polyamides, polyesters, and a few polyurethanes, as well as some miscellaneous polymers, may be made in this way.

By way of illustration, a polyamide would be prepared as follows (6). A quantity of "nylon salt" (Chapter 3, Preparation 1) is added to the tube through a funnel (Fig. 2.7) such that the tube is not more than

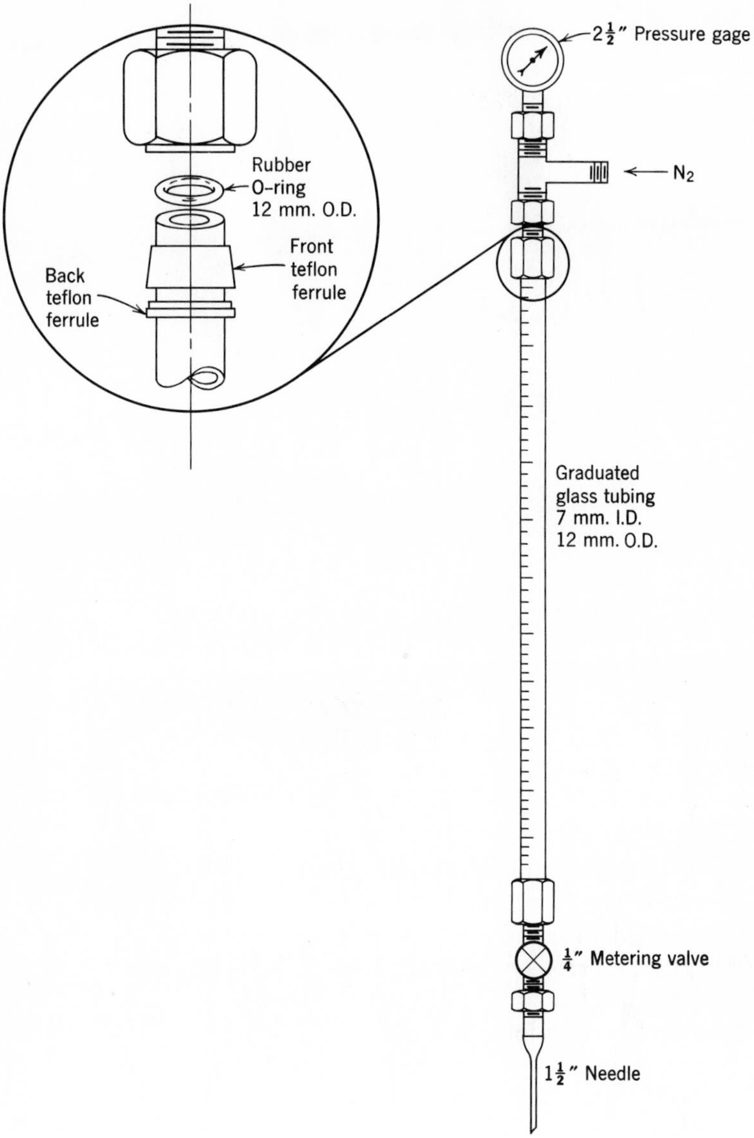

Fig. 2.6. High pressure buret.

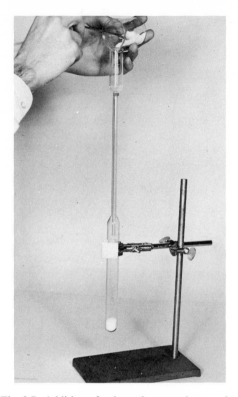

Fig. 2.7. Addition of nylon salt to a polymer tube.

one-third filled. The tube is constricted with an oxygen torch, alternately evacuated with an oil pump, flushed with nitrogen several times, and finally sealed under vacuum. The tube is heated, either in a vapor bath (Fig. 2.1) (dangerous with sealed tubes) or, better, in a salt bath, a heavy metal container holding a mixture of fused inorganic salts at a pre-determined temperature. Several eutectic salt mixtures may be obtained commercially, and they are convenient and safe to use. Such a mixture is easily prepared from a combination of sodium and potassium nitrites and nitrates, which are equimolar in the ions involved. For reasons of safety, the glass tube, either heated in a vapor bath or a salt bath, should be contained in a sleeve of glass cloth (see Section III and Fig. 2.4) or in a steel tube, with the open end directed away from the operator. After the heating cycle, the tube containing water and a non-volatile prepolymer is cooled, opened under nitrogen, and equipped with a capillary and a side arm for distillation (Fig. 2.8) which is either

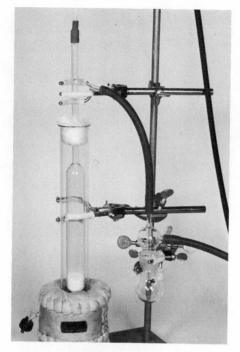

Fig. 2.8. Distillation from a polymer tube.

sealed or attached by heavy-walled pressure tubing. The nitrogen inlet should extend to the bottom of the polymer tube, below the surface of the prepolymer; if necessary, the tube may be heated under nitrogen to liquefy the polymer so the tip of the inlet can be introduced into the liquid. The tube is now evacuated, and nitrogen bubbled in for a prescribed time at a given temperature. The progress of polymerization often can be judged quite accurately by the rate of rise of the nitrogen bubbles in the liquid. Toward the end, the rate will be exceedingly slow. When the polymerization is considered to be complete, the mixture is cooled and treated as described in specific experiments in later chapters.

C. Use of Pipe Autoclave

An alternative to the above procedure, a pipe autoclave (Fig. 2.9) may be used in place of the glass tube (7). The ingredients (e.g., the nylon salt) are placed in a suitable liner, which may be a glass test tube or an aluminum cylinder with a closed end. The latter can be made from heavy foil and Sauereisen cement. The liner and contents are placed in the

Fig. 2.9. Pipe autoclave.

autoclave and the prescribed polymerization cycle is carried out as in Section I-3B. A nitrogen bubbler cannot be used.

D. Safety

The hazards involved in using sealed tubes are described above. It is essential to realize the potential hazards and take all possible precautions. For this reason, the operator should routinely manipulate the sealed tube behind a safety shield and should wear heavy leather gauntlets covering the hands and forearms. As with all laboratory work, safety glasses should be worn.

4. USE OF HIGH SPEED HOME MIXERS IN LABORATORY PREPARATION OF POLYMERS

The technique of interfacial polymerization (Chapter 3) has made possible the synthesis of a variety of polymers which could not be made in other ways. Basically, this technique involves the reaction of a diacid chloride dissolved in an inert solvent immiscible with water with, for example, a diamine in water containing an acid acceptor. Since the reaction occurs at the interface between the two solvents it is desirable to make the interface as large as possible to speed the polymerization and minimize side reactions.

One of the most convenient ways of doing this on a laboratory scale is to use a home blender, such as the Waring Blender, or the Osterizer.

The aqueous diamine solution is placed in the jar of the blender, and the motor turned on. The diacid chloride solution is run rapidly into the jar in a thin stream and is dispersed throughout the aqueous solution. Polymerizations run in this way are usually complete in a matter of seconds. Numerous examples will be found in Chapter 3. Note that household blenders must be modified to permit the use of flammable solvents, since otherwise a fire hazard exists.

5. Use of Resin Kettles

Resin kettles (Fig. 2.10) are essentially equivalent to three-necked flasks, and may be used to advantage in place of them, since, unlike the three-necked flask, the top can be separated from the bottom. When one is dealing with hard, tough polymers, or very viscous solutions or gel, use of a resin kettle may obviate the necessity for breaking the reaction vessel to remove the product. Resin kettles are widely available commercially in a variety of sizes.

A simple screw-cap jar can be converted into a resin kettle-like reactor (8) as shown in Fig. 2.11. No provision is made for condenser attachment, so the vessel is usually limited to room temperature and lower, such as would be encountered in cationic systems and low temperature solution polycondensations. The polymerization mixture can be stored for later work-up by simply removing the jar from the top-works and stirrer and capping it. The jar is inexpensive enough so that it can be thrown away when contaminated.

Many times it will be necessary to scale up a polymerization beyond the resin kettle level, either to obtain larger uniform quantities of polymer for testing or to study polymerization variables, at which point recourse to stirred reactors or autoclaves of several gallons capacity is necessary. For polymerizations under any level of pressure and of any size, stirred or rocking autoclaves are not only very functional but are safer than beverage bottles. The use of such equipment is particularly

Fig. 2.10. Resin kettle.

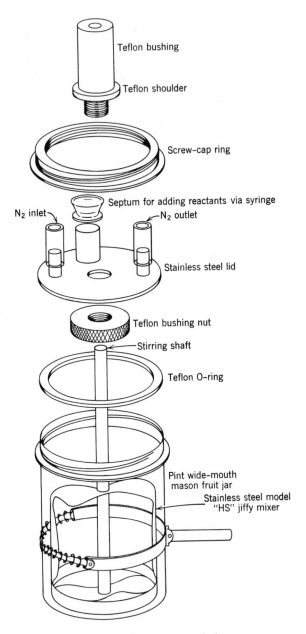

Teflon bushing

Teflon shoulder

Screw-cap ring

Septum for adding reactants via syringe

N₂ inlet

N₂ outlet

Stainless steel lid

Teflon bushing nut

Stirring shaft

Teflon O-ring

Pint wide-mouth mason fruit jar

Stainless steel model "HS" jiffy mixer

Fig. 2.11. A screw-cap resin jar.

valuable in polymerization via coordination (or, as they are sometimes called, Ziegler-Natta) catalysts, especially as it applies to ethylene and propylene. Even a lab-scale continuous reactor has been described (9). It should be noted, however, that resin kettles and ordinary three-necked flasks can be used for gaseous monomers at atmospheric pressure by passing the monomer through a slurry or solution of catalyst, provided the latter is reasonably active (10).

6. USE OF HYPODERMIC SYRINGES

In many vinyl polymerizations, particularly those proceeding by ionic mechanisms, it is necessary to add, for example, a catalyst to a very cold, anhydrous monomer under completely anhydrous and anaerobic conditions. This can be done conveniently by equipping the polymerization vessel with a serum-type stopper free of sulfur, etc., which would act as an inhibitor. The catalyst, or other ingredient, then is injected quantitatively through this closure from a graduated hypodermic syringe (Fig. 2.12).

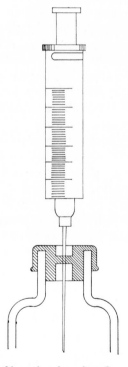

Fig. 2.12. Use of hypodermic syringe for catalyst transfer.

Besides the transfer of catalyst solutions, syringes can be used for suspensions of solids under the right circumstances (11). For example, commercial titanium trichloride (aluminum reduced) can be successfully dispensed from a suspension of known quantity in cyclohexane using an 18 gauge or larger needle, utilizing not more than two-thirds the capacity of the syringe. The "concentration" acquired in a typical syringe charge should be determined by evaporating the solvent under vacuum and weighing the residue. The method is generally satisfactory for other than quantitative work.

7. ISOLATION OF POLYMERS

Polymerizations may yield the desired polymer as a solution, a gel-like mass consisting of polymer swollen by solvent, an emulsion, a hard, solid lump, or an easily filtered, granular suspension. The first four conditions require special consideration.

A. Polymer Solution

A polymer solution may be fabricated directly. If it is desired to isolate the polymer, however, the solution should be mixed with a liquid which is a nonsolvent for the polymer but is miscible with the polymer solvent. The precipitation should be done with vigorous agitation to prevent formation of large lumps of polymer which could enclose unprecipitated solution. Washing the polymer to remove last traces of solvent, byproducts, and monomer can be done in a high-speed mixer, as in Section I-4. Solvent also may be removed by soaking in nonsolvent, followed by heating in a vacuum oven.

An elegant method for precipitation of polymer solutions into water has been devised (12) so that the polymer contacts a large volume of water, effectively removing water-soluble impurities, such as emulsifiers, and the solvent itself, yielding the polymer as easily handled, uniform, small particles.

The apparatus is shown in Fig. 2.13. Water is supplied to the precipitator at A. Air under pressure is introduced at B; the polymer solution is drawn up the capillary at C and atomized into a torrent of water.

B. Emulsions

Emulsions often are obtained from vinyl polymerizations. They are broken by addition of an ionic material, such as alum, sodium chloride, or hydrochloric acid, or sometimes simply by heating. The polymer usually precipitates as a curd, like cottage cheese, which is filtered,

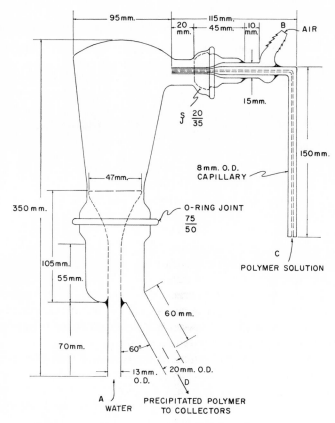

Fig. 2.13. Apparatus for precipitating polymer solutions.

washed thoroughly with water, and dried. Other nonfilterable suspensions can be separated by centrifugation.

C. Gel-Like Mass

Occasionally, an interfacial polymerization may yield an emulsion of
polymer solution (or highly swollen gel) in water. This is best broken by
stream distillation, or by addition of an organic nonsolvent for the
polymer.

Gel-like masses of precipitated polymer are best soaked or stirred
vigorously in a nonsolvent for the polymer to remove the gelling agent
and give a filterable solid. Alternatively, the solvent may be evaporated
or removed by steam to leave a solid lump (Section I-7D).

D. Solid Lump

Polymer obtained in a solid lump often may be fabricated from this form. However, for convenience in handling and extracting possible impurities, the polymer may first be cut up into smaller lumps, using a heavy knife and hammer or a small hatchet. These small pieces are then fed into a Wiley mill and cut to any desired fineness. This latter operation may cause trouble if the heat generated in the mill is sufficient to fuse the polymer. This fairly common problem can be solved by grinding Dry Ice together with the polymer.

8. DISSOLVING OF POLYMERS

Many polymers are soluble in organic media; it is customary to determine routinely the solubility spectrum of new polymers as they are obtained (Section III). However, there are two features of polymer solutions which make them different from ordinary solutions of organic compounds. The polymers may dissolve slowly, and the solutions are extremely viscous.

It is usually important in dissolving polymers to have the material as finely divided as possible and to have each particle thoroughly wetted by the solvent. Agitation of some kind is essential, since solvent penetration into the particles is kinetically very slow for high molecular weight polymers, and a viscous coating is usually formed over each particle which retards further solvent diffusion into the polymer. If finely divided polymer is dispersed into cold solvent to bring about wetting, solution is sometimes facilitated as the mixture is allowed to warm up.

A surprising increase in the rate of polymer dissolution can be brought about by the use of a shear-disk stirrer (Fig. 2.14), which consists simply of a steel shaft terminated by a steel disk, and rotated at high speed. The shear-disk stirrer may be modified with a second disk, mounted far enough up the shaft to be well above the level of the solution to be stirred. This will effectively prevent very viscous solutions from climbing the stirrer shaft. Once the solution is obtained, it cannot be freed of impurities by ordinary filtration unless it is very dilute. A pressure filter (Fig. 2.15) must be used for viscous solution. This consists of, from left to right in the figure, a cap to be attached to a compressed air source, screwed onto the body of the filter, with a gasket of an inert material in between. On the bottom of the tube is another cap with an exit tube, preceded by a perforated metal disk (slotted underneath), a piece of filter cloth, and another inert gasket. This equipment may be operated at 20–50 p.s.i. and will clean up very viscous solutions.

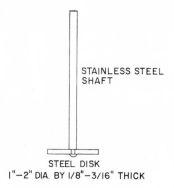

STAINLESS STEEL
SHAFT

STEEL DISK
1"–2" DIA. BY 1/8"–3/16" THICK

Fig. 2.14. Shear-disk stirrer.

Soluble polymers obtained in any form may be purified by preparing a solution which is then filtered, or centrifuged, and precipitated in a nonsolvent with vigorous stirring to give a granular product.

II. Fabrication of Polymers

A complete treatment of the fabrication of polymers would require a book at least the size of this one. It is the intent of this chapter to describe only the simplest and most elementary polymer fabricating methods.

Polymer fabrication may be classified roughly into two categories: melt methods and solution methods.

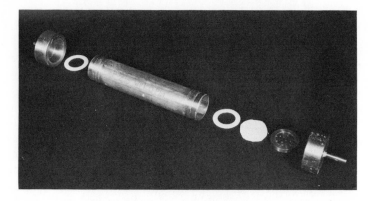

Fig. 2.15. Pressure filter.

1. Melt Methods

In this method, the polymer is heated until molten, formed into a desired shape, then cooled. This technique is applicable only to polymers that are stable at the temperatures involved.

A. Melt-Pressing of Films

For the preparation of small pieces of polymer film in the laboratory, a press (such as shown in Fig. 2.16) may be used.

The platens of the press are heated electrically to a temperature close to the polymer melt temperature, previously determined, according to Section III. The polymer is placed in a small pile in the center of a 4 in. × 4 in. sheet of aluminum foil (copper if the temperature is to be over 250°C.) (Fig. 2.17). It is covered with another piece of foil, and the sandwich is placed between the platens of the press. If desired, the thickness of the film may be predetermined by the use of metal shims or templates, which may be sandwiched between the pieces of foil.

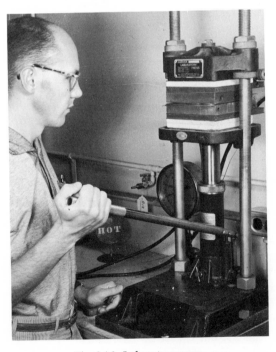

Fig. 2.16. Laboratory press.

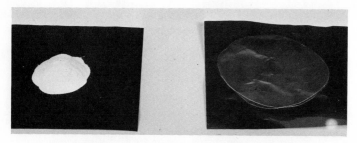

Fig. 2.17. Preparation of a film.

The platens are brought together by the hydraulic jack, and a pressure of 2000–5000 p.s.i. is applied for about 30 sec. The pressure is released, the foil removed and cooled in water, or on a cold metal plate. The two pieces of foil are separated, and the film sample (Fig. 2.17) removed.

If the film is not clear and completely coalesced, the temperature may not be high enough. If the film is too thin and shows evidence of excessive flow, or degradation, the press is too hot. Occasionally, a film will be difficult to remove from the foil. If the polymer is not affected by alkali or acid, the foil may be dissolved away. If the film is pressed between sheets of tin foil, the latter can be dissolved in mercury by amalgamation to free an acid- or base-sensitive film. Separation also is aided by prior spraying of the foil with a mold lubricant, or by placing the sandwich under cold water.

Much information can be obtained on a film sample. Thus the qualitative strength (or lack of it) will give an indication of whether or not the polymer has been prepared in a useful molecular weight. Drawability (Fig. 2.18) can be demonstrated on strips of film, and pieces of film are very useful for determining the crystalline melting point of a polymer (Section III).

If a commercial press, such as is shown, is not available, a fairly satisfactory substitute can be made. Mount two electric irons, with tops and handles removed, face to face in a large vise mounted perpendicularly. Wire the irons in parallel and control the temperature with a rheostat capable of handling the required wattage. Temperature may be measured by thermocouples in wells drilled in the bases of the irons. This apparatus may be calibrated, and a plot of rheostat setting versus temperature mounted conveniently nearby. No way of measuring pressure applied is available, but experience will allow the operator to have a reasonable feel for the apparatus.

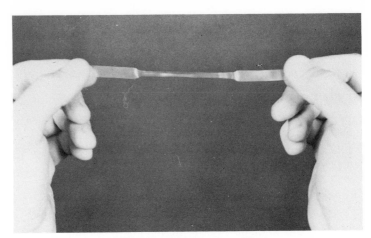

Fig. 2.18. Cold-drawing a film.

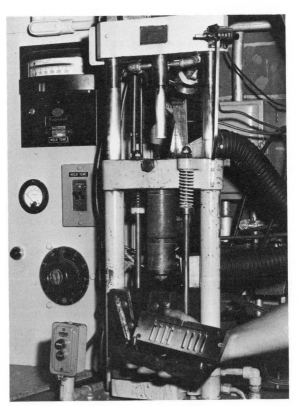

Fig. 2.19. Injection molding.

B. *Preparation of Molded Objects*

The preparation of molded objects such as bars, circular chips, cups, etc., may be done either by injection or compression molding.

Injection molding is done by an apparatus consisting of a molding chamber, into which molten polymer may be forced. Such an apparatus for simultaneously making eight molded bars is shown in Figs. 2.19 and 2.20. The molding chamber (Fig. 2.20) consists of two heavy plates hollowed in the desired shapes, with each compartment connected to the others by channels, through which the molten polymer may flow, and to a channel through which the molten polymer is forced into the mold. The objects so obtained (in this case, small test bars) are all connected. They are separated by cutting away the connecting polymer.

Even the simplest such machine represents a considerable capital outlay. Larger machines suitable for the production of larger and more complicated objects are quite costly and will be found only in laboratories specializing in this type of work or in commercial injection molding factories.

Compression molding of simple objects such as bars and chips may be done with simple and readily available equipment. In compression molding, an apparatus such as is shown in Fig. 2.21 for bars or Fig. 2.22 for disks or plugs may be used. The polymer is placed in the mold, on top of the bottom plate, and the piston is inserted. The mold is heated externally with, for example, an electric strip heater to fuse the polymer, and pressure is applied to the piston to compact the polymer. The pressure may be applied either by a press, such as is shown in Fig. 2.16, or

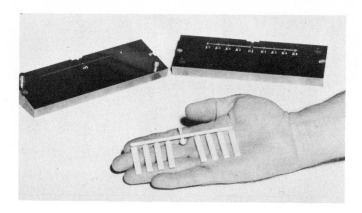

Fig. 2.20. Injection molding.

Fig. 2.21. Apparatus for compression molding of bars.

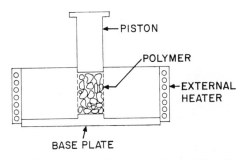

Fig. 2.22. Apparatus for compression molding disks.

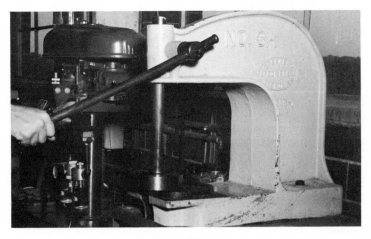

Fig. 2.23. Arbor press.

by an Arbor press (Fig. 2.23). The apparatus is cooled, the bottom plate and the piston removed, and the molded object knocked out.

C. *Melt Extrusion of Polymer to Fibers*

The simplest method for making short lengths of fiber is by manual spinning. The polymer is melted in a test tube, and threads removed with a glass rod (Fig. 2.24).

The simplest mechanical method for converting polymer to continuous lengths of fiber is to place it in a heavy walled, heated steel cylinder, equipped with a piston driven by a hydraulic ram, and a spinneret, a small disk drilled with one or more holes (Fig. 2.25).

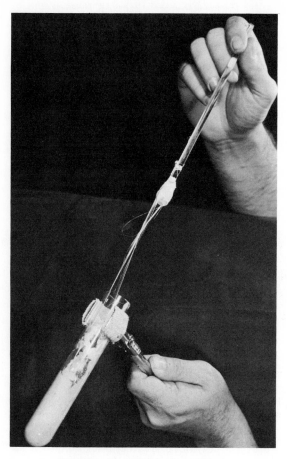

Fig. 2.24. Manual spinning of fibers.

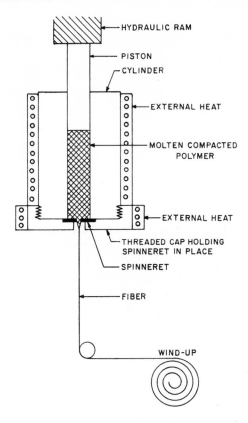

Fig. 2.25. Melt-spinning apparatus.

A photograph of the spinning cell is shown in Fig. 2.26 and the motor driven wind-up, equipped with a cylindrical, removable bobbin in Fig. 2.27. The bobbin (Fig. 2.28) is normally perforated for soaking or other aftertreatment of the yarn, an operation usually limited to solvent-spun yarns (Section II-2B).

The polymer should be compacted before placing it in the cylinder of the extruder to minimize entrapment of air, which would cause discoloration as well as produce bubbles in the extruded filament. The finely divided polymer may be compacted to a cylindrical plug in a heated mold such as is shown in Fig. 2.22. The plug is then dropped into the cylinder of the melt-spinning apparatus. A simpler, but less effective, method is to press the polymer to a rather thick film, then cut disks from the film with a sharp cork borer of the proper diameter to fit snugly in

Fig. 2.26. Melt-spinning cell.

Fig. 2.27. Winding up melt-spun yarn.

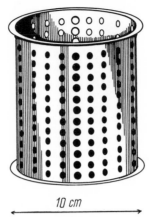

10 cm

Fig. 2.28. Perforated bobbin.

the barrel of the spinner. A stack of disks 1–2 in. in height will produce enough fiber for preliminary evaluation.

The production of melt-spun fibers also can be carried out using equipment described by Hardy (13) and shown in Fig. 2.29. In the figure, C is a 1 in. diameter glass tube drawn down to a stout capillary at one end. It is surrounded by a double-walled glass jacket (B) heated with the vapor of a boiling liquid from an attached flask (A). The jacket is constructed with an aperture at its base to permit the capillary jet (D) to pass through when desired. By adjusting the height of the jet relative to the aperture, it is possible to regulate the temperature of the jet when extruding filament. The jet is sealed initially to enable the vessel charged with polymer to be evacuated and filled with nitrogen (G, H). When the polymer is melted, the tip of the jet is cut off and a filament pulled out. True extrusion is impractical, but it is possible to produce continuous filament under a moderate pressure of nitrogen. The fiber can be passed over a guide roll (E) and wound up on a spool (F).

D. Plasticized Melt Fabrication

Occasionally, a polymer shows very high melt viscosity, or perhaps some instability at the temperature of fusion. In such a case, it is often possible to blend the polymer with a plasticizer, a high boiling liquid compatible with the polymer. The plasticized polymer can then be melt-fabricated at much lower temperatures. A number of polymers based on

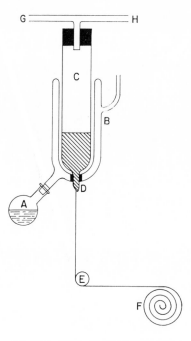

Fig. 2.29. Melt-spinning apparatus.

vinyl chloride and vinylidene chloride are fabricated commercially in this way—for example, Saran fibers.

The presence of a plasticizer will make a polymer more flexible. If this is desirable, the plasticizer may be left in the polymer after fabrication. Otherwise, it may be extracted by an organic solvent.

E. Compounding of Rubber

Elastomers are generally not used without incorporation of a variety of additives, and preparation of a rubber stock involves mixing the additives with the raw polymers. This is usually accomplished on a rubber mill, which has two massive heated rolls set parallel with only narrow separation, similar in appearance to a clothes wringer. These rolls turn in opposite directions, but at different speeds so that material on the mill is subjected to repeated kneading and shearing action.

The additives used cover a wide range of products, the exact nature of which will depend upon the polymer used and the ultimate end use of the product. The following partial list represents the types of additives which may be used.

1. A vulcanizing agent, such as sulfur, together with an accelerator, such as mercaptobenzthiazole and an activator, or retarder.

2. Fillers—carbon black is very useful, and increases tensile properties and elasticity. Other fillers include silica and various clays.

3. Pigment—if a filler other than carbon black is used, the product can be given a desired color by mixing in a pigment.

4. Softeners—plasticizers to improve workability.

5. Antioxidants—such as phenyl-β-naphthylamine, to protect the polymer from oxidative deterioration, both during processing and in service.

For further details, the reader is referred to one of the many excellent books on rubber technology (14).

2. Solution Methods

When a polymer cannot be melted, or is unstable at its melting point, a common technique for fabrication is to form a viscous solution in a volatile solvent, then cast to a film or spin to a fiber. Massive articles (corresponding to molded objects) cannot be made from solution, since removal of solvent becomes very difficult and form retention is almost impossible.

A. Casting Films

Solutions for casting should be prepared by methods suggested in Section I. They should be quite viscous to prevent the cast solution from "running" or spreading over the casting surface. Concentrations of the order of 20% are usually satisfactory, although much will depend on polymer properties. Only the trial and error method eventually will produce the optimum concentration. To cast a film, a viscous polymer solution is spread onto a glass plate with a doctor knife. This may be a glass rod wrapped at either end with a few turns of tape to give a uniform clearance when the rod is passed over the solution (Fig. 2.30). More precise work can be done with the knife shown in Figs. 2.31, 2.32, 2.34–2.36. It is made of brass or stainless steel, with the cross bar ground

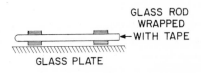

Fig. 2.30. A doctor knife.

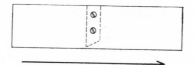

DIRECTION OF THE DRAW

Fig. 2.31. A doctor knife.

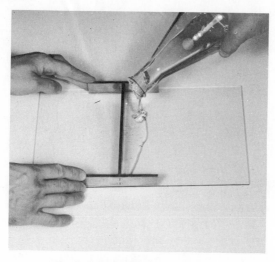

Fig. 2.32. Solution-casting a film.

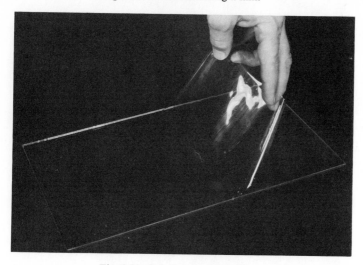

Fig. 2.33. Solution-casting a film.

Fig. 2.34. Using a casting table.

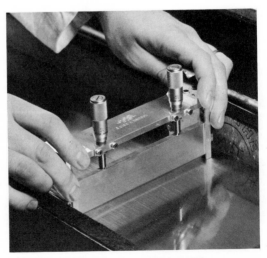

Fig. 2.35. Using a casting table.

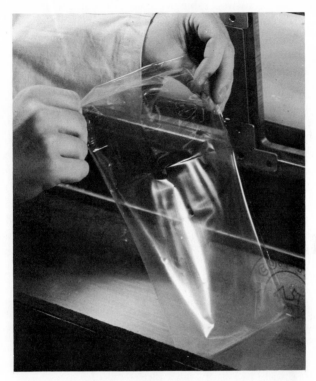

Fig. 2.36. Using a casting table.

back from the runners at an angle to give the desired thickness and clearance.

The operation of film casting is shown in Fig. 2.32. The prepared plate is placed in a forced draft oven to dry, at a temperature well below the boiling point of the solvent to avoid bubbling. The dried film is then stripped from the plate (Fig. 2.33).

If film adhesion to glass prevents its easy removal, the film can be cast onto aluminum or tin foil stretched smoothly over glass and the metal foil removed by dissolving in acid or base, or, for tin, in mercury, as already noted under melt fabrication methods (Section II-1-A). This approach constitutes a way of preparing samples of thermoset polymer films that may not ordinarily have the toughness to permit their being obtained in an unsupported state for testing (15).

More elaborate equipment, suitable for use in a laboratory specializing in polymer work, is shown in Figs. 2.34–2.36. The film is spread on a chrome-plated casting table with an adjustable doctor knife. The table is covered with a lid, and may be heated uniformly with steam. The lid allows an atmosphere rich in solvent to be above the drying film and prevents roo rapid drying of the surface with consequent wrinkling, development of orange peel, etc.

B. Spinning Fibers

There are two well-known methods for converting a polymer solution to fiber. These are dry spinning and wet spinning. In dry spinning, a viscous polymer solution is forced through a spinneret into a heated gas (air or nitrogen) which quickly evaporates the solvent, leaving a polymeric thread. This is very important commercially (Fig. 2.37). In wet spinning, polymer solution is injected into a precipitant (nonsolvent), which causes the solution to coagulate into a thread (Fig. 2.38).

In the laboratory, dry spinning is quite difficult to do because of the complexity of the process. The simplest set-up for continuous fiber

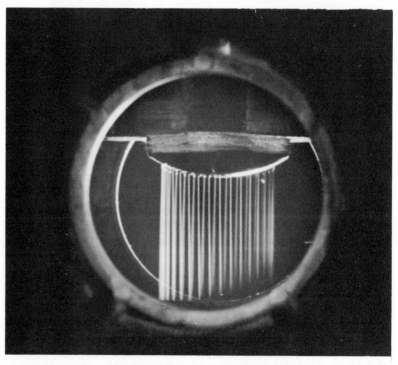

Fig. 2.37. Dry-spinning multifilament.

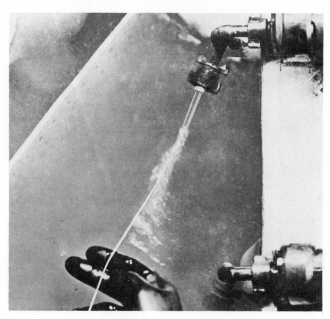

Fig. 2.38. Wet-spinning.

production, with adequate control of variables, will cost many thousands of dollars. However for the preparation of small amounts of fiber from easily spinnable polymers, such as acrylonitrile copolymers, a set-up shown in Fig. 2.39 may be constructed.

The column is a 3-ft. piece of Pyrex glass, 3 in. in diameter. Hot air is injected without undue turbulence by the scheme shown. Polymer solution is extruded into the hot air from, for example, a hypodermic syringe such as shown in Fig. 2.11, and collected on a variable speed windup (cf. Fig. 2.27).

Wet spinning on a small scale is more practical, although, again, choice of precipitant, temperature, etc., are very critical and will determine the quality of the fibers obtained. The choice of precipitating bath is particularly critical and must be determined experimentally for each situation. Precipitation should not be too abrupt, or a porous, weak fiber will be obtained. A near-solvent may be desirable to allow slower precipitation. For example, a dimethylformamide solution of a polymer might well be spun into dimethylformamide diluted with water. An ordinary hypodermic syringe is useful for preliminary work, the fiber being drawn from the tip with a pair of tweezers (Fig. 2.40). For

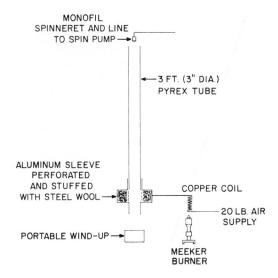

Fig. 2.39. A simple dry-spinning column.

Fig. 2.40. Small-scale wet spinning.

Fig. 2.41. Motor driven hypodermic.

more precise work, a motor-driven, metal hypodermic syringe can be used (Fig. 2.41).

III. Polymer Characterization

1. INTRODUCTION

The many desirable physical properties that are associated with polymeric materials, such as strength, plasticity, elasticity, and viscosity, are a direct consequence of the high molecular weight of the molecules composing the material. A related consequence is the need for special techniques to characterize these materials. The problem posed by the much greater molecular size of polymers is complicated further by the molecular inhomogeneity which prevails in as-prepared polymeric materials. Consequently, most of the standard organic characterization procedures must be modified or supplanted.

The characterization of polymers is a task which has been approached in many instances according to the class of polymers being investigated and the needs of the investigators. To cite one example, in amorphous polymers no true melting point can be determined; yet, such a material can be characterized as to the temperature (or temperature range) at which is just softens, or becomes molten, or is moldable, or begins to distort under a defined condition of stress. The same sample of polymer may give a different temperature for each category cited, and, depending on the interest of the investigator, any one of them may constitute a proper characterization of the thermal properties of the material. Thus, the conditions of measurement of a given property must always be stated. Where the property measured is a function of the molecular weight or molecular weight distribution of the sample, these constitute part of the conditions of the measurement in question. Fortunately, most of the physical properties of a given polymer change very little or not at all when a fairly high average molecular weight is reached.

Although a number of highly particularized characterization methods have been developed to meet specialized needs, as previously pointed out, a certain few basic properties have been widely used as fundamental starting points for the physical and chemical characterization of polymers. Among the first to be determined are thermal properties, i.e., temperature when polymer becomes molten (PMT), crystalline melting point (T_m), and glass transition temperature (T_g). Others are average molecular weight, amount of crystalline and amorphous character, solubility spectrum, and an establishment of chemical structure where any uncertainties may exist.

The latter area has acquired added significance in recent years as more understanding has been required about the detailed structure of polymers; e.g., the microtacticity (16) of polymer chains (especially those not largely of one stereochemical type), molecular motion, and chain flexibility (17). These last-mentioned fields have yielded to the use of nuclear magnetic resonance applied to polymer solutions. Advances in knowledge of the sequence distribution of copolymers have also been made (18).

In the following sections, the treatment of some of the above-mentioned areas of polymer characterization is primarily from the standpoint of the simplest laboratory methods available for estimating property or value in question. They are intended as a minimum framework of characterization which is applicable to most of the polymers prepared in subsequent chapters. In many cases the methods are things the organic polymer chemist can do himself. There are others, including many not directly considered here, that are in the realm of the characterization specialist; these are, of course, extremely important, but encompass a level of inquiry beyond the scope of the present treatment. Polymer characterization is indeed a very broad topic and reaches from the most basic aspects such as elemental analysis and molecular weight through mechanical properties, to environmental and end use properties such as light stability of fibers and burst strength of plastic pipes.

The organic polymer practitioner will find it necessary at times to develop a greater familiarity with some of these areas as a polymer that he has synthesized progresses in practical and theoretical importance. A fairly extensive bibliography is provided so that the reader can be initially directed to some of the extensive general and particular treatments of polymer characterization.

2. MOLECULAR WEIGHT DETERMINATION

The determination of molecular weight in polymeric materials yields a value which is always an average of the molecular weights of the molecules present. What kind of average is obtained depends on the method of measurement. The two most common average molecular weights are the number average, $\overline{M}_n$, and the weight average, $\overline{M}_w$. They are defined as:

$$\overline{M}_n = \sum NM/\sum N$$
$$\overline{M}_w = \sum NM^2/\sum NM$$

where N = number of molecules of molecular weight M.

The kind of average obtained depends upon the method used to obtain it. Osmometry gives a number average (19–21), while light scattering (19,22,23) and certain types of ultracentrifugation (24–26) give weight average molecular weights. The latter two of the above-mentioned methods require the use of highly specialized and expensive equipment and sophisticated operational skills. They are tools of the specialist in both equipment and training, and consequently outside the intended scope of this Section. The same can be said for osmometry, but with some qualification. There have now been developed highly automatic membrane osmometers which reach equilibrium in a few minutes so that analyses can be performed in a relatively routine manner, in contrast to the many hours required with prior conventional instruments (20). Number average molecular weights in the range of about 10,000–500,000 can be handled. Another development is the so called vapor pressure osmometer, which measures the temperature difference between two drops, one of solvent and one of polymer solution, exposed to the vapor of the solvent; the temperature difference results from the lower evaporation rate from the polymer solution and is detected by sensitive thermisters (21). It is effective up to a molecular weight of 20,000. While both of these methods involve rather expensive equipment, they effectively put absolute number average molecular weights within reach as routine characterization value to those laboratories so equipped.

All of the above methods have the advantage of being absolute methods, in that a molecular weight average may be determined without recourse to any previous measurement. As such, they are the ultimate basis for the use of polymer solution viscosity measurements for the determination of molecular weight (19).

A number of viscosity designations have been defined for dilute polymer solutions. For the sake of consistency the more common usage is adopted here, with the newer, but as yet less used, equivalent term given in parentheses. These are as follows:

1. Relative viscosity: (Viscosity ratio)

$\eta_{rel} = t/t_0$

t_0 is flow time through a viscometer of a reference liquid, and t is flow time through the same viscometer of a dilute solution of polymer in the reference liquid.

2. Specific viscosity:

$\eta_{sp} = \eta_{rel} - 1$

3. Reduced specific viscosity: (Viscosity number)

$\eta_{sp}/C = (\eta_{rel} - 1)/C$

4. Inherent viscosity: (Logarithmic viscosity number)

$\eta_{inh} = \ln \eta_{rel}/C$

5. Intrinsic viscosity: (Limiting viscosity number)

$$[\eta] = \lim_{c \to 0} \eta_{inh} = \lim_{c \to 0} \eta_{sp}/C$$

In the above, C is concentration of polymer solution in g./100 ml. of solvent. The units of intrinsic viscosity are deciliters per gram, therefore. The intrinsic viscosity is obtained by extrapolating to zero concentration a plot of either inherent or reduced specific viscosity versus concentration. The above viscosity numbers depend on the solvent, the concentration (except for intrinsic values) and the temperature at which the determination is made, though the latter is usually of little effect within 10–15°C. in a good solvent for the polymer.

A correlation of intrinsic viscosity with molecular weight for linear polymers can be achieved through the empirical equation proposed by Mark and Houwink (27), based on earlier work by Staudinger (28):

$$[\eta] = KM^a$$

where M is molecular weight, and K and a are constants for a particular polymer–solvent system. K and a are determined by the intercept and slope, respectively, for a plot of the log of intrinsic viscosity against the log of molecular weight of fractionated samples of polymer over a wide range of molecular weight values. If unfractionated polymer is used, the molecular weight distribution for each sample over its molecular weight range must be the same. The molecular weights for use in such a plot are determined by one of the absolute methods described earlier, e.g., light scattering. An approximate viscosity average molecular weight, $\overline{M}_v$, (rather than $\overline{M}_w$ or $\overline{M}_n$) is obtained when unfractionated, molecularly heterogeneous polymer is used in a determination using the appropriate values of K and a. For most high polymers, viscosity averages will be much closer to a weight average than a number average molecular weight. The value of a for most polymers has been found to be around 0.7. Where $a = 1$, $\overline{M}_v = \overline{M}_w$.

Thus, by determination of intrinsic viscosity, the magnitude of the polymer molecular weight can be estimated by choosing K and a values from a known polymer—solvent combination which has as much similarity as possible to the polymer–solvent system under consideration (29). Comparison of intrinsic viscosities of two similar polymers measured in the same solvent, one of which is of known molecular weight, also can be used to estimate molecular weight (30,31). The qualitative nature of such comparisons must be recognized, however, since minor structural differences may lead to large differences in viscosity.

Viscometric molecular weight determination has been extensively reviewed (33,34) and a large number of K and a values for various polymer–solvent combinations are given. The *Polymer Handbook* (35) is another excellent source. It is also worth noting that dilute solution viscosity measurement is the principal experimental method for obtaining information on the dimensions of polymer molecules (34–37).

It should be recalled that the ultimate correlation between intrinsic viscosity and molecular weights via the Mark-Houwink equation rests on determining K and a from samples of polymer having a narrow molecular weight distribution. Fairly homogeneous molecular weight polymer can be obtained by fractionation techniques (32), usually by a chromatographic (38), column elution (39), or fractional precipitation (40) method. Fractional precipitation can be very time consuming, so it is not surprising that it is giving way to the other methods. Large scale fractionations have been carried out by column methods; 100 g. samples of polystyrene (41), 200 g. of low-density polyethylene (42), and 1 lb. of high-density polyethylene (43) have been successfully handled.

Gel permeation chromatography (44,45), in particular, has transformed the fractionation of polymers. The commercially available equipment, though quite expensive, permits relatively rapid and, if desired, highly automated isolation of fractions and allows construction of a molecular weight distribution curve. The principle (38) involves the selective permeation of polymer molecules from a solution into the pores of a gel of crosslinked polymer (e.g., polystyrene), from which they are subsequently eluted. The smaller molecules permeate the gel more easily than the large and leave the column more slowly, forming the basis of the separation.

Where it is not necessary to arrive at a numerical value for the molecular weight of a polymer, it is often convenient simply to relate one given sample of polymer to other known samples by means of inherent viscosity or relative viscosity. If it is known, for instance, that poly(vinyl chloride) of a certain inherent viscosity value (under stated conditions) is required in order to achieve a desired level of film properties, it may be sufficient characterization to relate newly prepared poly(vinyl chloride) to anticipated properties by determining only the inherent or the reduced viscosity of the new sample. In some cases, relative viscosity may have advantages.

In the following procedures for viscosity determinations, per cent solutions are given as grams per 100 ml. of solvent; i.e., 0.5% is 0.5 g. per 100 ml.

A. Determination of Relative Viscosity

Relative viscosity can be taken as the ratio of the flow times of a polymer solution and the pure solvent in the same viscometer and at the same temperature. (Strictly, relative viscosity is the ratio of the kinematic viscosities of solution and solvent. Assuming the same density for dilute solution and solvent, and using the same viscometer for solvent and solution, the ratio of efflux time can be taken as relative viscosity in most cases.)

The following method is specifically designed for determining the relative viscosity of dilute (1% or less) solutions. Relative viscosity values generally are used for calculating the intrinsic or inherent viscosity of a polymer. Relative viscosity is easily determined, but its magnitude is more a function of polymer concentration than it is of molecular weight.

Relative viscosity measurements are conveniently made in a thermostatted bath at 30°C. This temperature is chosen so that the bath always will be above room temperature, even during hot weather, and therefore not require controlled cooling.

For viscometers, Cannon-Fenske, Series 100, 200, 300, 400, and 500, Fisher No. 13-616, or equivalent, are useful in these determinations. It is essential that viscometers be kept free of dust, residues, and other foreign matter.

The solvent to be used will depend on the polymer in question. In general, the solvent should completely dissolve the sample in less than 30 min. It is desirable that the polymer be dissolved at room temperature although heating is permissible if no degradation occurs. Degradation can be noted by determining the viscosity value at intervals of an hour or so.

Weigh 125 ± 1 mg. of the dry sample and transfer it quantitatively to a test tube. If some concentration other than 0.5% is run, use a proportionately larger or smaller sample. Weigh liquid samples directly into a test tube.

Accurately measure 25 ± 0.05 ml. of the required solvent into the test tube containing the sample. Manual or mechanical (e.g., spiral rod or disk stirrer, Fig. 2.14 attached to a motor) stirring will usually be required. Instead of a test tube, a small, stoppered Erlenmeyer flask may be used for making the solution. Here, a magnetic stirrer may be used. Solvent must in no case be allowed to evaporate and alter the concentration in any of the operations that follow.

When the sample has completely dissolved, filter about 10 ml. without vacuum through a coarse porosity sintered glass filter into a 50 ml. flask or other suitable container. While the solution is filtering, add about 10 ml. of the solvent used for dissolving the sample to a 50 ml. beaker. Select a viscometer through which the solvent will flow in not less than 100 sec. and, preferably, not more than 200 sec. Hold the viscometer in a vertical, inverted position and immerse the end of the capillary tube in the solvent. Apply suction to the other (wide) tube until the solvent fills both bulbs and most of the capillary (Fig. 2.42). Remove from the beaker and while the viscometer is still inverted, allow the liquid in the capillary tube to drain back until the meniscus just reaches the graduation mark around the working capillary. When the graduation has been reached, quickly invert and wipe the excess liquid off the tube.

Immerse the viscometer in a constant temperature bath in a vertical position. Allow the viscometer to remain in the bath long enough for its contents to come to the temperature of the bath. Ordinarily, 5 min. is sufficient for temperatures between 20 and 40°C.; 10 min. should be allowed for temperatures outside this range. During the temperature equilibrating stage, and later while making the measurement, the temperature of the bath must be held constant within $\pm 0.05°C$.

During the temperature equilibrating stage the solvent will drain into the lower reservoir bulb and while doing so a bubble may become trapped in the bend at the bottom of the instrument. Remove any such bubble by manipulating the solution with a suction bulb.

Fig. 2.42. Use of viscometer.

After the solvent has attained the temperature of the bath, apply pressure to the top of the wide arm (or suction to the capillary) until the liquid has filled the first bulb and is about 1 cm. above the mark between the bulbs. Make certain that no bubbles are trapped. Allow the liquid to flow freely and determine the time for the meniscus to pass from the upper to the lower mark.

Record this time as the flow time for the solvent. Draw the liquid up again and measure the flow time, which should agree with the first flow time within 0.2 sec. If it does not, continue until three flow times agreeing within 0.2 sec. are obtained.

When about 10 ml. of sample solution filtrate has been collected, immerse the same viscometer, which has been cleaned and dried, in the filtrate and fill as described above. Place in the water bath, allow to come to temperature equilibrium and determine the flow time as described above. Three values, agreeing within 0.2 sec. for solution flow times, should be obtained. The relative viscosity is given by:

$$\eta_{rel} = (\text{solution flow time, seconds/solvent flow time, seconds})$$

B. Determination of Inherent Viscosity

Inherent viscosity is calculated from the dilute solution (1% or less) relative viscosity of the polymer. The relative viscosity is determined as described in the preceding section.

While the nature of the solvent used and the polymer concentration have an influence on inherent viscosity values, the effect is far less than it is on relative viscosity. In general, the better the solvent, the higher the observed inherent viscosity for a given polymer. Similarly, the higher the concentration, the lower the observed inherent viscosity. Temperature is important only insofar as it influences solvent power and polymer degradation. Results obtained at 30 and 25°C. usually agree within the precision of this method. Results obtained by this method should be precise within 0.04 units, absolute, within the range of 0–5 inherent viscosity units. The inherent viscosity is calculated as:

$$\eta_{inh} = \ln \eta_{rel}/C$$

where C = concentration of the polymer in grams per 100 ml. of solvent; usually, $C = 0.50$; $\ln \eta_{rel}$ = natural logarithm of the relative viscosity of the dilute (1% or less) polymer solution.

For polymers of limited solubility at 30°C., it is necessary to use a constant temperature bath held at an elevated temperature. Polyhydrocarbons such as polyethylene or poly(4-methyl-1-pentene) are satisfactorily soluble only at 130°C. in solvents such as decahydronaphthalene containing 0.2% of an antioxidant such as phenyl-β-naphthylamine. The polymer is dissolved in decahydronaphthalene at a concentration of 0.1 g./100 ml. instead of the usual 0.5 g., using an ethylene glycol monomethyl ether bath at reflux (125°C.) to heat the polymer and solvent. The solution is filtered through a preheated 200 mesh stainless steel screen into a test tube immersed in the 130 ± 0.1°C. temperature bath. Ten ml. of the solution is transferred by means of a hot pipet (do not use mouth suction) to a suitable viscometer (a Cannon-Fenske, Series 75) immersed in the bath. After allowing 10 min. for temperature equilibrium to be established, the inherent viscosity is calculated as described above.

C. Determination of Intrinsic Viscosity

The intrinsic viscosity, $[\eta]$, is given by:

$$[\eta] = \lim_{C \to 0} \eta_{inh} = \lim_{C \to 0} (\eta_{sp})/C$$

Intrinsic viscosity is obtained from plotting inherent viscosity numbers or reduced viscosity numbers versus concentration and extrapolating to zero concentration. The viscosity number intercept at zero concentration is taken as the intrinsic viscosity. Customarily, curves for both inherent and reduced viscosities versus concentration are plotted. The intrinsic viscosity value obtained should be the same in each case. If they are not, the midpoint between them is usually taken.

The determination of intrinsic viscosity should be based on a minimum of three inherent or reduced viscosity measurements at different concentrations. Four or five such measurements are often preferable. Concentrations should be from 0.1 to 0.5 g. per 100 ml. of solvent. The experimental procedures are the same as those given for η_{rel} and η_{inh} in the preceding sections.

Molecular weight estimation by solution viscometry outlined in this section is necessarily brief and nonmathematical, and is designed primarily to present the experimental methods involved. The reader must seek elsewhere for the full theory, implications, and limitations of the subject (19,33,34). Additional experimental procedures, as applied to poly(vinyl chloride) and ethylene polymers, for example, are given in ASTM Standards (45).

D. End Group Methods

End group determinations, where applicable, are useful for molecular weights less than 25,000. This approach, which gives a number average value, depends on the polymer having a terminal group, or groups, on each chain which can be quantitatively measured. When there are no losses of end groups by side reaction, no production of additional end groups by branching, and when all ends can be accurately determined, a direct measure of the number average molecular weight can be made (19,46).

End groups can be determined in specific cases of vinyl polymers through the use of initiators having groups identifiable by functionality (47), elemental analysis (48), or presence of a radioactive element (49). It is essential that the mechanism of the polymerization be known and unambiguous, such that the location of initiator fragments at one or at both ends of the chain can be predicted.

In condensation polymers, where $-CO_2H$ or $-NH_2$ groups are present, direct titration is usually an effective means of end group determination (50–53). The procedures involve the use of a suitable inert solvent for acidic or basic titration, and consequently depend on the solubility limits of the polymer. Hydroxyl groups in polyesters have been determined by reaction of the —OH with a reagent that subsequently forms a titratable group; i.e., acetic anhydride followed by titration of the acetic acid after hydrolysis of the excess reagent (54), or succinic anhydride followed by titration of the free carboxyl of the succinic half ester (55). Hydroxyls in polyesters also have been determined through infrared methods (56).

The selection of the method to be used for determining a particular group is influenced by the following factors.

a. Solvent. The solvent used must dissolve the polymer but not interfere with the applicable analytical method. For example, formic acid is an excellent solvent for nylon, but the direct acidimetric titration cannot be carried out in it. Generally speaking, the sample need not be highly soluble in the solvent; 0.1% is ordinarily sufficient.

b. Impurities Present. In many cases, the impurities likely to be present in a polymer may be deduced by knowing how it was made. For example, polyamides made by melt polymerization are often free from impurities, while those prepared from acid chlorides usually contain salts which are difficult to remove and seriously interfere in many methods. Methods used for purifying the polymer, and the solvents with which it has been in contact, also must be considered.

c. Other Functional Groups Present. Interfering functional groups must be absent. For example, amine groups interfere with the determination of hydroxyl end groups.

d. Molecular Weight and Structure of the Polymer. If the molecular weight is greater than about 25,000, end group methods are, in general, not very reliable. The degree of crosslinking or branching are other factors which influence both the solubility of the polymer and the end group concentration.

Because the procedure to be used, in any case, depends so much on the individual polymer, no general methods are given here. However, in Chapter 3, Preparation 94, a method of terminal —OH and —CO₂H is given for the low molecular weight polyesters prepared there. This method is used also in the preparation of certain polyester resins in Chapter 7. Also in Chapter 7, a method is described for determining epoxide content (terminal group) in low molecular weight epoxy resins.

E. Other Methods

Both cryoscopic and ebullioscopic methods give a number average molecular weight (46). As the molecular weight of a solute increases, the molar quantity required to give the necessary observable melting point or boiling point change in the solvent becomes greater. Consequently, these methods have generally been restricted to polymers of

30,000 molecular weight or less, though higher values have been determined in some cases (57).

3. CRYSTALLINITY IN POLYMERS

It is a feature of polymeric materials that they may be entirely amorphous, partly amorphous and partly crystalline, or almost completely crystalline. The preparation of microscopic single crystals of many polymers from dilute solution has been demonstrated (58). The usual situation for a polymer cooled from its melt or simply precipitated from solution is to find that it is entirely amorphous or partly crystalline.

The most effective method of ascertaining the presence and extent of crystallinity in a polymer is x-ray diffraction, which has been one of the most informative and useful physical methods in polymer characterization (59,60). X-ray diffraction, in principle and practice, is beyond the intent of this section.

A convenient way of determining T_m is differential thermal analysis (DTA) (61), a simple, rapid method for measuring the heat–energy change in a substance as its temperature is raised. Only a small amount of polymer is required, and it may be used in powder form. DTA is also a very useful way to determine the glass temperature, as noted later. Commercial equipment is available for DTA measurements. DTA, besides its application to glass and crystalline changes, is applicable to a variety of characterizations involving reactions going on in the polymer (e.g., crosslinking, degradation, and oxidation).

Crystallinity is a phenomenon more generally observed in polymers which have (a) little or no random chain branching or crosslinking, (b) regularity and symmetry of structure along the backbone of the chain, and (c) polar or highly bonding groups. The effects of these structural features are much the same as they are in simple organic compounds; those effects that tend for the readier packing and mutual attraction of chains favor crystallinity in polymers. Polymers which are amorphous as prepared may sometimes be induced to crystallize, in part, by the action of heat, treatment with a near or partial solvent, slow cooling of the polymer melt, etc. Such treatments may permit the necessary amount of molecular motion in segments of the polymer chain to allow them to attain some of the alignment needed for crystallization. Theoretical treatment of polymer crystallinity has been given by Geil (58), Mandelkern (62), and others (63–66).

For polymers that are crystalline, the crystalline melting point, T_m, is taken as that temperature where the last trace of crystallinity disappears under equilibrium conditions. Elaborate techniques have been devised for determining this temperature with considerable accuracy (67). One of the better methods is via the disappearance of a crystalline x-ray diffraction pattern as the temperature is raised. The long heating time required (24 hr. or more) limits the usefulness of the method. The simplest laboratory method is to note the loss of crystalline birefringence in a polymer sample using a hot stage polarizing microscope.

A. Determination of Crystalline Melting Point (T_m)

The sample is heated on a hot stage microscope (Fig. 2.43), optionally under nitrogen, and the temperature at which the color between crossed optical polarizers disappears is noted.

This procedure is applicable to any fiber, film, or other material which exhibits color (birefringence) when placed between crossed optical polarizers, and does not decompose at elevated temperatures in the relatively short times required.

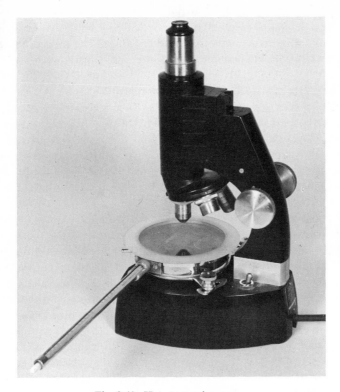

Fig. 2.43. Hot stage microscope.

There are two sources of birefringence in *unoriented* crystalline polymer samples: (a) birefringence due to strain within the sample which is characterized by a brilliant play of colors during the initial heating period and which disappears when the temperature approaches the melting point; and (b) birefringence due to sample crystallinity which is characterized by the bright yellow or white color of the sample which remains until the crystalline melting temperature is reached. This color disappears rapidly over a narrow temperature range and blends with the dark field. Inorganic impurities showing birefringence should be ignored. These are usually very high melting substances and can be easily recognized with a little practice.

For use in this determination, any good microscope equipped with $5 \times$ and $10 \times$ oculars and objectives, an optical polarizer and analyzer, and an insulated or metal stage is satisfactory. The Unitron Polarizing Microscope, Model MPS (United Scientific Co.), which has been modified to seat the Koefler hot stage accurately, is an example. A less elaborate instrument can be made by modifying a simple student microscope with a disk of Polaroid film on the eyepiece and another over the light source (Fig. 2.43). The optics must be raised by an insert in the mounting to accommodate the hot stage. The procedure below uses the Unitron Microscope, but is the basic operation for any instrument.

Using a film as an example, cut the sample into at least 10 pieces, each about $0.1 \times 1 \times 1$ mm., or smaller. Place the pieces in the center of a slide, taking care that the pieces are close to each other, but not overlapping. Cover the pieces with a cover glass. Place the slide on the stage, turn on the light and using the $5 \times$ objective and $10 \times$ eyepiece, select a field where the sample particles are well distributed with little bunching or clumping. Place the heat baffle over the slide and cover the stage with the glass cover.

If the approximate melting point of the sample is known ($\pm 10°C.$) adjust the heating rate to give a temperature rise of $0.1°C.$ per min. at $20°C.$ below the expected value. Allow the sample to anneal for 30 min. under these conditions. This is to relieve internal strains in this sample which may cause birefringence. Then adjust the heating rate to give a temperature rise to $1°C.$ per min. Refocus the microscope with the $10 \times$ objective and $10 \times$ eyepiece, move the analyzer into position and note the temperature at which the first polymer particle blends with the dark background as T_i. Note the temperature at which the last polymer particle disappears as T_f. Disregard any small isolated bright spots which persist well above the temperature at which the bulk of the sample particles have lost their color.

When the approximate melting point of the sample is not known, re-focus the microscope, using the $10\times$ objective and $10\times$ eyepiece. Move the analyzer into position. Set the heating rate to give a temperature rise of $10°$ per min. at $250°C$. Note the temperature at which the last sample particle disappears as T_m.

Place the cooling block, which has been precooled in ice water, on the hot stage. Prepare and mount a fresh portion of the sample on the stage as described above. Anneal the sample for 30 min., using the T_m value just determined as its approximate melting point and then determine the melting point as described.

On cooling the melted polymer, crystallinity will usually reappear and the determination can be repeated. If the sample does not become crystalline again on cooling, treatment with an appropriate solvent or mechanical working may reinduce crystallinity. Orientation in a crystalline polymer does not adversely affect determination of the crystalline melting point; in fact, it usually helps since oriented, crystalline samples are usually brighter and the disappearance of color is more apparent.

Calculation. Let $T_i = °C$. at which the first sample particle blends with the background; $T_f = °C$. at which the last sample particle blends with the background:

$$\text{Crystalline Melting Point} = T_m = (T_i + T_f)/2$$

It should be noted that amorphous polymers having some orientation of the molecules (as in a stretched film) will exhibit birefringence under a polarizing microscope. This will dissappear near the glass transition temperature and will not reappear on cooling. It should be noted also that cutting bulk, unoriented polymer will introduce some additional birefringence around the edges due to shear orientation, hence such samples will be more brilliant around the edges when viewed between crossed polarizers.

4. GLASS TRANSITION TEMPERATURE (T_g)

An amorphous polymer can be considered to be a hard glass below a certain temperature; above it, the material is usually soft or rubbery. The temperature that marks this division is the glass transition temperature, T_g (68). Above T_g, a freer movement of parts of the polymer chains can occur. An amorphous polymer is a hard solid or a soft rubber, accordingly, as it is below or above its glass transition temperature.

T_g is determined by measuring the change in some physical property of the solid polymer (e.g., thermal coefficient of expansion, specific volume, dynamic modulus of elasticity, heat capacity or dielectric constant) as a function of temperature. A change in slope of the curve so obtained is taken as the glass transition temperature. Probably the simplest method for determining T_g when it lies above room temperature is differential thermal analysis (DTA) (61), which was briefly described in Section III-3.

For most homopolymers having crystalline and amorphous regions it is a general rule of thumb that the glass transition temperature, T_g, is two-thirds of the crystalline melting point, T_m, both expressed in °K. (69). Laterally symmetrical polymers [e.g., polyethylene, poly(vinylidene fluoride)] appear to have T_g equal to one-half T_m in °K. (70). Polymers with in-chain carbonyls cannot be laterally symmetrical.

Table 2.2

Glass Transition Temperatures of Some Polymers

Polymer	T_m, °C.	T_g, °C.	$(T_g, °K.)/(T_m, °K.)$	Ref.
—CH₂—CH— (| Cl)	—	75	—	72
—CH₂—CH— (| CO₂CH₃)	—	0	—	73
cis-CH₂—C=CH—CH₂— (CH₃)	27	−72	0.67	69
trans-CH₂—C=CHCH₂— (CH₃)	60	−53	0.67	74
—NH(CH₂)₆NHC(=O)—(CH₂)₄—C(=O)—	265	50	0.60	69
—O(CH₂)₂O—C(=O)—(CH₂)₄—C(=O)—	50	−70	0.63	69
—O(CH₂)₂O—C(=O)—⟨C₆H₄⟩—C(=O)—	270	80	0.65	69
—Si—O— (CH₃ / CH₃)	—	−123	—	75

Since the determination of T_g experimentally requires somewhat specialized equipment, no procedure is given here. T_g is a rate phenomenon and not a true physical constant, although the matter is not without debate (71). It is one of the most difficult physical values to determine on polymers with precision. Experimenters using different methods, samples, and interpretation, frequently obtain values on the same polymer that differ markedly. For this reason, the two-thirds or one-half rule is considered here as a reasonable method of estimation. The limitation, of course, is that the polymers have a determinable crystalline melting point.

T_g is of value as an indication of temperatures for drawing films or fibers, and in other aspects of fabrication. Drawing of fibers, for instance, must usually be done at, or somewhat above, T_g. The position of T_g determines the basic character of the polymer, as either a rubber or a hard solid (plastic or fiber) depending on whether T_g is substantially above or below the use temperature of a polymer. Table 2.2 shows the approximate glass transition temperature of typical polymers, along with crystalline melting point, T_m, where applicable.

5. OTHER THERMAL CHARACTERIZATION METHODS

A. Polymer-Melt Temperature (PMT)

For many polymers, one of the simplest observations that can be made is the temperature at which a polymer sample simply becomes visually soft or molten. The polymer-melt temperature, PMT, is defined as that temperature where a polymer sample becomes molten and leaves a trail when moved across a hot metal surface with moderate pressure (7). A polymer may become rubbery or soften before becoming molten, particularly if largely amorphous. Where a polymer is of very high molecular weight, it may show an anomalously high PMT because of a high melt viscosity. Some polymers decompose before becoming molten. The temperature at which any such behavior occurs should be noted, as well as the best estimate of the PMT, or the PMT range.

This test reveals some practical information about the polymer in terms of fabrication. It can serve as a guide to proper temperatures for molding, melt extruding, melt pressing, and an indication of the thermal stability.

For highly crystalline polymers, the PMT may occur rather sharply, over a narrow range, usually a few degrees below the crystalline melting point. Amorphous polymers exhibit a PMT over a wider temperature range, frequently with noticeable softening at a lower temperature. The

Fig. 2.44. Determination of polymer-melt temperature.

PMT may be determined on polymer in any form, e.g., as powder stroked with a spatula along the heated surface, or as a film or solid plug manipulated by hand as in Fig. 2.44, where a modified Dennis bar (see below) is the hot surface. A tendency to thermoset on heating also may be observed in this test on polymers which soften or become molten, then resolidify. On cooling and reheating, such samples are usually found to be infusible.

A convenient apparatus is a modified Dennis bar (76), shown in Fig. 2.45; a temperature gradient between the ends of the bar is measured potentiometrically at a number of points. Such a bar may be used to

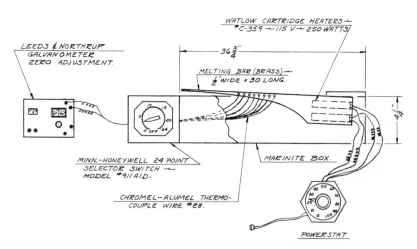

Fig. 2.45. Apparatus for determining PMT.

determine polymer-melt temperatures up to 350–400°C. The test is somewhat subjective, particularly for amorphous polymers, but has the advantage of speed and simplicity coupled with the observation of potentially useful thermal behavior of the polymer.

It should be noted that for amorphous polymers no "melting point" can be validly assigned, since melting is a phenomenon restricted to crystalline materials. Polymer-melt temperature means only what was said for it above; it is a temperature or temperature range where a polymer leaves a molten trail under the conditions given. It can be applied, therefore, to amorphous as well as crystalline material.

B. Durrans Mercury Method

In addition to the method described in the preceding section for estimating the polymer-melt temperature, other techniques have been developed that have found specific application to a class of polymers. One of these is the Durrans mercury method (77), which has been used extensively in the characterization of soluble, fusible epoxy resins before they are crosslinked. The method determines the temperature at which a given weight of mercury will break through a resin on which it is placed. The following procedure is recommended for use in characterizing the epoxy resins prepared in Chapter 7.

Three grams of resin is placed in a 17 × 150 mm. test tube and the contents heated to melt the resin. A thermometer is inserted in the melt. After the resin is allowed to cool to room temperature or cooled in ice in order to form a solid plug in the tube, 50 g. of mercury is added to the tube. The tube and contents are then heated in a bath to effect a temperature rise of 2°C./min. The temperature at which the resin first appears above the surface of the mercury is taken as the softening or melting point. This determination should be done in a hood.

The method can be applied to any class of polymers that are not degraded on heating and which flow sufficiently on heating to allow penetration by the mercury. Standardized conditions (weight of resin and mercury, size of tube, type of thermometer, heating rate, etc.) are necessary for making valid comparisons of different polymer samples. The Durrans mercury method requires no special equipment and can be carried out rapidly with a minimum of subjectivity under standardized conditions.

C. The Vicat Needle Method

For many hard plastic materials, thermal characterization consists in part, at least, of a determination of the temperature at which a given distortion occurs under specified condition of stress. For example, in the Vicat method (78–80), the standard sample (minimum width, $\frac{3}{4}$ in. and thickness, $\frac{1}{8}$ in.) is heated at a given rate (50°C./hr.) while a needle (having a point with an area 1 mm.^{2}) under a definite pressure (usually not exceeding 1 kg.) is applied to the surface of the sample. The temperature at which a 1 mm. penetration of the needle occurs is taken as the softening point. The test can be applied to polyethylene, polystyrene, and polyacrylics with a precision of 2°C. For nonrigid poly-(vinyl chloride), poly(vinylidene chloride), and some others, the Vicat softening range is too large to permit such precision. A Vicat apparatus may be purchased commercially.

D. Heat Deflection Temperature (HDT) (81)

This parameter is one of the most commonly cited for the characterization of plastics (81). It refers to the temperature at which a molded bar (5 in. × $\frac{1}{2}$ in. × $\frac{1}{8}$ – $\frac{1}{2}$ in.) supported at both ends undergoes a deflection of 0.010 in. when exposed to a temperature rise of 2°C./min. under a fiber stress of 66 or 264 p.s.i. applied across the center of the bar. There are again commercially available units for this purpose; some can be converted for determining the Vicat temperature as well as HDT. Often Vicat temperature is more convenient because less sample is required and the test specimen is easier to prepare. Vicat temperatures and HDT's have been correlated for several polymers (80).

E. Flow Properties

Although the crystalline melting and glass temperatures are those elements of thermal behavior usually first encountered in characterizing a polymer, especially for the organic chemist, the flow characteristics of a polymer melt or solution as a function of temperature and applied stress are a matter of great practical importance. The rheological characterization of polymers is beyond the scope of this book, but at least one method of flow determination should be noted because of its simplicity and the wide application it has had. This is the so-called melt index (82,83), which uses a heated barrel to melt the polymer and a variably weighted piston which fits the barrel and extrudes the melt through an orifice at the bottom of the barrel. Essentially any melt-stable polymer can be tested, providing it is not so fluid as to literally run freely from the barrel nor so stiff-flowing as to defy extrusion with the application of practical weight (force) levels. The test consists of simply weighing the amount of polymer extruded per time and expressing the results as g./10 min. The method is necessarily a one-point determination since shear stress and rate are not easily varied, whereas in more sophisticated methods (e.g., capillary rheometry at variable shear rates (84,85)) the shear stress developed at a wide range of shear rates (and, of course, temperatures) can be obtained.

The value of the melt index (sometimes also called melt flow index, depending somewhat capriciously on the polymer under examination) is in the rapid estimation of flow behavior relative to other samples, especially those of the same polymer type. The rheology of molten polymers is a function of molecular weight and of molecular weight distribution as well (86), and the principles involved have been reviewed (87–89).

F. Polymer Degradation via Thermal Gravimetric Analysis (TGA)

For polymers designed to withstand extremely high temperatures, e.g., 300–500°C., for varying periods, the retention of any mechanical properties at all may be sufficient to do the job in question. (Of course, the greater the property retention the better.) It is essential that the material resist degradation to volatile fragments, however, for if it does not, in time there simply may not be enough remaining to be effective. TGA provides an evaluation of weight loss as a function of temperature or of time at a specified temperature. The sample is exposed to a programmed or fixed temperature (dynamic or isothermal conditions, respectively) and the weight of the sample remaining is continuously recorded. The resulting plot of temperature or time versus per cent weight loss is valuable in characterizing would-be high-temperature polymers (90), and its use has proven well-nigh indispensable. TGA units are available commercially, but are quite expensive. For those laboratories engaged in high-temperature polymer work, however, they may be a routine piece of equipment.

TGA is only one method of studying polymer degradation, and is suited to very high temperature work. DTA has already been mentioned. Polymer degradation in light, under thermal processing conditions, and in corrosive chemical environments are other examples. TGA is mentioned particularly because it is a relatively new method and because it permits at least an introduction to the important area of polymer degradation, which is otherwise beyond the intended coverage of this chapter. Much information is available from degradation studies. As an example, gas–liquid chromatography has been combined with polymer pyrolysis to permit identification of unknown polymers to give information on composition and structure (e.g., degree of block copolymer character), and mechanism of degradation (91,92).

6. POLYMER SOLUBILITY

The solubility of a polymer is an important part of its characterization (93). For polymers that are not melt-stable, fabrication via their solutions is often the only method available. Determination of molecular weight by solution viscosity methods (see Molecular Weight Determination) requires that a suitable solvent be found.

The determination of chain dimensions, which can then be related to polymer microstructure, has already been noted under solution viscometric molecular weight determination (Section II).

As is to be expected, degree of crystallinity and molecular weight of a polymer affect its solubility. For these reasons solubility behavior may vary from sample to sample of a given polymer. As a generalization, the solubility relationships presented in Table 2.3 have been recognized. Table 2.3 is not an exhaustive list of solvents or solubilities, but shows some typical examples.

Crosslinked polymers do not show normal solubility. Such polymers may swell under the influence of certain solvents. The fact of swelling by itself is not proof of crosslinking, however, since a polymer on the borderline of solubility may exhibit this behavior. But, when a polymer resists solubility in a number of solvents typical for those of its class, and is infusible as well, it is usually considered to be crosslinked unless there is compelling evidence to the contrary.

Solubility in sulfuric acid is usually a characteristic of polymers with functional groups. Degradation may occur in this and other potent acidic solvents such as trifluoroacetic acid, however.

Solvent mixtures are sometimes more effective than a single solvent; e.g., alcohol–benzene for certain cellulose derivatives, carbon disulfide–acetone for poly(vinyl chloride), and nitromethane–water for polyacrylonitrile. Mixed solvents are usually most effective when each component is a near-solvent for the polymer or when the solvents mutually interact as, for example, by hydrogen bonding.

Many of the structural aspects of polymer molecules that affect solubility and melting point are those that affect these same properties in simple organic molecules also. For instance, crystallinity, high symmetry, hydrogen bonding, high polarity, chain stiffness, and stereoregularity in the chain, contribute to higher melting point and reduced solubility compared to an otherwise similar polymer lacking the feature in question. The following procedure is useful for a rapid, qualitative determination of solubility.

A small amount of polymer, about 0.1 g., is mixed with about 2 ml. of solvent in a test tube and stirred together thoroughly. An indication

Table 2.3

Some General Polymer–Solvent Systems

Polymer	Solvent
Polyamides	Acidic solvents; formic acid, *m*-cresol
Polysulfonamides (having —NH—)	Basic solvents; 10% aqueous sodium hydroxide, dimethyl formamide
Polyurethanes	Chlorinated solvents; methylene chloride, chloroform, mixtures of methylene chloride or chloroform with 10–20% by weight of methanol
Polyesters	Chlorinated solvents; trichloroethane, dichlorobenzene; see also polyurethanes
Vinyl polymers	Ketones, aromatic hydrocarbons, cyclic ethers, esters, chlorinated solvents; see specific examples below
Poly(vinyl alcohol)	Water
Poly(vinyl chloride)	Tetrahydrofuran, cyclohexanone, dimethylformamide, nitrobenzene
Poly(vinyl acetate)	Acetone, methyl ethyl ketone
Polystyrene	Xylene, butyl acetate, carbon tetrachloride
Polyacrylic and methacrylic esters	Methyl ethyl ketone, tetrahydrofuran
Polyacrylonitrile	Dimethylformamide, dimethyl sulfoxide, ethylene carbonate
Hydrocarbon polymers	Decalin,[a] benzene, xylene
Most O-, N-, or S-containing polymers (uncrosslinked)	Sulfuric acid, occasionally with decomposition
Resins in soluble stage, before crosslinking	Ketones, acids, alcohols, water, ethers, hydrocarbons, halogenated solvents; see examples below
Alkyds (phthalic acid–glycerol type; varies with extent and type of modification)	Acetone, methyl ethyl ketone, acetic acid, butyl acetate, toluene
Phenol–formaldehyde condensates	Alcohol, acetone, Cellosolve[b]
Urea or melamine–formaldehyde condensates	Water, butanol, toluene (when resin is partially etherified)
Epoxy	Ethylene dichloride, benzene, dioxane

[a] Trademark for du Pont's decahydronaphthalene solvent.
[b] Trademark for Union Carbide Corporation's solvent.

of solubility is "schlieren" as the mixture is stirred. Solubility is usually facilitated by the use of polymer in a finely divided state. If no sign of solubility occurs at room temperature, the mixture should be heated gently to the boiling point of the solvent, or near it. If polymer dissolves, the solution should be allowed to cool to see if polymer remains in solution or precipitates. If polymer is swollen by a solvent, but not dissolved, related solvents should be checked to see if they will effect solution, either singly or in combination. Swelling without dissolving, even in the most potent solvents for the polymer type, should be taken as an indication of crosslinking. However, many crosslinked resins will have extractable fractions which may be highly branched. These fractions are of relatively low molecular weight in most cases, having not yet reached the crosslinked stage.

Table 2.4

Designations for Effect of Solvent on Polymer Sample

0 = Unaffected by hot solvent
1 = Melted or sticky in hot solvent
2 = Partly soluble in hot solvent
3 = Soluble in hot solvent, precipitated cold
4 = Soluble in hot solvent, remains soluble cold
5 = Soluble in cold solvent

Solubility categories of polymers have been suggested by Beaman and Cramer (7) to describe the apparent interaction of polymer and solvent. These are given in Table 2.4.

Polymer purification is very often effected by dissolving the polymer in a solvent and precipitating by pouring the solution slowly, while stirring, into an excess of a nonsolvent which is miscible with the solvent. For careful analytical and characterization work, several reprecipitations may be necessary.

A variation (94) of this traditional approach involves dissolving the polymer in five to fifty volumes of what is ordinarily a borderline solvent or a nonsolvent (e.g., 6–6 nylon in ethanol, polyethylene in hexane, polystyrene in acetone) and heating the mixture to about 150°C. in a bomb to bring about solution. On cooling, the polymer is obtained in a fine, granular form, with most impurities retained by the solvent.

Dialysis can also be employed in polymer purification (94a).

Burrell (95) along with others has developed the solubility parameter concept to a very useful level in practical terms. Polymer solubilities become reasonably predictable, at least to the extent of reducing experiments to a minimum. The system is best adapted, but not entirely limited to, amorphous polymers. The solubility parameter of a material is defined as the square root of the cohesive energy density (energy of vaporization/cc.). Determinable or calculable for solvents, it must be estimated experimentally for polymers, for which a solubility parameter range is best stated. Tables of values have been compiled (96). Solvents are best chosen from those in the range of the solubility parameter for a given polymer. Reasonable choices of mixed solvents can also be made.

References

1. R. M. Fitch, M. B. Prenosil, and K. J. Sprick, *Polymer Div., Am. Chem. Soc., Polymer Preprints*, **7** (2), 707 (1966).
2. G. G. McClaflin, private communication.
3. M. Schütze, *Angew. Chem.*, **70**, 697 (1958).
4. L. F. Fieser, *Experiments in Organic Chemistry*, 3rd ed., Heath, Boston, 1955.
5. Donald Goodman, private communication.
5a. W. R. Sorenson, *J. Chem. Educ.*, **42**, 8 (1965); A. V. Tobolsky, U.S. Pat. 3,291,859 (Dec. 13, 1966).
5b. C. D. Kennedy, private communication.
6. D. D. Coffman, G. J. Berchet, W. R. Peterson, and E. W. Spanagel, *J. Polymer Sci.*, **2**, 306 (1947).
7. R. G. Beaman, and F. B. Cramer, *J. Polymer Sci.*, **21**, 223 (1956); R. N. Blomberg, U.S. Pat. 2,965, 437 (Dec. 20, 1960) (to du Pont).
8. P. A. Schwab and L. Rose, private communication.
9. D. E. Steutz, *J. Appl. Polymer Sci.*, **10**, 833 (1966).
10. G. Natta, G. Mazzanti, A. Valvassori, G. Sartori, and A. Barbagallo, *J. Polymer Sci.*, **51**, 429 (1961).
11. D. B. Miller and J. Heller, private communication.
12. R. W. Magin and H. G. Nunnamaker, *J. Polymer Sci. A-1*, **4**, 2328 (1966).
13. D. V. N. Hardy, *J. Soc. Chem. Ind., Trans.*, **67**, 426 (1948).
14. M. Morton, Ed., *Introduction to Rubber Technology*, Reinhold, New York, 1959.
15. J. D. Murdock and G. H. Segall, *Offic. Dig. Federation Soc. Paint Technol.*, **33**, 709 (1961).
16. R. L. Miller, *S.P.E. Trans.*, **3**, 123 (1963).
17. D. W. McCall and W. P. Schlichter, in *Newer Methods of Polymer Characterization*, B. Ke, Ed., Interscience, New York, 1964.
18. H. J. Harwood, *Angew. Chem. Intern. Ed. Engl.*, **4**, 1051 (1965).
19. P. W. Allen, Ed., *Techniques of Polymer Characterization*, Academic Press, New York, 1959: Butterworths, London, 1959.
20. F. B. Rolfson and H. Coll, *Anal. Chem.*, **36**, 888 (1964).
21. J. van Dam, *Rec. Trav. Chim.*, **83**, 129 (1964).

22. K. Stacey, *Light Scattering in Physical Chemistry*, Academic Press, New York, 1956.
23. F. W. Billmeyer, Jr., in *Treatise on Analytical Chemistry*, Vol. 5, Part 1, I. M. Kolthoff and P. J. Elving, Eds., Wiley, New York, 1964.
24. R. L. Baldwin and K. E. Van Holde, *Fortschr. Hochpolymer. Forsch.*, **1**, 451 (1960).
25. J. J. Hermans and H. A. Ende, in reference 17.
26. J. E. Blair, *J. Polymer Sci. C*, **8**, 287 (1965).
27. H. Mark, *Der Feste Korper*, 1938, 65–104; R. Houwink, *J. Prakt. Chem.*, **1957**, 15 (1940).
28. H. Staudinger and W. Heuer, *Ber.*, **63**, 222 (1930).
29. E. R. Blout and M. Idelson, *J. Am. Chem. Soc.*, **80**, 4909 (1958).
30. W. J. Bailey and H. R. Golden, *J. Am. Chem. Soc.*, **76**, 5418 (1954).
31. C. S. Marvel and R. D. Vest, *J. Am. Chem. Soc.*, **79**, 5771 (1957).
32. N. S. Schneider, *J. Polymer Sci. C*, **8**, 179 (1965).
33. G. Meyerhof, *Advan. Polymer Sci.*, **3**, 59 (1961).
34. M. Kurata and W. H. Stockmeyer, ibid,, **3**, 196 (1963).
35. J. Brandrup and E. H. Immergut, Eds., *Polymer Handbook*, Interscience, New York, 1966.
36. G. V. Schultz, W. Wunderlich, and R. Kirste, *Makromol. Chem.*, **74**, 22 (1964).
37. A. Nakajima and K. Kato, ibid., **95**, 52 (1966).
38. J. C. Moore, *J. Polymer Sci. A*, **2**, 1835 (1964).
39. R. M. Screaton, in reference 17.
40. G. M. Guyman in *Progress in High Polymers*, Vol. 1, J. C. Robb and F. W. Peaker, Eds., Academic Press, New York.
41. J. Klein and E. Killman, *Makromol. Chem.*, **96**, 193 (1966).
42. D. F. Slonamaker, R. L. Combs, J. E. Guillet, and H. W. Coover, Jr., *J. Polymer Sci. A-2*, **4**, 523 (1966).
43. A. S. Kenyon, I. O. Salyer, J. E. Kurz, and D. R. Brown, *J. Polymer Sci. C*, **8**, 205 (1965).
44. J. Cazes, *J. Chem. Educ.*, **43**, A567, A625 (1966).
45. Am. Soc. Testing Materials, ASTM Standards, Pt. 9, D 1243-58T and D 1601-58T, Philadelphia, 1958, pp. 530 and 534.
46. R. N. Bonnar, M. Dimbat, and F. H. Stross, *Number Average Molecular Weights*, Interscience, New York, 1958.
47. M. G. Evans, *J. Chem. Soc.*, **1947**, 266.
48. C. C. Price and B. E. Tate, *J. Am. Chem. Soc.*, **65**, 517 (1943).
49. J. C. Bevington, H. W. Melville, and R. P. Taylor, *J. Polymer Sci.*, **14**, 463 (1954); **12**, 449 (1954).
50. L. Mandelkern, *Chem. Rev.*, **56**, 903 (1956).
51. P. Fijolka, I. Lenz, and F. Runge, *Makromol. Chem.*, **23**, 60 (1957).
52. J. E. Waltz and G. B. Taylor, *Anal. Chem.*, **19**, 448 (1947).
53. H. Zahn and P. Rathgeber, *Melliand Textilber,*. **34**, 749 (1953).
54. C. L. Ogg, W. L. Porter, and C. O. Willits, *Ind. Eng. Chem., Anal. Ed.*, **17**, 394 (1945).
55. A. Conix, *Makromol. Chem.*, **26**, 226 (1958).
56. I. M. Ward, *Trans. Faraday Soc.*, **53**, 1406 (1957).
57. C. A. Glover and J. E. Kirn, *J. Polymer Sci.*, **B3**, 27 (1965).
58. P. H. Geil, *Polymer Single Crystals*, Interscience, New York, 1963.
59. W. O. Statton, ASTM Spec. Tech. Publ., **247**, Philadelphia, 1959.

60. C. W. Bunn, in *Fibers from Synthetic Polymers*, R. Hill, Ed., chaps. 10 and 11, Elsevier, New York, 1953.
61. B. Ke, in reference 17.
62. L. Mandelkern, *Crystallization of Polymers*, McGraw-Hill, New York, 1964.
63. J. D. Hoffman, *S.P.E. Trans.*, **4**, 315 (1964).
64. F. P. Price, *ibid.*, **4**, 1 (1964).
65. P. H. Lindenmeyer, *Science*, **147**, 1256 (1965); *S.P.E. Trans.*, **4**, 157 (1964).
66. H. G. Zachman, *Advan. Polymer Sci.*, **3**, 581 (1964).
67. P. J. Flory, L. Mandelkern, and H. K. Hall, Jr., *J. Am. Chem. Soc.*, **73**, 2532 (1951).
68. A. Tobolsky, *Properties and Structure in Polymers*, Wiley, New York, 1960.
69. R. G. Beaman, *J. Polymer Sci.*, **9**, 470 (1952).
70. R. F. Boyer, *J. Appl. Phys.*, **25**, 825 (1954).
71. E. A. Dimarzio and J. H. Gibbs, *J. Polymer Sci. A*, **1**, 1417 (1963).
72. R. F. Clash, Jr. and L. M. Rynkiewicz, *Ind. Eng. Chem.*, **36**, 279 (1944).
73. R. H. Wiley and G. M. Brauer, *J. Polymer Sci.*, **3**, 647 (1948).
74. K. Überreiter, *Z. Physik Chem.*, B**45**, 361 (1940).
75. C. E. Weir, W. H. Leser, and L. A. Wood, *Rubber Chem. Technol.*, **24**, 366 (1951).
76. L. M. Dennis and R. S. Shelton, *J. Am. Chem. Soc.*, **52**, 3128 (1930).
77. T. H. Durrans, *J. Oil Colour Chem. Assoc.*, **12**, 173 (1929), *Chem. Abstr.*, **23**, 4355 (1929).
78. *ASTM Bull.* D 1525-65T.
79. R. Houwink, *Plastomers and Elastomers*, Vol. III, p. 53. Elsevier, New York, 1948.
80. C. E. Stephenson and A. H. Willbourn, ASTM Spec. Tech. Publ. No. 247, Am. Soc. Testing Materials, Philadelphia, 1959.
81. *ASTM Bull* D648-58 (1961).
82. A. Rudin and H. P. Schreiber, *S.P.E. J.*, **20**, 533 (1964).
83. ASTM D1238-62T.
84. R. L. Ballman and J. J. Brown, *Instron Eng.*, *Tech. Bull.* SA-2.
85. E. H. Merz and R. E. Colwell, *ASTM Bull.* **232**, 63 (1958).
86. R. S. Hagan, D. P. Thomas, and W. R. Schlich, *Polymer Eng. Sci.*, **6**, 373 (1966).
87. G. Pezzin, *Materie Plastiche ed Elastomeri*, **14** (8), 80 (1962).
88. E. H. Merz, *S.P.E. J.*, **19**, 735 (1963).
89. A. B. Metzner, in *Processing of Thermoplastic Materials*, E. C. Bernhardt, Ed., Reinhold, New York, 1959.
90. J. Chiu, *Appl. Polymer Symp.*, **2**, 25 (1965).
91. J. Van Schooten and J. S. Evenhuis, *Polymer*, **6**, 343 (1965).
92. U. Gokcen and D. M. Cates, *Appl. Polymer Symp.*, **2**, 15 (1965).
93. F. W. Billmeyer, Jr., *Polymer Sci. Eng.*, **6**, 359 (1966).
94. R. M. Joshi, *J. Appl. Polymer Sci.*, **10**, 1806 (1966).
94a. C. H. H. Neufeld and C. S. Marvel, *J. Polymer Sci. A-1*, **4**, 2907 (1966).
95. H. Burrell, Preprints, *Org. Coating and Plastics Div.*, **28** (1), 682 (1968); *Offic. Dig. Federation Soc. Paint Technol.*, **34**, 131 (Feb., 1962).
96. H. Burrell, in reference 35, IV, p. 341.

CHAPTER 3

Polycondensation and Hydrogen Transfer Polymerization

Condensation reactions in organic chemistry are among the most useful reactions for the synthesis of organic compounds, so it is not surprising that many of them have been used successfully in the preparation of high polymers from difunctional molecules. The common attribute to all condensation reactions is the linking together of two molecules with the formation of a new bond, and the elimination of by-product molecule,

$$A + B \longrightarrow A—B + C$$

where A and B are coreactive function molecules and C is the by-product. If molecules having two condensable groups each are brought together, polymer will result if the reaction conditions are chosen properly. The polymerizable reactants may be of the AA and BB type, or the AB type. Polymerization would be represented as:

$$n\,AA + n\,BB \longrightarrow [—AA—BB—]_n + 2n\,C$$

and

$$n\,AB \longrightarrow [—A—B—]_n + n\,C$$

The following reactants are examples: AA = hexamethylenediamine, BB = adipic acid, AB = ϵ-aminocaproic acid.

The number of condensation reactions is very large, and many of them have been turned to the formation of polymers. A list of these (Table 3.1) would include the following, which could be used in either of the generalized types of equations above, where A and B represent various functional molecules.

Polymers formed by such polycondensation reactions are termed "condensation polymers." However, the term "condensation polymer" also includes any polymer whose structure indicates that it could have been prepared by a condensation reaction. For instance, the addition of a diol to a diisocyanate forms a polyurethane which is structurally a condensation polymer by this definition, although it was

Table 3.1

Examples of Condensation Types

A	B	Polymer formed	C
R—OH	R—CO$_2$H	Polyester	H$_2$O
R—NH$_2$	R—COCl	Polyamide	HCl
R—NH$_2$	R—NH—CO$_2$R	Polyurea	ROH
R—NH$_2$	R—CO$_2$H	Polyamide	H$_2$O
R—OH	R—COCl	Polyester	HCl
R—CO$_2$H	R—CO$_2$H	Polyanhydride	H$_2$O
R—SH	R—Cl	Polythioether	HCl
R—SO$_2$Cl	R—NH$_2$	Polysulfonamide	HCl
R—OCOCl	R—NH$_2$	Polyurethane	HCl
R—NH$_2$	R—NH—COSH	Polyurea	H$_2$S

prepared, not from a condensation, but from an addition reaction without by-product elimination:

$$\text{OCN—R—NCO} + \text{HO—R'—OH} \longrightarrow \left[\text{—NHR—NH—}\overset{\displaystyle O}{\overset{\displaystyle \|}{C}}\text{—O—R'—O—}\overset{\displaystyle O}{\overset{\displaystyle \|}{C}}\text{—} \right]_n$$

It is a condensation polymer because it could conceivably have been prepared from either of the condensation reactions:

$$\text{HO}_2\text{C—HN—R—NH—CO}_2\text{H} + \text{HO—R'—OH} \longrightarrow$$
$$\left[\text{—NH—R—NH—}\overset{\displaystyle O}{\overset{\displaystyle \|}{C}}\text{—O—R'—O—}\overset{\displaystyle O}{\overset{\displaystyle \|}{C}}\text{—} \right]_n + \text{H}_2\text{O}$$

$$\text{H}_2\text{N—R—NH}_2 + \text{Cl—}\overset{\displaystyle O}{\overset{\displaystyle \|}{C}}\text{—OR'—O—}\overset{\displaystyle O}{\overset{\displaystyle \|}{C}}\text{—Cl} \longrightarrow$$
$$\left[\text{NH—R—NH—}\overset{\displaystyle O}{\overset{\displaystyle \|}{C}}\text{—O—R'—O—}\overset{\displaystyle O}{\overset{\displaystyle \|}{C}} \right]_n + \text{HCl}$$

In this chapter, then, methods for preparing condensation polymers will be presented which involve true condensation reactions between functional groups, and those reactions which involve the addition of active hydrogen compounds to receptive molecules. The diol–diisocyanate reaction cited is an example of the latter. Before beginning a discussion of these polymerization processes, it would be well to point out that, although the condensation and addition reactions involved are those familiar in principle or practice to most organic chemists, the most important difference, besides the polyfunctionality of the reactants, is that only reactions which proceed in extremely high yield will form high polymer. While an organic reaction may be considered to be of excellent preparative value if it forms the desired product in 90% yield, it is immediately clear that in order to obtain high molecular weight condensation polymers, the yield must be essentially 100%. (See, however, examples of interfacial polycondensation for exceptions.) The last stage of the reaction brings together the ends of fairly large molecules to produce the desired very large molecules. In order to achieve this kind of efficiency, reactions must be substantially free of chain-terminating side reactions, and the reactants must be of the utmost purity. In most, but not all, polycondensations an exact equivalence of reactants is also required.

Branching may occur in certain types of condensation polymers. An example of branching is shown below, where, in an isocyanate–diol addition reaction, a urethane hydrogen along the polymer chain may add to a terminal isocyanate group of another growing chain:

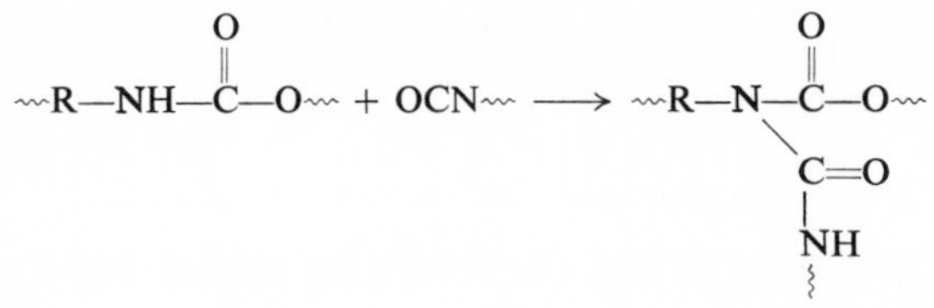

$$
\underset{\displaystyle \sim\!\!\text{R—NH—}\overset{\displaystyle \text{O}}{\overset{\|}{\text{C}}}\text{—O}\!\sim}{}\ +\ \text{OCN}\!\sim\ \longrightarrow\ \sim\!\!\text{R—N—}\overset{\displaystyle \text{O}}{\overset{\|}{\text{C}}}\text{—O}\!\sim
$$

with branch:
$$
\begin{array}{c}
\text{C}\!=\!\text{O} \\
| \\
\text{NH} \\
\{
\end{array}
$$

Such a reaction is not a favored one if any hydroxyl ends still remain; but in the presence of excess isocyanate ends and with sufficient heat, such a reaction becomes a threat to the linearity of the polymer. Cross-linking, the formation of a space network polymer, may result in the above example or one in which reactants are used with functionality greater than 2, for example a triamine or a tricarboxylic acid.

The molecular weight distribution in condensation polymers depends on the polymer type, on the kind of polymerization reactions involved, and on the conditions prevailing during the process.

The quantitative aspects of condensation polymerization, including kinetics, molecular weight distribution, and effect of polyfunctionality on branching and gelation, have been thoroughly treated elsewhere and will not be considered.

The polymer preparations in this chapter are arranged as far as possible, according to the polymer class: polyamide, polyurethane, polyurea, etc. Examples of specific polymer-forming reactions (e.g., reaction of an active hydrogen compound with an acid halide) are dispersed throughout the chapter. Discussion of some of the more important condensation and hydrogen transfer addition reactions precede the first usage of the reaction.

Some examples of reactions on polymers are also included, and follow the preparation of the polymer itself. They point up the applicability of normal organic reactions to polymers and demonstrate property changes due to structural alteration.

Because of the similarity of experimental procedure in several instances, certain preparations are repeatedly referred to because of the detailed directions provided. For example, the basic technique of melt polymerization is given for polyamides in the preparation of poly-(hexamethylenedipamide) and for polyesters with poly(ethylene terephthalate). A number of other polymer preparations use these procedures with variations as required. In most cases, vacuum cycles are necessary and in some a sealed tube heating cycle is used which involves considerable pressure build-up. In both cases, sufficient shielding of equipment is an essential and fundamental safety practice. Where direct handling of pressured or evacuated equipment is required, the operator should wear protective gloves and face mask or goggles. The routine use of safety glasses or goggles is a laboratory practice strongly recommended under any circumstances.

I. Polyamides and Related Polymers

The reaction of a primary or secondary amine with a carboxylic acid to form an amide is a well-known organic reaction. The same reaction involving difunctional molecules is a convenient way of preparing polyamides and related polymers. The reaction is carried out, customarily, by heating the reactants together above the melting point of the final product, and driving the process to completion by removing the last traces of water, usually with the assistance of a high vacuum and/or the sweep of an inert gas. The technique is limited to starting materials and products that are stable to heat above their melting points. For polymerization of AA with BB, stoichiometric amounts of reactants are essential, which is assured by the preparation of a balanced salt of the diamine and diacid. In the case of an amino acid, an AB reactant, the required balance of functionality is a built-in feature of the molecule.

Probably the classic example of a diamine–diacid condensation is the preparation of polyhexamethyleneadipamide from hexamethylene-diamine and adipic acid (1). The term "nylon" was originally coined as the generic name for all long chain synthetic polyamides, which were then distinguished by adding numbers to the generic title to designate the constituents of the polymers. Thus, the polymer named above became 6-6 nylon, or 6-6 polyamide since there are six carbons in the diamine chain (designated first) and six carbons in the diacid chain.

The nylon from tetramethylenediamine and sebacic acid is 4-10, and that from ϵ-aminocaproic acid is simply 6, the number of carbon atoms in the chain.

As a class, polyamides are high-melting materials whose properties depend, in large part, on the high interchain attraction due to the occurrence of hydrogen bonding sites (both donor, —NH—, and acceptor, —C=O) along the chains. They usually can be made to crystallize easily and are often found to be highly crystalline as prepared. In general, the longer the distance between amide groups, the lower the melting point of the polymer. The qualification must be added that as the number of carbons is increased in either the diamine or diacid portion, the melting point decreases in an alternating fashion, with the polymers from intermediates having an odd number of carbons melting lower than those having an even number. Table 3.2 illustrates this point.

Table 3.2

Polyamide	Polymer melt temperature, °C.	Polyamide	Polymer melt temperature, °C.
4–6	308	4–10	236
5–6	223	5–10	186
6–6	265	6–10	228

Polyamides have been made from diamines and diacids with exceptionally long methylene chain units, e.g., acids up to 22 carbons and amines up to 18 (2,3). As might be expected, melting points are generally lowered as the number of methylene units increases; some examples are:

Nylon	T_m, °C.
8–22	175
12–22	164
18–22	146
12–12	178
12–18	167

Isomorphism of —CH$_2$—, —O—, and —S— units was found in polymers of this type, including those with p-xylylenediamine.

The preparation of **6-6 polyamide,** which follows, is typical of the methods used in **melt-polymerization.** Most of the aliphatic polyamides can be made by the basic technique described. The most certain way of achieving reactant balance is through the use of the diamine salt of the dicarboxylic acid, as in the following example.

1. Preparation of Hexamethylenediamine-adipic Acid Salt (6-6 Salt)

In a 250 ml. Erlenmeyer flask is placed 14.60 g. (0.100 mole) adipic acid. The acid is dissolved in 110 ml. absolute ethyl alcohol by warming, and then is cooled to room temperature. A solution of 11.83 g. (0.012 mole) hexamethylenediamine (b.p. 90–92°C./14 mm., m.p. 41–42°C.) in 20 ml. absolute ethyl alcohol is added quantitatively to the adipic acid solution. The mixing is accompanied by spontaneous warming. Crystallization soon occurs. After standing overnight, the salt is filtered, washed with cold absolute alcohol, and air-dried to constant weight. The yield is 25.5 g. (97%). A 2% excess of diamine is used to promote a salt which is rich in diamine, since this is the more volatile component and may be lost during salt drying or during polycondensation. The white crystalline salt melts at 196–197C. and has a pH of about 7.6, determined on a 1% solution of salt in water, using a pH meter.

A pH tolerance of 0.5 unit is usually acceptable, especially on the high side because of possible diamine loss, as noted above. Salt imbalance may be corrected by recrystallization or the after-addition of a small amount of the indicated component. Salts of low and high pH may be mixed to give a balanced composition of the proper pH.

2. Preparation of Poly(hexamethyleneadipamide) (6-6 Nylon) (4)

$$\left[H_3\overset{+}{N}-(CH_2)_6-\overset{+}{N}H_3\right]\left[\overset{-}{O}-\overset{\overset{O}{\|}}{C}-(CH_2)_4-\overset{\overset{O}{\|}}{C}-\overset{-}{O}\right] \longrightarrow$$

$$\left[-NH-(CH_2)_6-NH-\overset{\overset{O}{\|}}{C}-(CH_2)_4-\overset{\overset{O}{\|}}{C}-\right]_n + H_2O$$

Twenty g. 6-6 salt is charged into a polymer tube using a polymer tube funnel (see Chapter 2). A constriction is made in the upper half of the neck of the tube with a glass-blowing torch. The tube is connected to a three-way stopcock, which connects to a vacuum pump and a source of low pressure (about 5 p.s.i.) nitrogen. The tube is purged of air by alternately evacuating to about 0.5 mm. and filling with nitrogen. After three or four such cycles, the constriction is sealed shut by means of a torch while the tube is evacuated.

The tube is placed in a steel tube open at the top and immersed in a salt bath heated at 215°C. for 1½–2 hr. The *heated tube is a potential bomb* and should be handled with due care. The salt bath is shielded in the front, with an access door at the side. The hand and arm used to manipulate the tube should be protected with a leather–asbestos glove and a leather gauntlet. The sealed tube step results in the formation of low molecular weight polymer under conditions which prevent escape of volatile diamine. If a shielded salt bath is not available, the tube can be heated in a metal tube immersed in a vapor bath or a Wood's metal bath. The metal shield should surround the tube completely, although it should be open at the top. The entire apparatus should then be shielded additionally, for example with a transparent safety shield.

After completion of this first heating cycle, the sealed polymer tube is removed from the heating bath and allowed to cool to room temperature. Then, the tube is opened behind a barrier after first scoring with a glass-cutting tool. In some melt polycondensations, uncondensed gases such as ammonia or carbon dioxide may be evolved during the sealed tube step, and the cold tubes may be under considerable pressure.

A neck bearing a side arm is sealed onto the polymer tube, the tube is clamped in an upright position and the side arm connected with pressure tubing to a trap which comprises a 50 ml. round-bottom flask fitted with an adapter. The trap is connected via a three-way stopcock, both to a vacuum pump and to a source of nitrogen. The top of the tube is fitted with a short section of rubber tubing. An inlet comprising a 7–8 mm. o.d. glass capillary tubing drawn out to a fine tip is fitted through the rubber tubing, with the end reaching to the bottom of the polymer tube. The inlet sometimes cannot be brought to the bottom of the tube until the polymer has been remelted. The inlet is connected to a source of low-pressure nitrogen.

The tube is purged of air by alternately evacuating and flushing with nitrogen. It is then heated by a 270°C. vapor bath (see Chapter 2). After 30–60 min. heating at atmospheric pressure, the polymer is gradually brought to high vacuum by manipulating the three-way stopcock. The heating is continued under vacuum of 0.2–1.5 mm. for about 1 hr. The polycondensation is discontinued when visual inspection of the rate of bubble rise indicates that the maximum melt viscosity has been reached.

Nitrogen is introduced through the stopcock, the inlet tube is raised, and the vapor bath is removed. The polymer is cooled under a gentle nitrogen stream entering through the side arm. The tube is wrapped with a towel during cooling to prevent glass from flying if the polymer tube spontaneously cracks. The tough, white, opaque polymer is removed by breaking the tube and separating the adhering glass by hammering and filing. The recovery is about 14 g. (80%). The inherent viscosity (0.5% conc., m-cresol) is about 1.0–1.4. The polymer has a melt temperature of 265°C., and is soluble in formic acid. Fibers and films may be obtained by melt methods or from formic acid solution.

The preceding method of polycondensation sometimes can be used starting with equivalents of diamine and dicarboxylic acid ester, weighed directly in the polymer tube (Preparation 14). In the latter instance, alcohol is removed instead of water. No "balancing" by salt preparation obtains in these instances.

An alternative method for carrying out polyamidations from a nylon salt is to use a pipe autoclave. This is safer and more convenient but does not allow visual observation of the polymerization (5).

Polymers which decompose below their melting points can sometimes be made by powder polymerization. The polycondensation is carried out to a low molecular weight product and the low polymer is ground in a suitable mill. Nylon salts of the type described above, which melt above 225°C., may be powder polymerized directly. The polycondensation is conducted by heating the ground polymer or high melting salt under vacuum with a nitrogen bleed to carry away the volatile by-Polymer types other than polyamides also may be prepared by powder methods. An example of the use of powder polymerization in the preparation of a polyester is found in Preparation 70.

A method of demonstrating the effect of *N*-alkylation in polyamides is the reaction of the polymer with formaldehyde and methanol to give a partially *N*-methoxymethylated product. The resultant decrease in amide hydrogen bonding has a profound effect on 6-6 polyamide. The polymer melt temperature is reduced, the solubility increased to include nonacidic solvents, and the polymer becomes somewhat rubber-like, depending on the degree of substitution. The following directions are for an *N*-methoxymethyl 6-6 having about 36% substitution on nitrogen. A small portion of the substitution is *N*-methylol. The melt temperature is reduced from 265°C. to 150°C., and the polymer is now soluble in 80% aqueous ethanol as well as in strong acids. The polymer used in this reaction may be prepared by the methods of the preceding example.

3. The *N*-Methoxymethylation of Poly(hexamethyleneadipamide) (6)

$$\left[-HN(CH_2)_6-NH-\overset{\overset{O}{\|}}{C}-(CH_2)_4-\overset{\overset{O}{\|}}{C}- \right]_n \xrightarrow[\text{CH}_3\text{OH}]{\text{CH}_2\text{O}}$$

$$\left[-HN(CH_2)_6-\underset{\underset{\underset{\underset{CH_3}{|}}{O}}{\underset{|}{CH_2}}}{N}-\overset{\overset{O}{\|}}{C}-(CH_2)_4-\overset{\overset{O}{\|}}{C}- \right]_n$$

A solution of 60 g. of 6-6 nylon in 180 g. of 90% formic acid is prepared by stirring at 60°C. To this is added a solution of 60 g. paraformaldehyde in 60 g. methanol, heated to 60°C. This latter solution is prepared by warming a suspension of paraformaldehyde in methanol to 60°C. and adding a trace of solid sodium hydroxide, whereupon the solution becomes perfectly clear. The rate of addition of the paraformaldehyde solution is very slow during the first minute in order not to precipitate the polymer, then is increased so that addition is complete at the end of three minutes. Ten min. after addition of the paraformaldehyde is begun, another 60 g. of methanol is added rapidly and the reaction allowed to proceed for 30 min. (If a time interval greater than 10 min. elapses before adding the second quantity of methanol, the degree of substitution is increased.) The solution is then poured into 1700 ml. of a water–acetone solution (50:50 by volume), and concentrated aqueous ammonia is gradually added, causing the *N*-methoxymethylated polymer to precipitate as fine white granules. After filtration, the polymer is washed thoroughly with water and dried over phosphorus pentoxide in a vacuum desiccator. Analysis for methoxyl content by the Zeisel method should give a value of about 7.1%. Analysis for methylol content is carried out by treating a solution of the polymer in 70% ethanol with sodium sulfite and titrating the liberated alkali with acid (7). Methylol content should be about 1.4%. This corresponds to a total amide substitution of about 36% from methoxymethyl and methylol.

The polymer melt temperature of the modified polyamide is about 150°C. It is soluble in 80% ethanol as well as formic acid and *m*-cresol. The polymer chain length is essentially unchanged. A film cast from ethanol is elastic, unlike a film of the parent polymer.

Another example of polyamide modification is the **reaction of ethylene oxide with 6-6 nylon** to give a polyamide where some of the nitrogens bear poly(ethylene oxide) chains (8). The product, therefore, is a graft copolymer, with many more of the hydrogen bond sites left intact than in the previous example of a methoxymethyl 6-6 polymer. Despite the large modification of 50% by weight ethylene oxide, the polymer melt temperature is lowered only slightly to around 220°C. (from 265°C.) and solubility is restricted to typical nylon solvents such as formic acid. The effect of the poly(ethylene oxide) side chain grafts is that of an internal plasticizer, producing a more rubbery, flexible polymer, but one still not possessing distinctly elastic properties. The side-chain effect is manifested in a marked lowering of the glass transition temperature from about 47°C. for unmodified 6-6, to below -40°C. for the modified polymer.

In the following reaction, modification should be as high as 50% by weight. It is necessary to start with polymer of low crystallinity, presumably because of the greater difficulty in penetration of ethylene oxide into crystalline regions. The growth of poly(ethylene oxide) chains rather than formation of *N*-hydroxyethylated polymer points to the preference of ethylene oxide for reaction with hydroxyl over amide hydrogen.

4. Preparation of Poly(ethylene oxide)-Grafted Poly(hexamethyleneadipamide) (8)

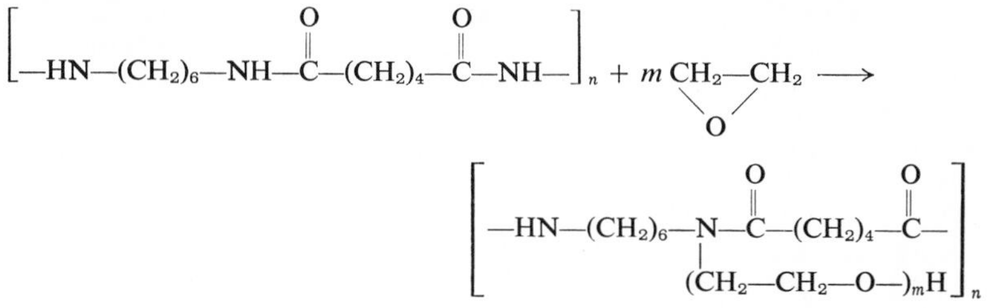

$$\left[-HN-(CH_2)_6-NH-\overset{\overset{O}{\|}}{C}-(CH_2)_4-\overset{\overset{O}{\|}}{C}-NH-\right]_n + m\ CH_2\overset{\diagdown}{}\overset{O}{}\overset{\diagup}{}CH_2 \longrightarrow$$

$$\left[-HN-(CH_2)_6-\underset{\underset{(CH_2-CH_2-O-)_mH}{|}}{N}-\overset{\overset{O}{\|}}{C}-(CH_2)_4-\overset{\overset{O}{\|}}{C}-\right]_n$$

To insure better reactivity of the polymer, a sample of 6-6 nylon which is of low crystallinity should be used. Amorphous 6-6 can be prepared by heating it to 280°C. in a polymer tube (in a vapor bath) in an atmosphere of nitrogen for a few minutes, then quenching the tube in ice-water. (*Caution!* Use a shield in case the tube shatters.) The polymer should be ground to pass a 30 mesh screen. Ten g. of polymer is placed in a stainless steel bomb and about 50–60 g. of ethylene oxide is then added to the bomb, which should be chilled to minimize loss of the volatile oxide when it is added. The bomb is sealed and heated in an 80°C. thermostatted oil bath or jacket behind a barricade for 40 hr. Shorter times will result in less take-up of the oxide by the polymer. The bomb is cooled in ice, opened with caution, and allowed to warm to vent excess ethylene oxide. The polymer remains as a swollen, rubbery mass, which is washed thoroughly with water (e.g., in a household blender several times), and dried over phosphorus pentoxide at 50°C. in vacuum. The increase in weight may be taken as the amount of ethylene oxide combined as poly(ethylene oxide) side chains. It should amount to about 50% in this case. The polymer melt temperature is then about 220°C., and the inherent viscosity should be only slightly less than that of the starting polymer, as determined in *m*-cresol for both. Films cast from formic acid are distinctly more flexible than ordinary 6-6 films. The degree of polymerization of the ethylene oxide in the side chains is about 5–7.

The **effect of intermolecular hydrogen bonding** on polyamide properties is again strikingly demonstrated by the difference in properties between poly(hexamethylenesebacamide) and the same polymer where 60% of the amide hydrogens have been replaced with alkyl groups. The following polymerization, where isobutyl is the alkyl substituent on nitrogen, illustrates this. The polymer melt temperature is reduced from 215°C. in 6-10 nylon to 145°C. in the 60% *N*-alkylated 6-10; and while 6-10 forms fibers similar in properties to those from 6-6 nylon, the *N*-alkylated polymer forms fibers that are quite elastic.

5. Preparation of *N,N'*-Diisobutylhexamethylenediamine (9)

$$H_2N-(CH_2)_6-NH_2 + 2\ (CH_3)_2CHC\overset{\displaystyle O}{\underset{\displaystyle H}{\diagup\diagdown}} \longrightarrow$$

$$(CH_3)_2CH-CH{=}N-(CH_2)_6-N{=}CH-CH(CH_3)_2 + 2H_2O$$
$$\text{(I)}$$

$$\text{(I)} \xrightarrow{\ (H)\ } (CH_3)_2CHCH_2-NH(CH_2)_6NH-CH_2CH(CH_3)_2$$

To 386 g. (2.0 moles) of a 60% aqueous hexamethylenediamine solution is added with stirring 288 g. (4.0 moles) of distilled isobutyraldehyde. The temperature is kept at 50–5°C. with an ice bath. The organic dialdimine layer is separated from the water layer and hydrogenated without purification as follows.

Platinum oxide (0.7 g.) is reduced in the absence of the hydrogen acceptor by shaking a suspension of the catalyst in 50 ml. of absolute alcohol with hydrogen for 10 min. in a low-pressure Parr catalytic apparatus equipped with a 1 l. Pyrex bottle. The dialdimine from above is added to the reduced catalyst in ethanol and the hydrogenation is started at 55 p.s.i. pressure and room temperature. When hydrogen is no longer absorbed, the catalyst is removed by filtration and the N,N'-diisobutylhexamethylenediamine is distilled through a 10 in. helixes-packed column at reduced pressure. The fraction boiling at 116–117°C./3 mm. weighs 365 g. (81%), and may be used in the following reaction without further purification.

6. Preparation of N,N'-Diisobutylhexamethylenediamine-sebacic Acid Salt (DIB6-10 Salt)

To a solution of 48.5 g. (0.24 mole) of sebacic acid in 200 ml. of absolute ethanol is added 56.5 g. (0.246 mole) of N,N'-diisobutylhexamethylenediamine in 100 ml. ether. After mixing the solution thoroughly, about 700 ml. of ether is added. The salt crystallizes on cooling in ice. It is filtered, washed well with ether on the filter, and air dried. The pH of a 1% solution of salt, thus prepared, is about 6.6. The salt is dissolved in 200 ml. of absolute ethanol. The yellow solution is treated with decolorizing charcoal, and after filtration 800 ml. ether containing 10 g. of the N,N'-diisobutylhexamethylenediamine is added. After crystallization the salt is filtered, washed with ether, and dried in a vacuum desiccator. The pH of the salt is then around 7.5. The dry salt melts at 137–138°C. The yield is 90 g. (See Preparation 1 for determination of pH and comments on obtaining a balanced salt.)

7. Preparation of Hexamethylenediamine-sebacic Acid Salt (6-10 Salt)

The subject compound can be made by the directions given in the "Preparation of 6-6 Salt," substituting sebacic for adipic acid and using the same molar quantities of reactants. The pH of a balanced 6-10 salt is about 7.6 (see Preparation 1). The melting point of 6-10 salt is 170–172°C., and the yield by the method described is about 85%.

8. Preparation of a Partially N-Isobutylated Poly(hexamethylenesebacamide) (10)

$$\left[\begin{array}{cc} \overset{+}{H_2N}-(CH_2)_6-\overset{+}{NH_2} \\ | \qquad\qquad | \\ i\text{-}Bu \qquad\quad i\text{-}Bu \end{array} \right] \left[\begin{array}{cc} O \qquad\quad O \\ \| \qquad\qquad \| \\ \bar{O}C-(CH_2)_8-C-\bar{O} \end{array} \right]$$

$$+ \left[\overset{+}{H_3N}-(CH_2)_6-\overset{+}{NH_3} \right] \left[\begin{array}{cc} O \qquad\quad O \\ \| \qquad\qquad \| \\ \bar{O}C-(CH_2)_8-C-\bar{O} \end{array} \right] \longrightarrow \text{Random copolymer}$$

By the technique and equipment described in the "Preparation of Poly-(hexamethyleneadipamide)" (Preparation 2), a mixture of 12.90 g. of DIB6-10 salt (0.03 mole) and 6.36 g. 6-10 salt (0.02 mole) is charged to a polymer tube and the tube filled with nitrogen and sealed. It is heated in a 202°C. vapor bath (m-cresol) for 16 hr. N,N'-Dialkyldiamines react more slowly than the corresponding diprimary diamines and a much longer sealed tube heating stage is required. The polymer tube is cooled and opened cautiously. (Observe precautions noted in 6-6 nylon preparation.) A capillary is introduced to the bottom of the tube and the tube flushed with nitrogen. It is then heated in a 218°C. vapor bath (naphthalene) for $\frac{1}{2}$ hr. at atmospheric pressure, when it is transferred to a 275°C. vapor bath (methyl naphthyl ether) for 45 min., still at atmospheric pressure and with a slow nitrogen flow through the capillary. Finally, the pressure is reduced to about 1 mm. for a period of 6 hr. The polymer has a polymer melt temperature of about 145°C. Elastic fiber can be melt-fabricated. Films can be cast from 98% formic acid or melt-pressed. The inherent viscosity (0.5% conc. in *m*-cresol, 25°C.) is 0.6–0.8.

A **series of polyamides** has been studied (11) **based on** *cis* **and** *trans* **isomers** of the cycloaliphatic diamine 1,4-cyclohexanebis(methylamine) (I) and a series of aliphatic diacids. By comparison with polyamides from the same acid series and *p*-xylene-α,α'-diamine, the cycloaliphatic diamine is at least as effective, and in some cases more so, in forming polymers with high melting points. *cis*-I produces polyamides with notably lower melting points than *trans*-I, and copolymers show a definite eutectic, indicating that the two isomers are not isomorphous in the polymer series in question. The crystalline melting point relationships are shown below.

Table 3.3
Melting Points of Polyamides[b]

Dicarboxylic acid	*trans*-I	*cis*-I	*p*-Xylene-α,α'diamine
Glutaric	280–290	163–167	—
Adipic	345[a]	242–246	333[a]
Pimelic	290–293	188–191	280–284
Suberic	308–311	210–215	300–305
Azelaic	270–275	190–195	259–263
Sebacic	295–300	205–208	279–281
Isophthalic	305–310	—	270–290

[a] Obtained by the extrapolation of the m.p. of a copolyamide series with 1,6-hexanediamine.
[b] Determined on a Fisher-Johns melting point block.

No salt balance is required when an **aminoacid** undergoes **polymerization.** In a pure compound, equivalence of reactive groups is guaranteed. An example is the polyamide from 11-aminoundecanoic acid (12,13). The monomer is prepared from undecylenic acid, which in turn is a derivative of castor oil. The polymer has an 11-carbon chain between amide nitrogens; the polymer melt temperature, 185–190°C., reflects the lower degree of hydrogen bonding per chain length (cf. polycaproamide) and the odd-numbered carbon skeleton. Solubility is restricted to strong acids and the phenols.

9. Preparation of 11-Aminoundecanoic Acid (12)

$$CH_2\!\!=\!\!CH\!-\!(CH_2)_8\!-\!CO_2H + HBr \longrightarrow Br\!-\!(CH_2)_{10}\!-\!CO_2H$$

$$Br(CH_2)_{10}\!-\!CO_2H + 2NH_3 \longrightarrow H_2N\!-\!(CH_2)_{10}\!-\!CO_2H + NH_4Br$$

A solution of 82 g. (0.44 moles) undecylenic acid (m.p. 24–25°C.) in 500 ml. of olefin-free hexane is stirred and cooled to 0°C. The hexane solution of the acid should be well exposed to the air in its preparation, and a trace of benzoyl peroxide should also be added. Hydrogen bromide gas is slowly passed into the reaction flask through an inlet tube that dips below the surface of the hexane. A trap should be provided for unabsorbed hydrogen bromide.

When the hydrogen bromide is no longer being absorbed, the mixture is cooled in ice-salt to -20°C. and the solid product separated by filtration. Some hexane can be evaporated if need be to aid precipitation of the product if at -20°C. no solid separates. The crude 11-bromoacid is twice recrystallized from petroleum ether to give a white, crystalline product melting at 50°C.

A mixture of 100 g. (0.38 mole) 11-bromoundecanoic acid, 300 g. of concentrated ammonium hydroxide, and 200 g. ethyl alcohol are stirred together at 30°C. for a total of 4 days. The excess ammonia and the alcohol are distilled at reduced pressure on the steam bath and the residue taken up in 1500 ml. boiling water, which is then cooled in ice. The resulting solid is filtered, washed with water, and, if necessary, recrystallized once more from about 1 l. of boiling water. The melting point of the product, dried in a vacuum oven at 50°C. for 5 hr., then over phosphorus pentoxide in a vacuum desiccator, is 176°C. The yield is about 49 g. (64%).

As an alternative to the above, the bromoacid and ammonia in the above amount may be heated at 60°C. in a bomb for 10 hr. with agitation and worked up as above. The yield is about 40 g. (53%).

10. Preparation of Poly(11-undecanoamide) (12)

$$H_2N\!-\!(CH_2)_{10}\!-\!CO_2H \longrightarrow \left[-(CH_2)_{10}\!-\!\overset{\displaystyle O}{\overset{\|}{C}}\!-\!NH- \right]_n + H_2O$$

Twenty-five g. of purified 11-aminoundecanoic acid is charged to a 200 ml. three-necked flask equipped with a stirrer having a stainless steel shaft and paddle, Claisen head for the distillation of water, and a nitrogen inlet. Nitrogen is passed in to purge the air and heating is begun by means of a metal or oil bath. The polymerization is heated at 220°C. for 10 hr. while a current of nitrogen is passed through the flask. After raising the stirrer from the molten mass, the reaction is cooled under nitrogen and the polymer is removed by breaking the flask.

The polymerization may be run in a polymer tube using smaller quantities (10–15 g.) of amino acid. A nitrogen inlet capillary to the bottom of the tube provides agitation of the melt. (See Preparation 2 for general directions. No vacuum cycle is needed in the present case.)

The product is obtained in a quantitative yield. Its polymer melt temperature is 185–190°C. The inherent viscosity in m-cresol (0.5% at 35°C.) is about 0.6–0.7. Films may be melt-pressed and fibers may be pulled from a melt of the polymer.

While most amine-acid condensations involve dicarboxylic acids with diamines (AA + BB reactions) or aminoacids with themselves (AB reactions), unusual polymers may be made by reactions involving a combination of these. For instance, hexamethylene bis(iminoacetic acid), a **diaminodicarboxylic acid**, undergoes a **polycondensation with itself to form diketopiperazine rings** linked through the nitrogens by hexamethylene units (14). The monomer in this case is an AB—BA type, whose reaction can be depicted as:

$$AB—BA + AB—BA \longrightarrow \begin{bmatrix} —BA \\ | \quad | \\ AB— \end{bmatrix}_n$$

Despite the tetrafunctionality of the monomer, a linear polymer is formed because of the ease of formation of the diketopiperazine ring.

11. Preparation of Hexamethylene Bis(iminoacetic Acid) (14)

$$H_2N—(CH_2)_6—NH_2 + HCN + CH_2O \longrightarrow$$

$$NCCH_2—NH—(CH_2)_6—NHCH_2CN$$

$$NCCH_2NH—(CH_2)_6—NHCH_2CN + H_2O \longrightarrow$$

$$\underset{\displaystyle HO—C—CH_2NH—(CH_2)_6—NHCH_2—C—OH}{\overset{\displaystyle O \qquad\qquad\qquad\qquad\qquad\qquad O}{\overset{\displaystyle \| \qquad\qquad\qquad\qquad\qquad\qquad \|}{}}}$$

Caution: Some Hydrogen Cyanide may be Formed. Run in a Good Hood.

A solution of 72.6 g. (0.62 mole) of hexamethylenediamine in 60 ml. of water is placed in a 1 l. three-necked flask equipped with stirrer, dropping funnel, and condenser. The solution is cooled in ice and the diamine is neutralized by the addition of 127 g. of concentrated (36%) hydrochloric acid. The solution is then maintained at 5–10°C. while 86.8 g. potassium cyanide (1.33 moles) in 120 ml. of water is added at such a rate that the temperature does not exceed 10°C. Then over a 1 hr. period, 97.5 g. of a 38% formalin solution (1.25 moles of formaldehyde) is added with stirring at 5–10°C. The mixture is stirred 3 hr. further at room temperature after addition. The solution is then filtered and 70 g. potassium carbonate added as a solid. The hexamethylene bis(iminoacetonitrile) separates as an oil, which is removed from the aqueous layer by decantation or by means of a separatory funnel. The oil is then taken up in 200 ml. methanol and the solution dried over anhydrous sodium sulfate, treated with 5 g. of decolorizing charcoal, and filtered. At this point, the bisiminoacetonitrile dihydrochloride may be precipitated, if desired, by addition of concentrated hydrochloric acid. After recrystallization from methanol, the dihydrochloride melts at 188–189°C. (dec.).

The crude bis(iminoacetonitrile) is obtained from the above methanol solution, after drying, by distilling the methanol at aspirator pressure through a Claisen head on the steam bath. The compound is freed from inorganic salts by dissolving in 200 ml. absolute ethanol, filtering and removing the ethanol under aspirator pressure. The hexamethylene bis(iminoacetonitrile) is obtained as a crystalline mass, in a yield of 84 g. (60%). This is hydrolyzed by refluxing the bisiminonitrile with 160 g. (0.5 mole) of barium hydroxide octahydrate in 3 l. of water for 13 hr. The mixture is cooled to room temperature and 49 g. (0.5 mole) of concentrated sulfuric acid is added to precipitate barium sulfate, which is removed by filtration. The filtrate is concentrated on the steam bath at water aspirator pressure until considerable separation of solid has occurred. This is filtered and ethanol added to the filtrate. The solid which precipitates is filtered and the combined solids recrystallized from a minimum of hot water by the addition of enough ethanol to induce precipitation. The hexamethylene bis(iminoacetic acid) is filtered, washed with a little ethanol, and dried in a vacuum desiccator over phosphorus pentoxide at 1 mm. pressure. The yield is about 68 g. (80%); the melting point on rapid heating is 265–266°C. (dec.) with sintering at 257°C.

12. Preparation of Poly(N,N'-hexamethylene-2,5-diketopiperazine) (14)

$$\text{HO—}\overset{\displaystyle O}{\overset{\|}{C}}\text{—CH}_2\text{NH—(CH}_2)_6\text{—NHCH}_2\text{—}\overset{\displaystyle O}{\overset{\|}{C}}\text{—OH} \longrightarrow \left[\text{—(CH}_2)_6\text{—N} \right]_n + 2H_2O$$

In a 100 ml. three-necked flask, with nitrogen capillary inlet tube reaching to the bottom of the flask, short air condenser, and dropping funnel, is placed 15 g. of hexamethylene bis(iminoacetic acid), and 35 g. of distilled m-cresol containing 0.04 g. phosphoric acid. The mixture is heated at 180°C. by means of an oil bath for 30 hr. (not necessarily continuously) while a slow stream of nitrogen is passed through the reaction. As the solvent is lost by evaporation, additional m-cresol is added from the dropping funnel. The temperature is then raised to 218°C. for 20 hr., then the pressure is reduced to 15–20 mm. for 3 hr. This removes the solvent and leaves a yellow-orange tough plug of polymer. It is cut up, ground to a powder, and extracted with boiling acetone to remove residual m-cresol. The inherent viscosity in m-cresol (0.5%, 25°C.) is about 0.6–1.0. The polymer melt temperature is around 240°C., and fibers may be pulled from the melt. Flexible, tough films may be melt-pressed, which become soft and pliable after water immersion. The polymer is soluble in formic and acetic acids as well as in m-cresol.

Polyamides can be prepared by **reaction of a diamine with a diester** in a typical aminolysis reaction. Usually, phenyl esters (or negatively substituted phenyl esters) or methyl esters are selected because of their greater reactivity. Thiol esters are more reactive than their oxy counterparts. In the following example, a disubstituted phenyl malonate is used; the unsubstituted or monosubstituted malonates do not condense well with diamines.

13. Preparation of Phenyl Di-*n*-butylmalonate (16)

In a 1 l. three-necked flask equipped with condenser and dropping funnel, a solution of 123 g. (2.46 moles) of potassium hydroxide in 500 ml. of absolute ethanol is heated to reflux, and 100 g. (0.38 mole) of ethyl di-*n*-butylmalonate gradually added from the funnel. Hydrolysis takes place almost immediately and some salt precipitates toward the end of the reaction. After complete addition of the ester, the mixture is refluxed for 1–2 hr. It is then cooled to room temperature and acidified with concentrated hydrochloric acid. The resulting mixture is filtered to remove the potassium chloride, which is washed with ether. The filtrate is extracted with ether and the ether extractions and washing combined. The ether solution is extracted with three 200 ml. portions of 10% aqueous sodium carbonate. The sodium carbonate solution is treated with activated charcoal, cooled, and acidified with concentrated hydrochloric acid. After cooling to room temperature, the crystallized di-*n*-butylmalonic acid is collected on a filter, washed with cold water, and dried at 50°C. in a vacuum oven; yield is about 78 g. (98%); m.p. 160°C.

The di-*n*-butylmalonic acid (78 g., 0.36 mole) is placed in a 500 ml. three-necked flask and 175 g. (0.84 mole) phosphorus pentachloride added portionwise with occasional cooling of the flask in ice. When the addition is complete and the initial reaction has subsided, the mixture is heated under reflux for $1\frac{1}{2}$ hr. Hydrogen chloride is evolved and should be trapped. The phosphorus oxychloride is distilled from the reaction at atmospheric pressure (b.p. 107°C.) through a 10 in. Vigreux column, and the residue fractionated at reduced pressure. The di-*n*-butylmalonyl chloride boils at 160–178°C./85 mm. The yield is about 48 g. (57%).

Fifty g. (0.2 mole) of the acid chloride is heated with 41 g. (0.44 mole) phenol at a temperature of 200°C. by means of an oil bath until the evolution of hydrogen chloride has essentially ceased, which may require up to 3 hr. The reaction is then fractionally distilled at reduced pressure to give the phenyl ester boiling at 191–192°C./2 mm. The phenyl di-*n*-butylmalonate melts at 49°C. and can be recrystallized from ethyl alcohol (about 1 g. ester/3 ml. alcohol). The yield is 44 g. (60%).

14. Preparation of Poly(hexamethylenedi-*n*-butylmalonamide) (15)

A carefully weighed mixture of 2.95 g. (0.0254 mole) of hexamethylenediamine and 9.20 g. (0.0250 mole) of phenyl di-*n*-butylmalonate is placed in a polymer tube, which is then evacuated and filled with nitrogen and finally evacuated as described in the melt preparation of 6-6 nylon (Preparation 2). The tube is sealed while evacuated and is then heated for 14 hr. in a vapor bath at 210°C. The tube is then opened and fitted with a nitrogen capillary bleed reaching to the bottom of the tube and a side arm for distilling. The tube is then heated in a 265°C. bath for 1 hr. at atmospheric pressure, for 15 min. at

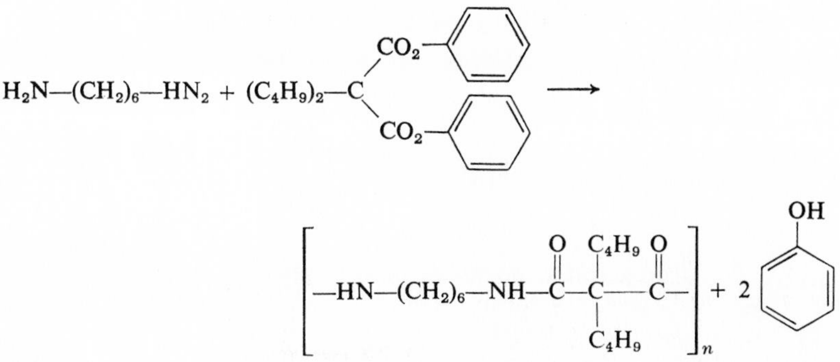

$$H_2N-(CH_2)_6-HN_2 + (C_4H_9)_2-C \begin{matrix} CO_2- \bigcirc \\ CO_2- \bigcirc \end{matrix} \longrightarrow$$

$$\left[-HN-(CH_2)_6-NH-\overset{O}{\overset{\|}{C}}-\overset{C_4H_9}{\underset{C_4H_9}{C}}-\overset{O}{\overset{\|}{C}}- \right]_n + 2 \bigcirc OH$$

30 mm. pressure, and finally for 5 hr. at 30 mm., all with a slow stream of nitrogen passing through the melt. The tube is allowed to cool to room temperature, then opened, and the glass broken away from the polymer plug. Except for mechanical losses in isolation, the yield of polymer is quantitative. The polyhexamethylenedibutylmalonamide has an inherent viscosity of about 0.5–0.7 in m-cresol (0.5% conc., 25°C.) and a polymer melt temperature of around 145°C. It can be melt-pressed or dry-cast to strong films from chloroform/methanol (88/12 by weight). The polymer is also soluble in ethanol as well as in the acidic polyamide solvents, e.g., m-cresol, formic acid.

From the standpoint of the diacid involved, the most readily aminolyzed esters are generally those from oxalic acid (16). For this reason, plus the fact that oxalic acid decomposes on melting, the preparation of **polyoxamides** usually involves the **reaction of an oxalate ester with a diamine** in some solvent at room temperature. The reaction in most cases is rapid and exothermic and a precipitate of prepolymer of low molecular weight forms. This is then polymerized to high molecular weight material in a melt system. Polyoxamides from short chain diamines (six carbons and less) have proved somewhat difficult to prepare in many instances because of a tendency to decompose at the high melt temperature involved. Polyoxamides have been prepared from such diamines as triethylenetetramine, H_2NCH_2-$CH_2NHCH_2CH_2NHCH_2CH_2NH_2$, which, with an excess of an oxalic ester, apparently gives polyoxamides having cyclic oxamide units in the chain (17), as

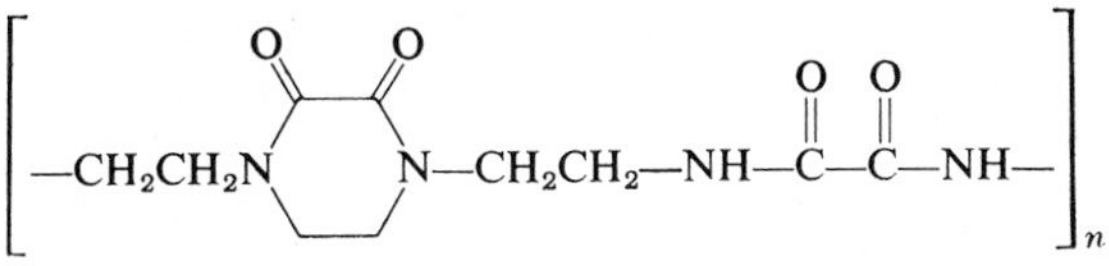

$$\left[-CH_2CH_2N \underset{\diagdown\diagup}{\overset{\overset{O}{\|} \quad \overset{O}{\|}}{\diagup\diagdown}} N-CH_2CH_2-NH-\overset{O}{\overset{\|}{C}}-\overset{O}{\overset{\|}{C}}-NH- \right]_n$$

Similarly, shorter chain diamines that are laterally substituted have also been used successfully to given melt-stable polyoxamides (18,19).

For instance, 3-methoxyhexamethylenediamine forms a polyoxamide having a polymer melt temperature of about 190°C. (18).

In the example below, the polyoxamide of decamethylenediamine is prepared.

15. Preparation of Decamethylenediamine (20)

$$NC—(CH_2)_8—CH \xrightarrow{(H)} H_2N—(CH_2)_{10}—NH_2$$

In a 1 l. hydrogenation bomb are placed 250 g. sebaconitrile, 250 ml. dioxane, and 15 g. Raney cobalt catalyst (as an ethanol paste, below). The bomb is flushed with hydrogen to remove air, and pressured to 5000 p.s.i. with hydrogen while at a temperature of 120°C. Hydrogen is pressured into the vessel at regular intervals until no more is taken up. The bomb is cooled to room temperature, bled to atmospheric pressure, and the solution filtered free of catalyst. The dioxane is stripped by distillation on the steam bath at water aspirator pressure using a short column. The residue can be fractionally distilled through an 8 in. helixes-packed column at reduced pressure in a stream of nitrogen to give about 160 g. (62%) of decamethylenediamine, boiling at 139–141°C./12 mm. The melting point is 60–61°C. If the hydrogenation is carried out in the presence of 180 g. anhydrous ammonia, yields may be as high as 97%. The diamine should be stored under nitrogen to avoid carbonate formation, and kept free from moisture.

The Raney cobalt catalyst used in this preparation can be prepared (21,22) by suspending 50 g. of finely powdered aluminum-cobalt alloy containing 50% by weight of each metal in 300 ml. boiling water in a 1 l. three-necked flask equipped with condenser and efficient stirrer. A solution of 50 g. sodium hydroxide in 100 ml. water is added slowly with good stirring and the mixture is boiled for 4 hr. After cooling, the supernatant liquid is decanted and the residue refluxed again for 4 hr. with a solution of 50 g. sodium hydroxide in 300 ml. water. The water is again decanted and the catalyst washed free from alkali by repeated stirring with fresh portions of water followed by decantation. The final washing and decantation is with 95% ethanol. The catalyst is stored under alcohol and should be used as an ethanol paste. It is pyrophoric and should be handled with caution.

16. Preparation of Poly(decamethyleneoxamide) (23)

$$H_2N(CH_2)_{10}NH_2 + C_4H_9OC\overset{O}{\underset{\|}{C}}—\overset{O}{\underset{\|}{C}}—OC_4H_9 \longrightarrow \left[—HN(CH_2)_{10}NH—\overset{O}{\underset{\|}{C}}—\overset{O}{\underset{\|}{C}}— \right]_n + 2C_4H_9OH$$

For use in this preparation, commercial dibutyl oxalate can be freed of acidic impurities by stirring overnight with 10% by weight of dry calcium hydroxide under anhydrous conditions. The mixture is filtered and the filtrate distilled under reduced pressure, b.p. 84°C./0.85 mm. Decamethylenediamine is prepared and purified as described in the preceding section.

To a solution of 17.23 g. (0.10 mole) decamethylenediamine in 25 ml. toluene (dried over sodium) in a 250 ml. three-necked flask equipped with stirrer, adjustable nitrogen inlet tube, and drying tube is added all at once 20.22 g. (0.10 mole) dibutyl oxalate with stirring under nitrogen. The residual oxalate ester is washed quickly into the flask with another 15 ml. portion of dry toluene. Heat is liberated and a white solid begins to form within a very short time. Stirring is continued until the mass becomes too thick to stir. The solid is a prepolymer with an inherent viscosity of about 0.15–0.25 (sulfuric acid, 0.5% conc., 25°C.). Two hours after the initial addition, the flask is heated to 270°C. in a Woods' metal bath with a current of nitrogen continually passing over the reaction mixture. The nitrogen inlet tube is located immediately above the reaction mass. The toluene distills as the temperature is raised. The 270°C. temperature is maintained for 1 hr., then the polymer is permitted to cool under nitrogen. A tough, white plug is obtained. The inherent viscosity is 0.6–0.7 in sulfuric acid (0.5% conc., 25°C.) and the polymer melt temperature is around 240°C. Fibers can be pulled from the melt.

The **reaction of diamines with** a diester of pyromellitic acid, **a tetrafunctional compound**, can form linear, soluble **polyimides.** This is an instance where a tetrafunctional compound is capable of producing linear, noncrosslinked polymers in reaction with a difunctional intermediate. The ease of intramolecular ring closure in the pyromellitimide system makes this effectively a difunctional molecule. (For an example of linear polymer from a tetraamine and diacid, see Preparation 34.) The polymerization is limited to the longer chain diamines in order to obtain melt-stable products. The stiff, inflexible pyromellitimide ring system gives rise to very high melting polymers, despite the lack of hydrogen bonding. This stiffness in the polymer chain is reflected in the higher glass transition temperature of the polyimides; for the polyimide from nonamethylenediamine with pyromellitic anhydride, it is about 100°C., while for 6-6 polyamide it is about 47°C.

17. Preparation of Nonamethylenediamine (27)

$$HO_2C(CH_2)_7CO_2H \xrightarrow{NH_3} NC(CH_2)_7CN$$

$$NC(CH_2)_7CN \xrightarrow{H_2} H_2N(CH_2)_9NH_2$$

In a 500 ml. three-necked flask, equipped with a gas inlet tube and straight distillation head with condenser, is placed a mixture of 250 g. azelaic acid and 10 g. polyphosphoric acid. The temperature is raised to about 115–120°C by means of a Woods' metal bath to melt the acid. Anhydrous ammonia is passed through the reaction at a fairly rapid rate by means of the gas inlet tube which reaches nearly to the bottom of the flask. The temperature is raised to 290–300°C. for a period of 8 hr. while the ammonia is added. Aqueous ammonia distills from the reaction. The residue in the flask is fractionated at reduced pressure to give about 150 g. (75%) azaleonitrile, boiling at 145–150°C./2 mm., which solidifies on standing.

Reduction is carried out as described for decamethylenediamine, Preparation 15, at a temperature of 135°C. Nonamethylenediamine is obtained in 70–80% yield; the boiling point is 80–82°C./3 mm.

18. Preparation of Polynonamethylenepyromellitimide (24)

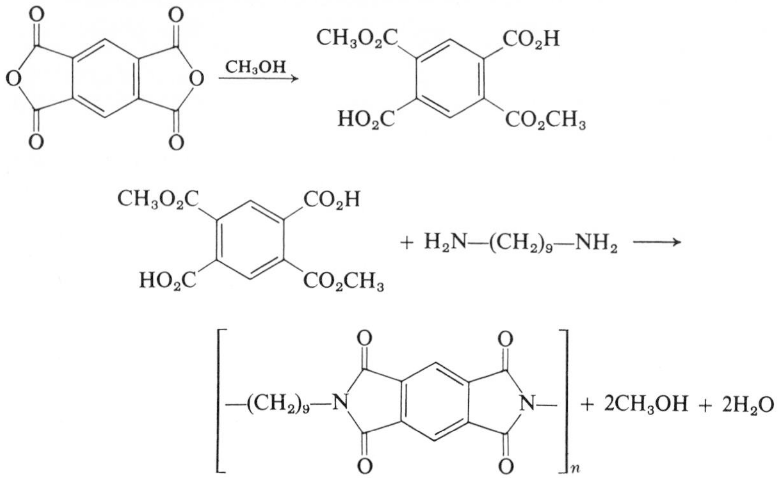

In a 100 ml. three-necked round-bottom flask protected by a drying tube is placed 6.08 g. (0.0279 mole) pyromellitic dianhydride and 30 ml. absolute methanol. (Pyromellitic dianhydride may be recrystallized from acetic anhydride.) The mixture is swirled by hand and gently warmed on the steam bath until a clear solution results. Then 4.414 g. (0.0279 mole) non-amethylenediamine is added quantitatively and the methanol distilled on the steam bath. The residual salt, which should be dry enough for easy handling, is transferred by means of a long stemmed funnel to a polymer tube having a side arm. The tube is then fitted with a capillary inlet reaching nearly to the bottom. (See Preparation 2 for general directions on melt-polymerization technique.) The tube is purged by alternate evacuation by means of an oil pump, and admission of nitrogen. At atmospheric pressure and in a slow stream of nitrogen, the temperature is raised to 139°C. by immersion in a m-xylene vapor bath for 2 hr., during which time water and methanol are driven off. The polymer tube is then transferred to a 325°C. vapor bath for another 2 hr. The tube is cooled after first raising the nitrogen capillary above the level of the melt. The polymer is removed by breaking the tube. The yield of polymer is quantitative except for mechanical losses. The polymer melt temperature is about 325°C., and the inherent viscosity is 0.8–1.2 in m-cresol (0.5% conc., at 25°C.). Tough films can be melt pressed at 340°C.

A "**copolymer effect**" is observed in condensation polymers **when more than two complementary difunctional molecules are caused to polymerize in a random arrangement** (5). Generally, for random condensation copolymers, properties such as polymer melt temperature and crystalline melting point pass through a minimum at some composition between the homopolymers. Solubility may show a maximum. An exception is to be found in those copolymers having constituents which are isomorphous, i.e., are capable of occupying interchangeably the same crystal lattice. Such copolymers show a linear dependence of physical properties on composition. For example, bis(3-aminopropyl)-ether, heptamethylenediamine, and adipic acid give a copolyamide (25) which is isomorphous with the homopolyamide from either diamine and adipic acid.

Complete randomness results from melt-polymerizations through amide interchange reactions (26), but from low temperature, non-reversible polymerization reactions (e.g., the diacid chloride–diamine reaction) ordered copolymers may result. Addition reactions involving hydrogen transfer give either random or block copolymers, depending on the monomers used and the polymerization conditions. The addition of a hydroxy-terminated polyester to a diisocyanate is an example of a block copolymer from a hydrogen transfer addition reaction.

In the following preparation of a random copolymer from hexa-methylene- and tetramethylenediamines with adipic and sebacic acids, the composition of 0.6 mole of 6-10 and 0.4 mole of 4-6 is used. This gives the minimum melting composition for the 6-10/4-6 copolymer series. It is nearly the maximum in solubility, being slightly exceeded by the 0.5/0.5 mole ratio copolymer in this respect. Some comparisons with the properties of the homopolymers are shown in Table 3.4 (5).

Table 3.4

Polymer	Polymer melt temperature, °C.	Crystalline m.p. (fibers), °C.	80% Ethanol
6–10	228	225	Insoluble
4–6	308	282	Insoluble
6–10/4–6 (0.6/0.4)	155	167	Soluble

19. Preparation of Poly(hexamethylenesebacamide-co-tetramethyleneadip-amide) (0.6/0.4 Molar) (5)

0.60 mole 6-10 salt + 0.40 mole 4-6 salt $\longrightarrow$

$$\left[-HN-R-NH-\overset{\overset{\displaystyle O}{\|}}{C}-R'-\overset{\overset{\displaystyle O}{\|}}{C}- \right]_n + 2H_2O$$

$R = -(CH_2)_4-$ and $-(CH_2)_6-$; $R' = -(CH_2)_4-$ and $-(CH_2)_8-$

The preparation of 6-10 salt is described in Preparation 8. The 4-6 salt used here is prepared as described (Preparation 1) for 6-6 salt, using a 2%

excess of tetramethylenediamine, which can be purified by distillation in a current of nitrogen and stored under nitrogen to protect it from atmospheric moisture and carbon dioxide. It boils at 158–160°C. at atmospheric pressure, and melts at 27–28°C. The 4-6 salt can be obtained in over 95% yield. The balanced salt melts at 193–194°C., and a 1% aqueous solution has a pH of about 7.1.

The polymerization may be conducted as described for the preparation of 6-6 nylon (Preparation 2) with the following modifications. Due precautions for handling tubes under pressure should be observed.

A mixture of 4.685 g. (0.02 mole) 4-6 salt and 9.553 g. (0.03 mole) 6-10 salt is charged to a polymer tube which is then evacuated and filled with nitrogen. The tube is sealed and heated at 220°C. (methyl salicylate bath) for 2 hr. A side arm is attached and vacuum is then gradually applied over a 15 min. period. The tube is heated for $1\frac{1}{2}$ hr. further at 220°C. at a pressure of 1.0 mm., or less, while a slow stream of nitrogen is passed through the melt via a capillary tube. The polymer is cooled under nitrogen after raising the capillary and is obtained as a tough translucent plug by breaking the tube. The copolyamide has a polymer melt temperature of about 170°C., and an inherent viscosity of 0.7–0.8 in m-cresol (0.5% conc., 25°C.). Fibers are slightly crystalline and exhibit a crystalline melting point of 179°C. The polymer is soluble in dimethylformamide, 80% ethanol, and ethylene chlorohydrin, as well as in the acidic polyamide solvents (phenols, formic acid, etc.).

There are, perhaps, no organic reactions that could be considered any more "classical" than the Schotten-Bauman reaction for acylating amines and alcohols, or the Hinsberg method of separating amines. Both involve the reaction of an acid halide with the active hydrogen of an alcohol or amine in the presence of an acid acceptor, and are usually carried out in an aqueous system. These simple, fast reactions have become the basis for an extremely versatile method for synthesizing polymers (27–31).

The method for carrying out the reaction on a polymer-forming basis has been termed **"interfacial polycondensation"** (27,31). The **reaction** apparently takes place **at the interface between** a solution of a **diacid chloride in a water immiscible organic solvent and a water solution of,** for example, **a diamine** containing an acid acceptor. The acid component may be aliphatic or aromatic dicarboxylic chlorides, bischloroformates, or disulfonyl chlorides. The active hydrogen compound may be aliphatic primary or secondary diamines, or diphenols as their sodium salts. Aromatic diamines and aliphatic diols apparently react too slowly to yield high polymer. Hydrolysis of the acyl halide, always a possible side reaction, may compete with the acylation sufficiently in these cases to prevent formation of high polymer.

Exact stoichiometry of reactants is not so important as it is in melt-polycondensations, presumably beacuse of the extremely rapid rate of interfacial polycondensation. In fact, enough excess diamine to act as the acid acceptor may be used in some cases without seriously reducing the molecular weight of the product. This is taken as evidence for a reaction site in the organic phase close to the interface, but apart from the excess diamine. Acid chloride enters the aqueous phase very little, thus avoiding hydrolysis. Reaction is so rapid that lack of precise equivalency of reactants in the solution does not prevent the formation of high molecular weight products at the surface contact of the two liquids.

Although interfacial polycondensation usually is very rapid, proper choice of a solvent system and reactant concentration is essential to ensure sufficient mobility of the growing chain to permit a high molecular weight to be reached.

The great utility of interfacial polycondensation stems from the fact that it is a low temperature process. Thus, polymers that are not stable at their melt temperatures can easily be prepared and unstable reactants can be used where melt-polycondensation would be useless. The method is very rapid, permitting the preparation of polymer in a matter of minutes, once the reactants are in hand. Little in the way of special equipment is needed. Rapid stirring is easily effected by use of the household blender. However, standard laboratory stirrers and flasks often may be used and, as one of the following preparations shows, a beaker may be the only apparatus required. The variety of polymer types that may be prepared is wide: **polyamides, polysulfonamides, polyurethanes,** and **polyphenyl esters.** Copolymers that would be difficult to obtain otherwise are easily prepared by interfacial polycondensation, e.g., **copolyamide-urethanes, copolyamidesulfonamides.** Substantially different reactivities of the different diacid chlorides with the other component may lead to the formation of nonrandom, ordered copolymer (32). The same will be true if two diamines of differing reactivity are polymerized with one acid chloride or if the reactants are mixed consecutively rather than all at once.

The average molecular weight of polymers from interfacial systems is usually at least as high as that in the comparable melt-prepared polymer and may, in the best of circumstances, be much higher.

Probably the simplest and the most dramatic example of interfacial polycondensation is the preparation of 6-6 or 6-10 nylon by the beaker method of Morgan and Kwolek (33). Their process (aptly called "The Nylon Rope Trick" for its something-out-of-nothing quality) consists simply of carefully pouring an aqueous solution of excess hexamethylenediamine onto a carbon tetrachloride solution of adipoyl or sebacoyl chloride, then steadily pulling away a coherent film of polyamide from the interface. No mixing is required, and the diamine can be used in excess to function as the acid acceptor. With purified intermediates, high molecular weights are obtained ($\overline{M}_n$ of 20,000 or more, and inherent viscosities of 1.8 in m-cresol), but even with as-purchased diamine and diacid chloride film and fiber-forming polymers are produced, but with lower molecular weight. The simplicity in comparison with, and the advantages over, melt-polymerization methods are obvious.

20. Preparation of Polyhexamethylenesebacamide (6-10 Nylon) (53)

$$H_2N-(CH_2)_6-NH_2 + Cl-\overset{O}{\overset{\|}{C}}-(CH_2)_8-\overset{O}{\overset{\|}{C}}-Cl \longrightarrow$$

$$\left[-HN-(CH_2)_6NH-\overset{O}{\overset{\|}{C}}-(CH_2)_8-\overset{O}{\overset{\|}{C}}-\right]$$

A solution of 3.0 ml. sebacoyl chloride in 100 ml. distilled tetrachloroethylene is placed in a 200 ml. tall-form beaker. (The diacid chloride should be

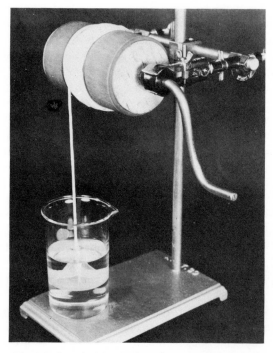

Fig. 3.1. Interfacial spinning with manual wind-up.

distilled material, for best results. The boiling point is 124°C./0.5 mm.; the pot temperature should not exceed 160°C., and the distillation should be as rapid as possible.) Over the acid chloride solution is carefully poured a solution of 4.4 g. hexamethylenediamine in 50 ml. water. (The diamine is handled most conveniently as a standardized stock solution of about 20% in water. The commercially available solid diamine may also be used without further purification.) The polymeric film which forms at the interface of the two solutions is grasped with tweezers and raised from the beaker as a continuously forming rope. If a mechanical wind-up device is placed above the beaker, the polymer may be wound up continuously (Fig. 3.1) until one of the reactants is exhausted. Figure 3.2 shows how the process can be made to operate automatically. The polymer can be washed several times with 50% aqueous ethanol or acetone and dried in a vacuum oven at 60°C. The product has an inherent viscosity of from 0.4 to 1.8 (*m*-cresol, 0.5% conc. at 25°C.), depending on the reaction conditions. The polymer melt temperature is 215°C. Fibers and films can be obtained from the melt or from formic acid solutions.

The following preparation is an example of the use of an **aromatic diacid chloride** in a **polycondensation with a secondary cyclic diamine,** *trans*-2,5-dimethylpiperazine. The polyamide so formed (from phthaloyl

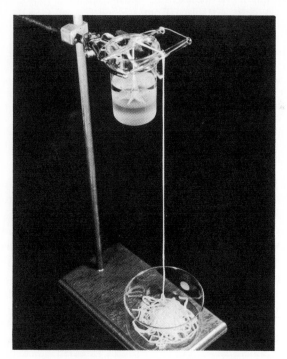

Fig. 3.2. Interfacial spinning—self-propelled.

chloride) is devoid of hydrogen bonds, but is still very high melting (>300°C.). The plurality of rings reduces the flexibility of the chain, increasing thereby the temperature required to put all the molecules in the condition of relatively free movement that obtains in the melt. However, because the strong interchain forces due to hydrogen bonding are not present, the polyamides are easily dissolved in a number of solvents.

21. Poly(*N,N'*-phthaloyl-*trans*-2,5-dimethylpiperazine) (34)

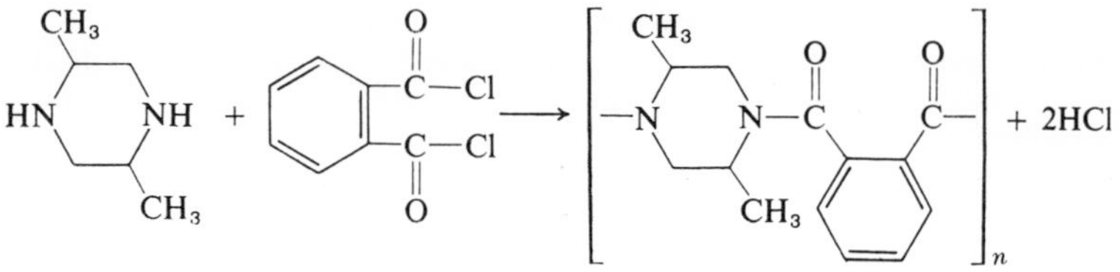

In a household blender jar is placed 6.50 g. (0.058 mole) of *trans*-2,5-dimethylpiperazine, 25 ml. methylene chloride, 20 ml. of a 5% Duponol* ME solution and 150 ml. of ice water containing 0.10 mole of sodium hydroxide, prepared by diluting a standardized caustic solution. *trans*-2,5-Dimethylpiperazine can be recrystallized from acetone (1 g./ml.); m.p. 117–118°C. To the rapidly stirred system is added all, at one time, 7.2 ml. (0.05 *m*.) of phthaloyl chloride in 25 ml. methylene chloride. The phthaloyl chloride should be fractionated at reduced pressure. The material boiling at 103°C./1.5 mm. through an 8 in., glass helixes-packed column gives satisfactory polymer. The polymerization mixture is stirred for 10 min., then poured into 1 l. of water and the methylene chloride boiled away on the steam bath. The polymer is filtered, washed in the blender three times with 200 ml. portions of water, and dried at 70°C. in a vacuum oven. The yield is 10 g. (80%), the polymer melt temperature is 350°C., and the inherent viscosity is 1.0–1.4 in *m*-cresol (0.5% conc. at 25°C.). The polymer is soluble in chloroform, acetic acid, and dioxane–water (82/18 vol.).

Extremely high melting polyamides can be prepared **from short chain** (2–6 carbon atoms) **primary aliphatic diamines** and **terephthaloyl chloride** (35). These polymers require very dilute conditions for best preparation. Because of their insolubility, they precipitate rapidly during polymerization and are unswollen by the reaction solvents used. Consequently, there is a tendency for low molecular weight products to form. The polyterephthalamide from ethylenediamine, whose preparation follows, is soluble in none of the customary polyamide solvents (*m*-cresol, formic acid), but only in the very strong acids, sulfuric and trifluoroacetic. Thus, the ring structure plus a high degree of hydrogen bonding combine to produce a high-melting, difficultly soluble polymer.

* Trademark for du Pont's surface-active agent.

22. Preparation of Polyethyleneterephthalamide (35)

$$H_2NCH_2CH_2NH_2 + Cl-\overset{\overset{O}{\|}}{C}-\underset{}{\bigcirc}-\overset{\overset{O}{\|}}{C}-Cl \longrightarrow$$

$$\left[-HNCH_2CH_2NH-\overset{\overset{O}{\|}}{C}-\underset{}{\bigcirc}-\overset{\overset{O}{\|}}{C}-\right]_n + 2HCl$$

For the following polymerization, ethylenediamine is purified by drying over potassium hydroxide pellets for 15 hr. It is then fractionated in a stream of nitrogen through a 10 in., glass helixes-packed column, taking care to protect the distillate from atmospheric carbon dioxide by means of soda-lime-packed tubes. Ethylenediamine boils at 117°C. at 760 mm. Terephthaloyl chloride can be prepared by refluxing 100 g. of terephthalic acid for 12 hr. in 500 g. of thionyl chloride and 2 ml. pyridine. The excess thionyl chloride is distilled at water aspirator pressure on the steam bath, and the residual acid chloride is distilled under vacuum through a short Vigreux column. The boiling point is 115–116°C. at 3.0 mm. It can be recrystallized from dry hexane (100 g./700 ml.); m.p., 81–82°C.

A solution of 3.78 g. (0.0630 mole) of ethylenediamine, and 0.126 mole of potassium hydroxide from a standardized solution in 4.5 l. of water is placed in an 8 l. stainless steel beaker and stirred by means of an efficient high speed stirrer. A large spatula is mounted vertically at the edge of the beaker with the blade perpendicular to the wall to act as a baffle for more efficient stirring. Next, 12.79 g. (0.0634 mole) of terephthaloyl chloride dissolved in 1 l. of methylene chloride is added rapidly to the stirred solution. The polymerization mixture is stirred for 10 min. at room temperature. The mixture is then filtered and the polymer placed in boiling distilled water to remove absorbed methylene chloride. The product is then filtered and washed twice with boiling distilled water. Finally, the polymer is dried in a vacuum oven at 80°C. to give a yield of 9.0 g. (75%). The polymer has an inherent viscosity of around 1.0 in sulfuric acid (0.5% conc., 30°C.). This corresponds to a weight average molecular weight of about 18,000. The polymer melt temperature is over 400°C. (The first transition above 400°C., determined by differential thermal analysis, is at 455°C., which may represent the polymer melt temperature.) The polymer is soluble in trifluoroacetic acid. Fibers can be dry-spun and films can be dry-cast from such a solution.

Polyamidation between an acid chloride and a diamine may also be carried out in a single, organic phase, in the presence of an organic acid acceptor. It is not necessary that the polymer be soluble in the organic phase; however, it is more convenient if both the polymer and the salt of the acid acceptor remain in solution. The system chloroform-triethylamine is often used. The preparation poly(N,N'-terephthaloyl-trans-2,5-dimethylpiperazine) is a representative example.

23. Preparation of Poly(2,5-dimethylpiperazine terephthalamide) Using Triethylamine Acid Acceptor (36)

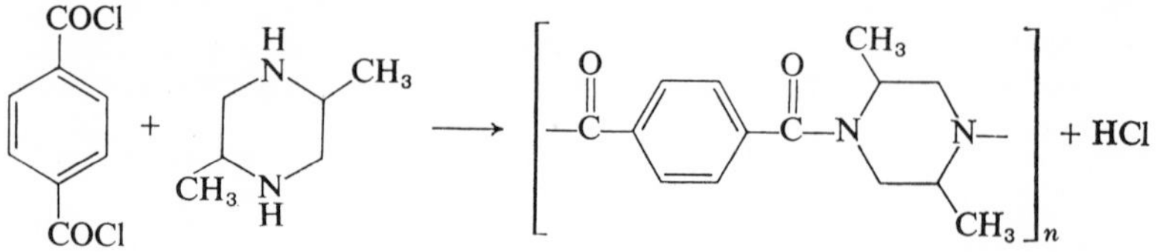

trans-2,5-Dimethylpiperazine (2.28 g.) and 5.6 ml. of pure triethylamine are dissolved in 100 ml. of washed and dried chloroform in a 500 ml. Erlenmeyer flask. To this mixture is added a solution of 4.06 g. of terephthaloyl chloride in 80 ml. of chloroform with swirling. More chloroform (20 ml.) is used to rinse in the residues of terephthaloyl chloride at once. The mixture remains clear, but the temperature rises quickly from 25 to 42°C. and there is an increase in solution viscosity. The solution can be dry-cast on glass to produce self-supporting films; however, they must be washed free of salt with water before they are completely solvent-free, if a tough, flexible product is desired.

After 5 min. the solution is coagulated by pouring into hexane with stirring. A fibrous precipitate is obtained, as well as crystals of triethylamine hydrochloride. If the precipitation is done slowly with no stirring or only slow stirring, long, coarse strings of polymer are obtained, which can readily be torn apart by hand or in a home blender. The precipitate is washed well with water and finally with acetone. After drying at 100°C., a 92% yield of polymer is obtained which has an inherent viscosity of about 3 (*m*-cresol, 0.5 g./100 ml., at 30°C.).

Excess diamine can also be used in solution polymerization. Other solvents and acid acceptors may be used, and the technique may be applied to formation of other classes of polymers. The entire subject of interfacial and solution polymerization is treated thoroughly by Morgan (37). The following example uses excess diamine as acid acceptor.

24. Preparation of Poly(2,5-dimethylpiperazine terephthalamide) Using Excess Diamine As Acid Acceptor (38)

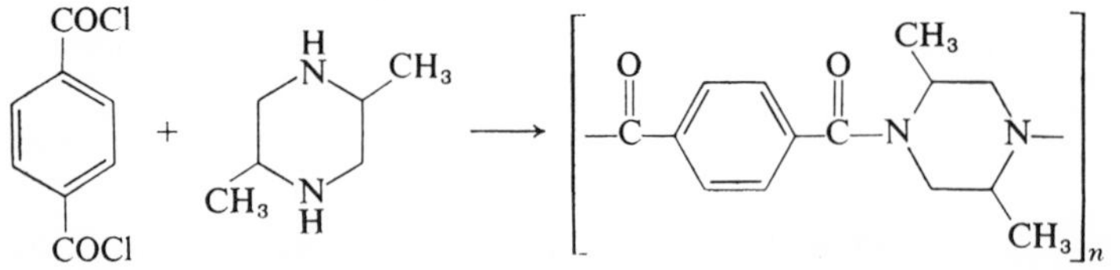

Terephthaloyl chloride (4.06 g., 0.02 mole) is dissolved in 150 ml. of chloroform in a 500 ml. flask equipped with a high speed stirrer. A solution of *trans*-2,5-dimethylpiperazine (4.456 g., 0.0390 mole) in 98 ml. of chloroform is added dropwise over a period of 45 min. A precipitate of diamine dihydrochloride forms as the diamine is added. Chloroform (40 ml.) is used to rinse the dropping funnel. At this point, the inherent viscosity of the polymer will be about 1.6.

Additional dimethylpiperazine (ca 0.2 g.) in 50 ml. of chloroform may be added over a period of 30 min. to increase molecular weight, if desired. During this time the dispersion of diamine salt becomes very viscous. The polymer is precipitated into hexane and is obtained in a fibrous form. The inherent viscosity should be about 5.0–6.0 (0.5 g./100 ml., m-cresol, 30°C.) and the total yield about 90% after washing and drying.

Coloration in polymers is usually a sign that degradation has taken place, but sometimes an inherently colored product can be made by inclusion of a chromophoric group in one of the monomers. An example is the azo group present in a fiber-forming polyamide, as described in the experiments that follow (39). Another system of an inherently colored polymer is that of the all-aromatic polyimides (Preparation no. 110).

25. Preparation of Azodibenzoyl Chloride

Azodibenzoic acid (33 g.; 0.122 mole), 150 ml. (248 g.; 2.08 moles) thionyl chloride and 0.5 ml. triethylamine was charged to a 500 ml. round-bottom flask equipped with stirrer and reflux condenser with drying tube. The reaction mixture was refluxed until a dark-red solution was obtained (4 hr.). Excess thionyl chloride was removed using a water pump and temperature below 50°C. Further drying at 1 mm. and temperature below 50°C. gave 37 g. (94% yield) of azodibenzoyl chloride. The acid chloride obtained in this manner was sufficiently pure for polymerization work. Recrystallization from dry hexane may be necessary if high molecular weight polymer is not obtained in the next experiment.

26. Preparation of Poly(azo-4,4′-dibenzoyl-*trans*-2,5-dimethylpiperazine) (39)*

In a household blender jar is placed 4.10 g. (0.036 mole) of *trans*-2,5-dimethylpiperazine and 6.31 g. (0.06 mole) of sodium carbonate and 250 ml. distilled water. After brief stirring to dissolve the reactants, 75 ml. methylene chloride is added. *trans*-2,5-Dimethylpiperazine can be recrystallized from acetone (1 g./ml.); m.p. 117–118°C. Then a solution 9.21 g. (0.03 mole) azodibenzoyl chloride in 150 ml. methylene chloride (slightly turbid solution)

---

* We are grateful to Dr. H. Wayne Hill, Jr., now of the Phillips Petroleum Co., for details of this and the previous preparation.

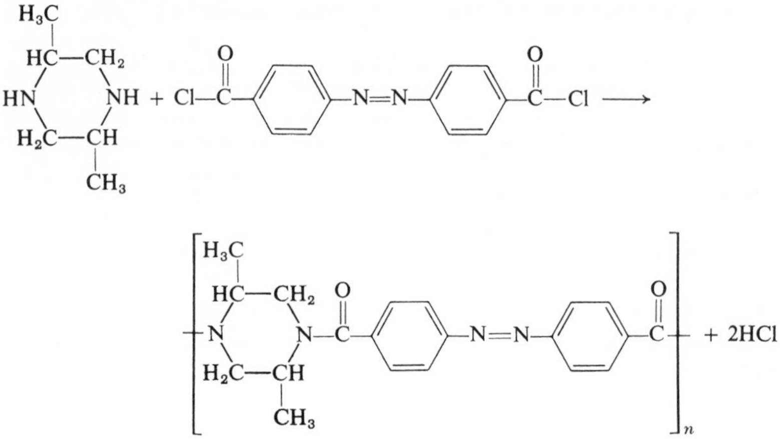

is added to the preformed emulsion in 1–2 sec. Rapid stirring is continued for about 7 min. and 300 ml. of hexane is added to precipitate the polymer. The polymer is separated by filtration, washed in the blender three times with 200 ml. portions of water, and dried at 70°C. in a vacuum oven. The yield is 8.6 g. (83%) of a bright-orange polymer and the inherent viscosity is about 2.2 in m-cresol (0.5% conc. at 25°C.). It is soluble in 98% formic acid, chloroform, and 1,1,2-trichloroethane/formic acid azeotrope (60/40 by weight). A tough, transparent, bright-orange film can be cast from a 10% solution in the trichloroethane/formic acid azeotrope. This film exhibits no change in color after 1300 hr. exposure in a Fade-O-Meter instrument (Atlas Electric Devices Company of Chicago) and is still quite tough.

The **effect of N-alkyl substitution in polyamides,** with the concurrent loss in interchain hydrogen bonding, is again demonstrated by a comparison of Preparation 22 with the completely N-ethylated polymer (40). In going to the latter, the polymer melt temperature is decreased over 200°C., and the solubility is raised to such a degree that 80% aqueous ethanol becomes a solvent. The N-substituted polymer is completely amorphous as prepared while the unsubstituted is moderately crystalline.

27. Preparation of N,N'-Diethylethylenediamine (35)

$$\text{ClCH}_2\text{CH}_2\text{Cl} + 2\text{CH}_3\text{CH}_2\text{NH}_2 \xrightarrow{\text{NaOH}} \text{CH}_3\text{CH}_2\text{NHCH}_2\text{CH}_2\text{NHCH}_2\text{CH}_3$$

A mixture of 148.5 g. (1.5 moles) ethylene dichloride and 450 g. (10.0 moles) ethylamine are heated together in a stainless steel bomb at 100°C. for 4 hr. The bomb is then allowed to cool, excess ethylamine vented, and the mixture transferred by rinsing with 500 ml. water to a 2 l. separatory funnel. About 500 g. of solid potassium hydroxide is added slowly. The diamine separates as an upper, oily layer; 20 ml. methanol is added to facilitate separation of the layers. The upper layer is separated and dried over potassium hydroxide pellets overnight. It is fractionated at atmospheric pressure through a precision column to give a forerun boiling at 52–138°C. which is discarded, followed by the main fraction, which is the desired dialkyldiamine, boiling at 149–151°C. The diamine is hygroscopic and must be protected from moisture and carbon dioxide of the air. The yield is 58 g. (33%). Also obtained from the distillation is 10–20 g. of N,N',N''-triethyldiethylenetriamine, b.p. 81–82°C./3 mm.

28. Preparation of Poly(N,N'-diethylethyleneterephthalamide) (35)

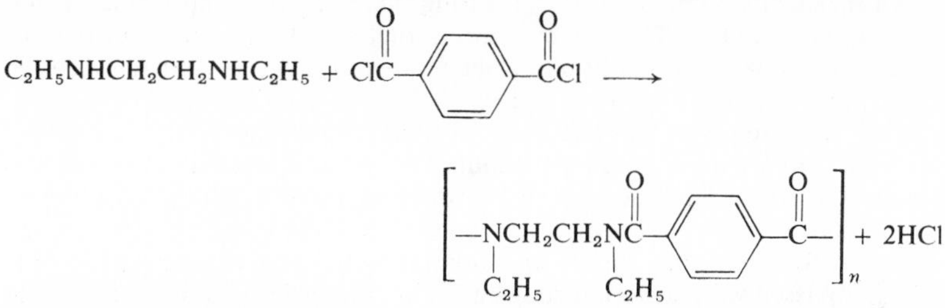

$$C_2H_5NHCH_2CH_2NHC_2H_5 + ClC{-}\!\!\bigcirc\!\!{-}CCl \longrightarrow$$

$$\left[-NCH_2CH_2NC{-}\!\!\bigcirc\!\!{-}C- \right]_n + 2HCl$$
$$\quad\quad\;\; C_2H_5 \quad\; C_2H_5$$

A solution of 5.8 g. (0.05 mole) of N,N'-diethylethylenediamine and 10.6 g. (0.1 mole) of sodium carbonate in 250 ml. water is stirred rapidly in a household blender. To this, a solution of 10.1 g. (0.05 mole) terephthaloyl chloride in 80 ml. of dry chloroform is quickly added and the resultant mixture is stirred for 10 min. at high speed. The product, consisting of two clear liquids, is heated to expel the chloroform and precipitate the polymer. The mixture is then filtered and the solid washed four times in a blender with water to give, upon drying, 10.1 g. (82% yield) of white polymer with an inherent viscosity of 1.93 in sulfuric acid (0.5% conc., 25°C.). The product has a polymer melt temperature of 230°C. and is soluble in m-cresol, formic acid, chloroform, acetone, and 80% ethanol.

Polysulfonamides can be prepared **from aromatic disulfonyl chlorides and aliphatic diamines** by interfacial polycondensation (41). Aliphatic disulfonyl chlorides give poorer results. Polysulfonamides having hydrogens on the amide nitrogen are in many cases soluble in strong alkali, just as their monomeric organic counterparts. With sodium hydroxide as the acid acceptor in the polymerization, branching and crosslinking can result from reaction of sulfonyl chloride with the sulfonamide anion, although conditions can be chosen to minimize these effects.

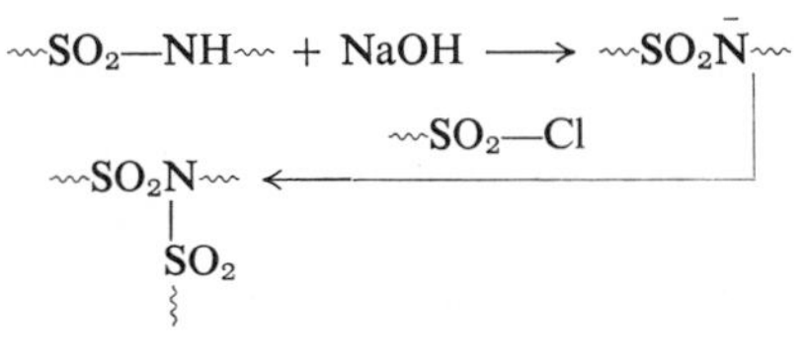

$$\sim\!\!\!\sim SO_2{-}NH\!\!\sim\!\!\!\sim + NaOH \longrightarrow \sim\!\!\!\sim SO_2\bar{N}\!\!\sim\!\!\!\sim$$
$$\sim\!\!\!\sim SO_2{-}Cl$$
$$\sim\!\!\!\sim SO_2\bar{N}\!\!\sim\!\!\!\sim \longleftarrow$$
$$\qquad\; SO_2$$

29. Preparation of *m*-Benzenedisulfonyl Chloride (41)

$$HO_3S-\underset{}{\bigcirc}-SO_3H \xrightarrow[PCl_5]{POCl_3} ClO_2S-\underset{}{\bigcirc}-SO_2Cl$$

In a 3 l. three-necked flask fitted with a condenser, thermometer, and stirrer is placed 1360 g. (6.55 moles) of ground phosphorus pentachloride and 727 g. of phosphorus oxychloride. To the stirred mixture is added 770 g. (2.94 moles) of *m*-benzenedisulfonic acid (90%) during 30 min. The temperature is not allowed to exceed 70°C. The mixture is refluxed 3 hr., then phosphorus oxychloride is distilled first at atmospheric pressure and later under vacuum until approximately 700 ml. is collected. The dark-colored liquid reaction mixture is poured with stirring into a 5 l. beaker two-thirds full of cracked ice. The cold mixture is stirred about 20 min. and filtered. The solid is dissolved in 1 l. of benzene and washed three times with 250 ml. portions of 5% sodium bicarbonate solution and once with 250 ml. water. After drying over anhydrous calcium sulfate and treating with decolorizing carbon, the filtrate is passed with suction through a $1\frac{1}{4}$ in. diameter column packed with 15 in. of activated alumina to remove the last traces of charcoal and to thoroughly dry the solution. The column is washed with 200 ml. benzene. To the solution is added 2500 ml. of olefin-free *n*-hexane, and the oil which separates is cooled to 20°C. and scratched to cause crystallization. The solid is filtered on a large Büchner funnel and washed twice with 500 ml. portions of olefin-free *n*-hexane to remove a slight yellow color. After drying in a desiccator containing calcium chloride for 3 hr. using a vacuum pump the solid weighs 553 g. (68%). It melts at 62.0–62.5°C. The filtrate is concentrated to 350 ml., and 500 ml. *n*-hexane added to give an oil which on seeding gives, after drying, 90 g. of crystalline material, melting at 61–61.5°C. The total yield is 643 g. (80%).

The hexamethylenediamine used in the following polymerization may be purified as described in the preparation of 6-6 nylon (Preparation 2) and weighed directly; or, it may be used in an aqueous solution, about 5–6N, which has been standardized by titration with hydrochloric acid. Such a solution should be stored under nitrogen.

30. Preparation of Poly(hexamethylene *m*-benzenedisulfonamide) (41)

$$H_2N-(CH_2)_6-NH_2 + ClO_2S-\underset{}{\bigcirc}-SO_2Cl \longrightarrow$$

$$\left[-HN-(CH_2)_6-NH-O_2S-\underset{}{\bigcirc}-SO_2-\right]_n + 2HCl$$

A household blender jar is charged with 145 ml. distilled water, 20 ml. of 10% aqueous Duponol* ME solution, 3.016 g. hexamethylenediamine (or

* Trademark for du Pont's surface active agent.

enough standardized aqueous diamine solution to give 0.026 mole), and
5.30 g. (0.05 mole) of sodium carbonate. To the stirred solution over a period of
20–30 sec. is added 6.88 g. (0.025 mole) of *m*-benzenedisulfonyl chloride dissolved in 200 ml. of methylene chloride. The mixture is then stirred 15 min.
After adding 100 ml. ethanol, the solid is filtered, washed on the funnel with
400 ml. water, and then washed in the blender with 200 ml. portions of ethanol
acetone, hot water, and acetone again. (Caution! If the blender motor
housing has not been modified with a compressed air inlet on the motor
housing for flame protection, do not use the flammable solvent washes listed,
or else wash the polymer in a beaker.) The sample is dried at 70–75°C. in
a vacuum oven overnight to give 4.9 g. polymer (63%). The inherent viscosity (0.5% conc. at 25°C.) measured in sulfuric acid should be about 2.0;
in dimethylformamide, 1.5. The polymer melt temperature is about 160–
170°C. when amorphous, about 200°C. when crystalline. The polymer is
fairly crystalline as prepared; melt-pressed films, however, are amorphous.
The polymer is soluble in the above-noted solvents as well as 6–10% sodium
hydroxide solutions.

The addition of a carboxylic acid to an isocyanate first forms a mixed
carboxylic–carbamic anhydride. In some cases, this intermediate has
been isolated. However, in most instances it decomposes directly to
the end products, either a mixture of the anhydride of the acid and the
urea based on the diamine (path 1); or, the substituted carboxamide
plus carbon dioxide (path 2), depending on the reactants used. Further
heating of the anhydride–urea mixture forms the substituted carboxamide of the acid and evolves carbon dioxide. Consequently, the eventual course of reaction leads to amide formation with the loss of carbon
dioxide (42). The over-all reaction is:

$$RNCO + R'CO_2H \longrightarrow$$

Dicarboxylic acids and diisocyanates or diisothiocyanates have given
polyamides by this reaction sequence (43). From diisothiocyanates,
carbon oxysulfide is evolved, indicating that in the decomposition of the

$RNH-\overset{\overset{\displaystyle O}{\|}}{C}-O-\overset{\overset{\displaystyle O}{\|}}{C}-R'$ mixed anhydride, the carbonyl oxygen in the
product amide is derived from that of the acid used. In the following

preparation of 10-10 polyamide, the diisocyanate is used; its preparation is given in Preparation 37.

31. Preparation of Polydecamethylenesebacamide (10-10 Polyamide) (43)

$$OCN(CH_2)_{10}NCO + HO-\overset{\overset{\displaystyle O}{\|}}{C}-(CH_2)_8-\overset{\overset{\displaystyle O}{\|}}{C}-OH \longrightarrow$$

$$\left[-HN-(CH_2)_{10}NH-\overset{\overset{\displaystyle O}{\|}}{C}-(CH_2)_8-\overset{\overset{\displaystyle O}{\|}}{C}-\right]_n + 2CO_2$$

In a polymer tube purged of air and flushed with nitrogen and having a capillary inlet tube reaching nearly to the bottom is placed a mixture of 7.5 g. sebacic acid and 8.41 g. decamethylenediisocyanate. (See Preparation 37.) The tube is heated at about 170°C. by means of a vapor bath for 1 hr. at atmospheric pressure as nitrogen is passed slowly through the melt which forms. A solid eventually forms during this period. The temperature is raised to 222°C. (methyl salicylate) for 3 hr. The polymer is then cooled under nitrogen. It has an inherent viscosity of about 0.4 in m-cresol (0.5% conc., 25°C.), and is soluble in the usual acidic aliphatic polyamide solvents (e.g., formic acid, phenol). The polymer melt temperature is about 185°C. Cold-drawable fibers may be pulled from the molten polymer.

An unusual example of a hydrogen addition to a double bond to form polymer is the Michael-type **addition of acrylamide to itself** to form poly(β-alanine), or 3-nylon (44). It represents the unusual case of an AB monomer in an anionic, proton transfer addition reaction. Although the polymerization gives a relatively low molecular weight product, it is included here because of the unusual character of the polymerization and the fact that 3-nylon is one of the lower possible homologs of the polyamide series derived from ω-aminoacids. Because of the short chain separation between amide groups the polymer melt temperature (320–330°C.) of 3-nylon is high (see Chapter 5). Hydrolysis of the polymer provides a short, high yield synthesis of β-alanine from the commercially available acrylamide.

Acrylamide also can be polymerized by a typical free radical route to vinyl polymer having pendant —$CONH_2$ groups. Polyacrylamide prepared in this way is a water-soluble, high molecular weight material, which forms polyacrylic acid on hydrolysis. (See Chapter 4).

32. Preparation of Poly(β-alanine) (3-Nylon) (44)

$$CH_2=CH-\overset{\overset{\displaystyle O}{\|}}{C}-NH_2 \xrightarrow{Na} \left[-CH_2-CH_2-\overset{\overset{\displaystyle O}{\|}}{C}-NH-\right]_n$$

The acrylamide used in this polymerization can be purified by recrystallization from ethyl acetate and sublimation at < 1 mm.; the melting point is 85°C. (Use care in handling; acrylamide is toxic!) The dimethylformamide must be dry; it can be distilled from a small quantity of phosphorus pentoxide at reduced pressure.

A solution of 4.4 g. acrylamide (0.062 mole) in 4 ml. dimethylformamide is prepared in a suitable small reaction vessel which is protected from the atmosphere by a nitrogen inlet tube attached to a mercury bubbler to vent nitrogen when the vessel is closed.

The solution is heated to 100°C. in an oil bath and 2 drops of 50% dispersion of sodium in xylene, which is approximately 0.018 g. (8×10^{-4} g.a.) of sodium is added. Polymerization occurs and is completed in 3–5 min. The reaction mixture is quenched in water, the polymer filtered and washed with water several times in a blender. The polymer, dried at 70°C. for 24 hr. in a vacuum, weighs 3.5–4.0 g. (80–90%), has a polymer melt temperature of 320–330°C., and an inherent viscosity of about 0.33 in 90% formic acid (0.5% conc., 25°C.). It is soluble in strong acids, such as formic acid, from which brittle films may be cast.

33. Preparation of β-Alanine (44)

$$\left[-CH_2-CH_2-\overset{\overset{\displaystyle O}{\|}}{C}-NH-\right]_n \xrightarrow{H_2O} H_2N-CH_2-CH_2-\overset{\overset{\displaystyle O}{\|}}{C}-OH$$

The 3-nylon polymer prepared above is refluxed with an excess of 50% aqueous sulfuric acid for 4 hr. The solution is then neutralized to pH 7 with hot aqueous barium hydroxide. The barium sulfate is filtered and washed twice by trituration with 50 ml. portions of water. The combined water filtrates are evaporated to dryness by heating at water aspirator pressure on the steam bath. The residual syrup crystallizes on cooling to give 80–90% yield of β-alanine, which may be recrystallized from hot methanol. The product melts at 195–196°C.

The preparation of a **soluble, linear polyimide from** the **tetrafunctional pyromellitic dianhydride** (Preparation 18) demonstates that polycondensation reactants may be more than difunctional and still produce linear, uncrosslinked products. Another example of this unusual situation involving a **tetrafunctional amine** rather than acid, is the preparation of the **polybenzimidazole** from 3,3′-diaminobenzidine and sebacic acid (45). The polybenzimidazole structure is a type not heretofore seen in polymers and is a striking example of the application of synthetic organic chemistry to the field of condensation polymers.

34. Preparation of Poly(2,2′-octamethylene-5,5′-dibenzimidazole) (45)

3,3′-Diaminobenzidine tetrahydrochloride is treated with decolorizing charcoal, and recrystallized twice from water by adding concentrated hydrochloric acid. The tetraamine is freed by adding a slight excess of sodium hydroxide in water to the tetrahydrochloride in water (1 g./30 ml.) and cooling. The slightly red solid is filtered, washed with water and dried in a vacuum desiccator over phosphorus pentoxide. The melting point of the free base is 173–174°C. The above operations should be conducted in boiled, oxygen-free water, with as many of the manipulations blanketed by nitrogen as possible, since the tetraamine is very sensitive to oxidation.

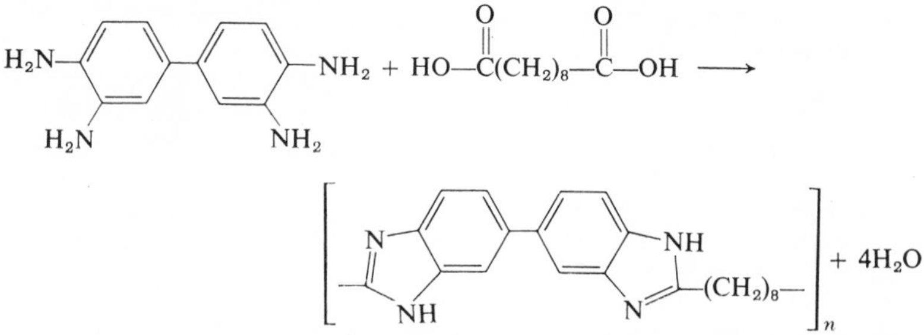

A mixture of 4.08 g. (0.019 mole) 3,3′-diaminobenzidine and 4.04 g. (0.020 mole) sebacic acid is heated in a polymer tube at atmospheric pressure for 3½ hr. at 265°C. by means of a vapor bath (diphenylmethane). A stream of nitrogen is admitted through a capillary reaching to the bottom of the tube. After allowing the melt to cool in nitrogen, the inherent viscosity of the pale yellow polymer is around 1.0 in *m*-cresol (0.5% conc., 25°C.) and the polymer melt temperature is about 750–255°C. A temperature of 340–370°C. is required to press films.

Hydrazine may be condensed at high temperature and under pressure **with a dicarboxylic acid, a dicarboxylic ester, a diamine or a dihydrazide** to produce high polymer through formation of the 4-amino-1,2,4-triazole ring (46).

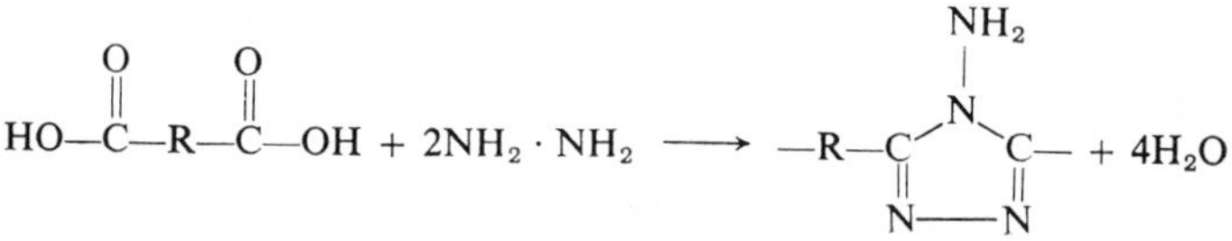

An advantage is gained in using the dihydrazide of the acid because a vacuum cycle is not needed in the polymerization. The polyaminotriazoles where —R— is $—(CH_2)_{6,\ 7,\ \text{and}\ 8}$ have been melt spun into fibers having good tensile properties and high dyeability with acid dyes (46,47); the presence of basic sites in the polymer accounts for the latter.

The polymer melt temperatures of the polyaminotriazoles are high (280°C. for that from adipic acid), the lower alkylene polymers (R = $—(CH_2)_{2,\ 3,\ \text{and}\ 4}$) are water soluble, and the class as a whole is soluble in the polyamide solvents (*m*-cresol, formic acid, etc.).

35. Preparation of Sebacic Dihydrazide

$$CH_3O—\overset{O}{\overset{\|}{C}}—(CH_2)_8\overset{O}{\overset{\|}{C}}—OCH_3 + 2N_2H_4 \longrightarrow$$

$$H_2NHN—\overset{O}{\overset{\|}{C}}—(CH_2)_8—\overset{O}{\overset{\|}{C}}—NHNH_2 + 2CH_3OH$$

A solution of 100 g. (2.0 moles) of hydrazine hydrate in 100 ml. methanol is refluxed gently in a 500 ml. three-necked flask equipped with condenser and dropping funnel. (**Caution!** Hydrazine is toxic.) A solution of 57 g. (0.25 mole) of dimethyl sebacate in 25 ml. methanol is added dropwise. Heating at reflux is continued 1 hr. after addition. The reaction mixture is cooled in ice, 100 ml. water added, and the solid filtered, washed with water, and recrystallized from water–methanol. Decolorizing charcoal is used if necessary. After drying a vacuum oven at 60°C. for several hours, the pure product melts at 186.5–188°C. The yield is 48–52 g. (85–91%).

36. Preparation of Poly(3,5-octamethylene-4-amino-1,2,4-triazole) (47)

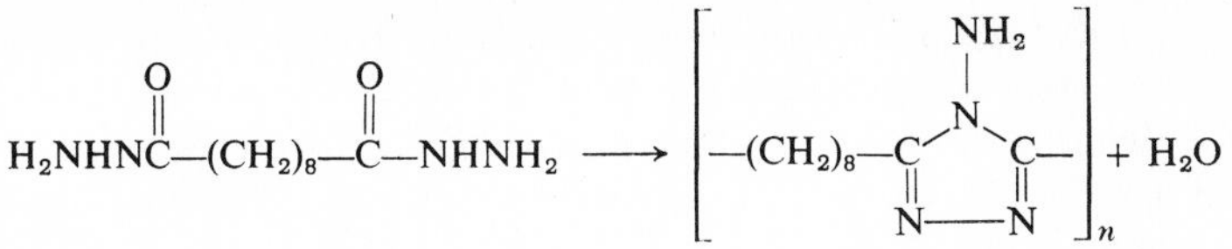

Twenty g. (0.087 mole) of sebacic dihydrazide and 5.0 g. (0.10 mole) of hydrazine hydrate are placed in a pipe autoclave (11) having an aluminum liner and a pressure gauge (see Chapter 2) The autoclave is flushed with nitrogen and sealed. The temperature is raised by means of a vapor bath or oil bath to 260°C. for 3 hr., then for 2 hr. further at 270°C. The pressure on the gauge may reach 800–900 p.s.i. It is important for safety reasons to use a pipe autoclave rated for use at these pressures and to have the reaction properly shielded. The pressure is released to about 100 p.s.i. after 3 hr. of the heating cycle. At the end of the polymerization the autoclave is allowed to cool and is cautiously bled to atmospheric pressure. The plug of off-white or light-gray polymer has a polymer melt temperature of around 250°C. and an inherent viscosity in *m*-cresol (0.5% conc., 25°C.) of 0.6–0.7. The polymer is soluble also in formic and acetic acids, from which the polymer can be spun into filaments or cast into films.

II. Polyureas and Related Polymers

The polyureas may be considered as polyamides derived from the lowest member in the homologous series of dicarboxylic acids, namely carbonic acid, and are therefore like the other polyamides and have a large number of sites available for interchain hydrogen bonding. The polyureas are generally higher melting and less soluble than the other polyamides having a similar amount of separation between functional groups. For instance, polyhexamethyleneurea has a polymer melt temperature of about 295°C., while that of 6-6 polyamide is about 265°C.

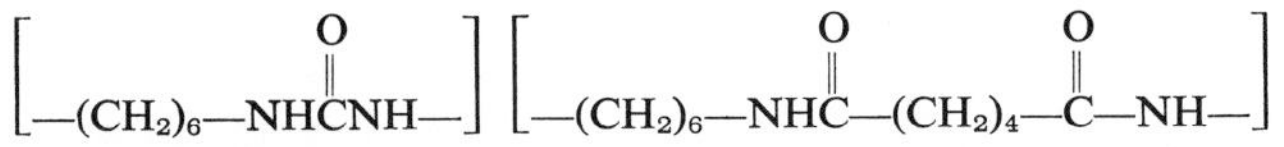

The greater extent of hydrogen bonding and higher polarity associated with the urea group are thought to account for the difference.

Polyureas can in some cases be made in melt systems, but high polymer melt temperatures and accompanying thermal instability frequently require solution techniques for preparation. A number of special methods have been developed for the preparation of polyureas.

Polyureas can be prepared in solution **from** the reaction of a **diisocyanate and diamine.** By taking advantage of the far greater reactivity of isocyanates with amines over phenols and alcohols, the polymerization may be conducted in hydroxylic solvents for the polymer (21). Polydecamethyleneurea can be prepared by a diisocyanate–diamine reaction carried out in m-cresol.

Following polyamide numeral nomenclature, polyureas would be called n-1 polyamides; n = the number of carbons in the diamine, and 1 = carbonic acid, the one-carbon diacid. The polyurea prepared below is 10-1 polyamide.

37. Preparation of Decamethylenediisocyanate (21)

$$ClH \cdot H_2N(CH_2)_{10}—NH_2 \cdot HCl + COCl_2 \longrightarrow OCN—(CH_2)_{10}—NCO + 4HCl$$

Caution!   Run in a Good Hood.

A solution of 86 g. (0.5 mole) of decamethylenediamine in 1000 ml. of dry xylene (isomer mixture is satisfactory) is prepared in a 2 l. three-necked flask equipped with gas inlet tube extending nearly to the bottom of the flask, and a condenser having an outlet to a trap or scrubber for .the off-gases of the reaction. Dry hydrogen chloride is passed through the diamine solution until no further precipitation occurs and the solution is saturated. The hydrogen chloride source is replaced by a phosgene cylinder and the solution is heated to reflux as a slow stream of phosgene is passed through it. (Phosgene is a highly toxic gas, and the reaction must be run in a good hood.) The gases from the reaction are hydrogen chloride and unreacted phosgene. When almost all the solid has dissolved (a period of about 6 hr. is required), the reaction mixture is cooled and filtered. The xylene is distilled at water aspirator pressure through a 10 in. Vigreux column. The residue is then fractionated through the same column at oil pump pressure to give 70–75 g. (62–67% yield) of decamethylenediisocyanate, boiling at 151–153°C./3.0 mm. The product should be stored under nitrogen in tightly stoppered flasks or in taped, screw-cap bottles, preferably in a dry box.

38. Preparation of Polydecamethyleneurea (21)

$$H_2N—(CH_2)_{10}—NH_2 + OCN—(CH_2)_{10}—NCO \longrightarrow$$

$$\left[—(CH_2)_{10}NH—\overset{\overset{\textstyle O}{\|}}{C}—NH \right]_n$$

In a 200 ml. three-necked flask which has been flushed with nitrogen and equipped with stirrer, dropping funnel, and condenser (the latter two protected with drying tubes) is placed a solution of 19.0 g. (0.11 mole) freshly distilled decamethylenediamine (Preparation 15) in 39 ml. of distilled *m*-cresol. With stirring, 24.8 g. (0.11 mole) decamethylenediisocyanate is added over a 10 min. period. Much heat is evolved and a precipitate forms. The dropping funnel is washed with 10 ml. *m*-cresol and the temperature is raised to 218°C. for a period of 5 hr. The original precipitate dissolves and the solution becomes viscous. The solution is then permitted to cool and is poured into 1500 ml. methanol with vigorous stirring. The polymer, which separates as a white solid, is filtered and washed several times by stirring (as in a household-type blender) with ethanol. The yield of polymer, when dried at 60°C. in a vacuum oven for 15 hr., is about 38–40 g. (90–95%), and the polymer melt temperature is about 210°C. The inherent viscosity in *m*-cresol (0.5% conc. at 25°C.) is about 0.3. Despite this low value, films may be melt-pressed and drawable fibers melt-spun.

Very high melting, soluble polyureas have also been prepared **from all-aromatic reactants** (48,49) by a solution method similar to that of the preceding example. If the polymer formed is soluble at room temperature in the reaction medium, no heating may be necessary, and a viscous polymer solution may result. The following polymerization, where *trans*-2,5-dimethylpiperazine is condensed with methylenebis(4 phenyl-isocyanate), exemplifies this type of reaction.

39. Preparation of Polyurea from *trans*-2,5-Dimethylpiperazine and Methylenebis(4 phenyl-isocyanate) (49)

A solution of 3.253 g. (0.013 mole) of methylenebis(4 phenyl-isocyanate) in 80 ml. of tetramethylene sulfone–chloroform (70/30 by volume) mixture is placed in a blender jar. A second solution of 1.484 g. of *trans*-2,5-dimethyl-piperazine in 80 ml. of the same solvent mixture is added rapidly with vigorous stirring. Stirring is continued at high speed for 7 min., then the reaction is stopped by addition of 100 ml. of 4 vol.% aqueous *n*-butylamine. More water is added to precipitate the polymer, which is then washed once with 50% aqueous acetone and repeatedly with water. The polymer may be dried at 80°C. under vacuum.

The yield of product is quantitative; the inherent viscosity should be about 3.0 (H_2SO_4).

Bis-*N,N'*-silyamines also undergo additions to diisocyanates to form high polymers, the R_3Si—N$\langle$ function adding to —NCO in the same way as H—N$\langle$. However, there is free inter-and intramolecular exchange of the R_3Si— and H— groups attached to nitrogen, so that an equilibrium distribution of silyl groups on nitrogen occurs as shown in the equation below.

40. *N*-Silyl-Substituted Polyurea from the Addition Reaction of Bis-*N,N'*-(trimethylsilyl)-*p,p'*-diaminodiphenyl Ether and Tolylene-2,4-diisocyanate (50)

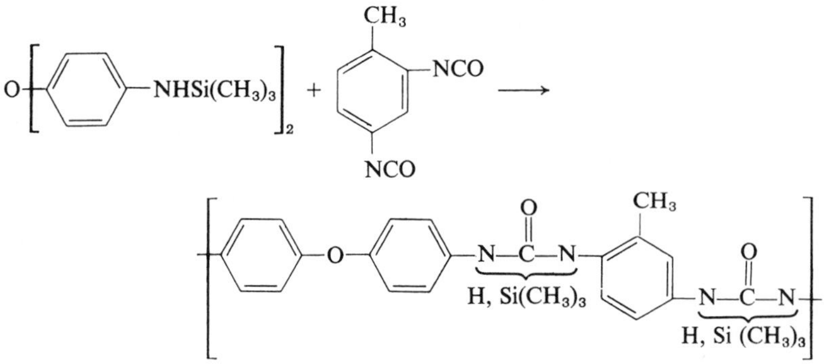

Bis-*N,N'*-(trimethylsilyl)-*p,p'*-diaminodiphenyl ether · is prepared from trimethylchlorosilane and the diamine. It boils at 196–197/1.4 min. and melts at 72–73°C. Tolylene-2,4-diisocyanate is purified by distillation (b.p. 75–78°C./1 mm.). Polymerization can be carried out in a stirred flask with condenser; care must be taken to thoroughly dry the glassware initially and to protect the system from moisture during charging and polymerization. Then, 3.48 g. (0.02 mole) of the diisocyanate is mixed with 6.89 g. (0.02 mole) of the bis-silylamine and 10 cc. of toluene which has been distilled from and stored over calcium hydride. The temperature of the mixture rises initially to about 60°C. The mixture is stirred for 3 hr. in a bath heated at 100°C. The colorless, clear solution becomes very viscous after this time, making stirring very difficult; 10 ml. of dry toluene is added and stirring is continued at 100°C. for an additional 3 hr. The solution is then diluted with 100 cc. of toluene; addition of 30 cc. of dry *n*-hexane precipitates the polymer in the form of a white, tough gum. It is washed several times in more dry hexane. The polymer melts over the range of 200–220°C.; unlike most polyureas, it decomposes well above its melting temperature.

The *N*-trimethylsilyl groups are slowly hydrolyzed on exposure to ambient moisture or rapidly in solution in contact with protonic solvents such as alcohols. The polymer should be handled accordingly.

For those polyureas that are stable above their melt temperatures the **reaction of a diamine with urea** in a melt-polymerization system with elimination of ammonia can sometimes be used in their preparation (51).

$$H_2N—R—NH_2 + H_2N—\overset{\overset{O}{\|}}{C}—NH_2 \longrightarrow \left[R—NH—\overset{\overset{O}{\|}}{C}—NH\right] + 2NH_3$$

In the following example of this reaction, the diamine is bis(γ-aminopropyl) ether. The resulting polyurea has the relatively low polymer melt temperature of 190°C. due, in part, to the odd number of atoms in the diamine chain.

41. Preparation of Bis(γ-aminopropyl) Ether (52)

$$CH_2=CHCN + HOCH_2CH_2CN \longrightarrow NCCH_2CH_2OCH_2CH_2CN$$

$$NCCH_2CH_2OCH_2CH_2CN \xrightarrow{(H)} H_2NCH_2CH_2CH_2OCH_2CH_2CH_2NH_2$$

A. Bis(β-cyanoethyl) Ether (53)

To a stirred mixture of 177 g. (2.5 moles) of ethylene cyanohydrin and 6 g. of a 20% potassium hydroxide solution in a 1 l. three-necked flask equipped with stirrer, dropping funnel and condenser is added dropwise 132 g. (2.5 mole) of acrylonitrile over $2\frac{3}{4}$ hr. The reaction is maintained at 40°C. during addition. When the addition is complete, the reaction is stirred for 18 hr. further at room temperature. It is neutralized with dilute hydrochloric acid and evaporated to dryness under water aspirator pressure (about 30 mm.) on the steam bath. The residue is fractionally distilled to yield about 266 g. (80%) of bis(β-cyanoethyl) ether, boiling at 159–162°C./5 mm.

B. Bis(γ-aminopropyl) Ether (52)

To a solution of 86 g. (0.69 mole) bis(β-cyanoethyl)ether in 340 ml. methanol containing 100 g. of anhydrous ammonia in a hydrogenation bomb is added 100 g. of Raney nickel catalyst (54). The dinitrile is hydrogenated at 1500 p.s.i. at 100–110°C. Hydrogen uptake should be complete in about $\frac{1}{2}$ hr. Prolonged heating of the reaction mixture reduces the yield of desired product by hydrogenolysis of the ether to γ-aminopropanol. The solution is filtered free of catalyst and the methanol and ammonia removed by distillation on the steam bath at atmospheric pressure. The residue is fractionally distilled through a precision distillation column. Bis(γ-aminopropyl)ether boils at 72–73°C./3 mm. The yield is about 60 g. (65%). The possible by-product, γ-aminopropanol, boils at 60°C./3 mm., and has the same refractive index (n_D^{25} 1.4605) as the desired diamino ether.

42. Preparation of Poly(4-oxaheptamethyleneurea) (51)

$$H_2N(CH_2)_3—O—(CH_2)_3NH_2 + H_2N—\overset{\overset{O}{\|}}{C}—NH_2 \longrightarrow$$

$$\left[(CH_2)_3—O—(CH_2)_3NH—\overset{\overset{O}{\|}}{C}—NH—\right]_n + 2NH_3$$

In a polymer tube with side arm is placed a mixture of 7.5 g. (0.125 mole) of urea and 16.5 g. (0.125 mole) of bis(γ-aminopropyl) ether.

Nitrogen is passed slowly through a capillary reaching to the bottom of the tube and the temperature is raised to 156°C. for 1 hr. by means of a vapor bath (cyclohexanone), during which time ammonia is evolved. The temperature is raised to 231°C. in a vapor bath for another 1 hr. period, and finally to 255°C. for 1 hr. During the last 20 min. of this part of the heating, an oil pump vacuum is cautiously applied; frothing may be serious if the vacuum is applied suddenly. The polymer is cooled under nitrogen and removed by breaking the tube. The inherent viscosity is about 0.6 in m-cresol (0.5% conc., 25°C.) and the polymer melt temperature is around 190°C. Strong films may be melt-pressed at or near this temperature.

Polyureas can be prepared also by the **aminolysis of a bisurethane,** with the elimination of an alcohol (55).

$$H_2N—R—NH_2 + EtO\overset{\overset{\displaystyle O}{\|}}{C}—NH—R—NH—\overset{\overset{\displaystyle O}{\|}}{C}OEt \longrightarrow$$

$$\left[—R—NH—\overset{\overset{\displaystyle O}{\|}}{C}—NH— \right]_n + 2EtOH$$

Carbonate esters are also reported to form polyureas by reaction with diamines, but the reaction is difficult to control.

The following polymer is a copolyurea of hexamethylene- and deca-methylenediamines.

43. Preparation of Poly(hexamethylene–decamethyleneurea) Copolymer (55)

$$H_2N(CH_2)_{10}NH_2 + C_2H_5O\overset{\overset{\displaystyle O}{\|}}{C}—NH(CH_2)_6NH—\overset{\overset{\displaystyle O}{\|}}{C}OC_2H_5 \longrightarrow$$

$$\left[(CH_2)_{10}—NH\overset{\overset{\displaystyle O}{\|}}{C}NH—(CH_2)_6—NH—\overset{\overset{\displaystyle O}{\|}}{C}NH \right]_n + 2C_2H_5OH$$

The hexamethylene bis(ethylurethane) is prepared (25) by the simultaneous addition from separate funnels of 130 g. (1.2 moles) ethyl chlorocarbonate and 48 g. (1.2 moles) sodium hydroxide in 400 ml. water to a rapidly stirred solution of 58 g. (0.5 mole) hexamethylenediamine in 200 ml. ether cooled in an ice bath and maintained at 10°C. or less during the addition. The reaction is stirred for 15 min. after the addition and the solid filtered. It is re-crystallized from benzene–petroleum ether. The melting point is 84°C.

A mixture of 12.37 g. (0.072 mole) of decamethylenediamine and 18.70 g. (0.072 mole) of hexamethylene bis(ethylurethane) is placed in a polymer tube which is then purged with nitrogen (Preparation 2) and heated to 202°C.

(*m*-cresol bath) for 3 hr. at atmospheric pressure while a slow stream of nitrogen is passed through the melt. The polymer is cooled under nitrogen and is obtained as a tough plug. It has an inherent viscosity of 0.2–0.4 in *m*-cresol (0.5% conc., 25°C.) and a polymer melt temperature of about 170°C. It can be pulled into fibers from the melt and melt pressed into films.

A preparation of **aliphatic polyureas from a diamine and carbon oxysulfide** was developed by Van der Kerk (56). This reaction involves, first, the formation of what can be depicted as the thiocarbamate salt,

$$\overset{+}{H_3N}-R-NH-\overset{\overset{\textstyle O}{\|}}{C}-S^-.$$ The salt is then heated to form polyurea with the loss of hydrogen sulfide. The polymerization is not carried out in the melt, but rather in the form of the solid salt, and is an example of powder polymerization.

Polyureas previously have been prepared in formally similar reactions of diamines with carbon dioxide (57) but these require high temperatures and pressures (100 atm.). Carbon disulfide reacts in like manner to give a polythiourea (58), and carbon oxysulfide has been stated to give a polythiourea also. The formation of a normal polyurea from carbon oxysulfide, as in the present case is, therefore, somewhat unusual.

The mechanism of the polymerization involves the formation, first, of low polymer during a mild heating cycle (110°C.), with the loss of some COS and diamine as well as H_2S. The low polymer, on heating at higher temperatures (150–180°C.) splits out more diamine by aminolysis of urea links near the end of a chain by H_2N— ends of another chain, forming higher polymer:

$$\overset{+}{H_3N}-R-NH-\overset{\overset{\textstyle O}{\|}}{C}-S^- \xrightarrow{\text{110°C.}} \left[H_2N-R-NH-\overset{\overset{\textstyle O}{\|}}{C}-NH\right]_x R-NH_2 + H_2S$$

$$\downarrow \text{150–180°C.}$$

$$\left[H_2N-R-NH-\overset{\overset{\textstyle O}{\|}}{C}-NH\right]_y R-NH_2 + (y-x)H_2N-R-NH_2$$

where y is larger than x. The later stages of the reaction bear a resemblance to the preparation of poly(ethylene terephthalate) from polymerization of bis(hydroxyethylterephthalate) by elimination of ethylene glycol. The reaction has been used for the preparation of polyureas from the six through ten and the twelve carbon diamines.

44. Preparation of the Thiocarbamate Salt of Decamethylenediamine (56)

$$2KCNS + 3H_2SO_4 + 2H_2O \longrightarrow 2COS + 2KHSO_4 + (NH_4)_4SO_4$$

$$H_2N-(CH_2)_{10}-NH_2 + COS \longrightarrow H_3\overset{+}{N}-(CH_2)_{10}-NH-\overset{\displaystyle O}{\overset{\|}{C}}-S^-$$

A 1 l. three-necked flask is set up as a carbon oxysulfide generator by providing it with a stirrer, dropping funnel, and a short air condenser topped with a gas outlet leading to a purification train. The latter consists, in order, of a U-tube filled with mercuric oxide dispersed on pumice or glass wool to remove hydrogen sulfide, a similarly prepared tube containing phosphorus pentoxide for drying the gas, a soda-lime-packed tube for removing carbon dioxide, and a kerosene bubbler to absorb carbon disulfide.

The generating flask is charged with 520 g. of concentrated sulfuric acid and 400 ml. of water. The purification train is then swept with nitrogen and connected to the gas generator and to the receiver, which is a 1 l. three-necked flask having a gas inlet tube reaching to the bottom of the flask, a stirrer, and an outlet (protected by a calcium chloride drying tube) leading to a solution of strong sodium hydroxide to absorb unreacted carbon oxysulfide. To the receiver is added 5 g. (0.029 mole) of distilled, carbonate-free, decamethylenediamine and 600 ml. of hexane. (The hexane is purified by shaking with concentrated sulfuric acid, then washing with aqueous sodium hydroxide and water, drying over anhydrous magnesium sulfate, and distilling over sodium.) The receiving flask should be flushed with nitrogen at the same time as the purification trap, and the diamine should be added to the flask under nitrogen.

To the sulfuric acid in the generator is added dropwise a solution of 48.0 g. (0.49 mole) potassium thiocyanate in water to give a total volume of 50 ml., with stirring at a temperature maintained at 30°C. by means of a warm water bath if necessary. The gas is passed into the diamine in the receiving flask with stirring and moderate ice cooling. The decamethylenediamine thiocarbamate precipitates as the reaction proceeds. When no more precipitate forms, the solid product is filtered with suction under a blanket of nitrogen, either in a dry box or under an inverted glass funnel which is attached to a nitrogen line. The salt is washed on the filter with dry hexane and dried in a vacuum desiccator at 0.5 mm. for 24 hr. It is stored under nitrogen in taped bottles, either in a desiccator or a dry box. The latter is preferred, since weighings of the solid can then be readily made under nitrogen.

The salt analyzes for the monothiocarbamate as shown in the equation for this reaction, but it is believed that the amine groups react at random and that various salt compositions are present. The simple equation represents the over-all composition of the salt, however.

45. Preparation of Poly(decamethyleneurea) (56)

$$H_3N-(CH_2)_{10}-NH-\overset{\displaystyle O}{\overset{\|}{C}}-S^- \longrightarrow \left[-(CH_2)_{10}-NH-\overset{\displaystyle O}{\overset{\|}{C}}-NH-\right]_n + H_2S$$

A 100 ml. one-necked flask is charged with 10 g. of decamethylenediamine thiocarbamate salt. The flask is fitted with a short bulb condenser, which has a vacuum take-off at the top. The condenser is attached to a vibrator, which is also a solid means of support, to agitate the contents of the flask continually during polymerization. The flask is not clamped, and depends on the aplication of vacuum to keep it attached to the condenser and its vibrator support. No water is used in the condenser (Fig. 3.3).

The pressure is reduced to 12 mm. and the flask is heated (with vibration) to about 110°C. for about 5 hr., when the evolution of hydrogen sulfide ceases. Some sublimate collects in the condenser; it should be noted whether the condenser is in danger of plugging. The pressure is reduced now to 1–2 mm. and the temperature raised to 150°C. for 2 hr., then 180°C. for 16 hr. Higher polymer results if an additional 3 hr. heating at 200°C. is used. The reaction mixture is permitted to cool, then opened to the air. The white, free flowing powder weighs 6.6–7.0 g. (99–95% of theory). The inherent viscosity should be at least 0.5 in *m*-cresol (0.5% at 25°C.). The polymer melt temperature is 210°C.; the polymer is stable enough its melting temperature to allow fabrication.

The highly versatile **interfacial polycondensation** method can be **applied to the preparation of polyureas** also. Phosgene is used as the

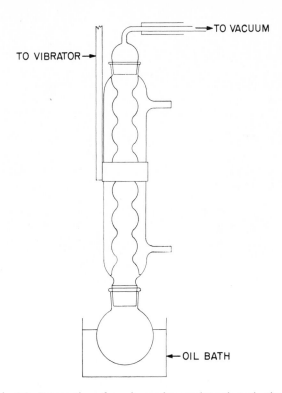

Fig. 3.3. Preparation of a polyurea by powder polymerization.

acid chloride in this instance. In the following preparation of poly-(hexamethyleneurea) a definite quantity of phosgene must be used. Bubbling phosgene through the diamine–alkali mixture in unmeasured amount gives lower molecular weights.

46. Preparation of Polyhexamethyleneurea (59)

$$H_2N(CH_2)_6NH_2 + COCl_2 \longrightarrow \left[(CH_2)_6-NH\overset{\overset{\displaystyle O}{\|}}{C}NH \right]_n + 2HCl$$

Caution!   Run in a Good Hood.

A solution of 5.8 g. (0.05 mole) hexamethylenediamine (Preparation 1) and 4 g. (0.10 mole) sodium hydroxide (preferably as an aliquot of a stock solution) in 70 ml. water is added with vigorous manual stirring to a solution of 4.95 g. (0.05 mole) phosgene in 200 ml. dry carbon tetrachloride contained in a 500 ml. wide mouth Erlenmeyer flask. The polyurea forms very rapidly and heat is evolved. After the reaction has been stirred briskly for 8–10 min., the carbon tetrachloride is evaporated on the steam bath and the polymer filtered, washed several times with water in a household blender, and air-dried overnight. The weight of polymer obtained is 5 g. (70%), having an inherent viscosity in *m*-cresol (0.5% conc., 30°C.) of about 0.90. The polymer melt temperature is about 295°C. Films can be melt-pressed.

The solution of phosgene in carbon tetrachloride used in the above polymerization can be prepared by condensing phosgene into dry carbon tetrachloride in a volumetric flask, and adding carbon tetrachloride to complete the volume. The solution is analyzed for g. of phosphene per ml. of solution by shaking thoroughly an aliquot with excess standard sodium hydroxide and titrating the excess sodium hydroxide in the aqueous layer using phenolphthalein indicator. The amount of phosgene, for convenience, should be 0.10–0.20 g./ml.

Certain **polyureas** may be **prepared in dimethyl sulfoxide** as the solvent **using the reaction of a diisocyanate with a monocarboxylic acid.** The solvent participates in the reaction, presumably interacting with the

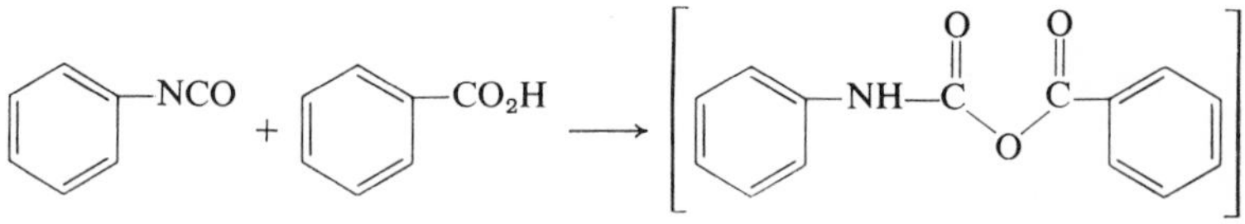

(I)

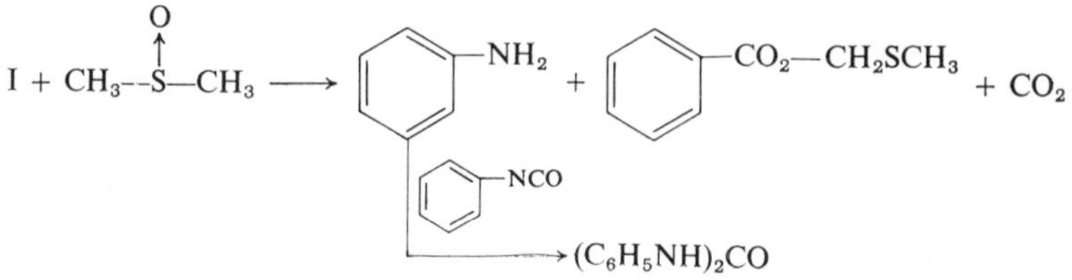

mixed anhydride (I) formed from the addition of the acid to the iso-cyanate group. As has been shown for the monofunctional reactants, the stoichiometry of the reaction is 2:1:1 for isocyanate:acid:sulfoxide (60). This reaction is considerably different from the 1:1 reaction of an acid and an isocyanate, alone or in an inert solvent, which leads ultimately to amide formation (see Preparation 31).

47. Preparation of Poly[methylene Bis(4-phenylurea)] (60)

$$OCN-\langle\bigcirc\rangle-CH_2-\langle\bigcirc\rangle-NCO + PhCO_2H + CH_3\overset{\overset{O}{\uparrow}}{S}CH_3 \longrightarrow$$

$$\left[-HN-\langle\bigcirc\rangle-CH_2-\langle\bigcirc\rangle-NH-\overset{\overset{O}{\|}}{C}-\right]_n + PhCO_2-CH_2SCH_3 + CO_2$$

This reaction should be carried out in a hood; sulfide odors are formed.

In a 100 ml. three-necked flask fitted with a stirrer and a calcium chloride drying tube is placed 4.84 g. (0.04 mole) dry benzoic acid and 40 ml. dimethyl sulfoxide. (The latter is dried by distillation at reduced pressure with a 20% forerun discarded to insure removal of water; the distillate collected is best stored in a taped, screw-cap bottle and opened under nitrogen or in a dry box.) When the benzoic acid has dissolved, 10.0 g. (0.04 mole) methylene bis(4-phenyl isocyanate) is added as a solid all at once to the flask to prevent possible introduction of moisture. (The diisocyanate is purified by distillation, b.p. 142–144°C./0.14 mm., through a short Vigreux column.) As the di-isocyanate dissolves, the reaction proceeds exothermically with the evolution of carbon dioxide. When the gas evolution has practically ceased, the reaction is warmed to 50–60°C. for $\frac{1}{2}$ hr. in a water bath, then stirred at room tem-perature until a total of 4 hr. has elapsed since the diisocyanate addition. The solution is now clear, viscous and yellow. Clear, tough films may be cast directly and dried in a vacuum oven at 60–80°C. The polymer may also be isolated from the original solution by precipitation in water, followed by thorough successive washings with water and ethanol in a home blender modified for use with flammable solvents. After drying in a vacuum oven at 60–80°C., the inherent viscosity in dimethyl sulfoxide is about 1.0 (0.5% conc., 25°C.). The polymer melt temperature is around 300°C., and the yield is quantitative (8.8 g.).

Polymer structures having a high concentration of amide groups can be made by the addition of hydrazine or a diacid hydrazide to a diisocyanate. In many cases, the polymer can be made in solution and cast directly into films or spun into fibers without the need for prior isolation.

The following is an example of **hydrazine–diisocyanate addition to give a polyureylene.** Although anhydrous hydrazine may be used, the hydrate is more convenient.

48. Preparation of Polymer from Methylene Bis(4-phenyl Isocyanate) and Hydrazine Hydrate: Poly[methylene Bis(4-phenylureylene)] (61)

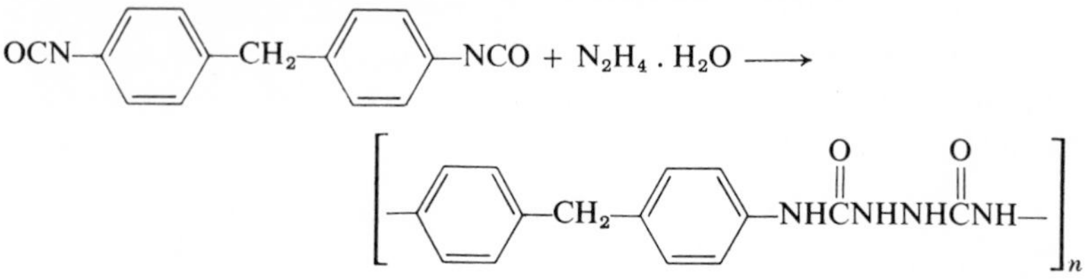

OCN—⟨benzene⟩—CH₂—⟨benzene⟩—NCO + $N_2H_4 \cdot H_2O$ ⟶

$$\left[-\text{⟨benzene⟩}-CH_2-\text{⟨benzene⟩}-NH\overset{O}{\overset{\|}{C}}NHNH\overset{O}{\overset{\|}{C}}NH- \right]_n$$

In a 300 ml. three-necked flask with stirrer, a mixture of 23.0 g. (0.092 mole) of methylene bis(4-phenyl isocyanate), purified as in Preparation 47, and 100 ml. of dry dimethylformamide is treated with a solution of 4.60 g. (0.092 mol) of hydrazine hydrate in 50 ml. of dimethylformamide with stirring. An immediate exothermic reaction occurs, and the solution becomes very viscous. This solution can be cast to clear, tough film by drying in a vacuum oven at 60°C. in a stream of nitrogen.

The polymer may be precipitated in water, filtered, and washed in a household mixer to cut it up. The yield is quantitative. However, the polymer cannot now be redissolved in dimethylformamide or dimethyl sulfoxide. The polymer decomposes at 300°C. without melting. If dianisidinediisocyanate is used in this preparation, the polymer will redissolve after precipitation.

If **isophthalic dihydrazide** is used in place of hydrazine in the preceding polymerization, the polymer formed is a **poly(isophthaloylsemicarbazide).** The structure differs from the preceding example by being less symmetrical and having two less urea-type —NH— groups per chemical repeat unit. The increased solubility in dimethylformamide and related solvents, and lower polymer melt temperature of the present case reflect this change. The reaction of the diisocyanate with the dihydrazide is initially less vigorous than with hydrazine because of the lower basicity of the hydrazide.

49. Preparation of Isophthalic Dihydrazide (62)

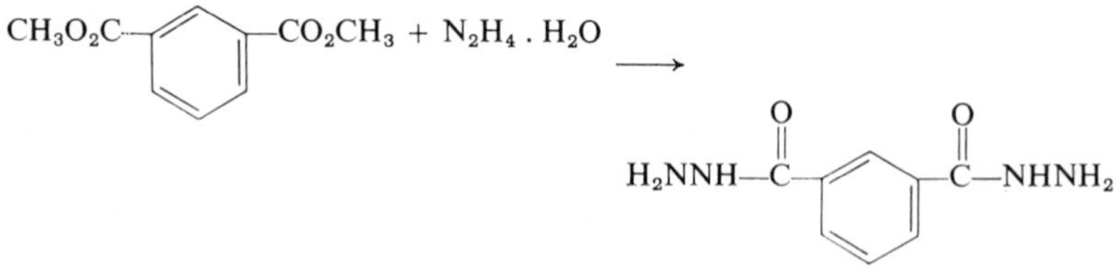

CH_3O_2C—⟨benzene⟩—CO_2CH_3 + $N_2H_4 \cdot H_2O$ ⟶

$$H_2NNH-\overset{O}{\overset{\|}{C}}-\text{⟨benzene⟩}-\overset{O}{\overset{\|}{C}}-NHNH_2$$

One hundred ninety-four g. (1.0 mole) of dimethyl isophthalate in 500 ml. of methanol is added to 350 g. (7.0 moles) hydrazine hydrate in 2 l. of methanol in a 4 l. Erlenmeyer flask. The solution is allowed to stand overnight. The solid which forms is separated by filtration, washed with methanol on the filter, and dried in a vacuum oven at 70°C. The melting point is 219–220°C. The yield is about 180 g. (93%). The isophthalic dihydrazide may be recrystallized from methanol-water, but this is usually not necessary.

50. Preparation of Polymer from Isophthalic Dihydrazide and Methylene Bis(4-phenyl Isocyanate) (61)

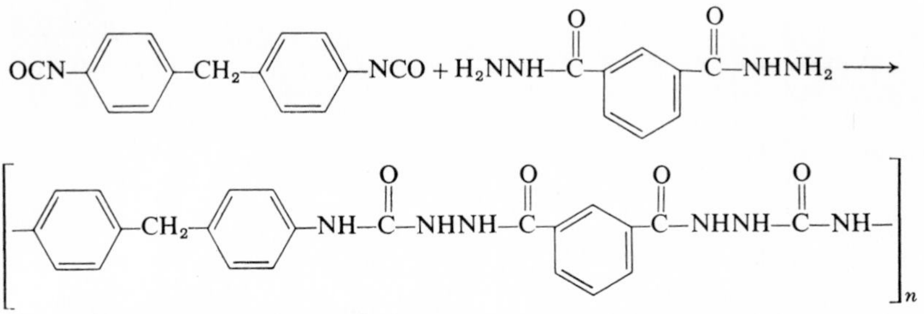

To a solution of 1.94 g. (0.01 mole) isophthalic dihydrazide in 50 ml. dry dimethyl sulfoxide in a three-necked 100 ml. flask equipped with a stirrer and nitrogen inlet is added at room temperature 2.50 g. (0.01 mole) methylene bis(4-phenyl isocyanate). (Preparation 47). The reaction mixture warms up slightly and becomes viscous very quickly. Stirring at room temperature under nitrogen is continued for 2 hr. The polymer is isolated by pouring the solution into 300 ml. of water, filtered, and is washed twice with water. The solid is dried in air, and has an inherent viscosity in dimethyl sulfoxide of about 1.8. The total yield is 3.5 g. (78%); the polymer melt temperature is 250°C. The polymer is soluble in cold N-methylpyrrolidone, sulfuric acid, dimethyl sulfoxide, dimethylformamide, and in hot hexamethylphosphoramide.

A 20% solution in dimethyl sulfoxide can be prepared and a tough, clear film cast.

Among the more unusual polymeric products from addition of active hydrogen compounds to diisocyanates is that from a dioxime (63). The reaction of dimethyl glyoxime with hexamethylene diisocyanate has given high molecular weight polymer:

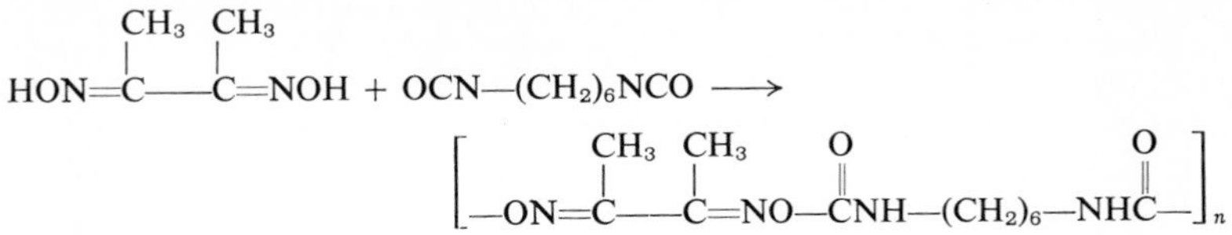

In the following example, cyclohexanedione dioxime and methylene bis(4-phenyl isocyanate) are the reactants. The products are poly-O-acyloximes. Although they can be fabricated to films and fibers, the polymers degrade at their melting point and in boiling water.

51. Preparation of Cyclohexanedione Dioxime (63)

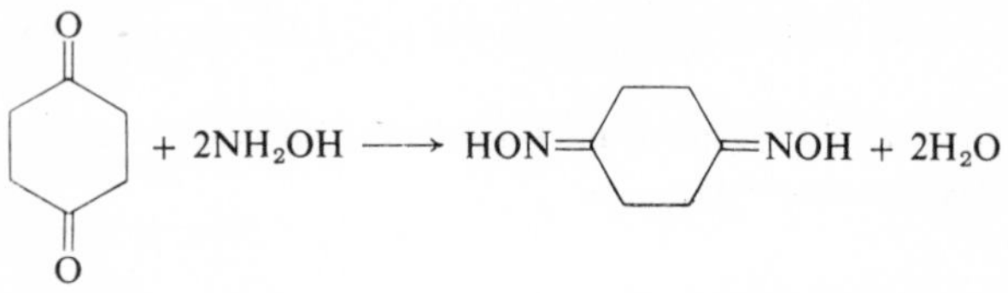

A mixture of 39 g. (0.35 mole) of 1,4-cyclohexanedione, 50 g. (0.72 mole) of hydroxylamine hydrochloride, 200 ml. of pyridine, and 200 ml. of absolute alcohol is refluxed for 4 hr. in a 1 l. round-bottom flask equipped with a condenser. The resulting solution is poured into a crystallizing dish and the solvents allowed to evaporate in a stream of air. Four hundred ml. of water is added and the solid is filtered. It is recrystallized from 90% ethanol, giving a white, crystalline solid melting at 201–202°C.

52. Preparation of Polymer from 1,4-Cyclohexanedione Dioxime and Biphenylene Diisocyanate (63)

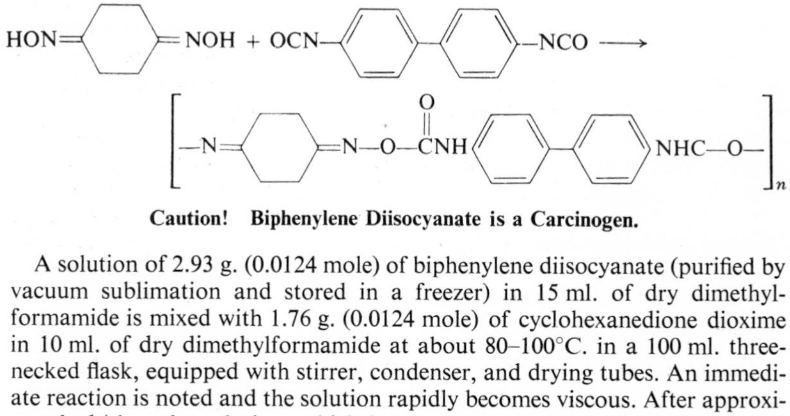

Caution!   Biphenylene Diisocyanate is a Carcinogen.

A solution of 2.93 g. (0.0124 mole) of biphenylene diisocyanate (purified by vacuum sublimation and stored in a freezer) in 15 ml. of dry dimethylformamide is mixed with 1.76 g. (0.0124 mole) of cyclohexanedione dioxime in 10 ml. of dry dimethylformamide at about 80–100°C. in a 100 ml. three-necked flask, equipped with stirrer, condenser, and drying tubes. An immediate reaction is noted and the solution rapidly becomes viscous. After approximately ½ hr., the solution, which has become somewhat cloudy, is poured into water and the polymer is isolated by filtration. It is ground up, washed thoroughly with water, and dried in a high vacuum. The yield is 4.35 g. (94%). The polymer decomposes without melting above 200°C.

The dry polymer is easily soluble in dimethyl sulfoxide. It has an inherent viscosity of 0.81–1.2 (0.5% conc. at 25°C.) in the solvent and can be cast to clear, tough film. A solution of polymer (about 15%) prepared as above can be extruded from a mechanically driven syringe into 50% aqueous dimethylformamide (see Chapter 2) to give fiber which is easily wound up on a mechanical windup.

Another unusual class of polymers are the polythiosemicarbazides, which have a very strong tendency to chelate with various metals. They are made by condensation of a bis-hydrazine with a diisothiocyanate.

53. Preparation of Diaminopiperazine (64,65)

(1)   HN⟨ ⟩NH + 2HONO ⟶ ON—N⟨ ⟩N—NO

(2)   ON—N⟨ ⟩N—NO ⟶ H_2N—N⟨ ⟩N—NH_2

A. N,N'-Dinitrosopiperazine

To a solution of 194 g. (1 mole) of piperazine hexahydrate, 500 ml. of water, and 250 ml. of concentrated hydrochloric acid is added at 15–25°C., dropwise and with stirring, 150 g. (2.1 moles) of 97% sodium nitrite in 300 ml. of water. The mixture is stirred for 2 hr., filtered, and the solid washed with water. Yield of N,N'-dinitrosopiperazine is 128.5 g. (89%); m.p. 162–164°C. (uncorrected). The reported m.p. is 158°C. (64).

B. N,N'-Diaminopiperazine Dihydrochloride

To a stirred mixture of 144 g. (1 mole of dinitrosopiperazine, 272 g. (4.16 atoms) of zinc dust, and 1000 ml. of water is added dropwise over a period of 2.5 hr. 600 ml. (10.5 moles) of glacial acetic acid, while the temperature is maintained at 20–30°C. The mixture is stirred at room temperature overnight and at 80–85°C. for 1 hr. On cooling, zinc acetate precipitates. This is removed by filtration and washed with 500 ml. of cold alcohol, the washings being added to the filtrate. Another 500 ml. of alcohol is added to the filtrate and 400 g. (11 moles) of hydrogen chloride is passed in. The mixture is cooled to 0°C., and filtered. Yield, 117.6 g. (62%) of N,N'-diaminopiperazine dihydrochloride.

C. N,N'-Diaminopiperazine

To 1500 ml. of ethanol is added 453 g. of potassium hydroxide and the mixture is stirred until solution is complete. To this is added in portions 378 g. (2 moles) of diaminopiperazine dihydrochloride. The mixture is heated at reflux for 2 hr. and filtered to remove the insoluble material. On evaporation of the filtrate to a small volume, and cooling in ice, a light-brown pasty solid precipitates. This is dried on a suction filter (under nitrogen) and recrystallized from 500 ml. of 1:1 alcohol–ether to give 140 g. (85.5%) of tan crystals. The tan product is sublimed to give 104 g. (63.5%) of white N,N'-diaminopiperazine; m.p. 117–119°C. Before use in a polymerization, the product should be further purified by recrystallization from chlorobenzene.

54. Preparation of Methylene Bis (4-phenyl isothiocyanate) (65)

NH_2⟨ ⟩—CH_2—⟨ ⟩NH_2 + $CSCl_2$ ⟶

SCN⟨ ⟩—CH_2—⟨ ⟩NCS

Caution!   Thiophosgene Is Highly Toxic and Should Be Handled Only in a Good Hood.

In a three-necked flask cooled with an ice bath is placed 150 g. of thio-phosgene and 1 l. of ice water. A solution of 87 g. of 4,4'-diaminodiphenyl-methane in 1 l. of chloroform is added with stirring over about 1 hr. The mixture is stirred at 0–10°C. for an additional 2 hr., then at room temperature overnight. The chloroform layer is separated and evaporated to dryness under a stream of nitrogen. The solid residue is dissolved in a mixture consisting of 400 ml. of benzene and 800 ml. of cyclohexane at the boiling point. The solution is decolorized, filtered, and allowed to cool. The fine needlelike precipitate is filtered, washed with cold cyclohexane, and recrystallized a second time from benzene–cyclohexane as described above. The yield of pure product (m.p. 141–142°C.) is 84 g. (66%).

The reaction mixture is ordinarily contaminated by traces of unidentified by-products with extremely repulsive odors. Rubber gloves should be worn at all times until the product is obtained in a reasonable state of purity, at which point it is essentially odorless.

55. Preparation of a Polythiosemicarbazide (65)

In a typical preparation, 56.4 g. of powdered methylene-bis(4-phenyl isothiocyanate) is stirred into a solution of 23.2 g. of diaminopiperazine in 600 ml. of dimethyl sulfoxide at about 50°C. The mixture rapidly becomes viscous, and heating and stirring are discontinued after 2 hr. The next day, the polymer is isolated by precipitation in water and is then chopped up in a home blender, washed thoroughly in water, and dried. The yield is quantitative and the product has an inherent viscosity of over 1.0 (0.5% in dimethyl sulfoxide); the PMT is about 230°C.

This polymerization is quite reproducible; inherent viscosities as high as 1.8 can be obtained with specially purified intermediates. It has been found that diaminopiperazine recrystallized from chlorobenzene is much more satisfactory than sublimed material. The polymer dissolves readily in di-methyl sulfoxide and can be cast to clear, tough films which can be drawn 2–3 times at about 175°C. The drawn film samples show strong birefringence under a polarizing microscope, the birefringence disappearing at about 220°C. However, x-ray diagrams from drawn and undrawn samples show the polymer to be completely amorphous.

56. Preparation of a Copper Chelate of a Polythiosemicarbazide (65)

To a solution of 0.4 g. of copper(II) chloride in 100 ml. of dimethylformamide is added a 0.35 g. of the polythiosemicarbazide prepared above in 10 ml. dimethyl sulfoxide. Then 10 ml. of triethylamine is added with vigorous stirring. The precipitated polymer is filtered, washed with water and dried. The polymer is black and contains 13% of copper (theory—13.8%).

The dihydrazides of aliphatic and aromatic diacids can be made to undergo reaction in solution with dialdehydes to give high molecular weight polymers (66). It appears necessary that the polymer remain soluble in order for a high molecular weight to be achieved. Polymers made in hexamethylphosphoramide from certain combinations of reactants were sometimes no longer soluble after isolation.

57. Polycondensation of Terephthaldehyde with Adipic and Isophthalic Acid Dihydrazides (66)

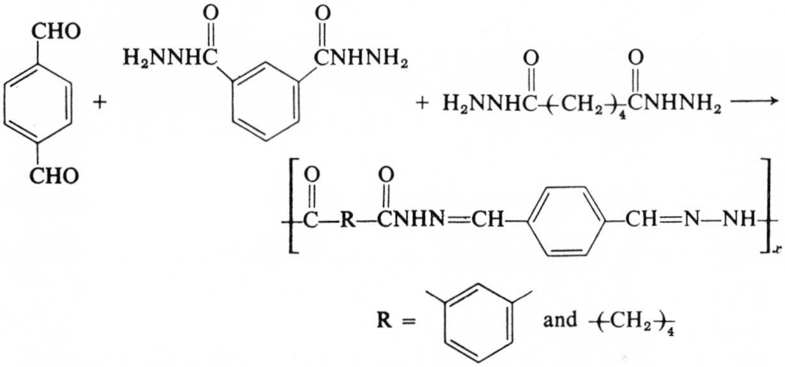

Adipic and isophthalic acid hydrazides are prepared in the same way. One mole of the dimethyl ester is stirred and refluxed with 1500 ml. benzene and 500 g. hydrazine hydrate for 16 hr. The mixture is then cooled, the resulting solid filtered, recrystallized once from water, and dried at 50°C. under vacuum. The yield is about 83%. The melting point of the isophthalic dihydrazide is 227°C., of the adipic dihydrazide, 180°C.

A 250 ml. three-necked flask with stirrer and two glass stoppers is charged with 100 ml. dimethylsulfoxide (distilled from Linde 4A Molecular Sieve), 3.48 g. adipic acid dihydrazide (0.02 mole), 3.88 g. isophthalic dihydrazide (0.02 mole) and 5.36 g. terephthaldehyde (0.04 mole). The solution is stirred for 48 hr. at room temperature, the polymer precipitated in a large amount of methanol, washed repeatedly in a blender with methanol, and finally dried in vacuum at 70°C. The polymer is soluble in hexamethyl-phosphoramide also, in which it has an inherent viscosity of about 1.3 (0.25 g./100 ml.; although finally determined at 30°C., it may be necessary to dissolve the polymer with vigorous stirring at 150°C. for half an hour). The polymer melt temperature is around 300°C., with decomposition. The polymer is essentially amorphous, in contrast to that from either hydrazide alone, but is still fairly resistant to hydrolysis; immersion in water for three days at 97°C. lowers the inherent viscosity to 0.86. Film of the original polymer, cast from dimethylsulfoxide, has a tensile modulus of 497,000 p.s.i., indicative of its stiffness; its tensile strength and elongation are about 13,000 p.s.i. and 22%, respectively.

III. Polyurethanes

The polyurethanes are related in properties to the polyamides because of the similar opportunity for interchain hydrogen bonding. Crystallinity is often induced in polyurethanes, or may be present as prepared. They are, however, usually lower melting than the polyamide having the same number of atoms in the chain, for example, as shown in Table 3.5.

Table 3.5

Polymer	Polymer melt temperature, °C.
$\left[\begin{array}{c} \quad\quad\quad\quad O \quad\quad\quad\quad O \\ -HN(CH_2)_6NH-C-O(CH_2)_4O-C- \end{array}\right]$	180
$\left[\begin{array}{c} \quad\quad\quad\quad O \quad\quad\quad O \\ -HN(CH_2)_6NH-C-(CH_2)_6-C- \end{array}\right]$	240

The most practical methods of preparing polyurethanes in the laboratory are: (a) the reaction of bischloroformates with diamines:

$$Cl-\overset{O}{\overset{\|}{C}}-O-R-O-\overset{O}{\overset{\|}{C}}-Cl + H_2N-R'-NH_2 \longrightarrow$$

$$\left[-\overset{O}{\overset{\|}{C}}-O-R-O-\overset{O}{\overset{\|}{C}}-NH-R'-NH-\right]_n + 2HCl$$

and (b) the addition of a diol to a diisocyanate:

$$HO-R-OH + OCN-R'-NCO \longrightarrow$$

$$\left[-\overset{O}{\overset{\|}{C}}-O-R-O-\overset{O}{\overset{\|}{C}}-NH-R'-NH-\right]_n$$

Direct melt-polycondensation of a diacid with diol or diamine to form the ester or amide bond, respectively, is impossible in polyurethane preparation because neither the required carbamic acid nor carbonic half-acid ester are stable compounds.

$$HO-\overset{O}{\overset{\|}{C}}-NH-R-NH-\overset{O}{\overset{\|}{C}}OH + HO-R'OH \xrightarrow{\;\;/\!/\;\;} \text{polyurethane}$$

$$HO-\overset{O}{\overset{\|}{C}}-O-R-O-\overset{O}{\overset{\|}{C}}-OH + H_2N-R'-NH_2 \xrightarrow{\;\;/\!/\;\;} \text{polyurethane}$$

Bischloroformates may be prepared from most aliphatic and aromatic diols by reacting them with an excess of phosgene at low temperature (67,68).

$$HO—R—OH + \text{excess } COCl_2 \longrightarrow Cl—\overset{\overset{\displaystyle O}{\|}}{C}—O—R—O—\overset{\overset{\displaystyle O}{\|}}{C}—Cl + 2HCl$$

Chloroformates are less reactive toward amines and alcohols than the comparable carboxylic acid chloride, but more reactive than the sulfonyl chlorides. When they are condensed with diamines, the products are polyurethanes; this type of reaction was the first usage of interfacial polycondensation (28).

The following example is the preparation of a **polyurethane from a cyclic disecondary diamine**, piperazine, **and ethylene bischloroformate.**

58. Preparation of Ethylene Bischloroformate (68)

$$HOCH_2CH_2OH + COCl_2 \longrightarrow Cl—\overset{\overset{\displaystyle O}{\|}}{C}—O—CH_2CH_2—O—\overset{\overset{\displaystyle O}{\|}}{C}—Cl + 2HCl$$

Carry out in a Good Hood. Phosgene is Toxic!

About 650 ml. (ca. 900 g., 9 moles) of phosgene is condensed into an ice-cooled, 1 l. three-necked flask equipped with a Dry Ice condenser, stirrer, and dropping funnel, all suitably protected by drying tubes. To the ice-cooled, stirred liquid is added dropwise 125 g. (2 moles) of ethylene glycol. The reaction is stirred from 3–4 hr. after addition is complete. The excess phosgene is allowed to evaporate or is trapped in aqueous alcohol-caustic if venting through the hood poses a safety hazard. The residue is heated at 40–50°C. at 20 mm. for a short time to remove any volatile material. On distillation at 1–2 mm. through a short path system, 340 g. (91%) of ethylene bischloroformate is obtained. It is redistilled through a 10 in. glass helices packed column to give a product boiling at 71–72°C./2.2 mm. If pure ethylene glycol is used, the product obtained after removal of the excess phosgene and other volatiles should be tested in a polymerization before distilling. Polymer grade material may sometimes be gotten without distillation.

59. Preparation of Poly(ethylene N,N'-piperazinedicarboxylate) (69,70)

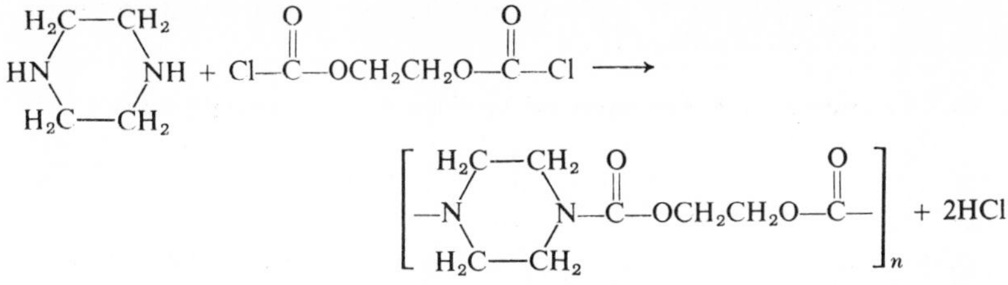

Four and five-tenths g. (0.052 mole) piperazine and 10.6 g. (0.10 mole) sodium carbonate are dissolved in 100 ml. ice cold water. (It is better to use a standardized piperazine stock solution and take aliquots than to weigh piperazine hexahydrate because of its variable moisture content.) The solution is stirred rapidly in a household blender and a solution of 6.4 ml. (9.35 g., 0.050 mole) ethylene bischloroformate in 30 ml. methylene chloride is added all at once. Polymer viscosity will be poorer if the acid chloride solution is added slowly. Using more (50 or 100 ml.) methylene chloride decreases viscosity only slightly.

The reaction mixture thickens rapidly, and in a few minutes it looks like cottage cheese. At that stage it is transferred to a 1 l. beaker with approximately 500 ml. water. The beaker is placed on a hot plate and methylene chloride is partially evaporated while stirring occasionally with a stirring rod. The methylene chloride should not be evaporated completely because then the polymer sets up in extremely tough chunks that can be cut up only with difficulty. As soon as the polymer is solid enough to stick together, it is ready to be chopped up.

The solid polymer is returned to the blender with some water and chopped up into small particles. It is filtered on a Büchner funnel and washed several times with warm water. It is dried in a vacuum oven at 90°C. for 24 hr. The yield is 9.5 g. (95%); the inherent viscosity (m-cresol at 25°C.) may be as high as 4.4 if intermediates are very pure, but 2.5 can easily be obtained. The polymer is soluble in formic acid. The polymer melt temperature is 238°C.

All of the polycondensations involving acid chlorides so far have been between AA and BB type reactants. It is possible, however, to use **AB monomers where one functional group is an acid chloride** if the **other functional site is blocked by a group, which when removed, permits polymerization** to take place. For instance, an amine group may be blocked by making the hydrochloride or p-toluenesulfonate salt, then freed for reaction by treatment with base:

$$\overset{-}{Cl}-\overset{+}{H_3N}-R-\overset{\overset{\displaystyle O}{\|}}{C}-Cl + 2\ base \longrightarrow \left[-HN-R-\overset{\overset{\displaystyle O}{\|}}{C}-\right]_n + 2\ base\cdot HCl$$

In the following preparation, pentanolamine is first formed from ω-hydroxyvaleraldehyde and ammonia. The pentanolamine is then converted to the tosylate salt of the amine group, followed by conversion to the chloroformate ester of the hydroxyl group (71). The amine group is then liberated by addition to a potassium carbonate solution and polymerization occurs.

60. Preparation of 5-Aminopentylchloroformate p-Toluenesulfonate (71)

$$HO(CH_2)_4-\overset{\overset{\displaystyle O}{\|}}{C}-H \xrightarrow[NH_3]{(H)} HO(CH_2)_5-NH_2$$

$$HO-(CH_2)_5-NH_2 \xrightarrow[p\text{-}CH_3\text{-Ph-SO}_3H]{} HO-(CH_2)_5-\overset{+}{N}H_3\overset{-}{O}_3S-Ph-CH_3\text{-}p$$

$$HO-(CH_2)_5-NH_3O_3S-Ph-CH_3\text{-}p \xrightarrow{COCl_2}$$

$$Cl-\overset{\overset{\displaystyle O}{\|}}{C}-O-(CH_2)_5-\overset{+}{N}H_3\overset{-}{O}_3S-Ph-CH_3\text{-}p$$

A 1 l. hydrogenation bomb (stainless steel) is charged with 102 g. (1.0 mole) hydroxyvaleraldehyde (72), 300 g. ammonia, and 20 g. Raney nickel (54). The mixture is heated to 110°C. and hydrogenated at 1600 p.s.i. for $3\frac{1}{2}$ hr. The product is separated from the catalyst by filtration and distilled through a 10 in. glass helixes-packed column. The boiling point of pentanolamine is 95°C./6 mm.; the yield is 57 g. (56%).

The p-toluenesulfonate salt of the pentanolamine is formed by mixing equimolar amounts of pentanolamine and p-toluenesulfonic acid mono-hydrate in ethyl acetate solution. The precipitated salt is recrystallized from ethyl acetate/ethanol mixture (90/10 by volume) to give 51% yield of the salt melting at 110°C.

One hundred ml. of phosgene (estimated by previously marking the reaction vessel at the desired capacity) is condensed into an ice-cooled 250 ml. three-necked flask containing 10 g. (0.41 mole) of the pentanolamine salt, and equipped with stirrer, Dry Ice condenser protected with drying tube, and a gas inlet tube for admitting phosgene. (**Caution! Phosgene Is Highly Toxic and Should be Used Only in a Properly Functioning Hood.**) The ice bath is removed and the salt suspension in phosgene allowed to stir and reflux at room temperature for $\frac{1}{2}$ hr., after which 50 g. of washed, dry chloroform is added and stirring is continued for another $\frac{1}{2}$ hr. The phosgene is then evaporated by replacing the Dry Ice condenser with an exit tube protected with a drying tube and placing a bath of warm water (45–50°C.) around the flask. The phosgene may be vented up the hood if the hood exit is sufficiently isolated. In larger runs (or in this one, if conditions require it) the phosgene should be trapped by passing it into an excess of aqueous alcoholic caustic. The chloroform is then evaporated by water aspirator (protect flask with dry-ing tube between it and aspirator) and the solid product recrystallized from dry benzene. The chloroformate salt is obtained as white needles melting at 114–116°C. The weight is 7.5 g. (60%).

61. Preparation of the Polyurethane of ε-Hydroxypentanecarbamic Acid (63)

$$Cl\text{---}\overset{\overset{\displaystyle O}{\|}}{C}\text{---}O\text{---}(CH_2)_5\text{---}\overset{+}{N}H_3\bar{O}_3S\text{---}\langle\bigcirc\rangle\text{---}CH_3 \xrightarrow{K_2CO_3} \left[\overset{\overset{\displaystyle O}{\|}}{-C}\text{--}O(CH_2)_5\text{---}NH\text{---}\right]_n$$

A solution of 1.0 g. of recrystallized 5-aminopentylchloroformate-p-toluene-sulfonate in 5 ml. dry chloroform is added to 5 ml. of $4M$ potassium carbonate in an 18 × 150 mm. test tube with vigorous stirring, provided by a motor driven glass rod with a paddle formed at the tip. An ice bath, placed around the tube just before polymerization is removed after 4–5 min. The mixture is stirred vigorously for 30 min., at which point the precipitated polymer is filtered and washed with both cold and hot water by trituration and filtration. It is dried at 60°C. in a vacuum oven. The yield is 0.4 g. (83%) of polymer having a polymer melt temperature of 150–155°C. and an inherent viscosity of 0.7–0.9 in m-cresol (0.5% conc. at 25°C.) It is soluble in chloroform/methanol, (85/15 by volume). It is sufficiently stable to be fabricated from the melt.

Although alcohols do not react with isocyanates as rapidly as do amines, the yield is sufficiently high to permit the formation of **high**

polymer from diol–diisocyanate reactions if the proper conditions are used. If the melt stability of the resulting polymer permits, the addition may be carried out without solvent at a sufficiently high temperature to keep the mixture molten. A solvent may be used, providing the polymer is either soluble or is swollen enough to permit reaction of the chain ends to proceed until a high molecular weight is reached.

The diol–diisocyanate addition reaction was used in Germany during World War II for the production on a modest scale of the polyurethane from tetramethylene glycol and hexamethylene diisocyanate (28).

62. Preparation of Poly(tetramethylene hexamethylenedicarbamate) by Melt Methods (28)

$$HO—(CH_2)_4—OH + OCN—(CH_2)_6—NCO \longrightarrow$$

$$\left[—(CH_2)_4—O—\overset{\overset{\displaystyle O}{\|}}{C}—NH(CH_2)_6NH—\overset{\overset{\displaystyle O}{\|}}{C}—O— \right]_n$$

A 250 ml. three-necked flask is fitted with a calcium chloride drying tube and an efficient stirring motor with a metal shaft and paddle. The eventual viscosity of the reaction may break glass stirring equipment. The flask is charged with 45.0 g. (0.500 mole) of tetramethylene glycol and a low pressure nitrogen flow is passed through the flask (above the surface of the liquid) through the third neck to displace the air. The tetramethylene glycol purity must be high; it should be subjected to careful fractional distillation (b.p. 120°C./10 mm.) to give a product melting at 19.7°C.

The nitrogen inlet tube is replaced by a stoppered, pressure-equalizing dropping funnel containing 83.16 g. (0.495 mole) of hexamethylene diisocyanate. The flask is heated to 50°C. in an oil bath and the diisocyanate is added with rapid stirring, over a period of 1 hr., during which time the temperature of the bath is raised to 190–195°C. The reaction is continued at this temperature until no further viscosity increase occurs. Good mixing is required to prevent local hot spots and the possible branched or crosslinked structure that could result. An insoluble, nonfluid product indicates the latter has occurred.

While the mixture is still molten, the stirrer paddle is raised and the mass allowed to cool. The hard, tough polymer is removed by breaking the flask. The polymer is cut up into pieces and ground through a 20 mesh screen in a mill. It is washed with methanol twice in a household blender and dried at 60°C. in a vacuum oven. The yield is essentially quantitative. The polymer melt temperature is about 180°C. and the inherent viscosity is 0.8–1.4 in *m*-cresol (0.5% conc. at 25°C.). Other solvents are phenol and formamide. The product can be melt-pressed to give films and can be melt spun to fibers, at a temperature of 190–200°C.

As an alternative to the melt-polymerization, one may carry out the **reaction in chlorobenzene/*o*-dichlorobenzene solution.** The polymer is soluble in the hot solvent mixture, but precipitates on cooling.

63. Preparation of Poly(tetramethylene hexamethylenedicarbamate) in Solution (73)

An 80/20 by volume mixture of chlorobenzene and o-dichlorobenzene, both purified by distillation over calcium hydride, is used as the solvent in the following reaction.

A dry, 1 l. three-necked flask equipped with a stirrer, nitrogen inlet, and reflux condenser with calcium chloride drying tube is flushed out with nitrogen and is then charged with 2.68 g. of pure tetramethylene glycol (Preparation 62) in 100 ml. of solvent. The nitrogen inlet is replaced by a dropping funnel and the solution heated to reflux. From the funnel is added 5.0 g. of hexamethylene diisocyanate in 50 ml. of solvent; about half the diisocyanate is added rapidly with vigorous stirring and the remainder over 3–4 hr. The solution is held at reflux for 1 hr. after addition. When the solution is cooled to room temperature, the polymer precipitates and the solvent is decanted. The polymer is dissolved in 50 ml. of hot dimethylformamide and 50 ml. of methanol is added to the still warm solution. The clear solution is cooled in a refrigerator overnight, and the precipitated polymer separated by filtration and dried at 0.1 mm. pressure in a vacuum desiccator overnight. The inherent viscosity is 0.5–0.7 in m-cresol (0.5% conc., 25°C.). The properties are essentially the same as the melt-prepared polymer.

64. Preparation of Poly(ethylene methylene bis(4-phenylcarbamate) (74)

$$\text{OCN}-\bigotimes-\text{CH}_2-\bigotimes-\text{NCO} + \text{HOCH}_2\text{CH}_2\text{OH} \longrightarrow$$

$$\left[-\overset{\overset{\displaystyle O}{\|}}{\text{C}}\text{NH}-\bigotimes-\text{CH}_2-\bigotimes-\text{NH}-\overset{\overset{\displaystyle O}{\|}}{\text{C}}-\text{OCH}_2\text{CH}_2\text{O}- \right]_n$$

The diisocyanate is purified by distillation through a vacuum-jacketed Vigreux column, b.p. 148–150°C./0.12 mm. The ethylene glycol is purified by distillation; b.p. 79°C./4.4 mm., $n_D^{25} = 1.4300$, and % $H_2O = 0.05$ or less. The solvents are purified by distillation: dimethylsulfoxide, b.p. 66°C./5 mm.; 4-methylpentanone-2, b.p. 115°C.

Forty ml. of 4-methylpentanone-2 and 25.02 g. of methylene bis(4-phenylisocyanate) are placed in a three-necked round-bottom flask equipped with stirrer and condenser and protected from moisture. To this rapidly stirred suspension is added 6.20 g. of ethylene glycol in 40 ml. of dimethylsulfoxide. The reaction is heated at 115°C. for 1½ hr. The clear, viscous solution is then poured into water to precipitate the polyurethane. The tough, white polymer is chopped up in a home blender, washed with water, then dried in a vacuum oven at 90°C. Inherent viscosity is 1.0 in N,N-dimethylformamide at room temperature (conc., 0.5%). Films may be dry cast from dimethylformamide or directly from the originally prepared polymerization solution. The polymer melt temperature is 255°C. and the glass transition temperature is 90°C.

The condensation of diacid chlorides with N,N'-disubstituted aromatic diamines of bisphenols can be carried out at reflux in an inert, high boiling solvent or swelling agent for the derived polymer, using magnesium as a catalyst. Although a relatively large amount of catalyst is required (ca. 25 mole% based on either reactant), it can be recovered and reused. There is evidence that an ionic magnesium species is the actual catalyst. This method is unusual in that fairly higher molecular weight polymers can be derived from such hindered and very weakly basic diamines as methylene bis(4-N-phenylaniline) and N,N'-diarylaryldiamines (75).

65. Preparation of 2,2-Bis(p-hydroxyphenyl)propane Bischloroformate (76)*

A 500 ml. three-necked flask is equipped with a thermometer, a magnetic stirrer, a water-cooled reflux condenser topped by a Dry Ice–acetone condenser, and a gas inlet tube that reaches below the liquid level. The apparatus is charged with 22.8 g. (0.1 mole) of 2,2-bis(p-hydroxyphenyl)propane, 3.45 g. (0.01 mole) of stearyltrimethylammonium chloride, and 250 ml. chlorobenzene. Phosgene, 21.8 g. (0.22 mole) which has previously been liquefied in a well-ventilated fume hood is added in one portion to the reaction mixture which has been cooled to 0°C. The cooling bath is removed and heat applied very cautiously to the reaction mixture with a heating mantle. At 20°C., phosgene refluxes in the Dry Ice condenser. Hydrogen chloride should be evolved at 40°C. Heat is applied to the mixture at a rate to keep the phosgene condensing vigorously on the Dry Ice condenser. At 80°C., solution should be complete. After a total reaction time of 3 hr., the reaction temperature will have been at 126°C. for 1.25 hr. After removing the heat, the mixture is cooled to room temperature. The catalyst is removed by filtration, washed with a little additional chlorobenzene on the filter, and the filtrate is stripped of volatiles under vacuum on a steam bath. The residue is dissolved in 150 ml. toluene at room temperature, filtered and the filtrate passed through a 3 × 30 cm. column of silica gel (Davison Grade 12, mesh 28–200). Elution of the column with 300 ml. toluene followed by removal of the toluene under vacuum gives a residue of 33.2 g. (94%) of the bischloroformate which crystallizes rapidly at room temperature. Recrystallization of this product from 150 ml. n-hexane gives the bischloroformate with a melting point of 93–95°C.

The stearyltrimethylammonium chloride used can be isolated from the commercially available products in aqueous solution (e.g., Aliquot 7, from

* We are indebted to Dr. Robert Barclay, Union Carbide Corp. for assistance in the details of this and the two subsequent experimental examples.

General Mills) by distilling most of the water under vacuum, azeotroping the viscous residue several times with benzene, and drying the solid residue at 50°C. in vacuum. The melting point should be in the range 185–221°C. (dec.).

The bisphenol can be recrystallized from toluene, as noted in Preparation 77.

66. Preparation of 4,4′-Methylenebis(*N*-methylaniline) (77)

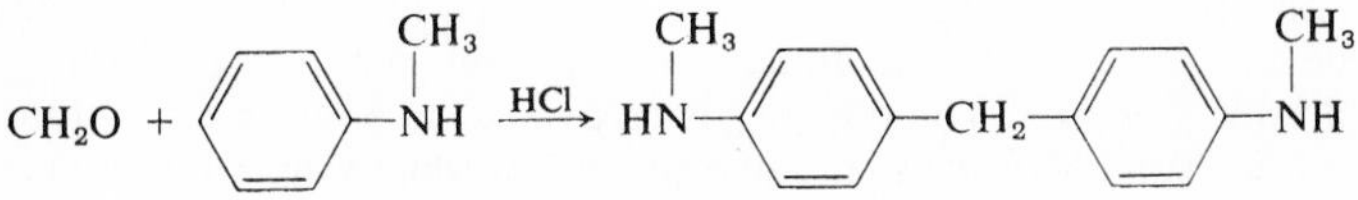

In a 5-l. three-necked flask equipped with a stirrer, a thermometer, a condenser, and a large dropping funnel are placed 644 g. (6.01 moles) of *N*-methylaniline and 270 ml. of water. To this mixture is added 495 ml. (6.04 moles) of 37.4% hydrochloric acid, the temperature being kept below about 20°C., and then 195 g. (2.38 moles) of 36.6% aqueous formaldehyde solution; addition of formaldehyde requires about 17 min., and the temperature is kept at 16–23°C. by cooling in ice water. After being stirred at 20°C. for 10 min., the solution is heated to boiling over about 35 min., heating under reflux is continued for 20 hr.

The solution is cooled and made alkaline by the cautious addition, with cooling, of a solution of 250 g. of sodium hydroxide in 2 l. of water. The solution is then steam-distilled until no further organic distillate is observed; 130.5 g. of wet *N*-methylaniline is recovered from the distillate. The residue is cooled and extracted with ether (total of about 2 l. in 6 portions), and the combined extract is washed with water until the washings are neutral, then dried over anhydrous potassium carbonate. After the ether has been removed by distillation at atmospheric pressure, distillation under reduced pressure gives 9.3 g. of *N*-methylaniline and 425.6 g. of crude diamine, b.p. 186–212°C./0.25 mm. Recrystallization of the latter from a mixture of ether and petroleum ether at −20°C. gives 355.2 g. (67%, based on *N*-methylaniline not recovered) of 4,4′-methylene bis(*N*-methylaniline), m.p. 54.4–56.2°C.

67. Polyurethane from 2,2-Bis(*p*-hydroxyphenyl)propane Bischloroformate and Methylene Bis(4-*N*-methylaniline) (78,79)

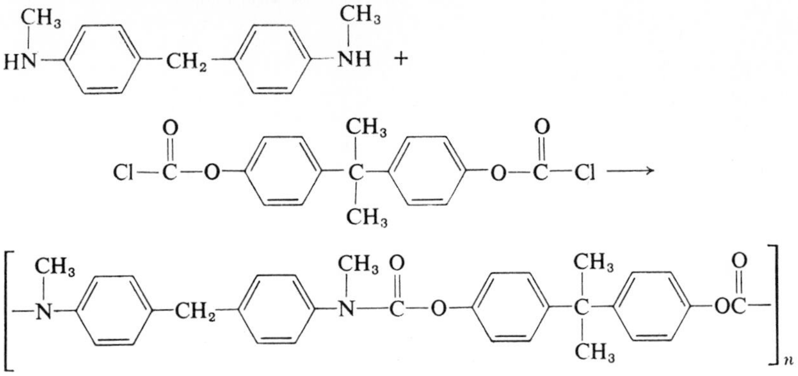

A 200 ml. three-necked flask is equipped with a condenser with drying tube, and a nitrogen inlet reaching to near the bottom of the flask. To the flask is added 2.263 g. (0.010 mole) methylene bis(4-N-methylaniline), 3.532 g. (0.010 mole) 2,2-bis(p-hydroxyphenyl)propane bischloroformate, 0.06 g. (0.0025 mole) magnesium powder, and 60 ml. dry, distilled sym-tetrachloro-ethane. (This solvent is sufficiently toxic to warrant great care in handling.) The mixture is heated at reflux in a stream of dry nitrogen for 22 hr. The evolution of HCl has essentially ceased at this point. The viscous, dark-red solution is allowed to cool, diluted with 100 ml. methylene chloride, and filtered under vacuum. The polymer is recovered by pouring the filtrate into 1 l. of isopropanol with stirring. The product is washed twice with isopropanol and once with methanol in a home blender and dried in a vacuum oven at 60°C. under nitrogen. The yield of nearly white polymer is 74%, and has a reduced viscosity in chloroform (25°C., 0.2 g./100 ml.) of 1.22.

IV. Polyesters and Related Copolymers

Virtually all the methods of esterification known in organic chemistry have been applied to the preparation of polyesters. Ester exchange, transesterification, and direct reaction of carboxyl or acid chloride groups are commonly used.

It may be necessary to use catalyst to increase the rate of reaction to a reasonable level. Acidic or basic catalysts, or combinations of the two, have been used, and the variety of both types has been great. For reactions involving aliphatic diols, weakly acidic or basic catalysts are usually required in order to prevent dehydration to ether or olefin. Metal oxides of the Group V metals, sodium alkoxytitanates, tetraal-kyltitanate esters, and alkaline earth salts of weak acids are among the catalyst types used (80–83).

The properties of polyesters vary widely, from the aliphatic esters that are viscous liquids just above room temperature, to the high-melting products from aromatic acids or bisphenols. Lacking the opportunity for interchain hydrogen bonds, the polyesters melt sub-

Table 3.6

Polymer	Polymer melt temperature, °C.	Solvents
$[-O(CH_2)_6O-\overset{O}{\overset{\|}{C}}-(CH_2)_4-\overset{O}{\overset{\|}{C}}-]$	60	Ethyl acetate, benzene
$[-NH(CH_2)_6NH-\overset{O}{\overset{\|}{C}}-(CH_2)_4-\overset{O}{\overset{\|}{C}}-]$	265	m-Cresol, formic acid

stantially lower than the polyamide of like structure (Table 3.6). Their solubilities differ considerably from polyamides also.

Unlike polyamidation reactions under melt conditions, the preparation of **polyesters** in the melt **from diols and** the **esters of diacids** does not always require exact reactant balance at the start. An excess of diol leads first to low molecular weight, hydroxy-ended polymer, which then goes over to high polymer by ester exchange reactions and evolution of the excess diol. Ester exchange occurs much more readily than amide exchange. For example, bis(hydroxyethyl) terephthalate is a suitable monomer for poly(ethylene terephthalate) preparation.

Poly(ethylene terephthalate) is a commercial example of a melt-polymerized polyester.

The following polymerization process is applicable in general to any system in which the monomers and polymers are thermally stable at temperatures above the polymer melting point, and the glycol is sufficiently volatile to permit the excess to be completely removed under vacuum. In this preparation there are two ester exchange reactions. The first forms "monomer," from excess glycol and dimethyl terephthalate, with elimination of methanol. The second eliminates glycol and forms the polymer.

68. Preparation of Poly(ethylene terephthalate) (81,82)

For the following preparation, dimethyl terephthalate may be purified by recrystallization from ethanol; the melting point is 141–142°C. The ethylene glycol is purified by dissolving metallic sodium in it (1 g./100 ml.) and refluxing in an atmosphere of nitrogen for 1 hr., followed by distillation (b.p. 196–197°C.)

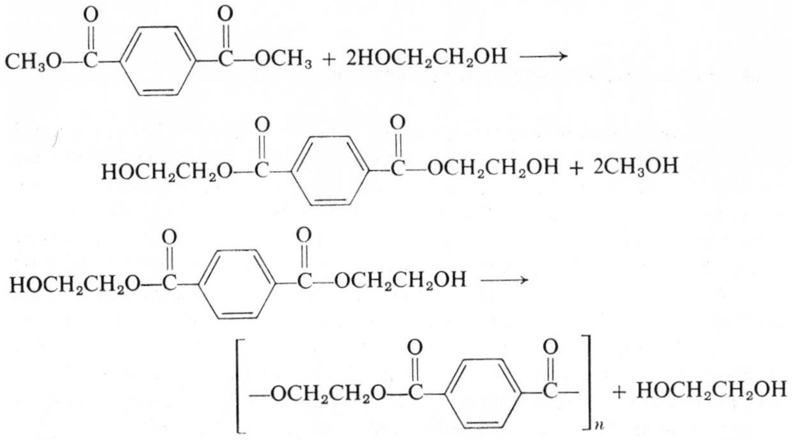

In a polymer tube bearing a side arm is placed 15.5 g. (0.08 mole) dimethyl terephthalate, 11.8 g. (0.19 mole) ethylene glycol, 0.025 g. calcium acetate dihydrate, and 0.006 g. antimony trioxide (80). The tube is partially immersed in a 197°C. vapor bath to melt the mixture, and a capillary tube is introduced which reaches to the bottom of the tube. A slow stream of nitrogen is passed through the melt. Methanol is distilled from the mixture during the course of 1 hr., after which time the polymer tube is immersed as far as is practical in the vapors of the heating bath. The mixture is heated another 2 hr. at 197°C. Removal of the last trace of methanol is a requisite for high polymer formation. It may become necessary to heat the side arm during this period to prevent clogging from the distillation of some dimethyl terephthalate.

The polymer tube is now heated by means of a 222°C. vapor bath (methyl salicylate) for 20 min., then is transferred to a 283°C. vapor bath (dimethyl phthalate). After 10 min., the pressure is reduced to 0.3 mm., or less, over 15–20 min. Due safety precautions, especially as to adequate shielding should be observed (see Preparation 2). The polymerization is continued for 3 hr.; the alteration in rate of bubble rise from the capillary indicates the change in viscosity. The polymer tube is wrapped in a towel and is allowed to cool under nitrogen; shattering of the tube may occur as the polymer contracts. The yield of polymer is quantitative if no dimethyl terephthalate was distilled in the early phases of the polymerization. The inherent viscosity in sym-tetrachloroethane/phenol (40/60 weight) should be about 0.6–0.7 (0.5% conc., 30°C.). Particularly flexible, tough films may be melt-pressed and strong, cold-drawable fibers pulled from the melt. The polymer melt temperature is about 270°C. The crystalline melting point is about 260°C.

The polymerization procedure, cited before, may be used to prepare a wide variety of polyesters. A number of different catalysts have been used in such reactions. Tetraisopropyl titanate is one of them, and use is made of it in the following **preparation of a polyester having a cyclic structure in the glycol as well as the acid portion of the repeating unit,** i.e., poly(1,4-cyclohexanedicarbinyl terephthalate).

69. Preparation of 1,4-Cyclohexanedicarbinol (84,85)

One hundred g. dimethyl terephthalate is hydrogenated in 800 ml. ethanol over 10 g. Raney nickel at 200°C. and 2000 p.s.i. When hydrogen uptake has ceased, the mixture is filtered, the alcohol distilled at reduced pressure and the residue fractionally distilled through a 10 in. Vigreux column. About 95 g. dimethylhexahydroterephthalate, b.p. 124°C./5 mm., is obtained. This diester is then hydrogenated over 8 g. copper chromite catalyst at 255°C. and 4000 p.s.i. When the hydrogenation is completed, the catalyst is separated and the residue distilled, first through a 6 in. Vigreux column, then through a precision distillation column. The boiling point of the diol is 117–120°C./0.5 mm. It distils as a viscous liquid which partially solidifies on standing. It is a mixture of cis- and trans-isomers. Chemical reduction of the hexahydrodiester by means of sodium and alcohol has also been carried out (86).

70. Preparation of Poly(1,4-cyclohexanedicarbinyl terephthalate) (87)

A mixture of 25.0 g. (0.148 mole) 1,4-cyclohexanedicarbinol, 13 g. (0.067 mole) dimethyl terephthalate, 0.02 g. tetraisopropyl titanate and 0.02 g. sodium isopropoxide is charged to a polymer tube. The mixture is heated in a nitrogen stream at 197°C. in a vapor bath for 3 hr., as described in the preceding preparation. The tube is then heated at 220°C for 15 min. to remove the last of the methanol and begin the polymerization. Heating is continued at 283°C. as a vacuum is slowly applied over a 15 min. period to bring the pressure to 0.2 mm. The polymerization is complete in about 3 hr. The polymer is removed from the tube after cooling (as in Preparation 68). It has an inherent viscosity of about 0.5–0.6 (0.5% conc., 30°C.) in tetrachloroethane/phenol (40/60 weight) and the polymer melt temperature is about 285–290°C. It is also soluble in sulfuric acid and hot o-dichlorobenzene. Films can be melt-pressed at 285°C. and fibers drawn from the molten polymer.

Polyesters from entirely aliphatic reactants are usually low melting even when of high molecular weight. Although these polymeric materials can be crystalline and fiber forming, they are of little utility in unmodified form. Direct esterification or ester interchange are the preparative methods most often used. Various catalysts have been used successfully. One of the most common of such catalysts is litharge, the use of which is demonstrated in the condensation of dimethyl sebacate with tetramethylene glycol. In the following example, equimolar amounts of reactants are used, and only one ester interchange reaction occurs. This is the polymer forming step.

71. Preparation of Poly(tetramethylene sebacate) (73)

A mixture of 4.95 g. (0.055 mole) of tetramethylene glycol 11.50 g. (0.050 mole) of dimethyl sebacate, 0.1 g. litharge, and 0.1 g. di-t-butylhydroquinone is placed in a polymer tube having a side arm and nitrogen capillary inlet reaching to the bottom of the tube, as described in Preparation 68. The reaction is heated at about 172°C. in a vapor bath for 2 hr. at atmospheric pressure in a current of nitrogen. Then, the pressure is slowly reduced over a 4 hr. period to 0.05 mm. The temperature is then raised to 215°C. for 4 hr. at the same reduced pressure. The reaction may be heated overnight without harm. The polymer, which is allowed to cool under nitrogen, is obtained as a white solid in nearly quantitative yield (12–13 g.). The inherent viscosity is around 1.0 in chloroform (0.5% conc., 25°C.). Its polymer melt temperature is 60–65°C. Fibers can be pulled from the melt and are cold-drawable.

In many difunctional molecules, the tendency to intramolecular cyclization is so great that intermolecular condensation is suppressed. An example of hydroxyacid having a great tendency to cyclize to a dimer is glycolic acid. However, **poly(glycollic ester)** can be formed **from glycolic acid** in favorable competition with the reaction leading to cyclic dimer (88).

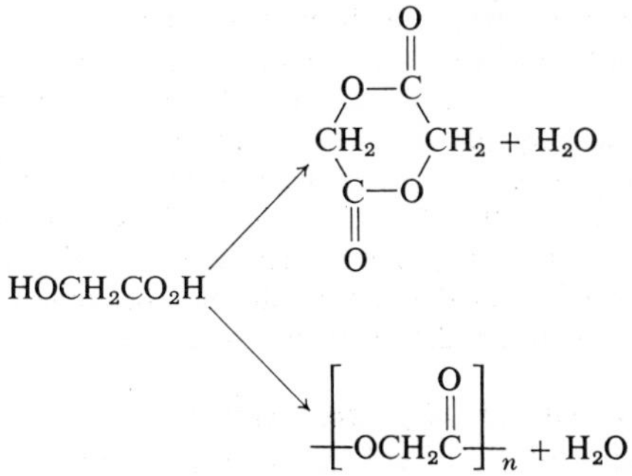

$$
HOCH_2CO_2H
\;\nearrow\;
\begin{array}{c}
\text{O} \\
\| \\
\text{O—C} \\
\diagup \quad \diagdown \\
CH_2 \quad\quad CH_2 \\
\diagdown \quad \diagup \\
C—O \\
\| \\
\text{O}
\end{array}
\;+\; H_2O
$$

$$
HOCH_2CO_2H \;\searrow\; \left[-OCH_2\overset{\displaystyle O}{\overset{\|}{C}} - \right]_n + H_2O
$$

72. Preparation of Poly(glycollic ester) (88)

$$
HO—CH_2—CO_2H \longrightarrow \left[-O—CH_2—\overset{\displaystyle O}{\overset{\|}{C}}- \right] + H_2O
$$

Fifteen g. (0.197 mole) of hydroxyacetic acid recrystallized from n-butyl alcohol, m.p. 80–80.5°C., is mixed with 0.015 g. triphenylphosphite color stabilizer and 0.001 g. antimony trioxide catalyst in a polymer tube with a nitrogen inlet capillary tube and a side arm. (See Preparations 2 and 68 for general directions on melt-polymerization technique). The tube is immersed in an ethylene glycol vapor bath at 197°C. for $\frac{1}{2}$–1 hr., during which time the acid melts and water is evolved vigorously. A slow stream of nitrogen is passed through the melted acid by lowering the capillary into the melt. When the reaction has subsided, the pressure is reduced to 1.0 mm. or less as quickly as possible. More water and a small quantity of glycolide (the cyclic dimer) distill during the next 70–80 min. It may be necessary to warm the side arm to prevent glycolide from solidifying. The polymer melt becomes cloudy and begins to crystallize. The polymer tube is quickly shifted to a naphthalene vapor bath (218°C.), previously heated to boiling. The polymer melts once more and is maintained at 218°C. at 1 mm. or less for 3–4 hr. Nitrogen is passed through the melt at the slow rate throughout. During this part of the heating cycle, the polymer may darken to some extent. At the end of this period the melt becomes very viscous and may partially solidify. The tube is removed from the bath and allowed to cool to room temperature under vacuum. The polymer is isolated by breaking the tube after releasing the vacuum.

The polymer plug, freed from any glass chips that might adhere, is ground in a mill to pass a 20 mesh screen. The powder is placed in a 50 ml. round-bottom flask equipped with a glass paddle stirrer, and a vacuum take-off and heated while stirring the solid, at a pressure of 1.0 mm. or lower in the 218°C. vapor bath. The powder polymerization is continued for 8 hr. at least; it may be left overnight (16 hr.).

The operations in the above polymerization cycle must be carried out carefully in order to obtain high polymer. Coloration can be reduced by using a very pure monomer and not exceeding 220°C. in any part of the polymerization.

The polymer removed from the tube may be tan to dark-brown in color. It weighs 9–11 g. (50–60%), has a polymer melt temperature of 230–235°C., and a crystalline melting point of 230°C. The inherent viscosity is 0.6–1.0, (0.5% conc. at 30°C. in phenol/trichlorophenol (60/40 weight)). The polymer is degraded slowly by contact with this solvent; the determination of inherent viscosity should be made as soon as possible after the solution is prepared. Poly(glycollic ester) can be melt-pressed at 240°C. to give clear, tough films which have a lower inherent viscosity than the original polymer, indicating degradation. However, the films can still be drawn to twice their original length at 50–60°C. with an increase in their toughness. The polymer is degraded severely by prolonged exposure to boiling water.

An unusual and interesting example of a **polyester** prepared **from a hydroxyacid** is that from the condensation product of protocatechuic acid, I, with epichlorohydrin (89). Protocatechuic acid is derived from wood pulp.

The hydroxyacid (II), an AB monomer, is obtained as a mixture of the 6- and 7-carboxy isomers. The polymer from the mixed isomers is

$$HO-\underset{HO}{\bigcirc}-CO_2H \;+\; CH_2-\overset{O}{CH}-CH_2-Cl \;\longrightarrow\; HOH_2C\underset{O}{\overset{O}{\bigcirc}}\{CO_2H$$

I   II

stable at its melt temperature of 210°C. and is prepared by melt-polymerization. The polymer prepared from a pure isomer of II (whether the 6- or 7-carboxy was not established) melts above 300°C.

with decomposition. Thus, only low polymer can be prepared by melt techniques. The mixture of the two isomers produces a copolymer which melts within the range of its thermal stability. The effect is typical of that usually found in random copolymers.

73. Preparation of 6- (and 7-)Carboxy-2-hydroxymethyl-1,4-benzodioxane (I) (89)

A flask equipped with a mechanical stirrer, gas inlet tube, and dropping funnel is charged with 187 g. (1.21 moles) of protocatechuic acid and flushed with nitrogen. A solution of 100 g. (2.5 moles) of sodium hydroxide in 945 ml. of water is added and the resulting solution cooled to 40–50°C. Epichlorohydrin (112 g.; 1.21 moles) is added over a period of 2 hr. with stirring; the temperature is kept at 40–50°C. and a nitrogen atmosphere is maintained. The reaction is continued under nitrogen for 7 hr. after addition is complete. The mixture is then poured into a cold solution of 240 g. concentrated hydrochloric acid in 240 g. of water with rapid stirring. The oil formed eventually solidifies. This is broken up, filtered, washed with water, and dried at 110°C. The yield is 168 g. of crude product (66%). The crude acid is esterified by dissolving in 400 ml. methanol, saturating with dry hydrogen chloride gas, and refluxing 24 hr. After removing the excess methanol and hydrogen chloride at water aspirator pressure, the residual methyl ester is distilled through a 10 in. Vigreux column at 175–196°C./0.4–1.5 mm. The yield of ester is 115 g. (43%). It is saponified by refluxing for 2 hr. under a nitrogen atmosphere in a solution of 60 g. sodium hydroxide in 250 ml. water, followed by acidification with hydrochloric acid. The oily acid solidifies quickly and is recrystallized from a minimum of boiling water, using decolorizing charcoal, and is dried in vacuum at 50–60°C. The melting point after two recrystallizations is 141–168°C.; the yield is 74 g. (35%) of colorless material. The calculated neutral equivalent is 210; the product should have an observed value of about 212. The product is a mixture of the 6- and 7-carboxy isomers.

74. Preparation of the Polyester from 6- (and 7-)Carboxy-2-hydroxymethyl-1,4-benzodioxane (89)

Ten g. (0.047 mole) of hydroxyacid(II) is placed in a polymer tube bearing a nitrogen inlet capillary reaching almost to the bottom and a side arm attached to an efficient vacuum pump. (See Preparation 2 and 68 for general instructions on melt-polymerization methods and precautions.) With a slow stream of nitrogen passing through it and under a vacuum of less than 1.0 mm., the tube is heated by the vapors of a 270°C. bath for a period of 17 hr. When cooled under nitrogen the polymer is a clear, glass-like solid, obtained in nearly quantitative yield, about 9 g. It has a polymer melt temperature of

210°C. and an inherent viscosity of 0.6–0.7 in *m*-cresol (0.5% conc. at 25°C.). Fibers may be melt-spun from the sample. The temperature used is 270°C., and, if provision is made to pass the threadline through an 80°C. water bath while effecting a draw of 140% by varying the speed of the windup rolls, fibers of considerable strength (4 g. per denier) can be obtained.

Unlike polymers from aliphatic components (discussed in Preparation 71) the **all-aromatic polyesters** are usually high melting materials. They can conveniently be prepared **from the sodium salts of diphenols by interfacial condensation** (40). In the following example, a copolyester is prepared which is more soluble and more readily fabricated than either of the corresponding homopolymers. The polymer melt temperature is high, around 280°C., once again pointing up the effect of ring structure on polymer properties.

The following polymerization procedure has been used successfully for preparing high molecular weight polymers from a number of bisphenols and appears to be generally applicable to the preparation of polyphenyl esters if the sodium salt of the bisphenol is water soluble. It has been very useful for preparing polymers using aromatic acid chlorides in particular, since these are not readily hydrolyzed by the strongly alkaline solution of the salt of the bisphenol.

75. Preparation of Poly[2,2-propane Bis(4-phenylisophthalate-co-terephthalate) (50/50)] (40)

A solution of 5.70 g. (0.025 mole) diphenylopropane (bisphenol A) and 2.0 g. (0.050 mole) sodium hydroxide in 150 ml. water is prepared in a household blender at very low speed stirring. (Bisphenol A is best purified as described in the preparation of its polycarbonate, Preparation 77). The sodium hydroxide should be added as a standardized carbonate-free solution since this will give a more accurate titre of alkali than weighing out pellets. The speed of the household blender motor can best be regulated by a Powerstat. A setting of about 20 is adequate for preparing the solution but the maximum setting is used for the polymerization. A second solution of 2.54 g. (0.0125 mole) isophthaloyl chloride and 2.54 g. (0.0125 mole) terephthaloyl chloride in 75 ml. chloroform is prepared in a 150 ml. beaker.

Isophthaloyl chloride can be recrystallized from dry hexane (50 ml. hexane for 100 g. acid chloride) at 21–24°C. Ice cooling should not be used. The melting point is 42–43°C. Terephthaloyl chloride can be purified as described in Preparation 27. The preparation of isophthaloyl chloride is essentially the same as that for terephthaloyl chloride, also given in Preparation 27. Both commercial grade and reagent grade chloroform must be washed with water before use to insure removal of the alcohol added as a stabilizer. The chloroform can then be dried over calcium hydride. To the solution in the blender is now added 15 ml. of a 10% aqueous solution of Duponol* ME and the blender is turned to a maximum speed. The chloroform solution of the acid

$$\text{HO—C}_6\text{H}_4\text{—}\overset{\overset{\displaystyle CH_3}{|}}{\underset{\underset{\displaystyle CH_3}{|}}{C}}\text{—C}_6\text{H}_4\text{—OH} + \quad \underset{\displaystyle Cl—\overset{\overset{\displaystyle O}{\|}}{C}}{}\text{...}\overset{\overset{\displaystyle O}{\|}}{C}\text{—Cl} +$$

$$Cl—\overset{\overset{\displaystyle O}{\|}}{C}\text{...}\overset{\overset{\displaystyle O}{\|}}{C}\text{—Cl} \longrightarrow$$

$$\left[—O—C_6H_4—\overset{\overset{\displaystyle CH_3}{|}}{\underset{\underset{\displaystyle CH_3}{|}}{C}}—C_6H_4—O\overset{\overset{\displaystyle O}{\|}}{C}\text{...}\overset{\overset{\displaystyle O}{\|}}{C}— \right]_n$$

$$\left[—O—C_6H_4—\overset{\overset{\displaystyle CH_3}{|}}{\underset{\underset{\displaystyle CH_3}{|}}{C}}—C_6H_4—O\overset{\overset{\displaystyle O}{\|}}{C}\text{...}\overset{\overset{\displaystyle O}{\|}}{C}— \right]_n + 4HCl$$

chlorides is added immediately and as rapidly as possible to the well stirred aqueous solution. The rapidly stirred solution has a tendency to foam over. The blender can be covered with aluminum foil, a top with a center hole added, and the acid chloride solution added through a powder funnel inserted through the covers. The emulsion so formed is stirred for 5 min. and the blender is stopped. The thin oil-in-water emulsion is poured into 1 l. of acetone to coagulate the polymer and extract the solvents. The polymer is filtered and washed once on the filter with acetone. The granular polymer is transferred back to the blender jar and washed in 500 ml. water to remove the salt and dispersing agent. The solid polymer is filtered again and washed on the filter with water. The water washing step is repeated twice more and the polymer is given a final wash on the filter with acetone. The polymer is dried 24 hr. in a vacuum oven at 90°C. The dried polymer weighs 8–8.5 g. (90–97%).

Polymer prepared in this way from purified intermediates should have an inherent viscosity in *sym*-tetrachloroethane-phenol (40/60 weight) of 1.8–2.2 (0.5% conc., 30°C.) and a polymer melt temperature of 280°C. It is very soluble in halogenated hydrocarbons, hot cyclohexanone, pyridine, and phenols and slightly soluble in hot dimethylformamide, dioxane, and tetrahydrofuran. It can be fabricated to films and fibers by casting or spinning from solutions in any of the good solvents listed.

Adipoyl chloride will react at an elevated temperature with **hydroquinone** in a rigorously anhydrous inert solvent such as nitrobenzene to form a high molecular weight **polyphenyl ester** (90). The evolved hydrogen chloride is removed from the refluxing solvent with the aid of an inert gas sweep and no acid acceptor is needed. The reac-

* Trademark for du Pont's surface-active reagent.

tion requires an unusually high degree of purification of reactants and solvents to produce high polymer, and the polymer must be soluble or highly swollen in the hot solvent in which the reaction is run.

76. Preparation of Poly(1,4-phenylene adipate) (90)

$$HO-\langle\bigcirc\rangle-OH \; + \; Cl-\overset{\overset{O}{\|}}{C}-(CH_2)_4-\overset{\overset{O}{\|}}{C}-Cl \longrightarrow$$

$$\left[-O-\langle\bigcirc\rangle-O-\overset{\overset{O}{\|}}{C}-(CH_2)_4-\overset{\overset{O}{\|}}{C}- \right]_n \; + \; 2HCl$$

For the following polymerization, the hydroquinone is purified by recrystallizing four times from water which has been deoxygenated by boiling and cooled with a stream of nitrogen bubbling through it. The adipoyl chloride used can be commercially available material which has been fractionally distilled twice at reduced pressure in a nitrogen atmosphere using an oil bath, not in excess of 150°C., as a heat source. The boiling point at 1 mm. pressure is about 70–72°C.; at 10 mm. it is 112–115°C. Distillation should be fairly rapid to avoid the decomposition which may result from prolonged heating. The nitrobenzene is purified by washing well with water and drying over calcium chloride. It is then distilled three times from phosphorus pentoxide at atmospheric pressure, then once from the same material at oil pump pressure. It should be stored under nitrogen under anhydrous conditions.

The flask is flamed out and cooled in a current of nitrogen admitted through a gas inlet tube reaching to the bottom of the flask. A mixture of 7.872 g. (0.0232 mole) adipoyl chloride, 4.728 g. (0.0233 mole) of hydroquinone, and 20.0 ml. nitrobenzene is placed in a 100 ml. three-necked flask equipped with a condenser protected with a drying tube.

The reaction mixture is heated slowly by means of an oil bath to 140–147°C. over a period of $2\frac{1}{2}$ hr., then maintained at that temperature for an additional 6 hr. A slow stream of nitrogen is passed through the reaction mixture during its course. Care must be taken to avoid heating above 150°C., since the acid chloride tends to decompose above this temperature. The nitrobenzene is then distilled at oil pump pressure with an oil bath temperature of about 147°C. The solid remaining is dried 2 hr. further at about 147°C. and 1.0 mm., or less. The white (or slightly off-white) solid obtained has an inherent viscosity of 1.0–1.4 in nitrobenzene/phenol (1:1 by weight, at 0.5% conc., 25°C.). The polymer melt temperature is about 240°C. and fibers can be pulled from the melt.

Phosgene, the simplest organic diacid chloride, can be used directly in reaction **with bisphenols to produce polycarbonates** (91,92). The reaction can be carried out readily in pyridine solution or in aqueous sodium hydroxide. Polycarbonates have also been prepared from bisphenols and dialkylcarbonates in ester exchange reactions (93,66).

77. Preparation of Poly[2,2-propanebis(4-phenyl carbonate)] (91,94)

Caution!   Phosgene is Toxic!   Run in a Good Hood!

A 1 l. three-necked flask is fitted with an efficient stirrer, a condenser with calcium chloride drying tube, a thermometer capable of being immersed in the reaction mixture, and a gas inlet tube reaching as nearly to the bottom of the flask as possible for admitting phosgene. The air is displaced from the flask with nitrogen and the flask charged with 98 g. (0.43 mole) of diphenylolpropane, m.p. 159–160°C., recrystallized from toluene, 80 g./l., and 700 ml. analytical grade pyridine. When the bisphenol has dissolved, phosgene is bubbled through the solution at the rate of about 1 g./min. with stirring. The temperature is maintained at 25–30°C. by means of an ice-water bath, applied as necessary. The phosgene flow may be followed by weighing the cylinder periodically or continuously, or a weighed amount of condensed phosgene may be vaporized into the reaction. The theoretical weight of phosgene is 42.6 g. (0.43 mole), but a 10–15 wt. % excess may be necessary because of loss of unreacted phosgene through the condenser. The exit gases from the reaction should be led to a suitable aqueous alcohol-caustic trap, or to a continuously flowing water scrubber and flushed down a drain with plenty of water. Loss of phosgene can be prevented by moderate stirring to avoid formation of a deep vortex.

At about the midpoint of phosgene consumption, crystals of pyridine hydrochloride begin to form. Toward the end of the reaction, the solution becomes viscous and the rate of phosgene addition is reduced to a very slow flow. At the endpoint of the reaction, a yellow-to-red color develops*, and the phosgene flow is stopped. The color may be discharged by the addition of a little bisphenol A in pyridine. The polymer is isolated by pouring the mixture into four times its volume of water with vigorous stirring. The polymer is filtered, washed on the filter with water, and suspended in 1 l. of water at 80°C. for 10 min. with stirring. It is filtered and washed again, and dried in a vacuum oven at 80°C. The inherent viscosity in *sym*-tetrachloroethane/phenol (40/60 weight) (0.5% conc., 25°C.) is 0.6–0.8. The polymer melt temperature is about 240°C., and strong, flexible films may be melt-pressed at that temperature. The polymer is soluble in chlorinated solvents, such as 1,1,2-trichloroethane.

As an alternate to the above procedure, a method using a methylene chloride–aqueous sodium hydroxide medium is also operable, as follows.

* The color change may reflect the source and purity of the bisphenol and may not always occur. No further change in viscosity also indicates the end point.

In a 3 l. three-necked flask equipped with stirrer, condenser, and gas inlet tube reaching to the bottom of the flask is placed 137 g. (0.6 mole) bisphenol A, 60 g. (1.5 moles) sodium hydroxide, 10 g. benzyltrimethylammonium chloride, 1 l. distilled water, and 500 ml. methylene chloride. The mixture is stirred rapidly and kept at 20°C. with ice cooling while phosgene is passed in at the rate of 2 g./min. Another 40 g. (1.0 mole) of sodium hydroxide is added in portions to keep the mixture strongly alkaline. The polymerization is estimated to be complete when a tough skin of polymer forms when a sample of the methylene chloride phase is evaporated. The methylene chloride is evaporated on a steam bath, finally, and the coarse polymer washed as described above. The polymer is essentially identical to that obtained above. The weight is about 140 g. (86%). The inherent viscosity (as before) is about 0.6.

Polycarbonates from bisphenols can be prepared, as described in Preparation 77, by condensation with phosgene at low temperatures. Many members of the polycarbonate class can also be prepared in a melt polycondensation with diphenyl carbonate, with phenol distilled as it is displaced. The principal limitation is that the product polymer be melt stable. The reaction is catalyzed by very small amounts of strong base. Cleavage of the bisphenol and rearrangement of in-chain carbonate groups occur with too great an amount of base, causing problems of discoloration, low molecular weight, and crosslinking. These reactions are known to occur.

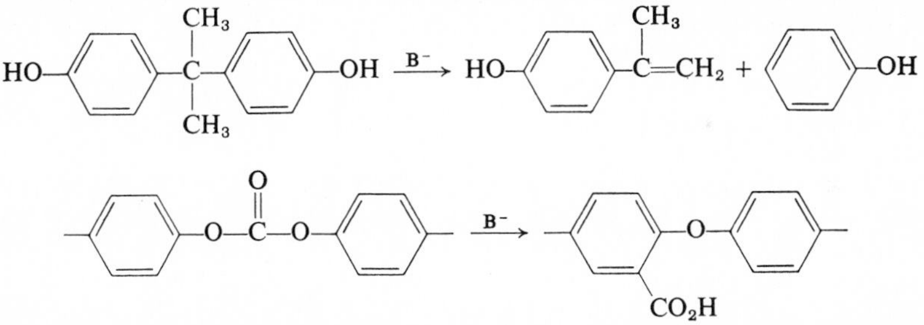

$$HO-\underset{CH_3}{\overset{CH_3}{\underset{|}{\overset{|}{C}}}}-OH \xrightarrow{B^-} HO-\underset{CH_3}{\overset{CH_3}{\underset{|}{\overset{|}{C}}}}=CH_2 + \bigcirc-OH$$

$$-\bigcirc-O-\overset{O}{\overset{||}{C}}-O-\bigcirc- \xrightarrow{B^-} -\bigcirc-O-\bigcirc- \quad CO_2H$$

The chemistry and physics of polycarbonates have been thoroughly reviewed in a book of that title by Schnell (95).

78. Preparation of Poly[2,2-propane-bis(4-phenyl carbonate)] (96)

A large polymer tube is flushed with nitrogen and charged with 22.8 g. bisphenol A (purified as in Preparation 77) (0.10 mole), 23.0 g. diphenyl carbonate (0.107 mole) and a minute quantity of lithium hydride (about 0.4 mg.), and melted under nitrogen flow through the customary capillary arrangement at a temperature up to 150°C. A Wood's metal bath is useful for the gradual temperature increases involved in this preparation. (Diphenyl carbonate, it is to be noted, is used in excess to assure the early conversion of phenolic-OH to phenyl carbonate groups; the latter are eliminated as diphenyl carbonate.) The pressure is slowly reduced to 20 mm. and the temperature is then raised slowly to 310°C. It is important to avoid distilling diphenyl carbonate along with the phenol which is eliminated during this phase. The pressure is again cautiously reduced to 0.2 mm. and the temperature brought to 250°C. over about 1 hr., followed by a rise to 280°C. over another 2 hr. Polycarbonates, as is typical of ring-containing polyesters generally, form extremely viscous melts. The product cools to a transparent solid which can be melt-pressed or solvent-cast (e.g., methylene chloride) to tough films. The catalyst should be destroyed in the melt if extensive melt processing is contemplated; this can be accomplished by adding a small portion of dimethyl sulfate (toxic!), the excess of which is removed during the last part of the operation. The polymer has an inherent viscosity of about 1.0 (0.5 g./100 ml. in methylene chloride, 20°C.).

An unusual situation exists in the preparation of **polyesters from phenolphthalein** by interfacial polycondensation (37,97). The action of alkali on phenolphthalein (I) produces not only colorless phenoxides but a tautomeric, highly colored quinomethine structure (II). Colorless carbinol compounds (III) may also be formed particularly in the presence of excess alkali.

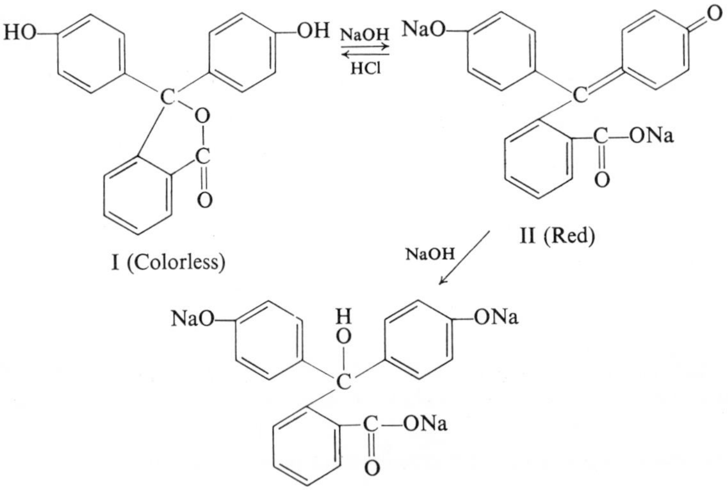

I (Colorless)   II (Red)

III (Colorless)

Upon reaction of phenolphthaleins with diacid chlorides in a two-phase system, the tautomeric equilibrium rapidly and continuously shifts toward the phthalide structure (I) and high yields of polyesters having phthalide substituents are obtained.

79. Preparation of Polyester from Phenolphthalein and Isophthaloyl Chloride (37,97)

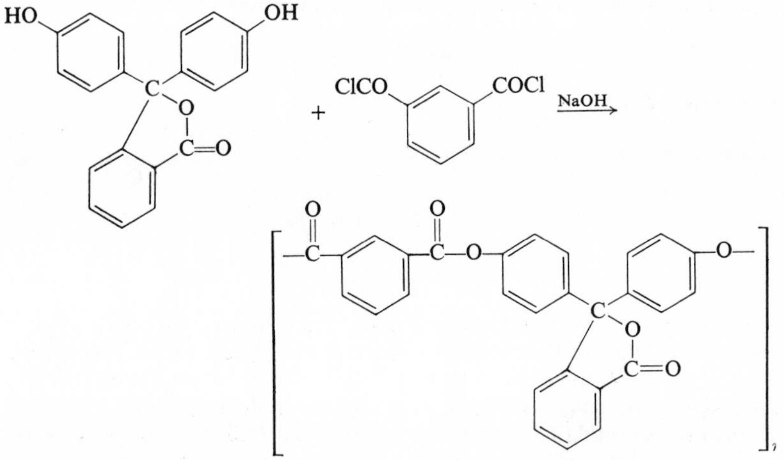

a. Interfacial Polycondensation

Phenolphthalein (3.18 g.) and 0.80 g. of sodium hydroxide are dissolved in 100 ml. of water in a blender jar. While the mixture is rapidly stirred, a solution of 2.03 g. of isophthaloyl chloride in 30 ml. of 1,2-dichloroethane is added all at once. The blood-red color is quickly reduced to a light pink. Stirring is continued for 5 min. Hexane (300 ml.) is added to precipitate the polymer, which is filtered and washed with water; yield 4.22 g.; η_{inh} about 1.0, determined in *sym*-tetrachloroethane/phenol (40/60 by weight) at 0.5 g./ 100 ml. and at 30°C.

b. Interfacial Polycondensation with Phosgene Gas

Phenolphthalein (3.98 g., 0.0125 mole), 1.0 g. of sodium hydroxide and 1.0 g. of tetraethylammonium chloride are dissolved in 120 ml. of water in a blender jar. 1,2-Dichloroethane (30 ml.) is added. While the mixture is stirred vigorously, phosgene gas is passed in until the color fades.

After the first loss of color, the color is returned by adding several drops of a 20% solution of sodium hydroxide, and phosgene is passed in again. This is repeated two more times. The total time is about 20 min. The polymer is isolated by adding acetone. The precipitate is filtered, washed thoroughly, and dried. The product is obtained in 93% yield with an η_{inh} of over 2.

The **reaction of a dicarboxylic acid chloride and a glycol** in an anhydrous melt system provides a methanol for preparing polyesters which is much faster than either the glycol–diacid or glycol–diester condensations (98, 99). The by-product is hydrogen chloride, which must be removed to prevent alkyl halide formation or etherification. The reaction is applicable in most cases to aliphatic glycols having at least a 3 atom chain between the hydroxyls, and to the aromatic diacid chlorides except for *o*-phthaloyl chloride.

80. Preparation of Poly(tetramethylene isophthalate) (98)

$$HO(CH_2)_4OH + Cl-\overset{\overset{O}{\|}}{C}-\underset{}{\bigcirc}-\overset{\overset{O}{\|}}{C}-Cl \longrightarrow$$

$$\left[-O(CH_2)_4O-\overset{\overset{O}{\|}}{C}-\underset{}{\bigcirc}-\overset{\overset{O}{\|}}{C}-\right]_n + 2HCl$$

A 100 ml. three-necked flask equipped with a nitrogen inlet tube extending below the surface of the reaction mixture, a mechanical stirrer, and an exit tube for nitrogen and evolved hydrogen chloride (provision should be made for trapping the latter) is flushed with nitrogen and charged first with 40.60 g. (0.20 mole) isophthaloyl chloride followed by 18.02 g. (0.20 mole) tetramethylene glycol (purification of the acid chloride is given in Preparation 75, the glycol in Preparation 62). The heat of reaction causes the isophthaloyl chloride to melt. The reaction is stirred vigorously and nitrogen is passed through the reaction to avoid accumulation of hydrogen chloride, which may bring about formation of tars. On a larger scale, the initial reaction should be controlled by ice cooling to maintain the temperature at 50°C., or below. In about 1 hr., the evolution of hydrogen chloride slows considerably and the mixture begins to solidify. The temperature of the reaction mixture is then raised to 180°C. by means of an oil bath and held at that temperature for 1 hr. During the last 10 min. of the 180°C. heating cycle, the last of the hydrogen chloride is removed by reducing the pressure to 0.5–1.0 mm.

The polymer is obtained as a white solid having an inherent viscosity of around 0.5 in *sym*-tetrachloroethane/phenol (40/60 weight) (0.5% conc., 25°C.). It is amorphous, as formed, and has a polymer melt temperature of 100–110°C. It is soluble in 1,2,2-trichloroethane, formic acid, dimethylformamide, and *m*-cresol. When the polyester is crystallized, the polymer melt temperature is increased to about 140°C., and the polymer is no longer soluble in dimethylformamide and formic acid. Films dry cast from trichlorethane or chloroform are crystalline; such films may be quite brittle because of the high degree of crystallinity. Amorphous films can be obtained by pouring the melted polymer onto plates and spreading with a rod, then crystallizing by heating for 3 hr. at 70°C. Fibers can be pulled from a melt of the polymer with a rod. Amorphous films or fibers can be cold-drawn by hand; the drawn sample then has a tendency to crystallize when held under tension. The amorphous fibers and films are somewhat rubbery.

Polyphosphonate esters can be prepared **from phosphonic acid dihalides and glycols.** Phenylphosphonyl dichloride, for instance, has been condensed with hydroquinone, or di- and tetrachlorohydroquinone to give fiber and film forming products (100,101). The phenylthiophos-phonyl polyesters also have been prepared.

81. Preparation of Poly(1,4-phenylene phenylphosphonate) (100)

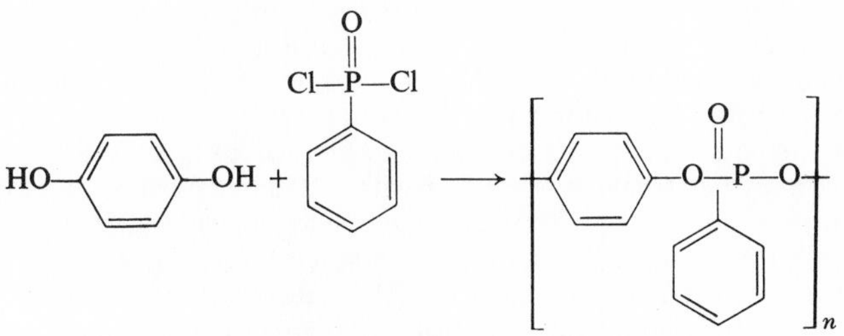

A polymer tube is charged with 10.2 g. (0.0525 mole) of freshly distilled (b.p. 104°C./4 mm.) phenylphosphonyl dichloride (102) and 5.50 g. (0.0500 mole) hydroquinone. The tube is filled with nitrogen (Preparation 2) and is heated at atmospheric pressure in a 139°C. vapor bath for 16 hr., during which time a slow stream of nitrogen is passed through the melt by means of a capillary reaching to the bottom of the tube. It is then heated for another 4 hr. in a 218°C. bath. Following this, the tube is heated in a 152°C. bath while the pressure is slowly reduced to 1–2 mm. over a period of 30 min. Heating is continued at this temperature and pressure for 4 hr. The tube is then switched to a 242°C. bath for 17 hr., with a nitrogen flow through the capillary, as in all phases of the polymerization. A final heating stage is carried out at 280–290°C. about 4 hr. at the same reduced pressure. The last heating stage is continued until the viscosity of the melt ceases to increase, as judged by the rate of rise of the nitrogen bubbles. The tube is cooled under nitrogen. The polyphosphonate ester has a polymer melt temperature of around 130°C. Fibers which are cold-drawable may be pulled from the melt. The polymer is soluble in chloroform and ethylene chloride. The inherent viscosity in the latter (0.5% conc., 25°C.) is about 0.4.

82. Preparation of Poly[2,2-propanebis(4-phenyl phenylphosphonate)]* (103)

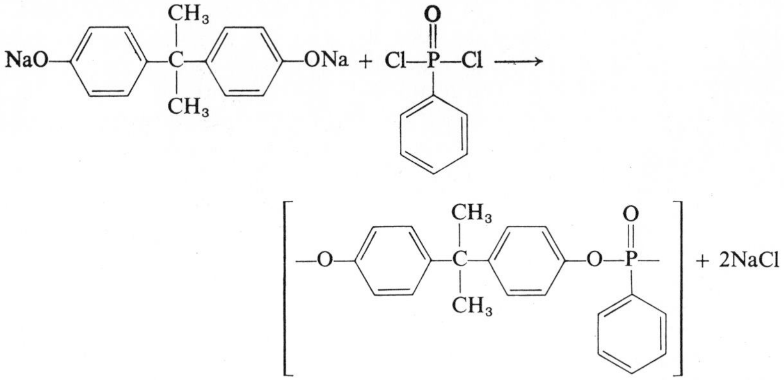

* We are indebted to Dr. Conix of Photoproducts Gevaert, for details of this preparation.

A 1 l. flask is fitted with a stirrer, a reflux condenser, a dropping funnel and a thermometer capable of being immersed in the reaction mixture. The flask is charged with 22.8 g. (0.1 mole) of diphenylopropane, 775 mg. (0.002 mole) of triphenylbenzylphosphonium chloride and 204 ml. of $1N$ aqeuous sodium hydroxide. When the bisphenol has dissolved, the mixture is cooled to $-8°C.$ by means of an ice-salt bath, and a solution of 19.5 g. (0.1 mole) of phenylphosphonyldichloride in 50 ml. of methylenechloride is added dropwise during 5 min. The temperature is held below 0°C. The polymerization mixture is stirred 1 hr. or more, the supernatant aqueous layer is decanted and the viscous polymer solution is washed with a 250 ml. portion of ice-water. The solution is diluted with 50 ml. of methylene chloride and the polymer is precipitated by pouring the solution into several volumes of ethanol. The precipitate is washed, and dried at 100°C. The yield of white, fibrous polymer is about 100% and the intrinsic viscosity in *sym*-tetrachloroethane at 25°C. is 0.54, corresponding to a molecular weight measured osmometrically, of 63,000. The polymer is soluble in chlorinated solvents, such as 1,1,2-trichloroethane, and also in dioxane and tetrahydrofuran. Very clear, strong, and flexible films can be cast from solution. The glass transition temperature of the polymer, determined refractometrically is 104°C.

André Conix was the first to prepare and report on all aromatic polysulfonate esters. A number of them are described in his patents and publications (e.g., 104–6). In general, they are quite soluble in many organic solvents, and are relatively low melting. Hydrolytic stability is usually very good.

83. Preparation of Biphenyldisulfonyl Chloride

$$HO_3S\text{—}\langle\!\!\langle\text{—}\rangle\!\!\rangle\text{—}\langle\!\!\langle\text{—}\rangle\!\!\rangle\text{—}SO_3H \longrightarrow ClO_2S\text{—}\langle\!\!\langle\text{—}\rangle\!\!\rangle\text{—}\langle\!\!\langle\text{—}\rangle\!\!\rangle\text{—}SO_2Cl$$

To 290 ml. of $POCl_3$ and 2 lb. of PCl_5 in a 3 l., three-necked flask fitted with stirrer and reflux condenser is added 500 g. of 4,4′-biphenyldisulfonic acid (Eastman Technical, 90%) over a period of 30 min. The temperature rises to 60°C. during this addition. The mixture is stirred and heated at reflux for 3 hr. and then cooled to room temperature. The slurry is slowly poured over a large amount of crushed ice with stirring. The light tan precipitate is vacuum filtered and sucked dry on the filter. This crude product is extracted four times with 1 l. of methylene chloride. This extract is washed twice with 250 ml. of 5% aqueous sodium bicarbonate solution and twice with 250 ml. water. After drying over anhydrous sodium sulfate, the solution is concentrated on a steam bath until crystallization starts, then hexane is added and the solution cooled to 0°C. The white crystalline diacid chloride is filtered; a second crop of crystals can be obtained by concentration and cooling of the filtrate. About 170 g. of biphenyldisulfonyl chloride having a melting point of 209–212°C. is obtained. One recrystallization from methylene chloride–hexane gives a product melting at 210.5°–212°C.

84. Preparation of a Polysulfonate (104,105)

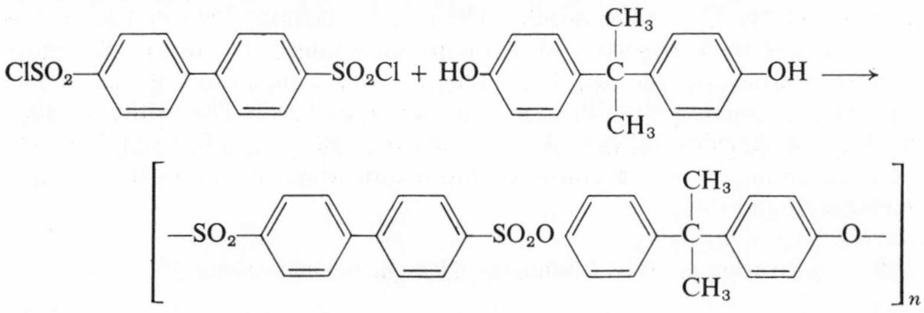

In a 250 ml. flask fitted with a stirrer are placed 80 ml. of $1.495M$ sodium hydroxide, 13.55 g. of diphenylol propane, 1 g. of tetraethyl ammonium chloride hydrate, and 1 g. of a detergent such as Duponol. The mixture is stirred until a clear solution is obtained, and cooled to 10°C. At this point, 21.00 g. of biphenyl disulfonyl chloride and 80 ml. of methylene chloride are added, and vigorous stirring is continued for about 1 hr. The white, doughlike semisolid is separated and boiled with water to remove the methylene chloride. The polysulfonate is obtained in quantitative yield; the inherent viscosity (0.5% in TCE/phenol) is 1.0–1.5. The polymer melts at about 210°C.

Recently, Hall has shown that certain substituted phenolsulfonic acids can be converted to stable, crystalline, phenolsulfonyl chlorides. These polymerize in this presence of triethylene diamine to high polymer. An intermediate such as

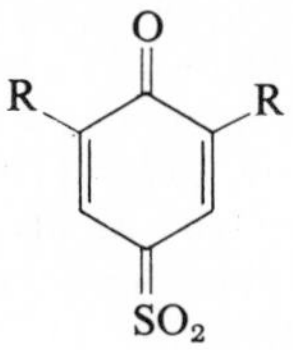

may be involved.

85. Preparation of 3,5-Dimethyl-4-hydroxybenzenesulfonyl Chloride (107)

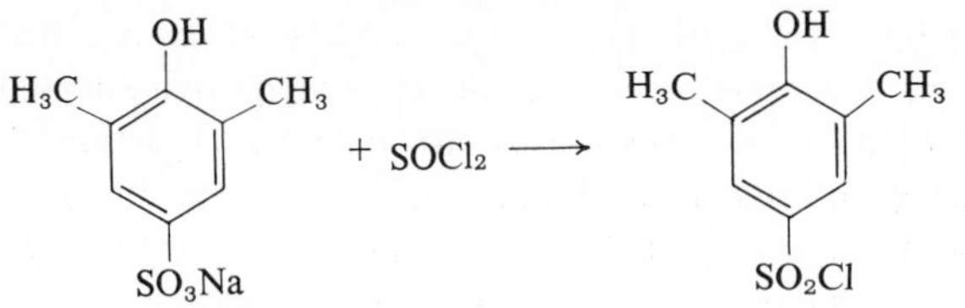

A solution containing 22.4 g. of sodium 3,5-dimethyl-4-hydroxybenzene-sulfonate (108) in 40 ml. of dimethylformamide is cooled to 0°C. with an ice-salt bath. To this solution 33 g. of thionyl chloride is added dropwise over a 10 min. period. The cooling bath is removed and the temperature rises to

39°C. After a reaction period of 52 min., the reaction mixture is added to 100 g. of ice. The white solid formed is isolated and washed several times with ice water. The crude product (19.8 g.) is vacuum dried at room temperature and then dissolved in a minimum amount of toluene. An equal volume of *n*-hexane was added and the solution is cooled to 0°C. The solids formed are isolated by filtration and vacuum dried. The white crystals (13.5 g.) are purified further by sublimation at 50°C. and 0.1 mm. Hg. The yield of monomer grade sulfonyl chloride melting at 134°C. is generally between 50 and 60%.

86. Preparation of Poly(3,5-dimethyl-1,4-phenylene sulfonate)*

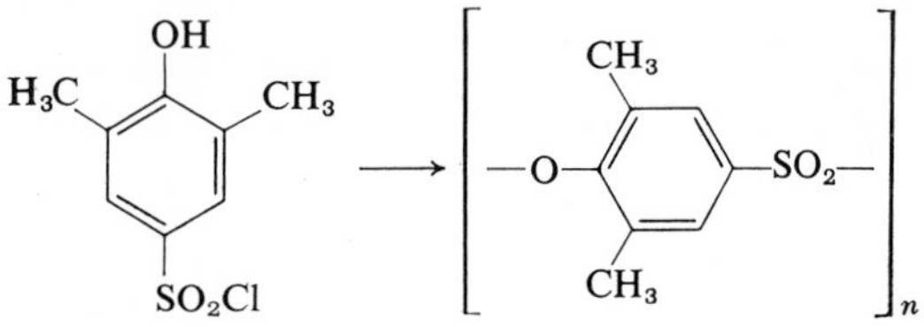

A solution of 9.2 g. of 3,5-dimethyl-4-hydroxybenzene-sulfonyl chloride in 20 ml. of dry nitrobenzene is prepared in a 100 ml. vaccine bottle under nitrogen. To this solution 6.6 g. of triethylene diamine in 20 ml. of nitrobenzene is added over a 15 min. period. After standing at room temperature for 15 hr. the contents of the bottle are added to ether and the precipitate is washed several times with water and ether. The crude product after vacuum drying weighs 6.7 g. (90%).

The product is separated into two fractions by extraction with 200 ml. of acetone. The insoluble material ($\sim 50\%$) is high molecular weight polymer with an intrinsic viscosity of 0.5–0.9 (25°C., nitrobenzene). A flexible film can be prepared on a hot stage press at 260°C. if the hot film is cooled quickly with ice water after removal from the press. (The polymer melt temperature is 225–250°C.) The film is amorphous as prepared, but crystallinity can be induced by treatment with organic solvents, e.g., acetone. The crystalline polymer is soluble in nitrobenzene.

The clear amorphous films show remarkable stability toward hydrolysis by hot acid and caustic.

The acetone soluble fraction of the crude product is a mixture of low molecular weight polymer and cyclic trimer and tetramer.

In previous preparations (71,94), polyphenyl esters were prepared from diacid chlorides and a bisphenol. **Polyphenyl esters of aliphatic diacids** can also be prepared **by an acidolysis reaction between the free acid and an ester of the bisphenol** (109). In the following example, the polysebacic ester of hydroquinone is prepared. The resorcinol polyester can be prepared by this same technique, as can poly(1,4-phenylene succinate). The latter is an "inverted" polyethylene terephthalate); the structures are formally identical, having a *p*-benzene ring

---

* We are indebted to Dr. Hall of General Electric for details prior to publication.

separated by an ethylene and two carbonyl groups. They are very
similar in properties.

Poly(ethylene terephthalate)   Poly(1,4-phenylene succinate)

87. Preparation of Poly(1,4-phenylene sebacate) (109)

For the following polymerization, p-phenylene diacetate (21) can be prepared by dissolving 11 g. (0.10 mole) hydroquinone in a solution of 9 g.
(0.22 mole) sodium hydroxide in 45 ml. water in a 250 ml. Erlenmeyer flask.
The mixture is cooled in an ice bath and a small quantity of ice is added to the
flask. Then 22.4 g. (0.22 mole) acetic anhydride is added at once and the flask
shaken vigorously by hand in the ice bath for 7 or 8 min. The white solid is
filtered, washed with water, and recrystallized from ethanol. It can be dried at
60°C. in a vacuum oven to give about 17 g. (88%) of product melting at
123–124°C.

A mixture of 9.70 g. p-phenylene diacetate (0.05 mole), 10.10 g. (0.05 mole)
sebacic acid, and 0.03 g. toluenesulfonic acid (monohydrate) is placed in a
polymer tube, the tube filled with nitrogen (Preparations 2 and 68) by a capillary inlet reaching to the bottom of the polymer tube. The temperature is then
raised to 180°C. Acetic acid distills as the temperature is slowly raised from
180°C. to 230°C. over a period of at least 30 min. The temperature is then
raised over 45 min. to 280°C. while the pressure is slowly reduced (about
10 min.) to about 0.3 mm. The temperature is maintained at 280°C. at this
pressure for 45 min. Nitrogen is passed slowly through the melt during the
heating. The product is a dark, tough solid, having an inherent viscosity in
m-cresol of 0.5–0.6 (0.5% conc., 30°C.) and a polymer melt temperature of
around 170°C. It may be melt-pressed to films at this temperature, and
drawable fibers may be pulled from the polymer melt.

The **acetates of** m- **and** p-**hydroxybenzoic acid** can undergo an **acidolysis reaction** with loss of acetic acid to form high molecular weight
copolymers. The meta isomer can be homopolymerized successfully,
but the para forms an intractable material.

88. Preparation of Poly(*m*-phenyl carboxylate) (110)

$$CH_3CO_2-\!\!\!\bigcirc\!\!\!-CO_2H \longrightarrow \left[-O-\!\!\!\bigcirc\!\!\!-\overset{\overset{\displaystyle O}{\|}}{C}-\right]_n + CH_3CO_2H$$

m-Acetoxybenzoic acid is prepared by heating *m*-hydroxybenzoic acid with excess acetic anhydride for 3 hr., concentrating the mixture under vacuum, and recrystallizing the solid residue from benzene–ligroin. The melting point is 130.5–131.5°C.

Ten g. of *m*-acetoxybenzoic acid and a small chip of magnesium (ca. 0.01% the weight of monomer) are placed in a polymer tube having a side arm and a nitrogen inlet which can be adjusted to reach the bottom of the tube. The tube is flushed with nitrogen (Preparations 2 and 68) and immersed in a 220°C. vapor bath. A slow stream of nitrogen is continually passed through the melt. The pressure is gradually reduced to 60 mm. Acetic acid distills from the tube. After 2 hr., the tube is immersed in a 300°C. vapor bath and the pressure brought to about 0.2 mm. This temperature is maintained until a maximum melt viscosity has been reached, as judged by the rate of bubble rise. The polymer is allowed to cool under nitrogen. The inherent viscosity is about 0.5 in *sym*-tetrachloroethane/phenol (40/60, weight) at 0.23% conc., 30°C. The polymer melts at 185–205°C., and is soluble in 1,1,2-trichloroethane, *m*-cresol, and *N*,*N*-dimethylaniline.

As an alternative to the above procedure, the polymerization can be carried out in a 100 ml. flask equipped with a nitrogen inlet, vacuum outlet, and a glass stirrer, using about 10–15 g. of *o*-terphenyl or a mixture of ditolyl sulfone isomers as a diluent to reduce the melt viscosity. Here, the temperature of reaction is 220–250°C. at a pressure which permits the solvent to reflux but not distill. The diluent is extracted from the anal polymer with acetone.

In either case, the polymer, so obtained, can be further powder polymerized by grinding to a fine particle size (0.8 mm. or less) and heating at 160–170°C. under high vacuum. Inherent viscosities as high as 0.9 may be obtained.

Hydrogen sulfide will add to diacrylates with sufficient thoroughness and lack of side reaction **to give thiodipropionate polyesters of high molecular** weight in favorable instance (111). The use of thiodipropionic acid itself in direct polyesterification has not met with much success. Tertiary or hindered secondary amine catalysis is used in the stepwise polyaddition described here, and the reaction is evidently ionic in character since oxygen and phenolic inhibitors are apparently without effect. A variety of diacrylate esters have been used; diacrylamides have also been tried, but low molecular weight polymers seem to generally be formed. One of the more interesting ester examples involves *p*-xylene diacrylate to give a rubbery polymer which is quite tough even when unvulcanized.

89. Preparation of *p*-Xylene Diacrylate (111)

A mixture of 14.0 g. *p*-xylylene glycol (0.10 mole), 15.8 g. acrylic acid (0.22 mole), 250 ml. benzene, 0.5 g. di-*tert*-amylhydroquinone, and 1.6 g.

$$CH_2{=}CHCO_2H + HOCH_2{-}\!\!\left\langle\!\!\bigcirc\!\!\right\rangle\!\!{-}CH_2OH \longrightarrow$$

$$CH_2{=}CH{-}CO_2CH_2{-}\!\!\left\langle\!\!\bigcirc\!\!\right\rangle\!\!{-}CH_2O_2C{-}CH{=}CH_2$$

p-toluenesulfonic acid is refluxed for 30 hr. in a 1 l. round-bottom flask equipped with a Dean-Stark trap for azeotropic removal of water. It is then washed with sodium bicarbonate solution and water. Distillation of the benzene from the solution leaves a solid residue which is recrystallized repeatedly from heptane to yield 8.6 g. of product, m.p. 67–72°C. Further recrystallization from heptane and aqueous ethanol produces white flakes, m.p. 74–75°C.

90. Preparation of Poly(p-xylylene thiodipropionate) (111)

$$CH_2{=}CH{-}\overset{\overset{O}{\|}}{C}{-}OCH_2{-}\!\!\left\langle\!\!\bigcirc\!\!\right\rangle\!\!{-}CH_2O{-}\overset{\overset{O}{\|}}{C}{-}CH{=}CH_2 + H_2S \longrightarrow$$

$$\left[\!{-}CH_2{-}\!\!\left\langle\!\!\bigcirc\!\!\right\rangle\!\!{-}CH_2O{-}\overset{\overset{O}{\|}}{C}{-}CH_2CH_2SCH_2CH_2{-}\overset{\overset{O}{\|}}{C}{-}O\!{-}\right]$$

Caution: Run Only in a Good Hood

In a 100 ml. three-necked flask equipped stirrer, condenser, and gas inlet tube is placed 50 ml. pyridine, 0.5 g. diisopropylamine, and 7.38 g. p-xylylene diacrylate (0.03 mole). Over a short period of six hr., hydrogen sulfide is passed into the solution in short, intermittent additions. In order to avoid overshooting the amount of hydrogen sulfide required, no further addition of gas should be made until the absence of H_2S is demonstrated after the previous addition by spotting the reaction mixture on lead acetate paper. When H_2S persists in the solution, the polymerization is complete. This method of creeping up on the end point by adding small quantities of H_2S at a time is capable of producing quite high polymer, as noted below. A more sophisticated approach using a calibrated flow meter to determine the approach to equivalence would permit a briefer experimental time.

When H_2S finally persists, the solution is poured into 400 ml. of heptane with stirring, the precipitated mass extricated whole and swelled in methylene chloride, and finally dropped in small pieces into heptane, and stirred vigorously. The supernatancy is decanted, fresh heptane added, and the process repeated. The polymer is finally dried at 50°C. in vacuum to give about 8 g. of rubbery polymer with an inherent viscosity around 0.5 (dimethylformamide, 0.5 g./100 ml., 30°C.). In pyridine, the inherent viscosity is around 0.8.

Preparations of various other polyesters will be found elsewhere. In this chapter, polyesters modified with diisocyanates are to be found in Section V, which follows. Crosslinked polyester resins are discussed in Chapter 7. The entire polyester field has been extensively treated in book form in terms of intermediates, processes, properties, and uses (112,113).

Copolyester–urethanes can be made by a variety of techniques. The next example describes the preparation of an alternating ester–urethane by reaction of piperazine with the bischloroformate of bis(hydroxyethyl) terephthalate.

91. Preparation of Bischloroformate of Bis-(hydroxyethyl) Terephthalate (114)

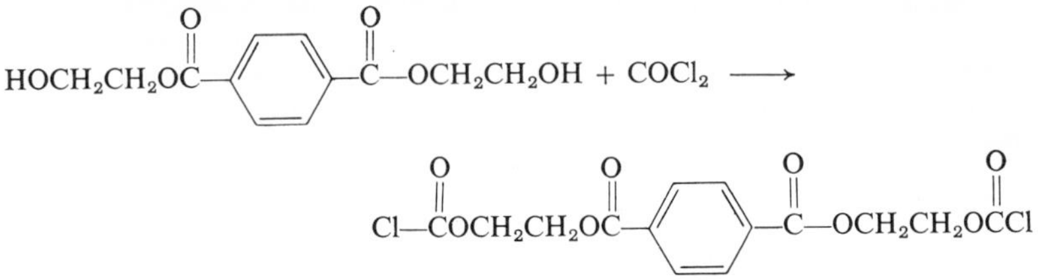

Caution: Phosgene Is Extremely Toxic

A round-bottom flask is charged with 97 g. of dimethyl terephthalate, 372 g. of ethylene glycol, and 0.3 g. of calcium acetate monohydrate as a catalyst. From this reaction mixture, methanol is removed by distillation to yield bis(2-hydroxyethyl) terephthalate. Distillation is stopped when the head temperature of the column rises to 150°C. The mixture is cooled to room temperature, poured into 1.5 l. of distilled water and filtered. The white solid product obtained in this manner is purified by recrystallization from boiling water, m.p. 107–108°C. The yield is 90–95 g.

To a mixture of 68.6 g. (0.27 mole) of bis(2-hydroxyethyl) terephthalate and 700 ml. of dioxane in a 2 l., three-necked flask equipped with a stirrer, Dry Ice condenser, and a dropping funnel is added a solution of 203 ml. of phosgene in 300 ml. of dioxane. There is no apparent reaction but after stirring 1 hr. a clear solution results. Stirring is continued for 4 hr. while keeping the temperature at about 40°C. The dioxane is removed by distillation under reduced pressure. The white crystals which remain are recrystallized from 900 ml. of cyclohexane and 150 ml. of benzene. The yield of bischloroformate is 91.6 g. (90% of the theoretical). The melting point is 101–104°C. After a second recrystallization the yield is 87.0 g. and the melting point 104°C.

92. Preparation of An Alternating Copolyester–urethane (114)

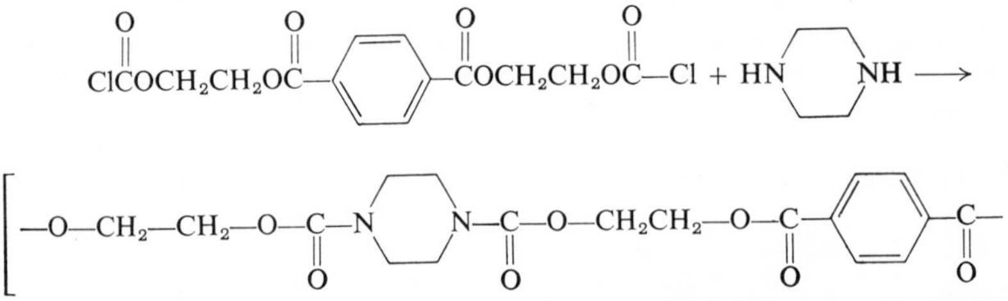

A Waring Blendor jar is charged with 210 ml. of distilled water, 15 ml. of a 5% solution of a synthetic wetting agent, 50 ml. of benzene, 6.36 g. of sodium carbonate, and 3.1 g. of piperazine dissolved in 30 ml. of water. To this rapidly stirred mixture is added a solution of 11.37 g. of the ester–bischloroformate in 50 ml. of benzene. The stirring is continued for 20 min. while the reaction temperature remains at approximately 25°C. At the end of 20 min. the agitation is stopped, and the polymer emulsion is broken with acetone. The polymer is collected on a filter, washed several times with distilled water and dried overnight in a vacuum oven at 70°C. About 10 g. of polymer is obtained. The polymer has an inherent viscosity of 1.2–1.3 (0.5% in trichloroethane/formic acid 90/10).

Polymer obtained as described above may be dissolved in a 90/10 percentage composition mixture of trichloroethane and formic acid to give a solution containing about 25% solids. Tough films can be cast; strips can be stretched 5–6 times.

Another approach to a copolyester–urethane involves starting with a polycarbonate. Solutions of polycarbonates are very readily degraded by amines. If the proper proportion of a diamine is added to a polycarbonate, the polycarbonate is degraded to a hydroxyl-terminated urethane macrosegment, which can be rebuilt by subsequent reaction with phosgene to give a copolymer.

93. Preparation of a Copolycarbonate-urethane (115)

(1)

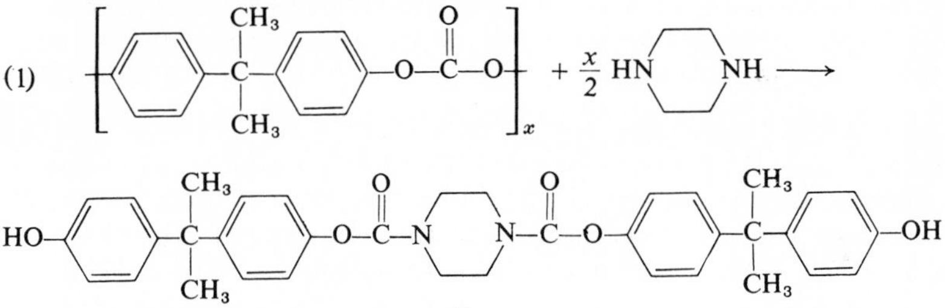

(2)   I + COCl$_2$ ⟶

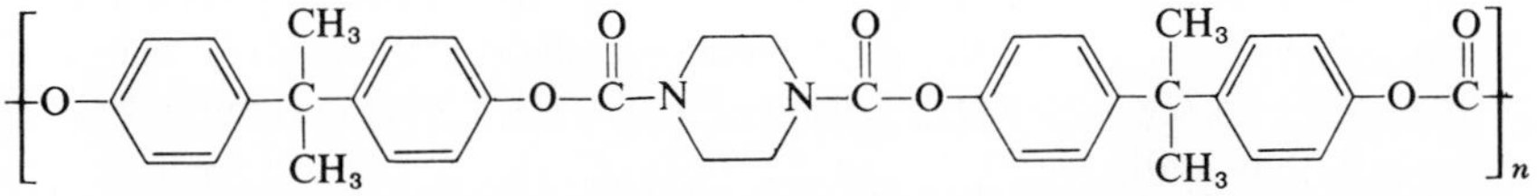

To 300 g. of a 0.3 molal solution of poly(diphenylolpropane carbonate) in methylene chloride is added at once at room temperature a solution of 3.87 g. (0.045 mole) piperazine in the same solvent. After standing at room temperature for 20 min. the solution is poured with stirring into a large excess of hexane. The precipitate is collected, washed twice with water and once with methanol, and is dried in an 80°C. vacuum oven overnight. This low polymer has an inherent viscosity of 0.12 in TCE/phenol (0.5% conc., 25°C.) and 2500 OH ends per 10^6 g.

In a 250 ml. three-necked flask provided with addition funnel, stirrer, and Dry Ice condenser 4 g. (0.005 mole, based on end-group analysis) of the above polymer is dissolved in a mixture of 20 ml. of methylene chloride and 10 ml.

of distilled pyridine. The solution is cooled in ice and a solution of 0.5 ml. (0.007 mole) phosgene in 10 ml. of methylene chloride is added with stirring over 10 min. A yellow precipitate forms during the course of the addition. The mixture is stirred for $\frac{1}{2}$ hr. at room temperature and is then poured into 400 ml. of methanol. A yellow polymer separates; it is collected, washed twice with water and once with methanol, and is dried in a vacuum oven at 80°C.

The polymer can be purified by washing its chloroform solution three times with water, and reprecipitating it as above. The color becomes a pale yellow. The polymer has a melting point of 260°C., an inherent viscosity of 0.6 in TCE/phenol, and it contains 3.4% N.

A film can be cast from a chloroform solution of the purified polymer. It is clear, tough, and drawable two times in hot water. The polymer is quite stable hydrolytically.

This procedure can, of course, be repeated by (*1*) adding calculated amounts of piperazine, (*2*) rebuilding the polymer with phosgene.

V. Block Condensation Elastomers

A class of synthetic elastomers has been developed from copolymer formulations based on low molecular weight aliphatic polyesters or polyethers having terminal hydroxyl and/or carboxyl groups which are capable of further reaction with other difunctional compounds. By far the most widely used are diisocyanates. This latter reaction can be used to couple the lower molecular weight polyester or polyether via urethane links (116), or the diisocyanate may be used in excess so that it becomes a terminal group (117,118). In the latter case, these macrodiisocyanates may be coupled by means of still another reagent, such as water, diols, aminoalcohols, or diamines (117), with the subsequent formation of high polymer. Such elastomeric products are complex block copolymers. The formulas written for these materials are approximations of the actual structure rather than precise representations, because of the complex nature of the starting materials.

The following examples represent typical preparations of difunctional, hydroxyl terminated soft segments. It should be noted that a number of such products, both polyether and polyester, are commercially available.

94. Preparation of Poly(ethylene-co-propylene adipate)

$$HOCH_2CH_2OH + HOCH_2\underset{\underset{CH_3}{|}}{C}HOH + HO-\overset{\overset{O}{\|}}{C}-(CH_2)_4-\overset{\overset{O}{\|}}{C}-OH \longrightarrow$$

$$H-\left[OCH_2CH_2O-\overset{\overset{O}{\|}}{C}-(CH_2)_4-\overset{\overset{O}{\|}}{C}-OCH_2\underset{\underset{CH_3}{|}}{C}HO-\right]_n-H-$$

In a 500 ml. three-necked flask equipped with stirrer, nitrogen inlet tube below the level of the reaction mixture, and a straight distilling head and condenser is placed 351.5 g. (2.40 moles) adipic acid, 106.4 g. (1.71 moles) distilled ethylene glycol, and 86.9 g. (1.14 moles) distilled 1,2-propylene glycol. The reaction mixture is heated to 140°C. by means of an oil bath, with stirring, and nitrogen is passed slowly through the mixture until the distillation of water ceases. This may require 10–15 hr. The temperature is then raised to 200°C. and the pressure gradually reduced to about 20 mm. by means of a water aspirator. The reaction mixture is stirred and the slow passage of nitrogen is continued. Part of the excess glycols are removed during this step, and the molecular weight is determined by this heating and vacuum cycle. After a period of 23 hr. total, the mixture is cooled under nitrogen to give a white, waxy solid. A viscous syrup may result if insufficient glycol is removed, and the resulting polyester is of very low molecular weight.

A sample of the polyester is removed and analyzed for hydroxyl and carboxyl ends in the following manner (119,120). About 2 g. of polyester is weighed to the nearest miligram into a 100 ml. round-bottom flask. To dissolve the sample, 25.0 ml. of a mixture of 12.0 ml. acetic anhydride and 500 ml. dry pyridine is added by pipet. The solution is refluxed for 1 hr. The condenser is then washed out by the addition of about 5 ml. water through the top, and the heating is continued for 5 min. The heat is then removed and the condenser tube and tip washed with 25 ml. methanol. When the mixture has cooled to room temperature, it is titrated with approximately $0.5N$ standard potassium hydroxide solution to a phenolphthalein endpoint. This is a value A, taken as mg. KOH per g. polymer. Value A should never be less than 65% of value B. If it is, insufficient acetic anhydride was added for complete acetylation.

A blank is then run on a mixture of the same volumes used above of acetic anhydride–pyridine reagent and water, which has been allowed to stand for 15 min. Methanol is added in the same amount, as in the preceding case, just before titrating. This value, in mg. KOH per g. polymer, is blank value B.

Another titration is carried out on a sample of polymer of about the same size as the first dissolved in 25 ml. pyridine, again with $0.5N$ KOH, to a phenolphthalein endpoint. Here, the number of mg. KOH per g. polymer, value C, gives the acid number of the polyester. The hydroxyl number of the polyester is obtained from value C + value B − value A, all as mg. KOH per g. sample.

[The method for hydroxyl number depends on a quantitative acetylation of —OH groups followed by titration of the acetic acid from the hydrolyzed, unreacted acetic anhydride, plus any carboxyls in the polymer. The latter are determined separately by titration as described. Other active hydrogen compounds, such as amines, interfere with —OH determination.

The sum of the acid and hydroxyl numbers permits a calculation of number average molecular weight:

(Acid No. + Hydroxyl No.)/(2 × 56.1 × 1000)

= moles of polymer per gram

mol wt = 1/moles of polymer per gram

Because there are two ends per polymer molecule, the total of hydroxyl and carboxyl ends equals twice the number of polymer molecules.

In polyester prepared as previously described, the hydroxyl number will be about 58–59 and the carboxyl number about 3–4.]

95. Preparation of Polycaprolactone Trimerized with 2,4-Tolylene Diisocyanate

In a dry 1 l. three-necked flask is placed 62 g. (1 mole) of freshly distilled ethylene glycol and 0.02 g. tetraisopropyl titanate catalyst. This mixture is is heated under nitrogen to 140–150°C. at which temperature 570 g. (5 moles) of epsilon-caprolactone containing 0.04 tetraisopropyl titanate catalyst is added over a period of 60–90 min. The temperature gradually increases to 180–185°C. during the lactone addition. The mixture is stirred an additional 2 hr. at 165–170°C. The polycaprolactone glycol is then cooled to 50–60°C. and placed under a vacuum of 0.05 mm. Hg. A slow stream of N_2 is allowed to pass intermittently through the glycol as its temperature is raised gradually to 95–100°C. at 0.05 mm. Hg. The distillate obtained (ca. 3 g.) primarily ethylene glycol. The colorless polycaprolactone glycol solidifies to a white wax on cooling to room temperature.

Glycol molecular weight (calculated)	670
Glycol molecular weight (by acetylation)	690

A mixture of 103.5 g. (0.15 mole) of catalyst-free polycaprolactone glycol (690) and 17.4 g. (0.10 mole) of freshly distilled 2,4-tolylene diisocyanate is stirred under dry nitrogen at 90–100°C. for 2 hr. An IR spectrum of the product shows that all of the TDI has reacted (no NCO band at 4.3μ).

96. Preparation of Polycaprolactone Glycol

In a 500 ml. three-necked round-bottom flask equipped with a stirrer, thermometer, and a pressure-equalizing dropping funnel with nitrogen inlet in the top is placed 8.02 g. of anhydrous ethylene glycol, and 16 mg. of dibutyltin dilaurate. The mixture is warmed to 150°C. and a mixture of 250 g. of caprolactone and 64 mg. of dibutyltin dilaurate is added dropwise. Addition is begun at a temperature of 150°C. and allowed to rise to 180°C. and held there until all the lactone is added, about 1.5 hr. After addition is complete, the reaction is continued 2 hr. to ensure completion. Molecular weight should be about 2000 as determined by reaction with acetic anhydride and titrating liberated acetic acid. The yield is essentially quantitative.

The next step in preparing a block elastomer is to react the polyether or polyester glycol with a diisocyanate. If one mole of diisocyanate is used per mole of glycol, chain extension to high polymer is complete in one step. The next preparation is such an example.

97. Chain Extension of Poly(ethylene-co-propylene adipate) with Methylene Bis(4-phenylisocyanate) (116)

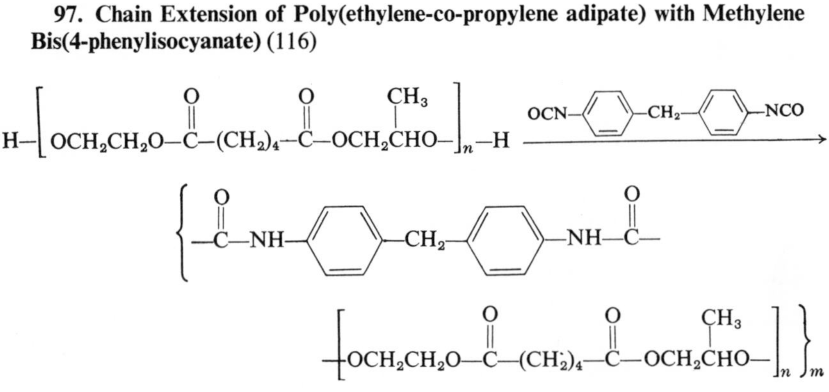

In a 500 ml. flask equipped with stirrer and nitrogen inlet tube reaching to the bottom of the flask is placed about 200 g. of the polyester prepared above. The polymer should have a molecular weight of around 2000–3000 and a ratio of hydroxyl to carboxyl numbers of at least 12. The polyester may be washed into the flask with a small quantity of methylene chloride. The temperature is raised to 120°C. by means of an oil bath, with stirring and passage of a slow stream of nitrogen through the liquid ester. A quantity of solid methylene bis(4-phenylisocyanate) (Preparation 47) is added corresponding to 96% of the theoretical amount based on the number of moles of polyester used, as determined by the end group analysis above. The mixture is stirred vigorously at 120°C. for 40 min. After cooling under nitrogen, the polymer obtained is a white or off-white solid. The inherent viscosity of the polymer is about 1.0–1.5 in dimethylformamide (0.5% conc., 30°C.). Films dry-cast from dimethylformamide are elastomeric.

A curable polyester–urethane can be prepared by thorough mixing with additional diisocyanate, e.g., on a rubber mill. When the polyester used has a molecular weight of 2000 and 96% of the theoretical diisocyanate is used in the chain extending reaction, 100 g. of the final polymer can be mixed with 5.5 g. of diisocyanate, molded or pressed into a desired shape, and cured at 150°C. for 70 min. to give a strong, useful elastomer.

As an alternative to chain-extending a hydroxy-ended polyester segment with a diisocyanate, the **initial low polymer** may be **terminated with a diisocyanate at each end** of the molecule (117,118). A **second difunctional molecule** is then **used for the chain-extending** step. The general reaction is:

$$HO\text{-}[\text{-polyester-}]\text{-}OH + 2\ R(NCO)_2 \longrightarrow$$

$$OCN\text{—}R\text{—}NH\overset{\overset{\displaystyle O}{\|}}{\text{—}C}\text{—}O\text{-}[\text{-polyester-}]\text{-}O\overset{\overset{\displaystyle O}{\|}}{\text{—}C}\text{—}NH\text{—}R\text{—}NCO \xrightarrow{H\text{—}X\text{—}H}$$

$$\left\{ \overset{\overset{\displaystyle O}{\|}}{\text{—}CN}\text{—}H\text{—}R\text{—}NH\overset{\overset{\displaystyle O}{\|}}{\text{—}C}\text{—}O\text{-}[\text{-polyester-}]\text{-}O\overset{\overset{\displaystyle O}{\|}}{\text{—}C}\text{—}NH\text{—}R\text{—}NH\overset{\overset{\displaystyle O}{\|}}{\text{—}C}\text{—}X\text{—} \right\}_n$$

H—X—H is a difunctional, active hydrogen compound, such as a glycol, diamine, or water. When water is used, carbon dioxide is evolved and a urea is the connecting linkage of the final product, as shown:

$$OCN\text{$\sim\!\!\sim$}NCO + H_2O \longrightarrow OCN\text{$\sim\!\!\sim$}NH\text{—}CO_2H \longrightarrow OCN\text{$\sim\!\!\sim$}NH_2 + CO_2$$

$$\downarrow$$

$$\text{$\sim\!\!\sim$}NH\overset{\overset{\displaystyle O}{\|}}{\text{—}C}\text{—}NH\text{$\sim\!\!\sim$}$$

98. Chain Extension of Isocyanate-Terminated Poly(ethylene–co–propylene adipate) with Water (117)

See reaction scheme, p. 158.

A sample of poly(ethylene–propylene adipate) prepared as described (above) is analyzed for the number of hydroxyl end groups. The following directions

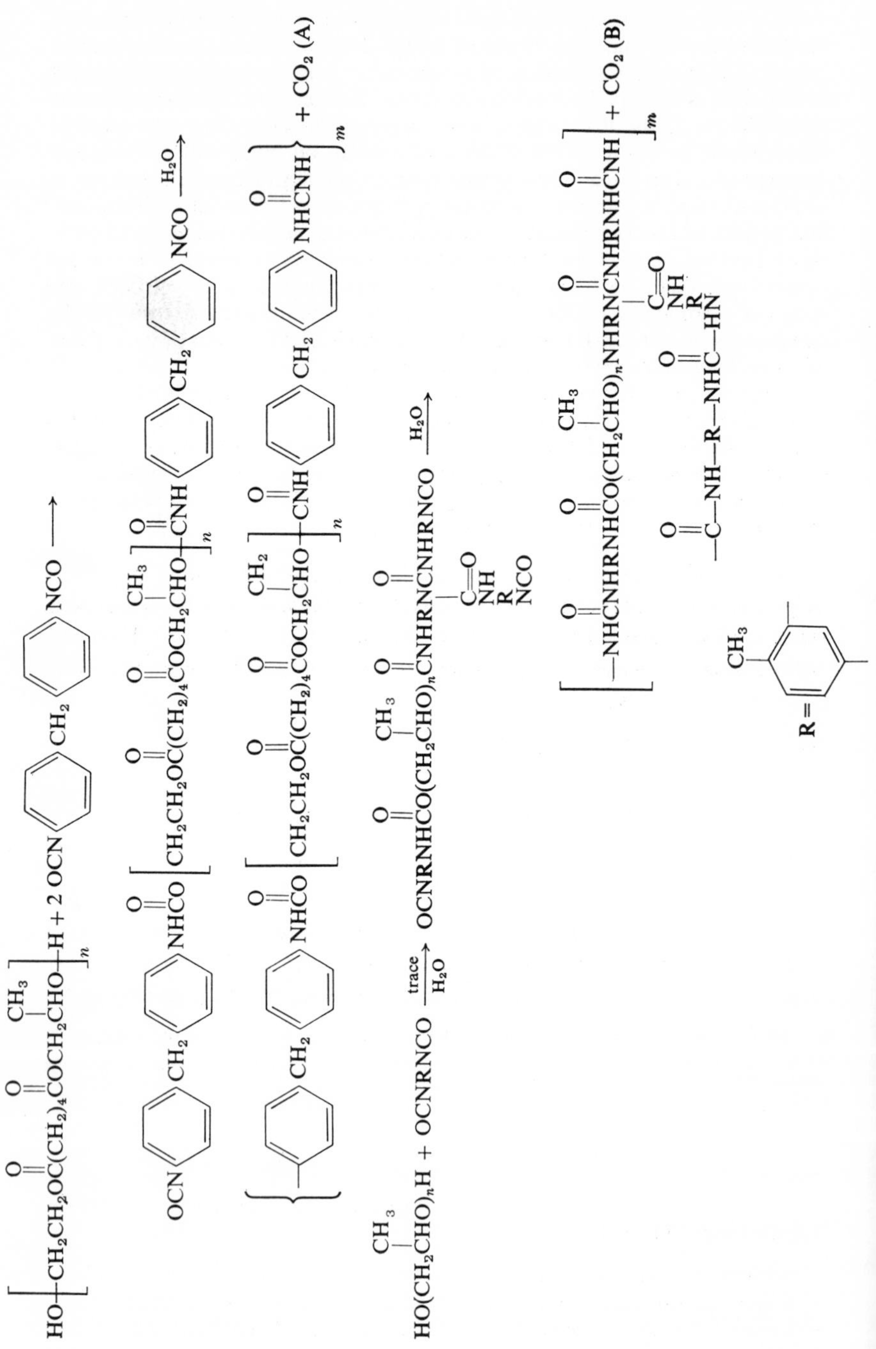

$$HO \left[CH_2CH_2O\overset{O}{C}(CH_2)_4\overset{O}{C}O\underset{CH_3}{CH}COCH_2CHO \right]_n H + 2\ OCN-\text{C}_6\text{H}_4-CH_2-\text{C}_6\text{H}_4-NCO \longrightarrow$$

$$OCN-\text{C}_6\text{H}_4-CH_2-\text{C}_6\text{H}_4-NHCO\left[CH_2CH_2O\overset{O}{C}(CH_2)_4\overset{O}{C}O\underset{CH_3}{CH}COCH_2CHO \right]_n \overset{O}{C}NH-\text{C}_6\text{H}_4-CH_2-\text{C}_6\text{H}_4-NCO \xrightarrow{H_2O}$$

$$\left\{ \text{C}_6\text{H}_4-CH_2-\text{C}_6\text{H}_4-NHCO\left[CH_2CH_2O\overset{O}{C}(CH_2)_4\overset{O}{C}O\underset{CH_2}{CH}COCH_2CHO \right]_n \overset{O}{C}NH-\text{C}_6\text{H}_4-CH_2-\text{C}_6\text{H}_4-NH\overset{O}{C}NH \right\}_m + CO_2 \quad (A)$$

$$HO(CH_2CHO)_nH + OCNRNCO \xrightarrow[H_2O]{trace} OCNRNHCO(CH_2CHO)_n\underset{CH_3}{\overset{O}{C}}NHRNCNHRNCO \xrightarrow{H_2O}$$

$$\left[-NHCNHRNHRNCO(CH_2CHO)_n\underset{CH_3}{}NHRNCNHRNHCNH- \right]_m + CO_2 \quad (B)$$

$$R = \quad \text{C}_6\text{H}_3(CH_3)_2$$

are for use with a copolyester having an average molecular weight of 2000–3000 and a hydroxyl number of 55–60. Two hundred g. of the polyester is placed in a 1 l. three-necked flask equipped with stirrer, condenser with drying tube, and nitrogen inlet. To the flask, flushed with nitrogen, is added two molar equivalents of methylene bis(4-phenylisocyanate) (Preparation 47), based on the number of moles of polyester used as derived from its observed molecular weight. The mixture is stirred vigorously at 80°C. under nitrogen for 3 hr. It is then cooled to room temperature and 500 ml. of dry dimethylformamide is added. The mixture is brought into solution as rapidly as possible by stirring at room temperature. Another 100 ml. of dimethylformamide, containing a quantity of water equivalent in moles to one-half the number of moles of diisocyanate used, is added. The over-all stoichiometry is: 1 mole polyester + 2 moles diisocyanate + 1 mole water. The resulting viscous solutions may be cast and dried in a vacuum oven at 50°C. to give elastomeric films, which may be somewhat tacky. The final film also may become insoluble after heating.

A low molecular weight **poly(propylene oxide) terminated with hydroxyls may be used to prepare foamed polymers** by reactions related to those of the two preceding examples. The polyether glycol is caused to react with excess diisocyanate, then treated with water. The foaming agent is the carbon dioxide liberated when water reacts with the free isocyanate groups in the prepolymer mixture (121). The foam effect is caused by the trapping of the gas in the polymeric mass. Polymerization reactions of this variety are used to make some of the widely employed urethane foam products.

99. Preparation of a Resilient Polyurethane Foam from Poly(propylene oxide) Glycol and 2,4-Tolylenediisocyanate (122)

In the following preparation, amounts specified correspond to the use of a poly(propylene oxide) glycol of molecular weight 2000, a hydroxyl number of 56.1, and an equivalent weight of 1000. If the poly(propylene oxide) glycol actually used has a different hydroxyl number of molecular weight, suitable corrections must be made in the amounts or reactants that follow.

A 500 ml. resin kettle equipped with stirrer, condenser with drying tube, thermometer, and gas inlet is flushed with nitrogen, and in it is placed 200 g. of poly(propylene oxide) glycol. Water is added, if necessary, to bring the total water content to 0.8 g. If the original water content of the polyether glycol is not known, and a water analysis cannot be conveniently carried out, the polyether glycol can be dried by heating to 160°C. under nitrogen at a pressure of 1 mm. or less for a period of 3–4 hr. To the dried macroglycol is then added 0.8 g. water. The macroglycol–water mixture is stirred and heated for 30 min. at 30–35°C. with a heating mantle. This and all subsequent operations must be carried out under nitrogen.

With continued stirring, but with removal of the heat source, 29.4 g. of 2,4-tolylenediisocyanate is added. This is an amount calculated to give an NCO/OH ratio of 1.25 and an NCO/H_2O ratio of 1.00. The reaction which occurs is slightly exothermic. After 30 min., the temperature is raised at the rate of about 2°C./min. to 120°C. ± 3°C., where it is maintained for 90 min. The mixture is then cooled to 80°C. If the molecular weight and hydroxyl number of the macroglycol used are not as stated for this preparation, the calculations for the amount of diisocyanate used are given by:

A. Wt. of diisocyanate (DI) for OH reaction = [(wt. of diol)/(equiv. wt. of diol)] × equiv. wt. of DI × 1.25.

B. Wt. of DI for reaction with H_2O present = [(wt. of water)/(equiv. wt. of H_2O)] × equiv. wt. of DI.

The sum of *A* and *B* is the required amount of diisocyanate. For the macrodiol stipulated above, this is 29.4 g. (The equivalent weight of the diisocyanate is 87; of water, 9.) At this point, a second addition of 2,4-tolylenediisocyanate is necessary to bring the total isocyanate content of the mixture to the desired level of 9.5%. In order to do this, the isocyanate content of the first reaction product must be determined, as follows.

Weigh about 0.5 g. of polymer from the resin kettle to the nearest milligram and transfer to a dry 250 ml. Erlenmeyer flask. Add 25 ml. dry toluene and stir magnetically for 5 min. to dissolve the polymer. Add 25.0 ml. of $0.1N$ butylamine in toluene (prepared as a primary standard from distilled butylamine and dry toluene) and continue stirring for 15 min. Add 100 ml. isopropyl alcohol and 4–6 drops of bromophenol blue indicator solution. Titrate with $0.1N$ HCl to a yellow-green endpoint. Run a blank including all reagents, but omitting the sample.

% NCO = [(ml. HCl for blank − ml. HCl for sample)
$$\times \text{ (normality of HCl)} \times 4.202]/[\text{weight of sample}]$$

In the present example, the NCO content of the polymer at the present stage should be about 1.5–1.8%. The amount of diisocyanate needed to bring the total isocyanate content to 9.5% would be about 45 g., and is obtained from the expression:

Wt. of diisocyanate to be added =
$$[(z - y)/(48.3 - z)] \times \text{ (wt. of polymer)}$$

where z = % NCO desired (9.5 in this experiment); and y = % NCO in polymer, determined as above.

Weight of polymer in this experiment, at the end of the reaction of the first amount of diisocyanate added, is about 229.4 g.

The amount of diisocyanate so determined is added to the reaction mixture at 80°C. Stirring is continued for 30 min. while the temperature is allowed to fall to 40°C. The product at this point, usually termed the prepolymer, is ready for the subsequent foaming step. The prepolymer may be safely stored under nitrogen at room temperature for 6 months or more.

Foaming can be carried out in a large beaker or other suitable container. It is suggested that small amount be tried initially to estimate the volume of the vessel needed to contain the foamed product. A blend of the following relative amounts is made at room temperature under nitrogen:

    100 parts prepolymer having 9.5% NCO
    0.5 part silicone oil, 50 centistokes (as Dow Corning DC-200)
    1.0 part *N*-methylmorpholine
    0.3 part triethylamine

To this mixture is added 2.25 parts of water (110% of theory). A foam results having a density of about 2.5 lb./cu. ft.

The following two preparations illustrate the use of a diamine in chain extension.

100. Preparation of Elastomer from Polycaprolactone Trimer Glycol Capped with Methylene Bis(4-phenylisocyanate) and Extended with Ethylenediamine

To 120.9 g. (0.05 mole) of the trimer glycol described above (cooled to 40–45°C.) is added 25.0 (0.1 mole) of methylenebis(4 phenylisocyanate). The mixture is stirred under nitrogen at 90–95°C. for 1 hr., then cooled to 75–80°C. and held for 2–3 hr. The theoretical isocyanate (NCO) analysis for the methylenebis(4 phenylisocyanate) capped trimer is 2.88%. The capped trimer is very viscous at room temperature, but flows readily at 75–80°C.

To 30 g. (0.0089 mole) of the above capped trimer is added 130 ml. of dry dimethylacetamide at room temperature. To this dilute prepolymer solution is added gradually with stirring a 1 molar ethylenediamine solution in DMAc. A viscous solution (about 2000 poises) is obtained after adding about 8–9 ml. of extender solution; further addition may cause gelation. The viscous polymer solution obtained is degassed at 75–80°C. for 2 hr. in a steam-heated oven. Clear, tough films may be cast in the usual way.

101. Preparation of Elastomer from Polycaprolactone (2000) Capped with Methylene Bis(4-phenylisocyanate) and Extended with Hydrazine

To cap the polycaprolactone glycol, 37 g. is mixed with 9 g. of methylene bis(4-phenylisocyanate) and the mixture is stirred under nitrogen at 80–90°C. for 1 hr. The resulting viscous material is diluted with 175 ml. of dimethylacetamide. To this solution, at room temperature, is slowly added stock solution of hydrazine in dimethylacetamide. This solution is prepared by adding 3.3 g. of hydrazine to 100 ml. of dimethylacetamide. The exact amount cannot be specified, but will be in the range of 14–15 ml. A good guide is solution viscosity. Addition should stop when the solution viscosity reaches about 2000 poises; if too much hydrazine is added a gel will form. At 2000 poises, clear tough films can be cast in the usual way.

The majority of commercial activity in polyurethanes is presently in flexible and rigid foams, with elastic fibers (spandex) accounting for a smaller, but well-publicized, poundage. Another important phase of polyurethane technology is the solid, cast elastomer. The chemistry is essentially like that of the other polyurethane categories, chain extension of lower molecular weight flexible chain segments primarily through urethane links. No blowing agent is added or generated, of course. The following example is based on a polyester soft segment from ε-caprolactone and methyl-ε-caprolactone; the mixed lactones reduce the tendency to crystallization. The use of caprolactones as the base for the polyester segment is said to provide advantages over diol-diacid polyesters in improved batch-to-batch reproducibility, as well as improved physical properties and processing characteristics.

The following structures are idealized and do not include crosslinking reactions of isocyanate with urethane —NH.

102. Preparation of a Solid, Cast Polyurethane Elastomer from a Polyester Based on Caprolactone (123)

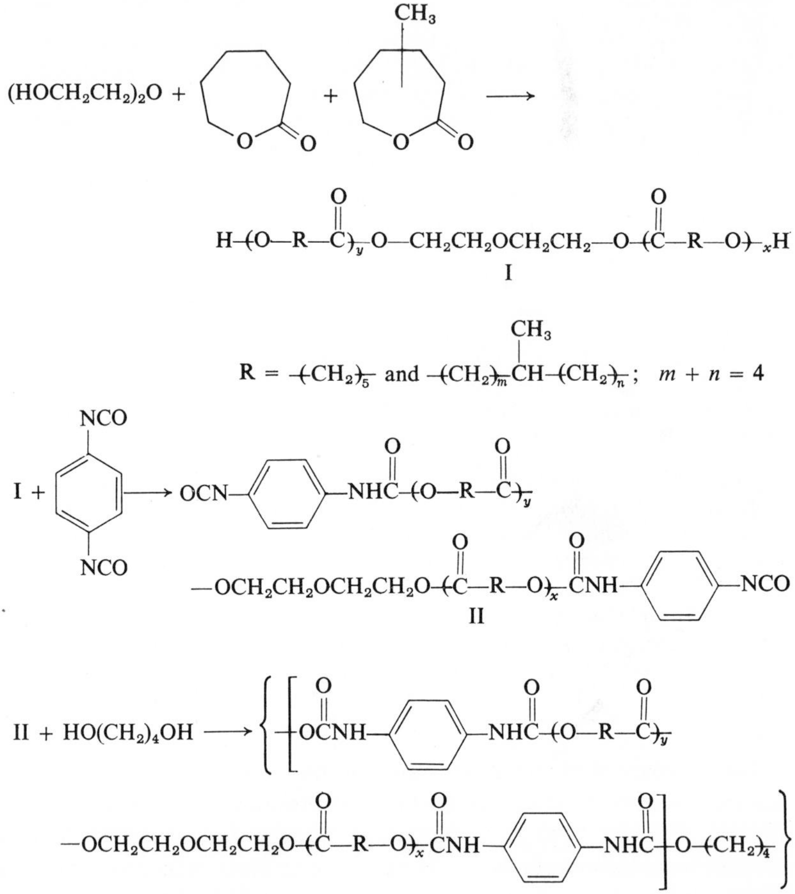

$$R = -(CH_2)_5- \text{ and } -(CH_2)_m-\overset{\displaystyle CH_3}{\underset{\displaystyle |}{CH}}-(CH_2)_n-; \quad m + n = 4$$

A 4 l. resin flask is charged with 191 g. (1.80 moles) of diethylene glycol, 1110 g. (8.67 moles) of methyl-ε-caprolactone, 2300 g. (20.18 moles of ε-caprolactone, and 200 ml. of benzene. The flask is fitted with an air stirrer, jacketed thermocouple, condenser, and Dean-Stark water trap, and nitrogen inlet tube, and is heated by a mantle. The mixture is stirred and heated to reflux under a nitrogen stream sufficient to produce an inert blanket. Residual water is removed by azeotropic distillation, thus reducing the possibility that it will cleave the lactone ring and form hydroxycaproic acid. After removal of the water, the benzene is distilled off until a reaction temperature of 190°C. is reached. This allows the polymerization reaction to proceed under anhydrous conditions. Benzoyl chloride (2.0 g.) is then added and the heating continued at 190°C. for 8–10 hr. until an acid number less than 1.0 is reached and the refractive index of the batch becomes constant. (Acid number determinations can be made only near the end of the polymerization reaction, as the alcoholic potassium hydroxide solution normally used tends to open the lactone ring, giving an unstable endpoint.) The residual benzene and unreacted lactone monomers are then stripped out by vacuum distillation. The finished ester is cooled. The hydroxyl number is about 56 ± 1.5, the acid number is 1.0, and the molecular weight is about 2000, the viscosity is about 3000 cp. at 25°C.

A 4 l. resin flask is charged with 600 g. (3.75 moles) of p-phenylene diisocyanate and 2.0 g. of benzoyl chloride. The flask is fitted with a stirrer, nitrogen inlet tube, reflux condenser, and heating mantle. A nitrogen stream sufficient to produce an inert blanket is introduced. The diisocyanate is melted and held at a temperature of 135°C. Agitation of the reaction mixture is started. Rapidly, 3380 g. of the polyester, above, preheated to 80–93°C. is added to the melted diisocyanate. The heating mantle is dropped and the exotherm temperature not allowed to go above 135°C. Agitation is continued until a reaction temperature of 85–92°C. is reached. The finished prepolymer is then transferred into a wide-mouth jar, and the top of the container flushed with dry nitrogen and sealed. This prepolymer is now ready for chain extension with a suitable difunctional curing agent. The viscosity of the prepolymer is about 28,000 cp. at 25°C.

With both components at room temperature, sufficient dry 1,4-butanediol is added to a weighed amount of the above prepolymer so that the OH/NCO mole ratio is 0.85. The NCO content of the prepolymer can be determined as in Preparation 99. The mixture is blended by hand mixing with a spatula and then thoroughly stirred by means of an air-driven stirrer. Where a casting formulation of extremely low viscosity is required, the prepolymer may be heated to 50–65°C. to facilitate rapid mixing with little loss of working life noted. The mixture of prepolymer and diol is degassed in a vacuum of 1–2 mm. of Hg, then poured into open-faced slab and button molds which are treated with a mold-release agent and preheated to approximately 80–90°C. The liquid resin is again degassed by vacuum, then cured in a forced draft oven at 135°F. for 8 hr.

The cured elastomer is crosslinked through reaction of the NCO in excess of that required for the curing reaction with diol; the former react with in-chain urethane NH to form allophanate links. Typical properties are: tensile strength, 3700 p.s.i.; elongation, 600%; compression set, 46%; and, tear strength, 269 lb./in.

Elastomers can be produced from macroglycols capped with 2 moles of a diisocyanate by methods not involving addition of a difunctional material such as water or a diamine. For example, elimination of CO_2 by use of the phospholene oxide catalyst described in Chapter 6.

$$OCN\!\sim\!\!NCO \longrightarrow [-N\!\!=\!\!C\!\!=\!\!N\!\sim\!]_n$$

103. Preparation of Preparation of a Polycarbodiimide Elastomer Based on Poly(tetramethylene ether) Glycol (124)

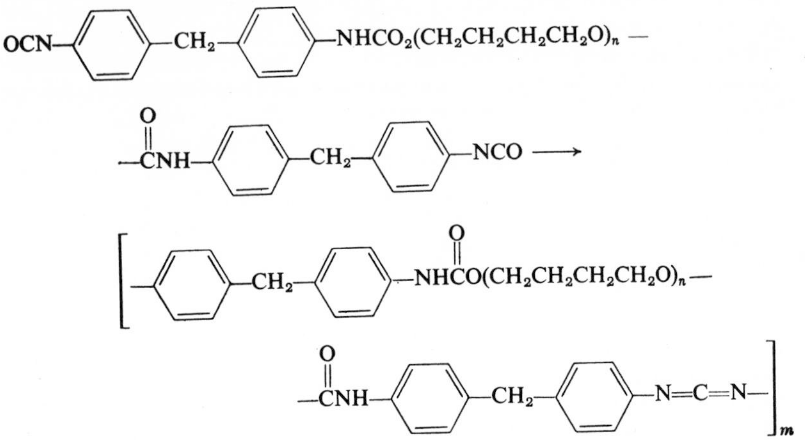

A mixture of 33.7 g. of poly(tetramethylene ether)glycol having an average molecular weight of about 2000 and 8.7 g. of methylenebis-(p-phenyl isocyanate) is heated on a steam bath for 90 min. The capped glycol is diluted with 200 ml. of xylene containing 0.1 g. of the preferred phospholene oxide catalyst. The mixture is refluxed and stirred for 1 hr. to give a very viscous solution. The viscous solution may be cast onto a glass plate, and the solvent evaporated. A clear, very tough, snappy sheet of an elastomer is obtained. This material may be elongated 600% or more and shows good recovery.

In a similar experiment, 145 g. of poly(tetramethylene ether) glycol with an average molecular weight of 3400 was capped with 171 g. of 2,4-tolylene diisocyanate on the steam bath for 2 hr. The cooled product is transferred to a Werner-Pfleiderer mixer, where the mass is blended at 80–100°C. for 4 hr. with 0.8 g. of the preferred phospholene oxide catalyst. The tough, rubbery mass which results is milled on a rubber mill to give a rough sheet. This product, molded under pressure for 1 hr. at 232°C., produces a slab of elastomer with the following properties at room temperature: tensile strength, 2400 p.s.i.; elongation, 500%; modulus at 300% elongation, 486 p.s.i.

The polycarbodiimide elastomer described in the preceding experiment has surprisingly good properties, despite the fact there are no hydrogen bonds, which are normally considered to be the "tie points" in the usual urethane–urea block polymer. It is probable that here the tie points are transient crosslinks of the type

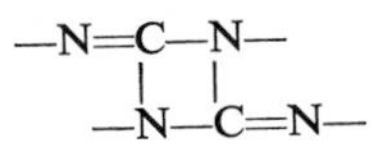

$$\begin{array}{c} -N{=}C-N- \\ \quad | \quad | \\ -N-C{=}N- \end{array}$$

Other nonhydrogen bonded elastomers have been described. One example is one in which the system is held together (i.e., chain slippage is prevented) by a very bulky hard segment. The preparation of such an elastomer is described in the next two experiments.

104. Preparation of 4,4′-Norbornylidene Bis(2,6-dichlorophenol) (125)

A 5 l., three-necked flask is fitted with a sweep, stirrer, a thermometer, and a water-cooled condenser. The top of the condenser is connected to a water trap to remove any HCl fumes that come off. To the flask are added 385 g. (3.5 moles) of distilled 2-norbornanone (b.p. 169–171°C.; m.p. 80–90°C.), 1320 g. (14 moles) of phenol, 2220 ml. of concentrated HCl, and 18 ml. of 3-mercaptopropionic acid. The mixture is then stirred at 50°C. for 7 hr. During the reaction, the product separates as pink balls about the size of small peas.

The mixture is allowed to stand overnight at room temperature, and the aqueous phase is decanted. The product is washed with water several times on a filter, then, while still moist, it is dissolved in 2500 ml. of hot acetic acid, treated with decolorizing carbon, filtered using a filter aid, and heated to about 100°C. Hot water (about 90°C.) is slowly added to the solution with stirring until crystallization begins. This requires 2500–2800 ml. of water. After crystallization is complete and the mixture cooled, the bisphenol is collected and washed with 50% aqueous acetic acid and with water, and dried. The product weighed 868 g. (83% yield, calculated as the hydrate).

If the bisphenol has a pink cast, it is dissolved in hot acetic acid (3 ml./g.), treated with an equal amount of hot water, and allowed to crystallize. It is then collected, washed with 50% aqueous acetic acid and water, and dried. The recovery from recrystallization is 90–95%. The bisphenol, small colorless prisms, melts at 177–179°C., and is a hydrate.

The unsolvated bisphenol is obtained by dissolving the hydrated compound in hot xylene–acetone (acetone is added to improve the solubility), removing the water as an azeotrope, and allowing the bisphenol to crystallize. It melts at 199–200°C.

A 2 l., three-necked flask is fitted with a stirrer, thermometer, gas inlet tube, and condenser. A glass tube extending 3–4 in. beneath the surface of the water in a small flask is connected to a trap, which is connected to the top of the condenser. A lecture bottle (small cylinder) of chlorine on a balance is connected to a bubbler containing H_2SO_4, which is attached to a trap connected to the gas inlet tube.

4,4′-(2-Norbornylidene)diphenol hydrate (149 g., 0.50 mole) and acetic acid (800 ml.) are placed in the flask. While the mixture is stirred, it is heated to 40°C. for about 10 min. The heat was then removed, and chlorine is passed in at such a rate that no bubbles are emitted under the water at the other end of the system. Since the reaction is slightly exothermic, it is necessary to cool the mixture occasionally with a water bath; the temperature is held as close to 45°C. as possible. During the chlorine addition, all of the bisphenol dissolves. In the later stages, the product begins to crystallize. The total amount of chlorine added is 149 g. (2.1 moles). Stirring is continued while the mixture cools to room temperature. The product is collected and thoroughly washed once with cool acetic acid. After drying, the chlorinated bisphenol weighs about 171 g. (82% yield). It consists of small white crystals melting at 182–184°C. When it is recrystallized from 1,2-dichlorethane (3 ml./g.), the recovery is about 81% and the melting point was 183–184°C.

105. Preparation of Polycarbonate Elastomer (126)

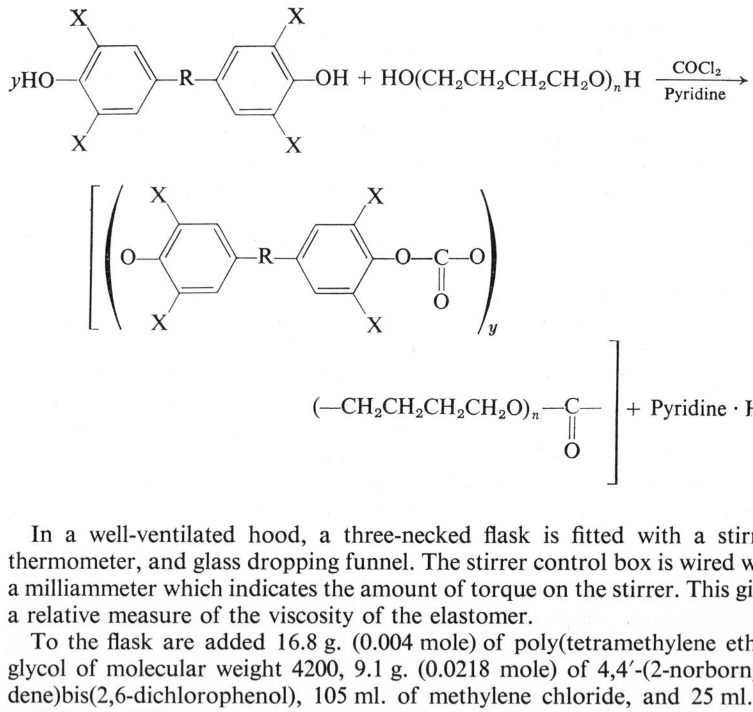

In a well-ventilated hood, a three-necked flask is fitted with a stirrer, thermometer, and glass dropping funnel. The stirrer control box is wired with a milliammeter which indicates the amount of torque on the stirrer. This gives a relative measure of the viscosity of the elastomer.

To the flask are added 16.8 g. (0.004 mole) of poly(tetramethylene ether) glycol of molecular weight 4200, 9.1 g. (0.0218 mole) of 4,4′-(2-norbornylidene)bis(2,6-dichlorophenol), 105 ml. of methylene chloride, and 25 ml. of pyridine. A 10% phosgene stock solution in methylene chloride is added to the rapidly stirred reaction mixture from a graduated dropping funnel. The temperature is maintained at 20–30°C. by means of a water bath. Thickening of the elastomer solution is indicated by the milliammeter attached to the stirrer control box. Slow addition of the phosgene solution is continued until the meter shows no further build-up; usually the mixture has wrapped around the stirrer. The volume of phosgene solution used is about 29 ml. (10–30 molar excess of phosgene is usually required). Water is added and the elastomer is diluted with methylene chloride. The solution is stirred with dilute hydrochloric acid and then washed with a large quantity of water to remove pyridine hydrochloride. After the aqueous layer is separated, 1.0 g. of antioxidant (an alkylated phenol) is added to the solution. The elastomer is precipitated in 50:50 acetone–methanol solution and dried overnight in a vacuum oven at 60°C. The inherent viscosity of the elastomers in chloroform is about 3.

VI. High Temperature Polymers

One of the most rapidly growing areas of polymer chemistry is synthesis of polymers which are tractable, yet which will withstand very high temperatures. Work has been directed toward both organic and inorganic structures, but greater success has been met with organic materials, with lower density and greater flexibility and toughness.

The impetus for this work has been principally for military and space age needs for films, fibers, fabrics, and plastics in general that would withstand temperatures greater than the currently available array of products. Several products are commercially available, for example, Nomex* is an all-aromatic polyamide obtainable as fiber and paper, while Kapton* is a polyimide, obtainable commercially as a film. Teflon* has been available for sometime, and the so-called Black Orlon*, a pyrolyzed polyacrylonitrile, has been known for many years (see Preparation in Chapter 4). It has limited utility, however.

In general, a necessary characteristic for a tough thermally stable polymer is a high degree of aromaticity. The following examples are illustrative. The first series of experiments leads to a novel alternating all-aromatic copolyamide.

106. Preparation of *N,N'-m*-Phenylenebis(*m*-nitrobenzamide) (127,128)

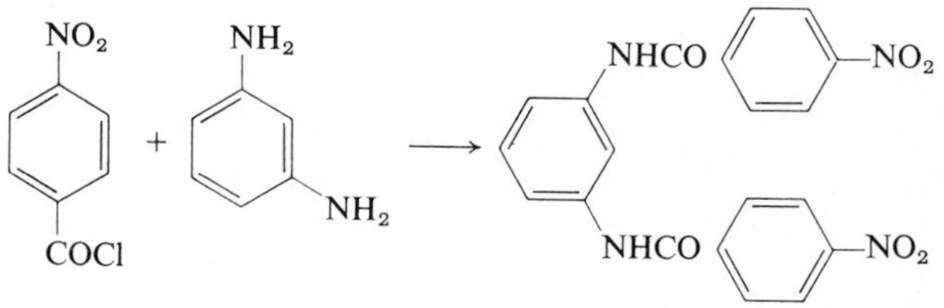

A solution of 0.4 mole (74.23 g.) of *m*-nitrobenzoyl chloride dissolved in 80 ml. of tetrahydrofuran is poured all at once into a Waring Blendor jar containing 0.2 mole (21.6 g.) of *m*-phenylenediamine and 0.4 mole (16.00 g.) of sodium hydroxide in 400 ml. of ice-cold water. The reaction mixture is blended for 5 min. and filtered with suction. The product is washed with

* Registered trademarks of the du Pont Company.

dilute hydrochloric acid, dilute sodium carbonate, and water. The product is dried for 1 hr. at 120°C. The dried product is dissolved in dimethylacetamide, and decolorizing carbon is added. The colorizing carbon is filtered, and the product is precipitated from the filtrate with methanol. The product is filtered with suction and dried. The melting point is 267–269°C.

107. Preparation of N,N′-m-Phenylenebis(m-aminobenzamide) (127,128)

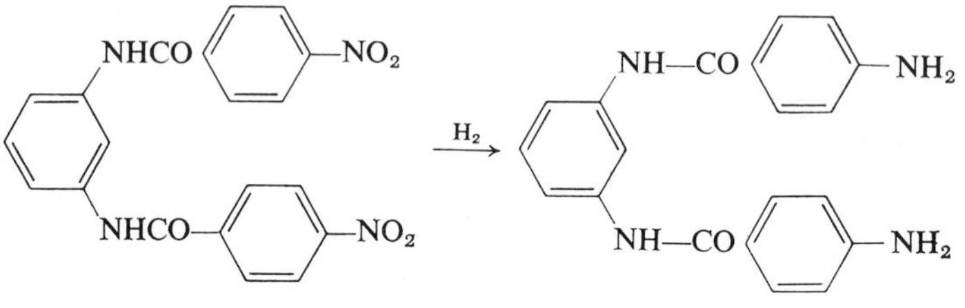

N,N′-m-Phenylenebis(m-nitrobenzamide) (0.1 mole, 40.6 g.) is dissolved in dimethylacetamide, and approximately 1 g. of 5% Pd on carbon is added. The solution is placed in a Parr low-pressure reaction apparatus at 60–65°C. Hydrogen is applied to the apparatus until no further drop in pressure is observed. The reaction is complete in approximately one hour. The catalyst is filtered by passing the solution through a fine sintered glass funnel. The product is precipitated as the dihydrochloride from the filtrate with an excess of dilute (18%) hydrochloric acid. The dihydrochloride is filtered with suction and dried. The dried dihydrochloride is heated in acetone to dissolve any unreacted dinitro compound, refiltered, and dried. The dihydrochloride is added to a solution of sodium carbonate. The product is filtered with suction, washed with water, and dried. The melting point obtained was 212–214°C., the product should be pure enough for the next step.

108. Preparation of Ordered Aromatic Copolyamide (127,128)

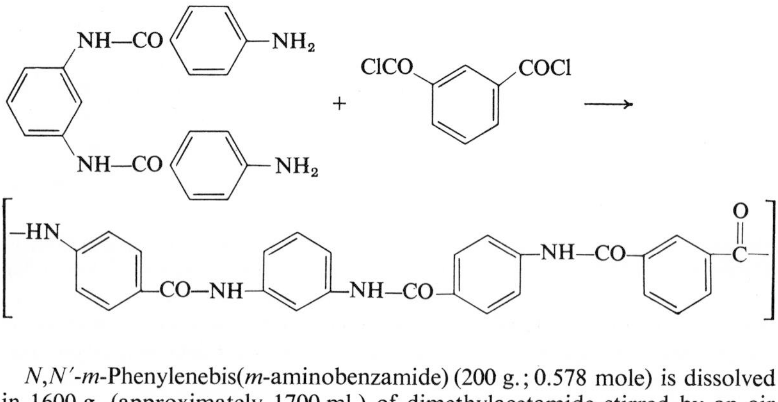

N,N′-m-Phenylenebis(m-aminobenzamide) (200 g.; 0.578 mole) is dissolved in 1600 g. (approximately 1700 ml.) of dimethylacetamide stirred by an air stirrer in a 3 l. resin pot. Liquid isophthaloyl chloride is added in portions from a weighing pipet until a clear solution is obtained in a spot test with dimethylaminobenzaldehyde, which gives a yellow color with aromatic amine end groups. About 122 g. of isophthaloyl chloride will be needed; theroetical amount is 117 g. The solution temperature is maintained between 0–25°C. during addition of the isophthaloyl chloride by keeping the solution in a Dry Ice bath. Lithium hydroxide is added to the solution until a green color is obtained with bromophenol blue (pH = 3.0–4.6). The polymer is precipitated into water. The inherent viscosity (0.5 g./100 mole, 30°C.) obtained in dimethylacetamide with 4% dissolved LiCl is about 2.2. Tough films may be cast from solution.

Aliphatic polybenzimidazoles are not high temperature polymers (see Preparation 18); however, all-aromatic polybenzimidazoles are; a series has been described by Marvel in a number of papers (129,130).

109. Preparation of Poly[2,2′(m-phenylene)-5,5′(6,6′-benzimidazole)] (129,130)

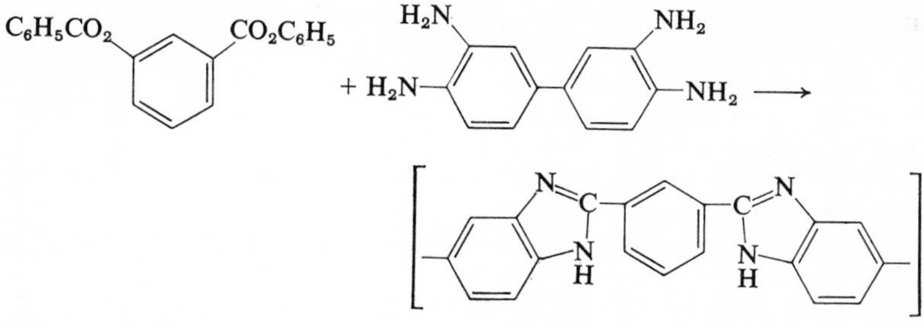

In a 1 l. one-neck flask equipped with nitrogen bleed, distillation head, condenser and vacuum line, 20.20 g. (0.094 mole) 3,3′-diaminobenzidine and 30.00 g. (0.094 mole) diphenyl isophthalate are mixed dry. After three-fold flushing with nitrogen, the contents are melted under 1 atm. nitrogen using a silicone oil bath set at 220°C. The temperature is raised to 260°C. for 15 min. The bubbling brownish mixture begins to change to a yellow color, and phenol condenses in the distillation receiver. The evacuation from 1 atm. to 5–10 mm. is then accomplished in stages, allowing a chance for the foam to collapse between each application of vacuum. When the polymer has hardened completely to a yellow spongy mass, the vacuum is left on and the temperature raised to 300°C. for 3 hr. After cooling, this "prepolymer" is broken out of the flask and ground to 40 mesh powder. The yield is about 31.0 g. of yellow prepolymer having an inherent viscosity of 0.14 (DMSO).

A large-sized polymer tube with a capillary bleed tube reaching almost to its bottom is charged with 30 g. of the above prepolymer. After evacuation for 1 hr., the system is flushed 4 times with nitrogen and evacuated to 0.25 mm. The nitrogen bleed agitates the powder vigorously. Excessive agitation is prevented by applying the vacuum slowly. After complete evacuation and flushing, the tube is placed in a salt bath at 220°C. The following heating schedule is used: 220°C. 1 hr.; 220–250°C., ½ hr.; 250°C., 3 hr.; 250–300°C.,

1 hr.; 300°C., 3 hr.; 300–350°C., 1 hr.; 350°C., 3 hr.; 350–375°C., ½ hr.; 375°C., 5 hr. The polymer is cooled under nitrogen before removal from the tube. The product is 25.6 g. (90.5%) of orange polybenzimidazole powder having an inherent viscosity (0.5 g./100 mole) of about 1.0 (DMSO).

Polyimides, made from an aromatic diamine and a bisanhydride are thermally quite stable. The first step in the synthesis is the formation of a soluble amide–acid. This is then, for example, cast to a film, and imide formation brought about by heating to elevated temperatures.

110. Preparation of Polypyromellitimide of 4,4′-Diaminodiphenyl Ether (131,132)

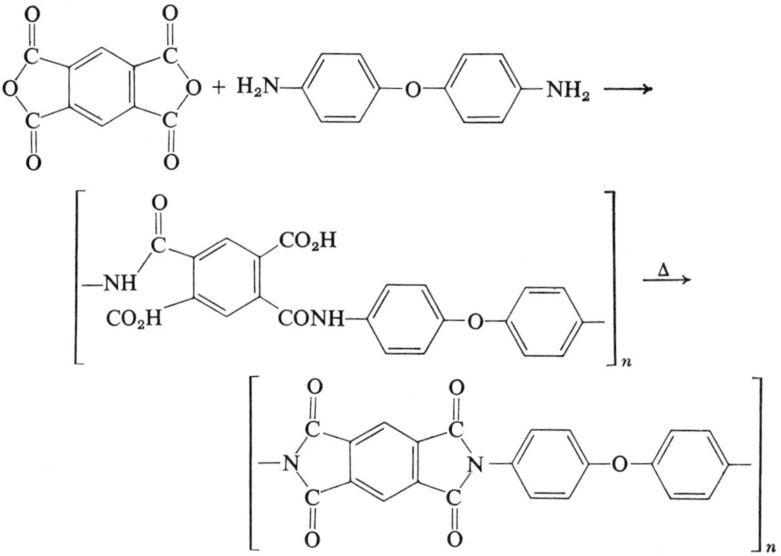

Materials and equipment must be anhydrous. Pyromellitic dianhydride is preferably dried at 180°C. for 24 hr. *in vacuo* with a nitrogen bleed. 4,4′-Diaminodiphenyl ether may be dried under the same conditions, at 100°C., but is usually sufficiently anhydrous. Anhydrous pyridine is prepared by redistillation from maleic anhydride and passage through a column of 5 Å molecular sieves; its water content should not exceed 100 parts per million.

4,4′-Diaminodiphenyl ether (66.7 g.; 0.33 mole) is dissolved in pyridine (665 ml.) in a 2 l. resin flask, with a slow current of dry nitrogen passing over the liquid. The solution is cooled to 10–15°C. Pyromellitic dianhydride (69.8 g.; 0.32 mole; 0.97 equivalents) is added to the solution in four approximately equal portions. Time is allowed after each addition for complete reaction, indicated by the disappearance of all solid particles. External cooling is applied to maintain the temperature below 40°C. The polymerization is completed by careful, portionwise addition of very small amounts of a 10% solution of the dianhydride in pyridine; near the equivalent point the viscosity increases sharply so care must be exercised to avoid formation of a high viscosity gel. This procedure yields typically a 17% solution of polyamic-acid, of inherent viscosity 1.0 (0.5 g./100 mole; in pyridine or dimethylacetamide), and solution viscosity of 2,500 poises. Attractive solvents for this polymerization include dimethylacetamide and N-methylpyrolidone, in addition to pyridine.

Another class of very stable polymers are based on post-reaction of a polyhydrazide. Two examples are given; one, a polyoxadiazole, from a series of papers by Frazer et al., the other an N-phenyl triazole.

111. Preparation of Alternating Copolyhydrazide of Terephthalic and Isophthalic Acids (133)

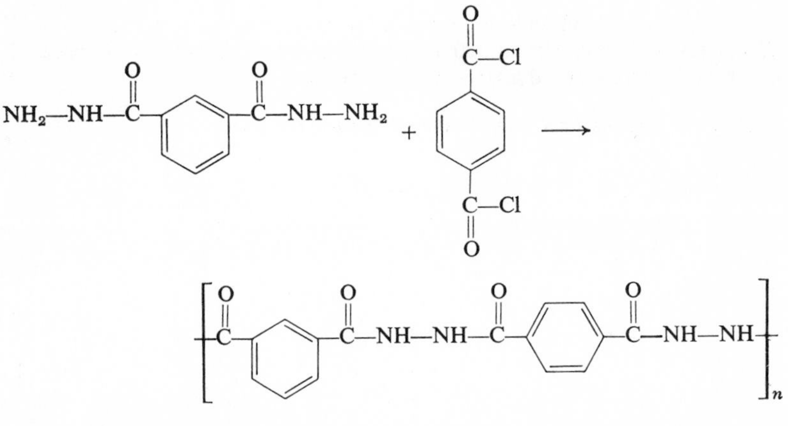

It is very important in the following procedure to avoid all traces of H_2O. Viscosity can then be regulated by moisture content of the solvent.

In a nitrogen filled dry box, 250 ml. of hexamethylphosphoramide (~ 80 ppm. H_2O) and isophthalic dihydrazide (19.10 g., 0.0984 mole) (dried 48 hr. 120°C. at 1 mm.) are placed in a 500 ml. resin kettle fitted with nitrogen bleed, drying tube, air-driven shear stirrer, and stoppered openings for addition of dry solids. The sealed system is transferred to a hood for connection to a nitrogen line and attachment of the shear stirrer to an air motor. The hydrazide is dissolved by stirring at a water bath temperature of 50°C. When solution is complete, the hot water bath is replaced with an ice bath.

After cooling to ice bath temperature, the first portion of terephthaloyl chloride (10 g.) is rapidly added with stirring. After cooling with stirring for ½ hr., a second portion (10 g.) of terephthaloyl chloride is added (total 20.0 g., 0.094 mole). The solution rapidly becomes thick and excessively difficult to stir. After 1 hr. of cooling with stirring the ice bath is removed and slow stirring continued for 1 hr.

The viscous polymer solution is poured into distilled water, with rapid stirring in a Waring Blendor. The polymer is collected on a sintered glass filter, washed twice in the Waring Blendor with water and finally with methanol. After drying overnight at 100°C. in a vacuum oven under nitrogen, polymer of η_{inh} of 1.8 (0.5 g./100 moles, hexamethylphosphoramide, 30°C.) and a PMT of 390°C. is obtained.

112. Preparation of Preparation of a Polyoxadiazole (134)

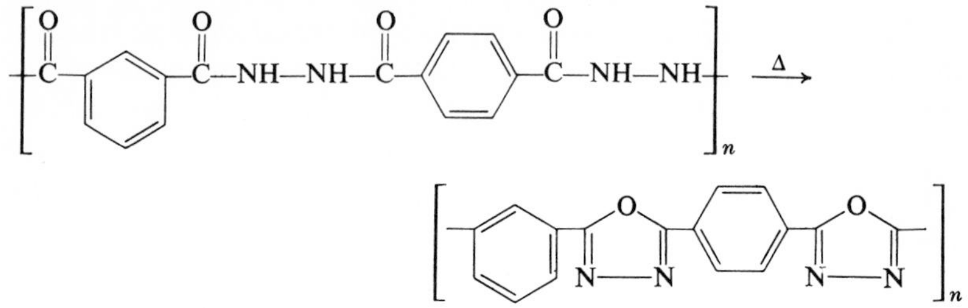

The dried polyhydrazide is heated in a nitrogen filled oven for 24 hr. at 275°C. followed by 24 hr. at 320°C. The product is a golden-yellow material, η_{inh} 1.0 (H_2SO_4) which does not melt or degrade below 450°C.

113. Preparation of a Poly(N-phenyl triazole) (135)

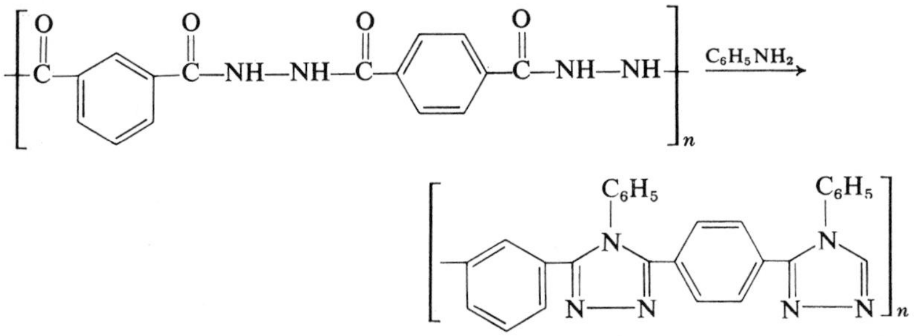

A 3000 g. portion of polyphosphoric acid (PPA) is heated to 150°C. and stirred under dry nitrogen. Aniline, 751 g. (8.1 moles), is added dropwise with stirring at such a rate that the temperature of the reaction mixture does not exceed 190°C. The temperature of the resulting solution is adjusted to 175°C. and 97.2 g. of poly(m-,p-phenylene) hydrazide (η_{inh} about 3.0) then added. The mixture is stirred and heated at 174–176°C. for 140 hr., during which time the polyhydrazide dissolves to form a homogeneous solution. The clear, light-orange, fairly viscous solution is poured hot into deionized water in two operating 1 gal. Waring Blendors. Sodium hydroxide pellets are added cautiously to the resulting hot slurries until the agglomeration points are reached. The mixtures are filtered and the combined residue reslurried in a Waring Blendor, first in 5% sodium hydroxide solution and then twice in deionized water. The residue is then extracted continuously with hot ethanol in Soxhlet extractors until the effluent liquid is colorless. The combined residue is then dried in a vacuum oven at 80–120°C.

There should be no formic acid-insoluble prepolymer present in this product. This may be checked by dissolving 0.2000 g. of the product in 20 ml. of boiling 98–100% formic acid in a centrifuge tube. This solution is cooled and centrifuged. The supernatant solution is decanted and 10 ml. of fresh formic acid added. This mixture is heated to the boil and then filtered through a tared coarse-grade fritted glass filter. The transfer to the filter is aided by additional formic acid wash. The residue is dried on the filter and weighed. The percentage formic acid insoluble product may then be calculated.

The poly(m-,p-phenylene)4-phenyl-1,2,4-triazole obtained from the above described reaction should have a number-average molecular weight of about 28,000. If lower inherent polyhydrazide samples are used, the triazole polymers will have correspondingly lower molecular weights.

Polyquinoxalines represent another class of all-ring heterocyclic polymers.

114. Preparation of 4,4′-Diglyoxalyldiphenyl Ether Dihydrate (136)*

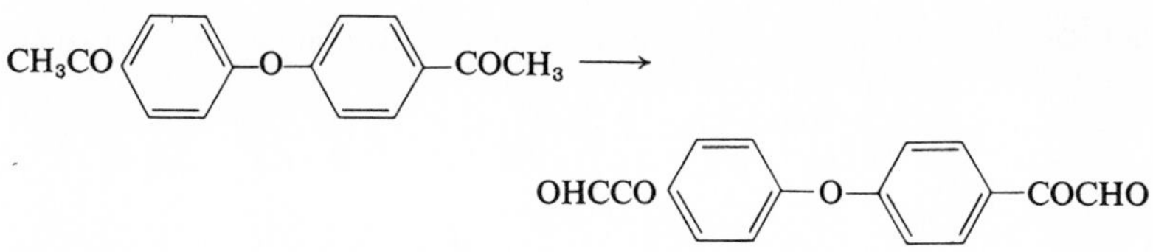

A. 4,4′-Diacetyldiphenyl ether

Anhydrous aluminum chloride, 249.4 g. (1.875 moles), is suspended in 2 l. of tetrachloroethane in a 5 l. three-necked flask, equipped with a reflux condenser, a sealed mercury stirrer, and a dropping funnel. Acetyl chloride, 147 g. (1.875 moles), and 100 g. (0.625 mole) of diphenyl ether are dissolved in 100 ml. of tetrachloroethane and added to the rapidly stirred suspension over a period of 20 min. The temperature is raised to 60°C. on a steam bath and kept at 60°C. for 4 hr. The reaction mixture is then cooled to room temperature and poured carefully into 800 ml. of cold water. The water layer is extracted with four 100 ml. portions of ether; the ether extract is added to the tetrachloroethane layer. The solvent is removed under reduced pressure and on standing a yellow solid crystallizes, m.p. 96–98°C. The yellow solid is recrystallized from 95% ethanol using charcoal to remove the color. The yield of the purified white 4,4′-diacetyldiphenyl ether is about 126 g. (63%) m.p. 98–99°C.

To a solution containing 29.7 g. (0.268 mole) of selenium dioxide dissolved in 150 ml. of dioxane and 4 ml. of water containing 3 drops of hydrochloric acid is added 34 g. (0.134 mole) of 4,4′-diacetyldiphenyl ether. On addition of the diacetyl adduct, the solution turns red and after refluxing for 6 hr., black, indicating the precipitation of selenium. Filtration of the hot reaction

* Our thanks to Professor Stille, Dr. Williamson, and Dr. Arnold for details in Preparations 114–116 not appearing in the reference.

mixture gives a red solution. The dioxane mixture is heated to reflux with 4 g. of charcoal. After filtration a yellow liquid is obtained, and upon addition of water a light tan solid precipitates. The compound is recrystallized from a 50/50 dioxane–water mixture to give about 20 g. of a white solid m.p. 120–121°C.

115. Preparation of 3,3′,4,4′-Tetraminodiphenyl Ether (136)

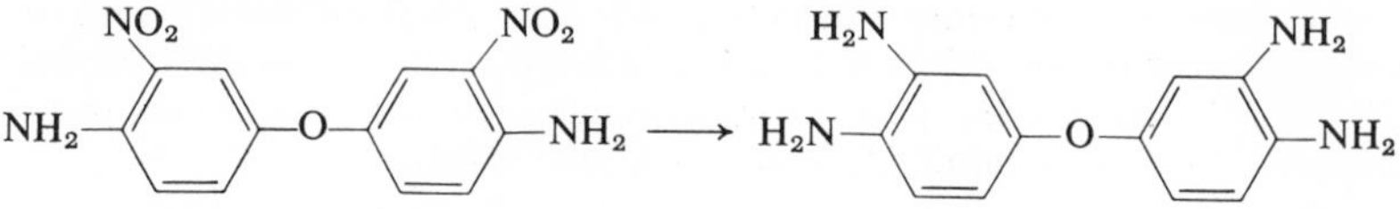

A. 4,4′-Diacetamidodiphenyl Ether

To a solution of 140 g. (0.70 mole) of p-oxydianiline in 500 ml. of glacial acetic acid is added dropwise 173 g. (1.6 moles) of acetic anhydride at such a rate as to maintain a temperature of 50–60°C. The temperature is maintained at 90–100°C. for an additional hour; then the solution is allowed to stand overnight. The precipitate which forms is collected and dried in air, then under reduced pressure for 24 hr. to give 147 g. of 4,4′-diacetamidodiphenyl ether. The filtrate from the above reaction is poured into 1 kg. of ice and the precipitate is collected by filtration and dried under reduced pressure to give an additional 12 g. of acetylated product. The combined yield is about 80%, m.p. 227–228°C.

B. 3,3′-Dinitro-4,4′-diacetamidodiphenyl Ether

To 700 ml. of cold acetic anhydride is slowly added 95 ml. of colorless 70% nitric acid at such a rate to keep the temperature below 10°C. (Extreme Caution!). The acetyl nitrate formed is cooled to 0°C. and 75 g. (0.265 mole) of 4,4′-diacetamidodiphenyl ether is added in small portions while the temperature is maintained between 10–15°C. The yellow mixture is stirred for 30 min. at room temperature and then poured slowly into 3 l. of a 1:1 mixture of ice and water. The yellow precipitate is filtered to give a quantitative yield of 3,3′-dinitro-4,4′-diacetamidodiphenyl ether, m.p. 210–213°C.

C. 3,3′-Dinitro-4,4′-aminodiphenyl Ether

To a solution of 199 g. (0.53 mole) of 3,3′-dinitro-4,4′-diacetamido-diphenyl ether in 1.3 l. of methanol is added a solution of 84 g. of potassium hydroxide in 300 ml. of methanol, dropwise with stirring. After 1 hr., an additional 56 g. of potassium hydroxide in methanol is added and the mixture is stirred for 3 hr. more. The mixture is poured into 5.0 l. of water and an orange solid precipitates which is collected by filtration. The combined precipitate, m.p. 174–177°C., is recrystallized from 95% ethanol to give about 130 g. of 3,3′-dinitro-4,4′-diaminodiphenyl ether.

D. 3,3′-4,4′-Tetraminodiphenyl Ether (VI)

To a warmed, vigorously stirred solution of 240 g. of stannous chloride dihydrate in 500 ml. of concentrated hydrochloric acid is added 46.4 (0.116 mole) of 3,3′-dinitro-4,4′-diaminodiphenyl ether at such a rate as to maintain the temperature at 50–60°C. The mixture is heated to 65–70°C. for 3 hr., and then cooled to $-10°C$. to yield a pink solid. The tetrahydrochloride is collected by filtration and dissolved in 300 ml. of hot water. To the solution is added 300 ml. of concentrated hydrochloric acid. Cooling produces white needles of the tetrahydrochloride salt which are collected and pressed dry under a stream of nitrogen. The salt is then dissolved in water and added dropwise to a stirred solution of 60 g. of sodium hydroxide in 300 ml. of deoxygenated water which is cooled in an ice bath. The gray-white precipitate (45 g.) is collected by filtration under nitrogen, washed with cold water and dried under reduced pressure to yield 31 g. (84%) of product m.p. 150–151°C. The tetraamine is purified by sublimation before each polymerization.

The polymer synthesis is carried out in two stages. The first consists of a solution polymerization, under a nitrogen atmosphere, in hexamethylphosphoramide. The hexamethylphosphoramide is freshly distilled under nitrogen before use into the reaction vessel. Monomers should always be quickly transferred from a nitrogen atmosphere to the nitrogen swept reaction flask. The work-up of the polymers is to first carry out a precipitation with methanol and then an extraction with benzene by means of a Soxhlet extractor to remove any occluded hexamethylphosphoramide.

116. Preparation of Poly[2,2′-(4,4′-oxydiphenylene)-6,6′-oxydiquinoxaline] (136)

To a solution containing 5.682 g. (0.01785 mole) of 4,4′-diglyoxaldiphenyl ether dihydrate dissolved in 100 ml. of hexamethylphosphoramide is added 4.111 g. (0.01785 mole) of 3,3′,4,4′-tetraaminodiphenyl ether dissolved in 70 ml. of hexamethylphosphoramide. The weighing of the monomers and the monomer additions are carried out under a nitrogen atmosphere in a dry box. After stirring in the dry box for 30 min. at 30°C., the flask is heated to 100°C. 2.5 hr., then overnight at 160°C.

The polymer is precipitated by the addition of 700 ml. of absolute methanol. The yellow polymer is washed with methanol and dried under reduced pressure over phosphorus pentoxide. The inherent viscosity is about 0.7 (0.5 g./100 mole, in the reaction solvent, 30°C.).

The polymer is treated to a second-stage high temperature heating cycle after initial polymerization, to complete the cyclization. The polymers are placed in a 50 ml. rotating flask and heated to 375°C. under reduced pressure (0.1 mm.) for 2 hr. Two 8 mm. diameter steel ball bearings are placed in the flask to facilitate mixing.

The so-called **"ladder" type structure,** i.e., a polymer chain in which each unit is held to the next by two bonds instead of one, **provides a further step in thermal stability.** The **polybenzobenzimidazoles** can provide true "ladders," as well as nonladders. The following examples cover two such polymers. The first, based on tetraaminobiphenyl, is not a true ladder, but the second, from tetraaminobenzene, is. Just as in the case of the polyimide, the final product is produced by thermal closure of an intermediate poly(imide-amine).

117. Preparation of a Polybenzobenzimidazole from Pyromellitic Dianhydride and Tetraminobiphenyl (137)

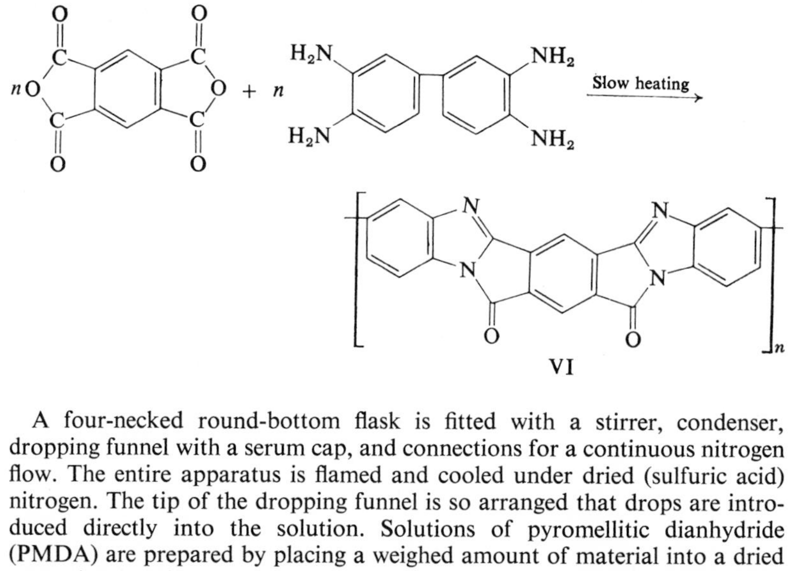

VI

A four-necked round-bottom flask is fitted with a stirrer, condenser, dropping funnel with a serum cap, and connections for a continuous nitrogen flow. The entire apparatus is flamed and cooled under dried (sulfuric acid) nitrogen. The tip of the dropping funnel is so arranged that drops are introduced directly into the solution. Solutions of pyromellitic dianhydride (PMDA) are prepared by placing a weighed amount of material into a dried serum bottle. The requisite volume of solvent is added and the PMDA dissolved. The solution is injected into the dropping funnel. The amine is placed in the flask and dried dimethylacetamide added. The flask is externally cooled with ice water during the polymerization. A typical polymerization requires about 4–5 hr.

In the apparatus described above a solution containing 2.181 g. of pyromellitic dianhydride in 25 ml. of dimethylacetamide is added slowly to a stirring solution of 2.143 g. of 3,3'-diaminobenzidine in 25 ml. of dimethylacetamide at a rate of 20–25 drops/min. After the addition is completed, an aliquot is removed and diluted to 0.5% with dry dimethylacetamide, and the inherent viscosity is determined at 30°C. These viscosities are usually between 1.0 and 1.6. Slight deviation from stoichiometry cause low viscosity, gross gelation, or gel particles.

This solution is concentrated to 10–15% solids under vacuum (0.01 mm.) at room temperature and then the barely pourable mixture is cast on a glass plate in a nitrogen dry box. The plate is heated to 45°C. in a vacuum oven at 1 mm. overnight.

The film can be removed easily (especially when cast from higher viscosity polymer). It is a tough yellow film, soluble in dimethylacetamide. The infrared spectrum shows a complex carbonyl centered at 6.1 μ.

The above film, on heating at 150°C. for 5–8 hr., is converted to a yellow-brown film exhibiting a carbonyl vibration at 5.85 μ. It is then heated at 225°C. overnight and then to 400°C. for 10 min. At this time the carbonyl frequency at 5.85 μ has sharpened considerably and there is essentially no N—H stretching at 3 μ. The dark-red film is creasable, but insoluble.

118. Preparation of 1,2,4,5-Tetraaminobenzene (138)

Tetraaminobenzene tetrahydrochloride is best prepared from *m*-dichlorobenzene by nitration, reaction with ammonia, and reduction. Since this amine is difficult to obtain, a more detailed description of its preparation is given in this part.

The best results are obtained by carrying out the amination in the presence of a mixture of ammonium acetate and an inert, high-boiling solvent, such as nitrobenzene; the reaction is run at 180°C. for 48 hr. in the presence of excess ammonia gas. By pouring the cooled reaction mixture into a controlled amount of methanol, it is possible to isolate pure dinitrodiaminobenzene (m.p. 309–310°C.) in an 88% yield, from unreacted dinitrochlorobenzene (2% yield, m.p. 102–103°C.) and from monoamino–monochlorodinitrobenzene (6% yield, m.p. 176–177°C.).

The tetraamine is obtained by catalytic reduction of dinitrodiaminobenzene in solution in diglyme at 50°C. in the presence of a palladium catalyst on charcoal with hydrogen under a pressure at 50 p.s.i. Most of the tetraamino compound remains adsorbed on the palladium catalyst but can be recovered with 90% yield by pouring the reaction mixture under inert atmosphere into concentrated hydrochloric acid. The tetrahydrochloride is purified by dissolution in distilled water, filtration to separate carbon and palladium chloride, and precipitation in ice-cold concentrated hydrochloric acid.

The liberation of 1,2,4,5-tetraaminobenzene from the tetrahydrochloride is carried out by shaking under nitrogen a cold solution of the tetrahydrochloride in boiled oxygen-free water with an ice-cold 15% sodium hydroxide solution, also in deoxygenated water. The precipitate is filtered with suction under nitrogen, washed with ice-cold ethanol, and finally dried to constant weight at 50°C. at 0.1 mm., and sealed under nitrogen. The yield is about 70%, m.p. 274–276°C.

119. Preparation of Polybenzobenzimidazole from Tetraaminobenzene and Pyromellitic Dianhydride (138)

A 0.85 g. portion of 1,2,4,5-tetraaminobenzene tetrahydrochloride is dissolved in 120 g. of 116% polyphosphoric acid; 0.65 g. of pyromellitic dianhydride is added under nitrogen to the solution and the reaction mixture is heated at 200°C. for 2 hr. The yield of ladder-type polymer is 86%, and the intrinsic viscosity measured in concentrated sulfuric acid is about 1.10.

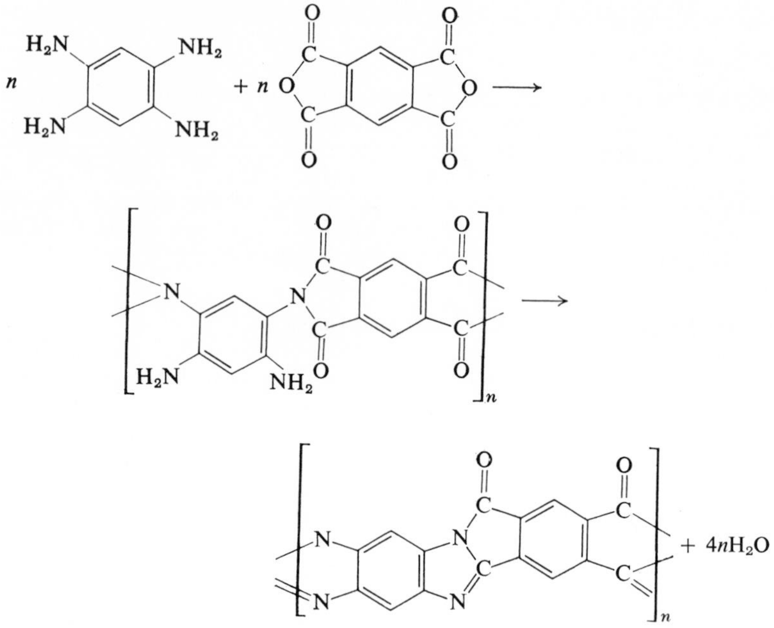

Other examples of polynuclear polymers continue to appear in the literature. Recent examples include a polyphenylpyrazole (139)

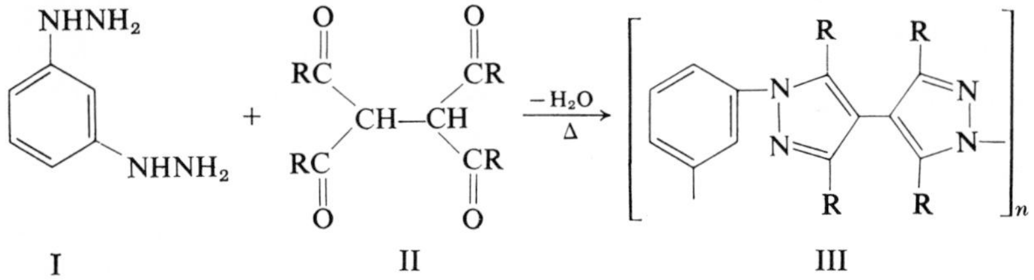

and polybenzimidazo–benzophenanthrolines (140) such as

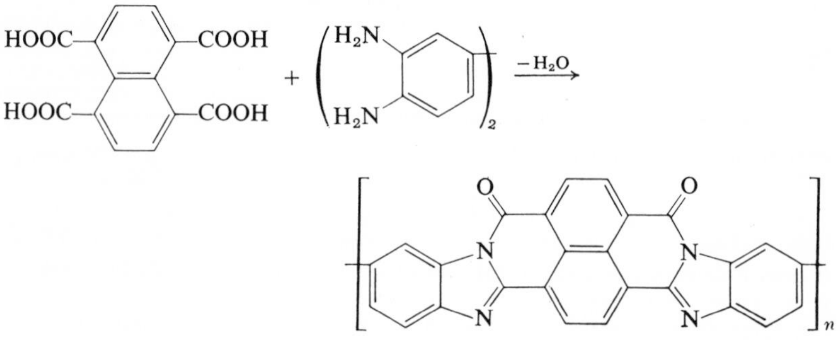

VII. Miscellaneous Condensation Polymers

The condensation of α,α'-dichloroxylene and similar reactive halides with difunctional silylamines leads to the formation of high molecular weight polyamines by elimination of a halosilane. The latter is inert in this system and actually acts as a solvent for the polymer in most cases.

The more obvious route to polyamines through condensation of disecondary diamines with active dihalides has never successfully given high molecular weight polymer because of such difficulties as salt formation with the hydrogen halide formed, leading to reactant imbalances, and, side reaction of the active halide when basic acid acceptors are added. In the silylamine system, the halide is eliminated in a neutral form. This polymerization is catalyzed by ammonium chloride or tetramethylenesulfone, but the function of these materials is unclear.

120. Preparation of Bis- N,N'-(phenyldimethylsilyl)-2-methylpiperazine (141)

$$2Ph(CH_3)_2SiCl + HN\!\!\overset{CH_3}{\diagdown}\!\!NH \longrightarrow Ph(CH_3)_2Si-N\!\!\overset{CH_3}{\diagdown}\!\!N-Si(CH_3)Ph + 2HCl$$

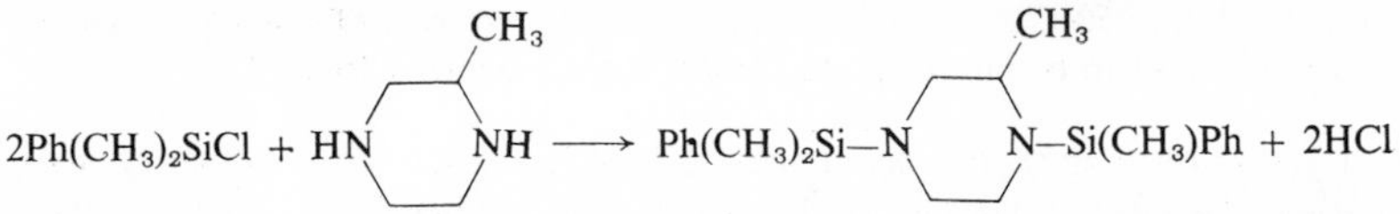

To 100 g. (1.0 mole) 2-methylpiperazine dissolved in 1 l. of dry toluene in a 3 l. flask protected from atmospheric moisture was added 341 g. (2.0 moles) phenyldimethylchlorosilane with stirring. The rate of addition is not critical; it is guided by the exothermic nature of the reaction. A white precipitate forms. When the heat of reaction has subsided, 253 g. (2.5 moles) dry triethylamine is added and stirring is continued 12–15 hr. The precipitate of triethylamine hydrochloride is filtered and the filtrate distilled. The product boils at 198°C./2.8 mm. A second distillation through a spinning band column is usually necessary to get a product of sufficient purity for successful polymerization. The refractive index of the pure material is 1.5417. The yield is about 70%.

121. Poly(1,4-xylylenyl)-2-methylpiperazine (141)

$$Ph(CH_3)_2Si-N\!\!\overset{CH_3}{\diagdown}\!\!N-Si(CH_3)_2Ph + ClCH_2-\!\!\bigcirc\!\!-CH_2Cl \longrightarrow$$

$$\left[\!\!-N\!\!\overset{CH_3}{\diagdown}\!\!N-CH_2-\!\!\bigcirc\!\!-CH_2\!\!-\right] + 2Ph(CH_3)_2SiCl$$

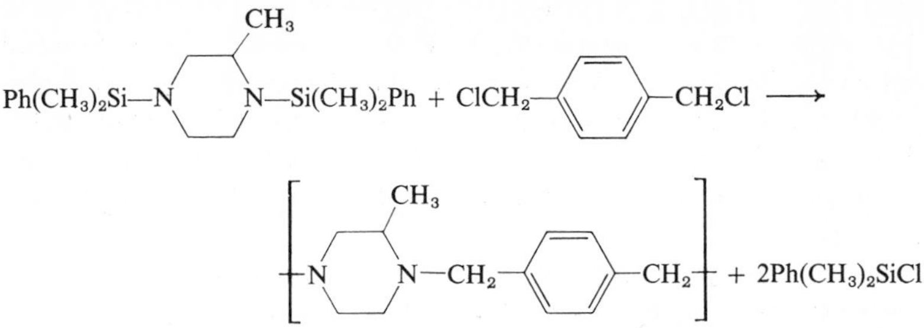

A 200 mole flask is equipped with a short Vigreux column and a nitrogen inlet. The flask is flamed dry, flushed with nitrogen, and to it is added 36.87 g. bis-N,N'-(phenyldimethylsilyl)-2-methylpiperazine and 17.50 g. α,α'-dichloro-p-xylene. The latter can be purified by recrystallization from ethanol. As catalyst, 0.2 g. ammonium chloride is also added. The mixture is then heated in an oil bath at 150°C. for 4–6 hr. under a blanket of nitrogen. An increase in viscosity should be evident after about 1 hr., and at the end of the heating period a highly viscous yellow mass is obtained.

Vacuum is then slowly applied and the phenyldimethylchlorosilane is distilled off, requiring about 10 hr. at 150°C. and 0.1 mm. for thorough removal. The tough, yellow foam is dissolved in chloroform and filtered through a coarse sintered glass funnel lined with glass wool to remove gel particles. The filtrate is concentrated to a fairly viscous solution and poured into a large excess of stirred ethanol in a home blender. The fibrous, nearly white polymer is washed twice more in the blender with ethanol and dried in a vacuum oven at 85°C. overnight. About 10–15 g. of polymer is obtained (50–75%). About equal amounts (2–5 g.) of crosslinked and low molecular weight (unprecipitated) polymer is also formed. The desired polymer is slightly crystalline and melts above 240°C. The intrinsic viscosity in chloroform should be around 1.9, corresponding to a number average molecular weight of about 40,000. Strong films can be cast from chloroform or melt pressed above 250°C. Chloroform is tenaciously retained and requires heating at 150°C., 10.1 mm. for 60 hr. to reduce the Cl content to 0.7%.

It is known that simple aromatic halides react with difficulty with ordinary nucleophiles in common solvents. Substitution in the halide with powerful electron-withdrawing groups, however, considerably enhances their reaction towards basic substances (142).

By taking advantage of this fact, a variety of aromatic polyethers has been prepared by reaction of alkali metal salts of typical dihydric phenols with certain activated aromatic dihalides (143). The choice of solvent is critical. Dimethyl sulfoxide is preferred although certain of the other dipolar aprotic solvents will function. No other type of solvent is known to work. Since this is a classical condensation polymerization of the A—A plus B—B type, the customary control of stoichiometry is necessary.

The disodium salts are generally used and are prepared *in situ* by the addition of exactly 2 moles of 50% caustic per mole of the bisphenol. The water which is present in the system at this point must be removed before addition of the activated dihalide. Otherwise a side reaction, which is believed to involve attack of caustic from hydrolysis of the disodium salt, on the activated dihalide and reactive chain ends, may occur. This upsets monomer stoichiometry and gives rise to inactive chain ends.

The following example is a preparation of the polysulfone polyaryl ether designated by the generic term "polysulfone."

122. Preparation of a Polysulfone from Bisphenol A and Dichlorodiphenyl Sulfone (143)*

Into a 1 l. stainless steel resin kettle, fitted with an inert gas sparge tube, thermocouple, mechanical stirrer, dropping funnel, and take-off to a ca. 6 plate (glass helix) fractionating column connected to a moisture trap and condenser, is placed 51.36 g. (0.225 mole) of high purity bisphenol A such as the UCAR HP grade sold by Union Carbide, 115 g. of dimethyl sulfoxide (DMSO), and 330 g. of chlorobenzene. Glass may be used but severe etching of the vessel is to be expected owing to the caustic nature of the reaction mixture. This can result in the consumption of some of the base needed for the polymerization but if contact times are kept to the minimum, little difficulty will be experienced. (**Caution!** Dimethyl sulfoxide is believed nontoxic. It is known, however, to penetrate body tissue very rapidly and could act as a carrier for more undesirable substances such as chlorobenzene. Handling of solutions throughout should be carried out, therefore, with due respect.)

The mixture is heated to 60–80°C. whereupon a clear solution is obtained. Air is displaced from the system by flushing with nitrogen or argon and exactly 0.450 mole of 50.0% caustic (e.g., 35.86 g. of 50.20% solution) is added with good stirring over about 10 min. In so doing, two liquid phases will appear: one predominantly chlorobenzene, the other disodium salt dissolved in aqueous DMSO.

The system is brought to reflux with inert gas sparging through the reaction mixture. The system must be maintained under an inert gas blanket throughout after the caustic addition to prevent oxidation of aryloxide moieties. Sparging is believed to aid in the removal of volatiles. Water is removed from the system, continuously returning the chlorobenzene that co-distills. In so doing, the temperature of the contents will rise from about 120°C. initially to 140°C. at the conclusion of this step. When this point is reached, most of the water originally present will have distilled and the disodium salt of bisphenol A will appear as a precipitate. Good stirring, of course, is essential particularly during the polymerization step to insure adequate thermal contact. Care must also be taken during dehydration to avoid broadcasting the precipitate much above the liquid level as it will prove inconvenient to effect re-solution of this material later.

* We are grateful to Dr. R. N. Johnson, Union Carbide Corp., for the following synthesis.

Excess azeotrope solvent is distilled from the system until the temperature of the contents reaches 155–160°C. At this point, the precipitate will redissolve with the formation of a very viscous solution. It is believed that at this point only traces of water remain.

A 50% solution of 64.61 g. (0.225 mole) of 4,4′-dichlorodiphenyl sulfone in dry chlorobenzene maintained at 110°C. is added over a period of about 10 min., allowing the excess solvent to distill in so doing sufficiently to hold the material temperature at about 160°C. The temperature must not drop below about 150°C. until the polymerization is well along as sodium-ended low polymer may precipitate on the walls of the vessel. This material which is polymeric is very difficult to redissolve upon heating owing to the familiar solvent migration problem. Too high a temperature during addition of the sulfone and subsequent polymerization is to be avoided as the reaction is mildly exothermic, extremely rapid above 160°C., and excessive solvent decomposition and/or discoloration or even gelation of the reaction may occur. To prevent danger of excessive overheating of the reaction mass, use of oil baths for heating is recommended.

When all the sulfone has been added, polymerization is continued until the desired degree of polymerization is reached. Upon addition of the sulfone, the reaction mixture becomes vividly colored. Orange to yellow but often deep greens are observed. The color is believed due to the formation of the Meisenheimer type π-complex or possibly a charge transfer complex composed of the reactants and the DMSO solvent. A reduced viscosity as measured in chloroform solution (0.2 g./100 mole) at 25°C. of about 1 or higher is reached in about 1 hr. at 160°C. after addition of all the sulfone. This would correspond to a number average molecular weight of about 80,000.

The polymerization may be terminated in a variety of ways, one of which is to pass methyl chloride into the polymerizing mixture when the desired degree of polymerization is reached. The color of the reaction mixture will fade in so doing to a light amber signalling the completion of the termination. The methyl chloride reaction, which is very rapid and efficient, involves the conversion of pendant aryloxide groups to their respective methyl ethers, thus preventing further polymerization.

The viscous polymer solution is then cooled and diluted with about 700 g. of chlorobenzene which provides a solution convenient for workup. The by-product sodium chloride is removed by simple pressure or vacuum filtration and the clear light-amber solution is coagulated in about 3–4 volumes of ethanol. The resulting fluff is dried in a vacuum oven at 135°C. for several hours. The yield is about 90% of theory or higher, depending on the severity of losses during the workup.

The polymer is soluble in dipolar aprotic solvents, cyclic ethers such as THF, polar aromatic solvents, most chlorinated hydrocarbons and some carbonyls such as cyclohexanone. Hazy solutions may be noted upon dissolving in certain of these solvents. The haze which may not develop immediately is due to the precipitation of cyclic oligomers which are crystalline; the polymer is amorphous.

Films may be obtained by casting or by pressing at about 280°C.; the polymer softens at about 200°C. Fibers may be obtained by pulling from the melt.

Dithiols add to nonconjugated diolefins in solution or in emulsion using a free radical catalyst **to give a polythioether** (144). The course of the reaction in all likelihood involves a radical initiated anti-Markownikoff addition of the sulfhydryl to the olefin:

$$R\cdot + -CH_2-SH \longrightarrow -CH_2-S\cdot + RH$$

$$-CH_2-S\cdot + CH_2\!\!=\!\!CH-CH_2- \longrightarrow -CH_2S-CH_2-CH-CH_2-$$

$$-CH_2-S-CH_2-CH-CH_2- + -CH_2SH \longrightarrow$$
$$- -CH_2-S-CH_2-CH_2-CH_2- + -CH_2-S\cdot$$

The polythioethers are usually low melting (100°C.), but are fiber forming when of high molecular weight. They show some crystallinity as well.

123. Preparation of Poly(hexamethylene thioether) (144)

$$CH_2\!\!=\!\!CH-CH_2-CH_2-CH\!\!=\!\!CH_2 + HS-(CH_2)_6-SH \longrightarrow [-(CH_2)_6-S-]_5$$

Caution. Dithiols may cause dermatitis, especially on prolonged exposure. Use care in handling.

A mixture of 12.30 g. (0.0819 mole) hexamethylenedithiol and 6.72 g. (0.0819 mole) biallyl, both freshly distilled, is prepared and stored in a nitrogen-filled, 10 oz. screw-cap bottle. One hundred twenty-five ml. of an emulsifier solution prepared from 5 g. emulsifier (as, MP-189-EF, a sodium salt of a hydrocarbon sulfonate in 500 ml. distilled water is added to the mixture of monomers, using a nitrogen line at the mouth of the bottle to keep air out. The bottle is capped and cooled to about 5°C. in an ice bath.

A catalyst solution is prepared no more than 5 hr. before the polymerization from the following, using 2.5 ml. of each solution: 1.46 g. ammonium persulfate in 20 ml. distilled water; 0.37 g. sodium metabisulfite in 10 ml. distilled water; 0.37 g. copper sulfate (hydrate) in 100 ml. distilled water. The catalyst mixture is added, again using a nitrogen line for exclusion of air, and the bottle is capped tightly and put on a tumbler at 30°C. in a constant temperature bath. This may be accomplished by wiring the bottle very firmly to the end of the metal stirrer shaft which is then placed in the bath at an acute angle so that the bottle is turned mainly end-over-end.

After 24 hr. the polymer is precipitated by adding 35 ml. of a 10% solution of potassium aluminum sulfate to which is added 4 ml. of concentrated hydrochloric acid. The polymer is filtered and dissolved in 250 ml. benzene. The wet benzene solution is filtered into 500 ml. methanol with stirring and the precipitated polymer filtered. It is washed with methanol and dried in a vacuum dessicator at 1 mm. pressure. The yield of white, solid polymer is 17 g. (95%). The polymer melt temperature is 70-75°C., and the inherent viscosity is 0.5-0.7 in benzene (0.5% conc. at 25°C.). If the inherent viscosity is above about 0.45, it should be possible to put cold-drawable fibers from the melt.

Polythioethers may also be prepared **by the condensation of the disodium salt of a dithiol with an alkylene dihalide** (145,146).

$$NaS—R—SNa + X—R'—X \longrightarrow [—S—R—S—R'—]_n + 2NaX$$

The following is an example of such a reaction.

124. Preparation of Alternating Poly(hexamethylene tetramethylene thioether) (145)

$$NaS(CH_2)_6SNa + Br(CH_2)_4Br \longrightarrow [—S—(CH_2)_6—S—(CH_2)_4—]_5 + 2NaBr$$

Into a 200 ml. three-necked flask equipped with dropping funnel and condenser with drying tube is distilled 30 ml. of absolute ethanol (147). To it is added 0.92 g. (0.04 mole) of sodium. When the sodium has dissolved, 3.0 g. (0.02 mole) distilled hexamethylenedithiol is added. The salt of the dithiol precipitates, but redissolves on heating the solution to reflux. To this boiling solution is added first 40 ml. of dry benzene (thiophene free), followed by 4.30 g. (0.02 mole) of distilled tetramethylene bromide in 10 ml. of benzene as rapidly as possible. A vigorous reaction results. When it subsides, another 25 ml. of benzene is added to the solution and the mixture is refluxed overnight, then cooled to room temperature. Some polymer separates and is removed by filtration. This collected polymer is freed of inorganic solids, by stirring with three successive 100 ml. portions of water and filtering. Only about 0.5 g. of polymer is recovered in this way, having an inherent viscosity of about 0.5–0.6 in benzene (0.5% conc., 25°C.), after drying at 0.01 mm. in a vacuum desiccator over phosphorus pentoxide. The polymer melt temperature is around 65°C.

Additional polymer can be recovered by pouring the filtrate from the original reaction into 500 ml. methanol with stirring. The precipitated polymer is removed by filtration, washed well with methanol and dried under vacuum. The inherent viscosity, as above, is about 0.3, and the polymer weighs about 2.1 g.

Polythioethers have been quantitatively **oxidized to** the corresponding **polysulfone** without degradation in a mixture of formic acid–hydrogen peroxide (147,148). The polymer melt temperatures of the polysulfones are much higher than the precursor polymer. Where the hydrocarbon unit is hexamethylene, the sulfone has a polymer melt temperature of about 212°C., as compared to 75°C. for the thioether. The melt temperature increases linearly in the polysulfones as the hydrocarbon portion decreases in length. A number of polysulfones have been prepared and melt-spun into fibers which were cold drawable and of good tensile properties (148). The alkylene portions of the chain had at least 4 carbons. In contrast, the polysulfone from propylene and sulfur dioxide (prepared in Chapter 4), having only 2 carbons in the chain unit, decomposes before it melts.

125. Preparation of Poly(hexamethylene sulfone) (148)

$$\text{-}(CH_2)_6\text{—}S\text{-}_n \xrightarrow{H_2O_2} [(CH_2)_6\text{—}SO_2\text{-}]_n$$

Ten g. (0.067 mole of repeated unit) of finely divided poly(hexamethylene thioether) with an inherent viscosity of at least 0.5 (see Preparation 123) is suspended in 400 ml. of 90% formic acid in a 1 l. three-necked flask fitted with condenser, dropping funnel, thermometer, and stirrer. The reaction is heated to 50°C. with stirring and 40 g. of 30% hydrogen peroxide (0.35 mole) is added dropwise at such a rate that the temperature of reaction does not materially change. Slightly over halfway through this addition, the suspended polymer goes into solution, then shortly begins to separate again. Presumably, the sulfoxide polymer is the soluble intermediate form. The solution is stirred and heated 1 hr. after the addition is complete. The mixture is then poured with stirring into 4 l. of water, the polymer filtered, and washed thoroughly with water and dried at 60°C. in a vacuum oven. The polymer melt temperature is about 212°C. and the yield should be 12–12.5 g. (95–100%). The polysulfone has about the same inherent viscosity (*m*-cresol, 0.5% at 30°C.) as the original polymer.

Unlike the alkylene polythioethers and sulfones which have found no industrial application, the **alkylene polysulfides** (149) are the basis of the Thiokol-type rubbers, noted for their resistance to solvents, oils, oxidation and light. These polymers are prepared by the **condensation of an alkylene dihalide**, usually the chloride, **with a sodium polysulfide.**

$$Cl—R—Cl + Na_2S_x \longrightarrow -[R—S_x-]_5 + NaCl$$

R may be almost any aliphatic grouping, while the value of x, called the "rank," is usually from 2 to 4, although it may be higher. Ethylene dichloride and dichloroethyl formal have been the most generally used dihalides in commercial practice. The polymers so formed are linear. To obtain crosslinked products, about 2 mol. % of the dihalide used is replaced by a trihalide, such as 1,2,3-trichloropropane. The following preparations of a polysulfide polymer may be so modified. The crosslinked polymers are resistant to cold flow, but are more difficult to process in latex compounding operations. The polymerization in either event, may be carried out simply by mixing the reactants in water and heating, either alone or in the presence of a dispersing agent. In the first case, bulk polymer is obtained, while a polymer dispersion results in the second.

126. Preparation of Poly(ethylene tetrasulfide) (150)

$$Na_2S + S \longrightarrow Na_2S_4$$
$$Na_2S_4 + Cl—CH_2CH_2—Cl \longrightarrow -[CH_2CH_2—SSSS-]_5$$

A. In a 500 ml. three-necked flask equipped with stirrer, condenser, thermometer, and dropping funnel, 38.4 g. (0.40 mole) of sodium sulfide monohydrate is dissolved in 150 ml. water. To this is added 37.5 g. (1.17 mole) of sulfur and the mixture heated to reflux for 1 hr. with stirring. To this solution at 70°C. is added 40 g. (0.40 mole) of ethylene dichloride with stirring over a period of 1 hr. The dark-red color of the polysulfide solution disappears by the time the last of the dichloride is added. The reaction is heated at 70°C. for another hour after addition. The reaction is cooled and the supernatant liquid decanted from the yellow, rubbery solid. The solid in the flask is washed three times by boiling with water and decanting. The polymeric product is dried over phosphorus pentoxide in a vacuum desiccator to give 50–54 g. (79–86%) of polymer. The offensive odor of the product is thought to be due to low molecular weight dithiols or cyclic disulfides. Carbon disulfide swells and partially dissolves the polymer; carbon tetrachloride and benzene swell the polymer to some extent also. On a hot bar, the polymer melt temperature is about 130°C.

B. To prepare the above polymer in a more easily handled, dispersed form, the polymerization is conducted in the presence of a magnesium hydroxide suspension (157). The reaction sequence in A is modified by addition of 8.5 g. (0.04 mole) magnesium chloride hexahydrate and 3.6 g. sodium hydroxide to the sodium tetrasulfide solution just before the addition of the ethylene dichloride. The addition of 5 g. of a dispersing agent such as a sodium alkylnaphthalene sulfonate will facilitate reaction of the water insoluble dichloride. The polymerization is carried out as in A with vigorous stirring. When the reaction is completed, the polymer particles are allowed to settle for 2 hr., and the supernatant liquid decanted. The polymer is redispersed in 600 ml. water, stirred, and once again separated from the wash liquid. This is repeated twice to remove inorganic salts. Centrifugation hastens the washing process. For some uses, a polymer suspension in water is a preferred form for handling. To coagulate to a bulk rubber, 10 ml. of concentrated hydrochloric acid is added with stirring. The spongy, rubbery polymer is yellowish to white in color; it is removed and dried in a vacuum desiccator as above.

Bis(tin hydrides) add to **diacetylenes** to give unusual high molecular weight and unsaturated elastomers.

$$
\begin{array}{c} R' \quad R' \\ | \quad | \\ HSnR\ SnH \\ | \quad | \\ R' \quad R' \end{array} + CH{\equiv}C{-}R''{-}C{\equiv}CH \longrightarrow
$$

$$
\left[\begin{array}{c} R' \quad\quad R' \\ | \quad\quad | \\ {-}Sn{-}R{-}Sn{-}CH{=}CH{-}R''{-}CH{=}CH{-} \\ | \quad\quad | \\ R' \quad\quad R' \end{array} \right]_n
$$

127. Preparation of p-Phenylene-bis(dimethyltin hydride) (152)

$$
2Me_2SnCl_2 + p\text{-}BrMgC_6H_4MgBr \xrightarrow{\text{THF}} p\text{-}ClMe_2SnC_6H_4SnMe_2Cl \xrightarrow[\text{Et}_2\text{O}]{\text{LiAlH4}}
$$

$$
p\text{-}HMe_2SnC_6H_4SnMe_2H
$$

The preformed Grignard reagent from 86.6 g. (0.367 mole) of p-dibromobenzene and 18.1 g. (0.745 atom) of magnesium in 400 ml. of tetrahydrofuran (THF) is added dropwise with vigorous stirring to a solution of 177 g. (0.806 mole) of dimethyltin dichloride in 100 ml. of THF. The mixture is refluxed for 2 hr., evaporated to dryness *in vacuo* and the residue extracted 3 times with hot benzene. The solvent is removed from the combined extracts by evaporation and the residue thus obtained crystallized from ligroin, yielding a crystalline product melting over a wide range ($\sim 130°C$.). A solution of this product in ether–THF is extracted with a saturated aqueous solution of ammonium chloride, in order to remove unreacted dimethyltin dichloride, which is soluble in the latter. The ether solution is evaporated to dryness and the residue crystallized from ligroin, affording 53.1 g. (30% yield) of colorless p-bischlorodimethylstannyl) benzene with m.p. 160–162°C.

A solution of 33.4 g. (0.075 mole) of the bis-halide in 60 ml. of THF is added dropwise with stirring to a suspension of 6.0 g. of $LiAlH_4$ in 260 ml. of anhydrous diethylether under nitrogen. The mixture is kept at 40°C. for 1 hr. and after cooling to 0°C., 18 ml. of water is added dropwise with vigorous stirring. Solids are then removed by rapid filtration (Büchner funnel) and the clear organic layer is dried over anhydrous sodium sulphate. After removal of solvents *in vacuo*, the residue is fractionally distilled using a Vigreux column. The fraction with b.p. 93–94°C. at 0.2 mm. (n_{20}^D 1.5732, d^{20} 1.599) was collected. Yield 14.8 g. (53% yield).

128. Polyaddition of p-Phenylene-bis(dimethyltin hydride) and 1,5-Hexadiyne (152)

$$p\text{-}HMe_2SnC_6H_4SnMe_2H + HC{\equiv}C{-}CH_2{-}CH_2{-}C{\equiv}CH \longrightarrow$$

$$\left[\begin{array}{c} \quad\;\; Me \qquad\quad Me \\ \;\; | \qquad\qquad | \\ {-}Sn{-}C_6H_4{-}Sn{-}CH{=}CH{-}CH_2{-}CH_2{-}CH{=}CH{-} \\ \;\; | \qquad\qquad | \\ \quad\;\; Me \qquad\quad Me \end{array} \right]_n$$

A mixture of 6.78 g. (0.185 mole) of p-phenylene-bis(dimethyltin hydride) (see previous Preparation), 1.41 g. (0.185 mole) of 1,5-hexadiyne and 30 ml. of benzene is heated at reflux temperature for 12 hr. (N_2 atmosphere). Benzene is removed by evaporation *in vacuo* and the residue heated at 90°C. for 4 hr. The product thus obtained is dissolved in a small volume of benzene. The polymer is precipitated by adding this solution dropwise to a large, vigorously stirred volume of methanol. The resulting precipitate is freed from volatiles at 50°C. in a vacuum, affording 7.1 g. (87%) of a rubbery polymer, the IR spectrum of which was devoid of residual Sn—H or ${\equiv}CH$ absorption.

An interesting linear, high molecular weight **polysiloxane** has been prepared by melt and solution condensation of **p-phenylene bis-(dimethylsilanol)** with the elimination of water. The polymer is partially crystalline (T_m, 148°C.), and shows a greater oxidative and thermal resistance in the range 200°C.–305°C. than polydimethylsiloxane (154). The following synthesis is preferred.

129. Preparation of p-Phenylene Bis(dimethylsilanol) [p-Bis(dimethyl-hydroxylsilyl)benzene] (153)

Tetrahydrofuran is dried by distillation from lithium aluminum hydride. Commercially available dimethylchlorosilane is redistilled before use.

To 36.5 g. magnesium (1.5 g. atom) and 212.5 g. dimethylchlorosilane (2.25 moles) in 180 ml. of tetrahydrofuran in a 1 l. three-necked flask with

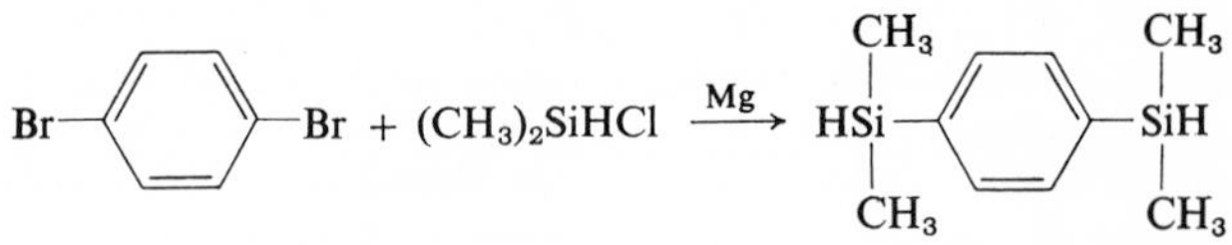

$$Br-\langle\bigcirc\rangle-Br + (CH_3)_2SiHCl \xrightarrow{Mg} \underset{CH_3}{\overset{CH_3}{HSi}}-\langle\bigcirc\rangle-\underset{CH_3}{\overset{CH_3}{SiH}}$$

I

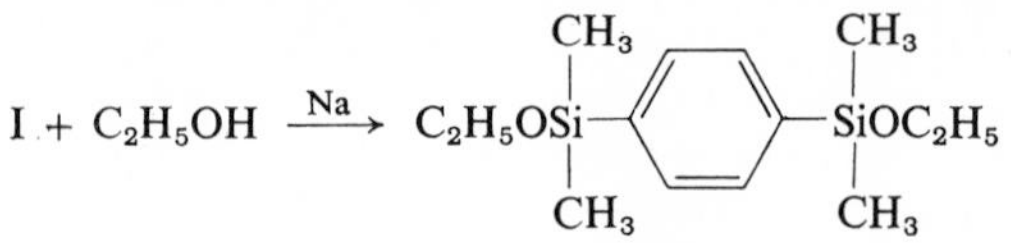

$$I + C_2H_5OH \xrightarrow{Na} \underset{CH_3}{\overset{CH_3}{C_2H_5OSi}}-\langle\bigcirc\rangle-\underset{CH_3}{\overset{CH_3}{SiOC_2H_5}}$$

II

$$II + H_2O \xrightarrow[CH_3OH]{NaOH} \underset{CH_3}{\overset{CH_3}{HOSi}}-\langle\bigcirc\rangle-\underset{CH_3}{\overset{CH_3}{SiOH}}$$

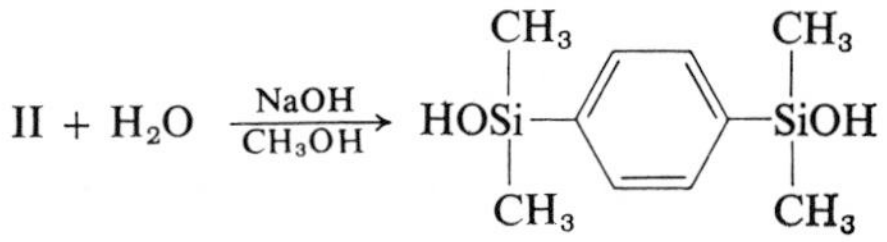

stirrer and condenser with a drying tube is added dropwise a solution of 177 g. p-dibromobenzene (0.75 mole) in 300 ml. tetrahydrofuran. The rate of addition is governed by the refluxing of the solvent from the heat of reaction. The reaction products are refluxed 1 hr. further when addition is complete, poured over crushed ice, washed with water, and dried over sodium sulfate. The solvents were removed and the mixture distilled under vacuum. About 95 g. (65%) of p-bis(dimethylhydrogensilyl)-benzene is obtained: n_D^{25} 1.5007; d_4^{25} 0.0032; b.p., 58–61°C./1.5 mm.

In a 500 ml. three-necked flask with stirrer, condenser, and drying tube, and pressure regulating dropping funnel, is placed 100 ml. refluxing absolute ethanol to which is added a small piece of sodium and 95 g. (0.49 mole) p-bis(dimethylhydrogensilyl)benzene is added dropwise. After the evolution of hydrogen has ceased, the reaction products are poured with constant stirring into a mixture of 57 g. NaOH, 343 ml. CH_3OH, and 38 ml. H_2O. To this was added a solution of 57 g. NaOH in 380 ml. H_2O. After standing 30 min., this mixture is poured with constant stirring into a solution of 505 g. KH_2PO_4 in excess ice and water. The precipitate which immediately forms is removed by filtration, dissolved in tetrahydrofuran, and washed with water. Evaporation of solvents provides about 220 g. crude products which are recrystallized from a mixture of hexane and tetrahydrofuran, giving a final yield of about 93 g. (85%) of p-phenylene bis(dimethylsilanol).

130. Preparation of Poly[p-Phenylene Bis(dimethylsiloxane)] [Poly(tetra-methyl-p-silylphenylenesiloxane] (153)*

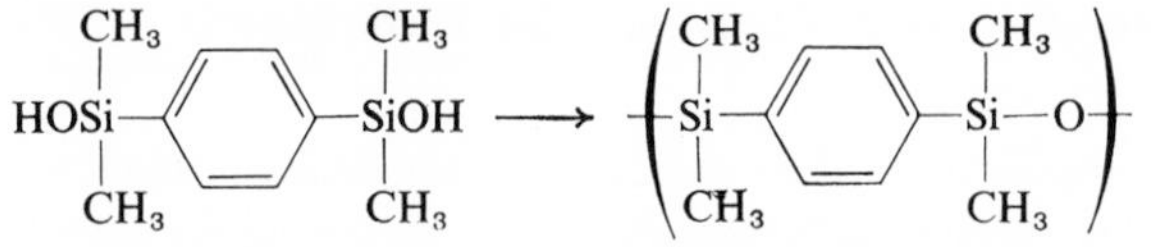

$$\underset{CH_3}{\overset{CH_3}{HOSi}}-\langle\bigcirc\rangle-\underset{CH_3}{\overset{CH_3}{SiOH}} \longrightarrow \left(\underset{CH_3}{\overset{CH_3}{Si}}-\langle\bigcirc\rangle-\underset{CH_3}{\overset{CH_3}{Si}}-O\right)$$

* We are happy to acknowlege the helpful commentary of Dr. R. L. Merker, Mellon Institute, on the details of this and the preceding synthesis.

In a 200 ml. flask equipped with a Dean-Stark trap for azeotropic removal of water is placed 50 g. of p-phenylene bis(dimethylsilanol), 35 ml. benzene and 0.1 g. n-hexylammonium 2-ethylhexoate. The solution is refluxed and the water removed from the trap as formed. After 6 hr., when the evolution of water has essentially ceased, the solution is poured with stirring into a large excess of methanol to give a tough, fibrous polymer. After filtration and repeated washing of the polymer in methanol, the polymer is dried in vacuum at 70°C. The yield of polymer is virtually quantitative. The intrinsic viscosity in toluene is about 2.0 (25°C.). From light-scattering molecular weight determinations on fractionated polymer and corresponding intrinsic viscosities, the relationship $[\eta] = 1.12 \times 10^{-4} \overline{M}_w 0.75$ has been determined. The crystalline melting point of the polymer is 148°C. by the polarizing microscope method, when the stage is heated very slowly to within 10°C. of the melting point, then raised to the final temperature over 2 hr. When heated to 305°C. for 16 hr. in air, the polymer yellows slightly, is swelled in benzene, but remains pliable; if polydimethylsiloxane is heated similarly, it decomposes to a hard, colorless, brittle gel.

The **elimination of water between carboxyl groups can give rise to polyanhydrides** when a dicarboxylic acid is used, which has the spatial requirements that favor the formation of linear, rather than cyclic, anhydride molecules. The behavior of diacids toward anhydride formation was studied by Carothers (1). Malonic acid forms only a polymeric anhydride, while succinic and glutaric acids form only the cyclic anhydrides. Adipic acid forms both a monomeric and polymeric anhydride, but higher diacids yield only linear products. Carothers investigated a large number of diacids and found that from sebacic acid a linear polyanhydride was first formed with a molecular weight of about 5000. When this polyanhydride (which was called α-anhydride) was subjected to molecular distillation, a cyclic dimer (β-anhydride) distilled and much higher molecular weight (ca. 20,000) ω-polyanhydride residue remained. The β-anhydride was converted to γ-anhydride on standing or remelting. The latter was practically identical with α-anhydride, and was thought to contain very large ring structures while the α-form was linear.

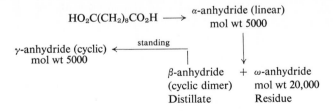

The ω-anhydride polymers are melt-spinnable to strong, lustrous, crystalline fibers. However, the aliphatic polyanhydrides are all so hydrolytically unstable that the polymers and fibers degrade rapidly on standing.

131. Preparation of Poly(sebacic anhydride) (1)

$$HO-\overset{\overset{\displaystyle O}{\|}}{C}(CH_2)_8\overset{\overset{\displaystyle O}{\|}}{C}OH \xrightarrow{(CH_3CO)_2O} \left[(CH_2)_8\overset{\overset{\displaystyle O}{\|}}{C}-O-\overset{\overset{\displaystyle O}{\|}}{C}\right]_n + H_2O$$

A solution of 20 g. sebacic acid in 100 ml. acetic anhydride in a 200 ml. flask equipped with a reflux condenser protected by a drying tube, is refluxed for 6 hr. The solvent is removed by warming on the steam bath under water aspirator vacuum. The crude anhydride is dissolved in 200 ml. of hot, dry benzene, and filtered through a fluted filter. Dry petroleum ether is added to precipitate the polymer (α-anhydride) which is stored over phosphorus pentoxide in a desiccator. This product melts at 75–80°C. to give a viscous liquid.

The polyanhydride prepared as before (α-polyanhydride) is placed in a flat or slightly round-bottom sublimation apparatus to form a thin layer of solid. The water-cooled condensing bulb or finger of the sublimator is adjusted to be about 2–3 cm. from the bottom of the heated portion of the apparatus. The pressure is reduced to at least 0.01 mm. by use of a mercury diffusion pump backed by an oil pump. The sublimator, which functions as a molecular still in this case, is then heated by means of a Wood's metal bath to 200°C. A crystalline distillate gradually accumulates on the condenser. The amount of distillate collected in a given time depends on the surface area of the anhydride being heated and the pressure. When an amount estimated to be about one-eighth the original anhydride used has collected, the distillation is stopped. The solid which has collected on the condenser is cyclic, dimeric sebacic anhydride (β-anhydride), which melts at 68°C. When cooled and remelted, it melts at about 82°C. and is now very viscous in the liquid form. This change represents the repolymerization of the cyclic dimer (β) to cyclic polyanhydride (γ). The residue from the distillation (high molecular weight ω-anhydride) melts at about 83°C. and is then extremely viscous. If it is heated to 130°C. strong filaments may be pulled from the melt; these can be cold drawn. They are rapidly degraded on standing at normal room humidity. Inherent viscosity determinations on solutions of the polymer are unreliable because of trace moisture pick-up even in hydrocarbons.

A series of **polyanhydrides based on aromatic diacids** of the type

$$HO-\overset{\overset{\displaystyle O}{\|}}{C}-\hspace{-0.3em}\left\langle\!\!\!\bigcirc\!\!\!\right\rangle\hspace{-0.3em}-O(CH_2)_n\,O-\hspace{-0.3em}\left\langle\!\!\!\bigcirc\!\!\!\right\rangle\hspace{-0.3em}-\overset{\overset{\displaystyle O}{\|}}{C}-OH \qquad n = 1-4$$

has been prepared by Conix (154). These polymers are much more stable to hydrolysis than their aliphatic counterparts. Preparation is best accomplished by forming the mixed anhydride of the diacid with acetic acid and heating that intermediate under vacuum to eliminate acetic anhydride.

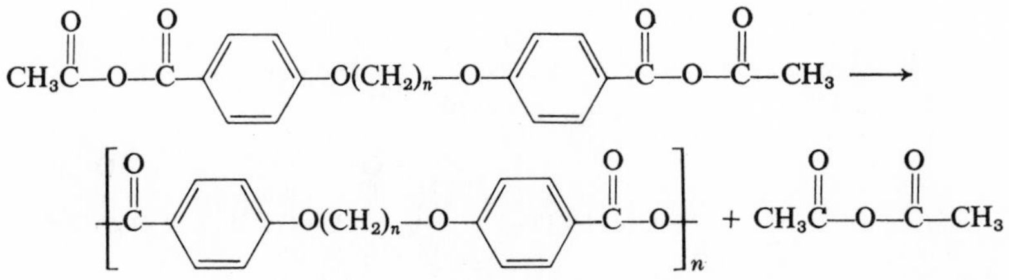

The products are crystalline, high melting and thermally stable enough to permit fibers to be melt spun. Polyanhydrides from related diacids have been reported by Yoda (155), using essentially the same reaction described above.

132. Preparation of 1,3-Bis(p-carboxyphenoxy)propane*

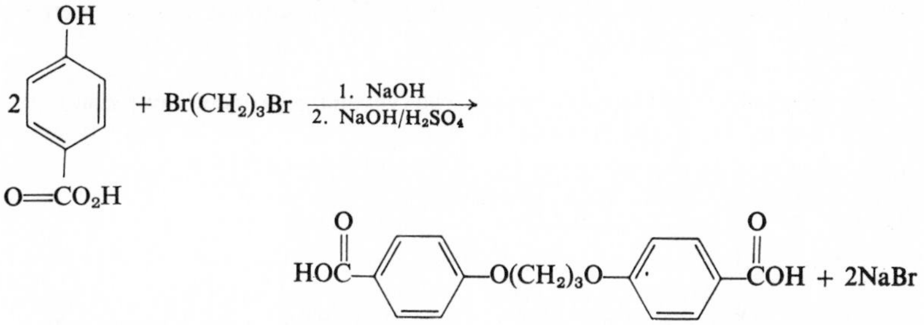

One hundred thirty-eight g. (1.0 mole) of p-hydroxybenzoic acid is dissolved in a solution of 80 g. (2.0 moles) sodium hydroxide in 400 ml. water in a 1 l. three-necked flask, fitted with a reflux condenser, stirrer, and dropping funnel. Through the funnel, 102 g. (0.5 mole) 1,3-dibromopropane is added over a period of 1 hr. while the contents of the flask are stirred and kept at reflux temperature. After this addition, the reaction mixture is heated under reflux for $3\frac{1}{2}$ hr. At this time, 20 g. (0.5 mole) solid sodium hydroxide is added to the mixture, which is further heated for 2 hr. at reflux. Heating is discontinued, and the reaction mixture is left standing overnight. The fine, powdery, white precipitate of the disodium salt is filtered and washed with 200 ml. of methanol. The wet precipitate is dissolved in 1 l. of distilled water and acidified with $6N$ sulfuric acid. The dibasic acid is isolated by filtration and dried in a vacuum oven at 80°C. The yield is 79 g. (50%). The neutralization equivalent is 157; calculated, 158. The 1,3-dibromopropane can be replaced by 1,3-dichloropropane using the same procedure but a longer reaction time (6 hr.). The yield is unchanged.

* We wish to thank Dr. Andre Conix and Photo-Produits Gevaert, S. A., Mortsel, Belgium, for making available to us the detailed preparation of the polyanhydride.

133. Preparation of the Mixed Anhydride of 1,3-Bis(p-carboxyphenoxy)propane and Acetic Acid

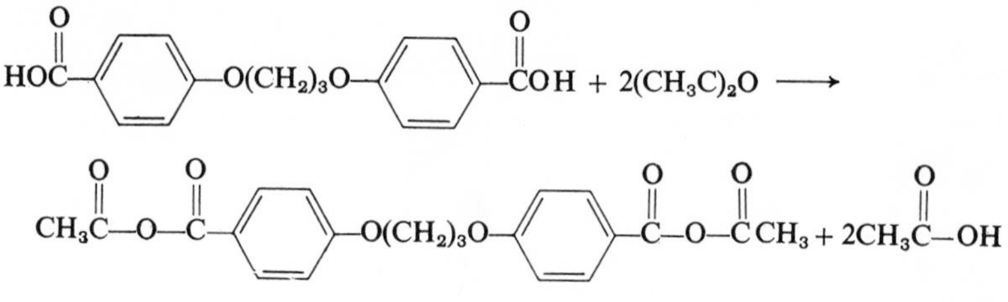

$$HOC\text{—}\langle\text{ring}\rangle\text{—}O(CH_2)_3O\text{—}\langle\text{ring}\rangle\text{—}COH + 2(CH_3C)_2O \longrightarrow$$

$$CH_3C\text{—}O\text{—}C\text{—}\langle\text{ring}\rangle\text{—}O(CH_2)_3O\text{—}\langle\text{ring}\rangle\text{—}C\text{—}O\text{—}CCH_3 + 2CH_3C\text{—}OH$$

Sixty g. (0.19 mole) of 1,3-bis(p-carboxyphenoxy)propane is refluxed with 650 ml. of acetic anhydride while a slow stream of dry nitrogen is bubbled through the solution. After 30 min. almost all the dibasic acid is dissolved. The mixture is filtered while still hot. The filtrate, which is colored slightly yellow, is concentrated to a volume of about 60 ml. by distilling acetic anhydride (contaminated with acetic acid) under vacuum at a temperature of 65°C. The concentrated reaction mixture is stored in a refrigerator overnight. The white, needle-like crystals which are formed are separated by filtration and washed with dry ether. The yield is 66 g. (87%), and the melting point is 102–103°C.

134. Preparation of Poly(1,3-bis(p-carboxyphenoxy)propane anhydride)

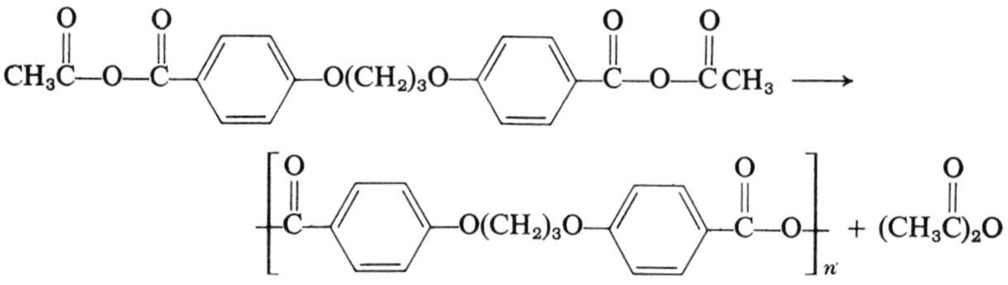

$$CH_3C\text{—}O\text{—}C\text{—}\langle\text{ring}\rangle\text{—}O(CH_2)_3O\text{—}\langle\text{ring}\rangle\text{—}C\text{—}O\text{—}CCH_3 \longrightarrow$$

$$\left[C\text{—}\langle\text{ring}\rangle\text{—}O(CH_2)_3O\text{—}\langle\text{ring}\rangle\text{—}C\text{—}O\right]_n + (CH_3C)_2O$$

In a polymer tube equipped with a side arm leading to a receiving flask is placed 20 g. of the mixed anhydride of 1,3-bis(p-carboxyphenoxy)propane with acetic acid. A capillary reaching to the bottom of the tube is inserted. The polymer tube is heated in a 280°C. (dimethyl phthalate) vapor bath which is brought to that temperature after the tube is in position. Nitrogen is passed through the mixture and acetic anhydride distils. After 30 min. at 280°C., a vacuum of about 1 mm., or less, is applied. A stream of nitrogen is continually passed through the increasingly viscous melt. Periodically, the vacuum may be released and a strong current of nitrogen flushed through the viscous melt for additional mixing. At the end of 30 min., the polycondensation is terminated.

On cooling the tube, adhesion of the polymer to the walls of the vessel and shrinkage during crystallization may cause the tube to shatter.

The polymer is obtained in the form of a yellowish, opaque hard block, which can be crystallized further by annealing at 130°C. in an oven for about 30 min. The crystalline melting point is about 267°C. From the melt, yellowish lustrous fibers can be drawn which show the typical phenomenon of cold drawing.

When potassium dihydrogenphosphate is heated to an elevated temperature, water is eliminated and an essentially linear inorganic polymer is formed which is a **polyanhydride of phosphoric acid** (156).

$$
\begin{array}{c}
\quad\quad O \\
\quad\quad \| \\
HO\!-\!P\!-\!OH \\
\quad\quad | \\
\quad\quad O \\
\quad\quad K
\end{array}
\longrightarrow
\begin{array}{c}
\left[\begin{array}{c}
O \\
\| \\
P\!-\!O \\
| \\
O \\
K
\end{array}\right]_n
\end{array}
+ \; H_2O
$$

The chemical repeat unit has the composition of potassium metaphosphate, KPO_3. Molecular weights of 100,000 or more have been obtained. However, the polymer is very readily hydrolyzed in water, particularly under acidic conditions.

In order to obtain linear polymer, a potassium-to-phosphorus atomic ratio of 1.0 or slightly greater is necessary in the starting material ($K/P \geqq 1.0$). At K/P of 0.98, a completely insoluble, crosslinked polymer results. At a K/P ratio of 0.9996 ± 0.0002, an appreciable amount of crosslinking occurs. In such cases, the small amount of trifunctional $O = P(OH)_3$ present accounts for the crosslinking.

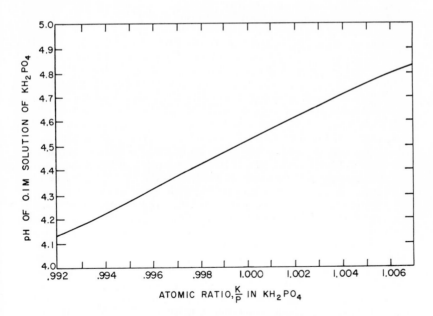

Fig. 3.4. pH of KH_2PO_4 solution as function of K:P.

The K/P atomic ratio is determined by measuring the pH of a $0.1M$ solution of potassium dihydrogenphosphate in carbon dioxide-free water. From Fig. 3.4, which relates pH and K/P atomic ratio, the latter may be obtained directly. In practice, most samples of KH_2PO_4 have a K/P ratio slightly less than one, in which case the ratio is adjusted to 1.00, or slightly greater, by the addition of potassium hydroxide. Addition of phosphoric acid is used to lower a K/P ratio which is substantially greater than 1.00. In the following example, directions are given for adjusting a K H_2PO_4 sample of K/P = 0.9996 to K/P = 1.001. The K/P ratio of the adjusted sample should be checked to verify that the desired ratio was achieved.

135. Preparation of Potassium Polymetaphosphate (156)

$$
\underset{\substack{|\\ \text{K}}}{\overset{\substack{\text{O}\\ \|}}{\text{HO}-\text{P}-\text{OH}}} \longrightarrow \left[\underset{\substack{|\\ \text{K}}}{\overset{\substack{\text{O}\\ \|}}{-\text{P}-\text{O}-}} \right]_n + \text{H}_2\text{O}
$$

To 188 g. of potassium dihydrogenphosphate (K/P ratio = 0.9996) in a 500 ml. stainless steel beaker is added enough 95% ethyl alcohol to just cover the crystals. Then 0.18 g. of potassium hydroxide, dissolved in a mixture 1 ml. of water and 10 ml. of ethyl alcohol, is slowly added to the mixture in the beaker with continuous stirring.

The alcohol is then evaporated on the steam bath with continuous stirring. A 3 in. diameter platinum dish containing 100 g. of the treated potassium dihydrogenphosphate (K/P ratio 1.001) is then placed in a furnace at 850°C. After 30 min., the molten material is cooled to 800°C., which is just below its melting point, then gradually lowered over a 4 hr. period to 775°C. The temperature is maintained at 775°C. for 40 min. The sample is then removed from the furnace and chilled by holding the lower part of the dish in water. The polymer is obtained as a transparent crystalline product. It is less than 0.004% soluble in water, but dissolves readily in an aqueous solution of a sodium salt, as sodium chloride.

After grinding to a powder in a laboratory mill, the polymer may be dissolved in water for a viscosity determination in the following way. A 1% slurry of polymer in boiled distilled water is placed in a three-necked flask equipped with stirrer and pH electrodes. With vigorous stirring, the pH is brought to 8.0 with 0.1N sodium hydroxide. Freshly washed sodium salt of Nalcite HCR ion exchange resin is then added, in the ratio of 6 g. air-dried resin per gram of polymer. The polymer begins to swell immediately. The pH tends to drop slightly, but is maintained between 7.5 and 8.5 by the addition of more alkali. Vigorous stirring is continued for 40 min. to disperse any lumps and the temperature is kept at 25–30°C. The resulting solution at pH 8.0–8.5 is filtered under slight vacuum through a mat of glass wool to remove the ion exchange resin. The filtrate is then a solution of poly(sodium–potassium metaphosphate) in water at a concentration of 1%. The specific viscosity (see Chapter 2), of the solution is determined at 25°C., using water as the reference liquid. Determinations must be made within 2 hr. after preparing the solution or degradation will be significant; molecular weight, estimated by means of endgroup determinations, has been correlated with specific viscosity measurements on 1% solutions of the mixed sodium–potassium salt of the polymer.

The following empirical relationship has been derived,

$$y = 0.61x + 2.12$$

where $y = \log_{10}$(degree of polymerization); and $x = \log_{10}$(specific viscosity).

From the above preparation, specific viscosities of 30–100 may be obtained. Films may be cast from freshly prepared solutions of the mixed sodium-potassium salt at about 11% solids concentration and pH 7.5–8.0 by drying in a stream of air. The film is too brittle, when dry, to be removed from the glass casting plate.

Another unusual inorganic polymer, similar in structure to $(PNCl_2)_n$ (see Chapter 5) is obtained by elimination of HF from imino-sulfur oxydifluoride.

$$HN{=}SOF_2 \longrightarrow \left[\begin{array}{c} O \\ \| \\ {-}N{=}S{-} \\ | \\ F \end{array} \right]_n$$

136. Preparation of Sulfur Oxytetrafluoride (157)

$$SF_4 + \tfrac{1}{2}O_2 \longrightarrow SOF_4$$

Warning: Sulfur Tetrafluoride Is About As Toxic As Phosgene

In a typical experiment, 108 g. (1.00 mole) of SF_4* (158), 16.0 g. (0.50 mole) of oxygen and 9.0 g. (0.21 mole) of NO_2 are heated at 200°C. for $7\frac{1}{2}$ hr. in a 400 ml. stainless steel bomb. The bomb is bled to atmospheric pressure through a trap cooled in solid carbon dioxide–acetone. The liquid condensed in the trap is transferred to a cylinder cooled in liquid nitrogen; the small amount of less volatile solid product is discarded. The liquid phase contains 86.0% SOF_4, 8.7% SOF_2, 2.5% SO_2F_2, 1.4% NO and/or NOF, and trace amounts of SF_6, N_2O, SiF_4, N_2 and O_2; no SF_4 is present. The yield of SOF_4 is 80% based on the SF_4 employed in the reaction.

All of the major impurities in the SOF_4, except SO_2F_2 are removed from the crude product by selective absorption in dimethylformamide. In a typical purification, 85 g. of crude SOF_4 is scrubbed twice with 50 ml. portions of dimethylformamide; this is done by condensing the crude SOF_4 in a stainless steel cylinder containing the dimethylformamide cooled in Dry Ice/acetone, and allowing the sealed cylinder to warm and stand for $\frac{1}{2}$ hr. at room temperature. The SOF_4 (which is a low boiling gas) is then bled to a second cooled cylinder of DMF. In the first wash 11 g. of impurities is retained by the solvent and in the second an additional 2 g. is removed. The SOF_4 is now sufficiently pure for the next step, and may be transferred directly from the second DMF cylinder.

*Air Products and Chemicals, Speciality Gas Department, Allentown.

137. Preparation of Synthesis of Imino-sulfur oxydifluoride (159)

$$NH_3 + SOF_4 + 2NaF \xrightarrow{(C_2H_5)_2O}$$

$$HN{=}SOF_2 \cdot 0.85(C_2H_5)_2O + 2NaHF_2 \xrightarrow{BF_3} HN{=}SOF_2 + BF_3 \cdot O(C_2H_5)_2$$

A mixture of 105 g. (2.5 moles) of anhydrous sodium fluoride and 500 ml. of ether is cooled to $-80°C$. and 125 g. (1 mole) of sulfur oxytetrafluoride is added. The solution is warmed to $-35°C$. and 15 g. (0.8 mole) of ammonia is introduced at the rate of 3 ml./sec. at that temperature. The mixture is then distilled at atmospheric pressure. The portion boiling up to 40°C. is discarded, and fractions boiling at 40–50°C. (42 g.) and 50–55°C. (66 g.) are collected. Chromatographic analysis shows about 12% imino-sulfur oxydifluoride in the second fraction and 50% in the third. The total yield of imino-sulfur oxydifluoride is about 53 g. (53% based on sulfur oxytetrafluoride or 67% based on ammonia). Temperature control during ammonia addition is critical; lower temperatures promote plugging of the inlet tube and greater solids formation.

Distillation of the above fractions provides an azeotrope fraction at 57.7°C., with a composition corresponding to $HNSOF_2$ $[(C_2H_5)_2O]0.85$. To isolate pure imino-sulfur oxydifluoride, a 150 ml. stainless steel cylinder is charged with 47 g. of imino-sulfur oxydifluoride–ether azeotrope and 19 g. (0.28 mole) of boron trifluoride and allowed to stand for 24 hr. Distillation of the mixture gives about 24.5 g. (84%) of imino-sulfur oxydifluoride, b.p. 43°C. It is important not to use an excess of boron trifluoride since it appears to form a nonvolatile complex with imino-sulfur oxydifluoride.

138. Polymerization of Imino-sulfur Oxydifluoride (159)

$$n HN{=}SOF_2 \longrightarrow \left[\begin{array}{c} O \\ \parallel \\ {-}N{=}S{-} \\ | \\ F \end{array} \right]_n + HF$$

A slurry of 35 g. (0.25 mole) anhydrous cesium fluoride in 50 ml. of benzene is stirred while 5.5 g. (0.055 mole) of imino-sulfur oxydifluoride is added. An exothermic reaction occurs, and the temperature of the mixture rises to about 40°C., then drops to 30°C., over a period of 1 hr. The mixture is boiled under reflux for 1 hr., and the supernatant liquid decanted. The residual solid was washed with water to leave white, tough, elastic poly(oxofluorosulfur nitride).

Imino-sulfur oxydifluoride–ether azeotrope also can be converted into poly(oxofluorosulfur nitride) by refluxing a solution in benzene with cesium fluoride.

A polymer having **tractability, low-temperature flexibility and an inorganic backbone is,** apart from the silicones, a distinct rarity. **Such materials are the zinc(II) and cobalt(II) mixed dialkyl phosphinate polymers** derived from the reaction of metal acetates with mixed di-alkylphosphinic acids (160). The polymers appear to have a double-bridged structure. The key to their flexibility and organic solubility is evidently in the structural disorder resulting from the mixed components and the alkyl side chains which together restrain the tendency to crystallization and the strong interpolar attraction, normally so destructive to the mechanical properties and tractability of poly-inorganics. These polymers are not thoroughbred inorganic polymers, but are rather hybrids. They are nevertheless of important scientific interest.

139. Preparation of Dibutylphosphinic Acid (161)

$$2C_4H_9MgBr + POCl_3 \longrightarrow (C_4H_9)_2PO(OH)$$

To a solution of 77 g. of phosphorus oxychloride in 250 ml. of dry ether, there is added dropwise with stirring 40 g. of dry pyridine and the resulting mixture is immediately treated dropwise, over the course of 50 min., with the Grignard reagent (filtered) prepared from 137 g. (1 mole) of n-butyl bromide and 24 g. of magnesium in 400 ml. of dry ether.

After stirring for 2 hr., the mixture is allowed to stand overnight, after which the decomposition of the mixture with ice-water (300 g.), followed by extraction of the organic layer with three 300 ml. portions of 5% sodium hydroxide solution and distillation of the organic residue, yields about 1 g. of tri-n-butylphosphine oxide, a hygroscopic solid, boiling at 185–186°C. at 18 mm.

The alkaline solution is concentrated under an infrared lamp to approximately 300 ml. and is then acidified with hydrochloric acid. The oil which separates is taken up in 100 ml. of benzene and the extract evaporated and chilled, when di-n-butylphosphinic acid crystallizes in stubby needles. After recrystallization from water the product melts at 70–71°C.; yield 42 g. or 47% (based on butylbromide).

140. Preparation of Dioctylphosphinic Acid (162,163)*

$$2C_6H_{13}CH=CH_2 + H_3PO_2 \longrightarrow (C_8H_{17})PO(OH)$$

A mixture of 471 g. (4.2 moles) of octene-1, 264 g. of "50%" aqueous hypophosphorous acid (2.0 moles of H_2PO_2H), 132 g. of water, 700 ml. of ethanol and 24.2 g. (0.10 mole) of benzoyl peroxide is refluxed for 24 hr.

To the cooled mixture (approximately 20°C.) is added 0.5 l. of benzene and 2.0 l. of 1.0M HCl. The lower phase is removed, and the upper (benzene) phase containing the product is washed with two 0.5 l. portions of 1.0M HCl. Following removal of the benzene by evaporation, the product is converted to its sodium salt by solution in 1.5 l. of 2.0M NaOH. The cooled solution (approximately 10°C.) is added to 2.0 l. of diethyl ether in a 5 l. separatory funnel. Following thorough agitation and subsequent phase disengagement, the lower phase is discarded. The ether solution of the sodium salt of the product is washed with six 1.0 l. portions of 1.0M NaOH. (The purpose of this step is to remove (n-octyl) (H)PO(OH) which is preferentially re-extracted into the aqueous NaOH.)

The ether phase is then contacted with 1.0 l. of 3.0M HCl. Following removal of the lower (aqueous) phase, the ether phase containing the product as free acid is washed with two 1.0 l. portions of 1.0M HCl. The ether is then

* We wish to thank Dr. B. P. Block, Pennsalt Corp., for his helpful comments on this and the polymer synthesis that follows.

removed by evaporation. The yield of essentially pure product is 540 g. (93% based upon H_2PO_2H).

141. Preparation of Poly(zinc(II) dibutyl-*co*-dioctyl phosphinate) (161)

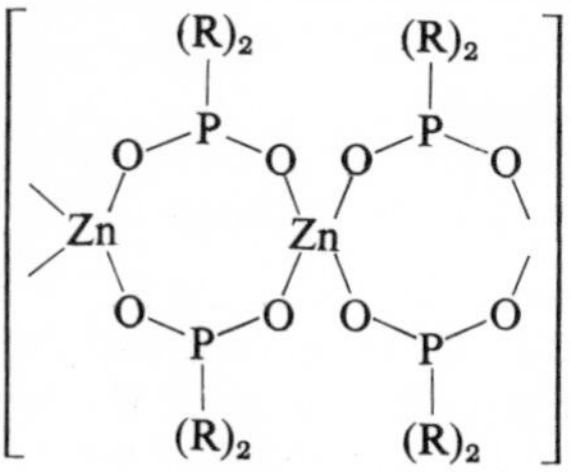

$$R = (C_4H_9)_2 \text{ or } (C_8H_{17})_2$$

To a 3 l. three-necked flask equipped with stirrer and condenser is charged with 1 l. of ethanol, 8.91 g. of dibutylphosphinic acid (0.05 mole) and 14.52 g. of dioctylphosphinic acid (0.05 mole). The mixture is heated to about 60°C. and 10.47 g. of zinc acetate dihydrate (0.05 mole) is added slowly (about 1 g. at a time) with stirring. When addition is complete, the mixture is heated to reflux. If a clear solution has not resulted, a short period of continued reflux should bring it about. The solution is then concentrated to about 800 ml. and then allowed to cool to room temperature with vigorous stirring to break up the large clumps that tend to form. The polymer is filtered, washed with ethanol and dried in a vacuum oven at 60°C. The polymer appears crystalline when viewed in a microscope under polarized light and melts at around 150°C. to give an amorphous form after cooling which is stable virtually indefinitely. It can be molded under light pressure at 200°C. to films that are transparent and flexible, remaining fairly so to −78°C. The intrinsic viscosity is about 0.4–0.5 dl/g. in chloroform.

REFERENCES

1. H. F. Mark and S. B. Whitby, Eds., *Collected Papers of Wallace Hume Carothers*, Interscience, New York, 1940.

The following references relate to specific topics mentioned in this chapter:

2. K. Saotome, H. Komoto, and T. Yamazaki, *Bull. Chem. Soc. Japan*, **39**, 485 (1966).
3. K. Saotome and H. Komoto, *J. Polymer Sci. A-1*, **4**, 1463, 1475 (1966).
4. D. D. Coffman, G. J. Berchet, W. R. Peterson, and E. W. Spanagel, *J. Polymer Sci.*, **2**, 306 (1947).
5. R. G. Beaman and F. B. Cramer, *J. Polymer Sci.*, **21**, 223 (1956).
6. T. L. Cairns, H. D. Foster, A. W. Larchar, A. K. Schneider, and R. S. Schreiber, *J. Am. Chem. Soc.*, **71**, 651 (1949).
7. S. Siggia, *Quantitative Organic Analyses via Functional Groups*, Wiley, New York, 1954, p. 21.
8. H. C. Haas, S. G. Cohen, A. C. Oglesby, and E. R. Karlin, *J. Polymer Sci.*, **15**, 427 (1955).
9. E. L. Wittbecker, R. C. Houtz, and W. W. Watkins, *J. Am. Chem. Soc.*, **69**, 579 (1947).

10. E. L. Wittbecker, W. W. Watkins, and R. C. Houtz, *Ind. Eng. Chem.*, **40**, 875 (1948).
11. A. Bell, J. G. Smith, and C. J. Kibler, *J. Polymer Sci. A.*, **3**, 19 (1965).
12. R. Aelion, *Ann. Chim.*, **3**, 5 (1948).
13. British Pat. 591,027 (August 5, 1947).
14. S. J. Allen and J. G. N. Drewitt, British Pat. 610,304 (October 14, 1948).
15. S. B. Speck, *J. Am. Chem. Soc.*, **74**, 2876 (1952).
16. J. A. Somers, *Man-Made Textiles*, **32**, No. 381, 60 (1956).
17. S. J. Allen and J. G. N. Drewitt, U. S. Pat. 2,483,514 (October 4, 1949).
18. G. S. Stamatoff, U. S. Pat. 2,704,282 (March 15, 1955).
19. British Pat. 737,939 (October 5, 1955).
20. F. K. Signaigo, U. S. Pat. 2,166,183 (July 18, 1939).
21. British Pat. 535,139 (March 31, 1941).
22. R. Schröter in *Newer Methods of Preparative Organic Chemistry*, Interscience, New York, 1948, p. 76.
23. S. J. Allen and J. G. N. Drewitt, U. S. Pat. 2,558,031 (June 26, 1951).
24. W. M. Edwards and I. M. Robinson, U. S. Pat. 2,710,853 (June 14, 1955).
25. F. B. Cramer and R. G. Beaman, *J. Polymer Sci.*, **21**, 237 (1956).
26. L. F. Beste and R. C. Houtz, *J. Polymer Sci.*, **8**, 395 (1952).
27. E. L.Wittbecker and P. W. Morgan, *J. Polymer Sci.*, **40**, 289 (1960).
28. P. Alexander and C. S. Whewell, *Some Aspects of Textile Research in Germany*, H. M. Stationery Office, London, 1947. BIOS Report No. 1472.
29. E. E. Magat, U. S. Pat. 2,831,834 (April 22, 1958).
30. E. E. Magat and D. R. Strachan, U. S. Pat. 2,708,617 (May 17, 1955).
31. P. W. Morgan, *Soc. Plastics Eng. J.*, **15**, 485 (1959).
32. D. J. Lyman and S. L. Jung, *J. Polymer Sci.*, **40**, 407 (1959).
33. P. W. Morgan and S. L. Kwolek, *J. Chem. Ed.*, **36**, 182 (1959).
34. M. Katz, *J. Polymer Sci.*, **40**, 237 (1959).
35. V. E. Shashoua and W. M. Eareckson, *J. Polymer Sci.*, **40**, 343 (1959).
36. P. W. Morgan and S. L. Kwolek, *J. Polymer Sci. A*, **2**, 185 (1964).
37. P. W. Morgan, *Condensation Polymers by Interfacial and Solution Methods*, Interscience, New York, 1965.
38. P. W. Morgan and S. L. Kwolek, *J. Polymer Sci. A*, **2**, 191 (1964).
39. N. Blake and H. W. Hill, Jr., (to du Pont), U. S. Pat. 2,994,693 (August 1, 1961).
40. W. M. Eareckson, *J. Polymer Sci.*, **40**, 399 (1959); see also A. Conix, *Ind. Eng. Chem.*, **51**, 147 (1959).
41. S. A. Sundet, W. A. Murphey, and S. B. Speck, *J. Polymer Sci.*, **40**, 389 (1959).
42. C. Naegli and A. Tyabji, *Helv. Chim. Acta*, **17**, 931 (1934); **18**, 142 (1935).
43. British Pat., 543,297 (February 18, 1942).
44. A. S. Matlack, U. S. Pat. 2,672,480 (March 16, 1954).
45. K. C. Brinker and I. M. Robinson, German Pat. 1,038,280 (September 4, 1959); Can. Pat. 575,411 (May 5, 1959); U. S. Pat. 2,895,948 (July 21, 1959).
46. J. W. Fisher, *Chem. Ind.*, **71**, 244 (1952).
47. R. Moncrieff, U. S. Pat. 2,512,667 (June 27, 1950).
48. M. Katz, U. S. Pat. 2,888,438 (May 26, 1959).
49. S. L. Kwolek, *J. Polymer Sci. A*, **2**, 5149 (1964).
50. J. F. Klebe, *J. Polymer Sci. B*, **2**, 1079 (1964).
51. British Pat. 530,267 (December 9, 1940).

52. P. F. Wiley, *J. Am. Chem. Soc.*, **68**, 1867 (1946).
53. H. A. Bruson and T. W. Riener, *J. Am. Chem. Soc.*, **65**, 23 (1943).
54. R. Mozingo, *Organic Synthesis*, vol. 21, Wiley, New York, p. 15.
55. British Pat. 528,437 (October 29, 1940).
56. G. J. M. Van der Kerk, H. G. J. Overmars, and G. M. Van der Want, *Rec. Trav. Chim.*, **74**, 1301 (1955).
57. G. D. Buckley and N. H. Ray, U. S. Pat. 2,550,767 (May 1, 1951).
58. W. E. Hanford and P. L. Salzburg, U. S. Pat. 2,313,871 (March 16, 1943).
59. E. L. Wittbecker, U. S. Pat. 2,816,879 (December 17, 1957).
60. W. R. Sorenson, *J. Org. Chem.*, **24**, 978 (1959).
61. T. W. Campbell, V. S. Foldi, and J. Farago, *J. Appl. Polymer Sci.*, **2**, 155 (1959).
62. W. Sweeny, private communication.
63. T. W. Campbell, V. S. Foldi, and R. G. Parrish, *J. Appl. Polymer Sci.*, **2**, 81 (1959).
64. A. Schmidt and G. Wichman, *Ber.*, **24**, 3245 (1891).
65. T. W. Campbell and E. A. Tomic, *J. Polymer Sci.*, **62**, 379 (1962).
66. R. H. Michel and W. A. Murphey, *J. Appl. Polymer Sci.*, **7**, 617 (1963).
67. W. Broker, R. E. Oesper, and W. A. Cook, *J. Am. Chem. Soc.*, **47**, 2609 (1925).
68. N. Rabjohn, *Am. Chem. Soc.*, **70**, 1181 (1948).
69. E. L. Wittbecker, U. S. Pat. 2,731,446 (January 17, 1956).
70. E. L. Wittbecker and M. Katz, *J. Polymer Sci.*, **40**, 367 (1959).
71. J. R. Schaefgen, F. H. Koontz, and R. F. Tietz, *J. Polymer Sci.*, **40**, 377 (1959).
72. G. F. Woods and H. Saunders, *J. Am. Chem. Soc.*, **68**, 2111 (1946).
73. C. S. Marvel and J. H. Johnson, *J. Am. Chem. Soc.*, **72**, 1674 (1950).
74. D. J. Lyman, *J. Polymer Sci.*, 1960, in press.
75. R. Barclay, Jr., *Can. J. Chem.*, **43**, 2125 (1965).
76. R. J. Cotter, M. Matzner, and R. P. Kurkjy, *Chem. Ind.*, **1965**, 791 (May 8).
77. J. V. Braun, *Ber.*, **41**, 2145 (1908).
78. M. Matzner, R. P. Kurkjy, R. J. Cotter, and R. Barclay, Jr., *J. Polymer Sci. B*, **3**, 389 (1965).
79. M. Matzner, R. P. Kurkjy, R. J. Cotter, R. Barclay, and C. N. Merriam, *J. Appl. Polymer Sci.*, **9**, 3295–3350 (1965).
80. J. C. Shivers, Can. Pat. 563,070 (September 9, 1958).
81. J. R. Whinfield, *Nature*, **158**, 930 (1946).
82. J. R. Whinfield and J. T. Dickson, British Pat. 578,079 (June, 1946).
83. French Pat. 1,158,755 (June 19, 1958); *Jap. Pat. Publn.*, 2,595 (1959).
84. G. A. Haggis and L. N. Owen, *J. Chem. Soc.*, **1953**, 404.
85. W. A. Lazier and H. R. Arnold, *Organic Synthesis*, Coll. Vol. II, A. H. Blatt, Ed., Wiley, New York, p. 144.
86. R. Malachowski, J. J. Wasowska, and S. Jozkiewicz, *Ber.*, **71**, 759 (1938).
87. C. J. Kibler, A. Bell, and J. G. Smith, U. S. Pat. 2,901,466 (Aug. 25, 1959).
88. N. A. Higgins, U. S. Pat. 2,676,945 (April 27, 1954).
89. L. H. Bock and J. K. Anderson, *J. Polymer Sci.*, **28**, 121 (1958).
90. K. Yamaguchi, M. Takayanagi, and S. Kuriyama, *J. Chem. Soc. Japan*, Ind. Chem. Sec., **58**, 358 (1955); *C. A.* **49**, 14373g (1955).
91. H. Schnell, *Angew. Chem.*, **68**, 633 (1956).
92. H. Schnell and L. Bottenburch, German Pat. 1,046,311 (Dec. 11, 1958).
93. Belgian Pats. 546,376 and 546,377 (March 23, 1956).
94. H. Schnell, *Ind. Eng. Chem.*, **51**, 157 (1959).

95. H. Schnell, *Chemistry and Physics of Polycarbonates*, Interscience, New York, 1964.
96. H. Schnell and G. Fritz, German Pat. 1,031,512 (to Bayer) (1958).
97. P. W. Morgan, *J. Polymer Sci. A*, **2**, 437 (1964).
98. P. J. Flory and F. S. Leutner, U. S. Pat. 2,623,034 (December 23, 1952).
99. P. J. Flory and F. S. Leutner, U. S. Pat. 2,589,688 (March 18, 1952).
100. A. D. F. Toy, U. S. Pat. 2,435,252 (February 3, 1948).
101. A. D. F. Toy, U. S. Pat. 2,572,076 (October 23, 1951).
102. A. D. F. Toy, *J. Am. Chem. Soc.*, **70**, 186 (1948).
103. A. Conix, private communication.
104. A. Conix and U. Laridon, Abstracts of *Symposium Uber Makromolecule in Wiesbaden*, Vol. IV, B 9, October 17–19, 1959.
105. A. Conix and U. Laridon, French Pat. 1,272,208 (November 24, 1961).
106. A. Conix, German Pat. 1,159,646 (December 19, 1963).
107. W. L. Hall, *J. Org. Chem.*, **31**, 2672 (1966).
108. P. Karrer and P. Leiser, *Helv. Chim. Acta.*, **27**, 678 (1944).
109. E. R. Walsgrove and F. Reeder, British Pat. 636,429 (April 26, 1950).
110. R. Gilkey and J. R. Caldwell, *J. Appl. Polymer Sci.*, **2**, 198 (1959).
111. J. G. Erickson, *J. Polymer Sci. A-1*, **4**, 519 (1966).
112. I. Goodman and J. A. Rhys, *Polyesters*, Iliffe Books, London, 1965.
113. Bjorksten Research Laboratories, Inc., *Polyesters and Their Applications*, Reinhold, New York, 1956.
114. E. L. Wittbecker, U. S. Pat. 3,036,979 (May 29, 1962).
115. V. S. Foldi and T. W. Campbell, *J. Polymer Sci.* **56**, 1 (1962).
116. T. G. Mastin and N. V. Seeger, U. S. Pat. 2,625,535 (January 13, 1953).
117. W. Brenschede, U. S. Pat. 2,755,266 (July, 1956).
118. F. W. Schmidt, U. S. Pat. 2,621,166 (December 9, 1952).
119. T. E. Mackay, private communication.
120. C. L. Ogg, W. L. Porter, and C. O. Willits, *Ind. Eng. Chem., Anal. Educ*, **17**, 394 (1945).
121. F. B. Hill, U. S. Pat. 2,929,800 (March 22, 1960).
122. C. M. Barringer, HR-26, Elastomer Chemicals Dept. Bulletin, April 1958, E. I. du Pont de Nemours & Co., Inc.
123. C. H. Smith, *Ind. Chem. Prod. Res. Develop.*, **4**, 9 (1965).
124. T. W. Campbell and K. C. Smeltz, *J. Org. Chem.*, **28**, 2069 (1963).
125. W. J. Jackson, Jr., and J. R. Caldwell, *Ind. Eng. Chem. Prod. Res. Develop.*, **2**,246 (1963).
126. K. P. Perry, W. J. Jackson, Jr., and J. R. Caldwell, *J. Appl. Polymer Sci.*, **9**, 3451 (1965).
127. J. Preston, *J. Polymer Sci. B*, **2**, 1171 (1964).
128. J. Preston, R. W. Smith, and C. J. Stehman, Paper presented at High Temperature Fiber Symposium, Phoenix, Arizona, January, 1966.
129. H. Vogel and C. S. Marvel, *J. Polymer Sci.*, **50**, 511 (1961).
130. H. Vogel and C. S. Marvel, *J. Polymer Sci. A*, **1**, 1531 (1963).
131. W. M. Edwards, U. S. Pat. 3,179,614 and 3,179,634, April 20, 1965.
132. C. E. Sroog, A. L. Endry, S. V. Abramo, C. E. Berr, W. M. Edwards, and K. L. Olivier, *J. Polymer Sci. A*, **13**, 1373–1390 (1965).
133. A. H. Frazer and F. T. Wallenberger, *J. Polymer Sci. A*, **2**, 1147 (1964).
134. A. H. Frazer, W. Sweeny, and F. T. Wallenberger, *J. Polymer Sci. A*, **2**, 1157 (1964).

135. J. R. Holsten and M. R. Lilyquist, *J. Polymer Sci. A*, **3**, 3905 (1965).
136. J. K. Stille, J. R. Williamson, and F. E. Arnold, *J. Polymer Sci. A*, **3**, 1013 (1965).
137. J. G. Colson, R. H. Michel, and R. M. Paufler, *J. Polymer Sci. A*, **4**, 59 (1966).
138. F. Dawans and C. S. Marvel, *J. Polymer Sci. A*, **3**, 3549 (1965).
139. J. P. Schaefer and J. L. Bertram, *Polymer Letters*, **3**, 95 (1965).
140. R. L. Van Deusen, *Polymer Letters*, **4**, 211 (1966).
141. J. F. Klebe, *J. Polymer Sci. A*, **2**, 2673 (1964).
142. J. F. Bunnett and R. E. Zahler, *Chem. Rev.*, **49**, 273 (1951).
143. R. N. Johnson, A. G. Farnham, R. A. Clendinning, W. F. Hale, and C. N. Merriam, Jr., Abstr. of Papers, 3rd Biennial Polymer Symposium, Cleveland, Ohio, June 22–24, 1966.
144. C. S. Marvel and P. H. Aldrich, *J. Am. Chem. Soc.*, **72**, 1978 (1950).
145. C. S. Marvel and A. Kotch, *J. Am. Chem. Soc.*, **73**, 481 (1951).
146. H. D. Noether, *Textile Res. J.*, **28**, 533 (1958).
147. L. F. Fieser, *Experiments in Organic Chemistry*, 3rd ed., Heath, New York, 1957, p. 285.
148. H. D. Noether, U. S. Pat. 2,534,366 (December 19, 1950).
149. E. M. Fettes and J. S. Jorczak in *Polymer Processes*, C. E. Schildknecht, Ed., Interscience, New York, 1956.
150. J. C. Patrick, U. S. Pat. 1,890,191 (December 6, 1933).
151. J. C. Patrick, U. S. Pat. 1,950,744 (March 13, 1934).
152. A. J. Leusink, J. G. Noltes, H. A. Budding, and G. J. M. Van der Kerk, *Rec. Trav. Chim.*, **83**, 609 (1964).
153. R. L. Merker and M. J. Scott, *J. Polymer Sci. A*, **2**, 15 (1964).
154. A. Conix, *J. Polymer Sci.*, **29**, 343 (1958).
155. N. Yoda, *Makromol. Chem.*, **32**, 1 (1959).
156. R. Pfanstiel and R. K. Iler, *J. Am. Chem. Soc.*, **74**, 6059 (1952).
157. W. C. Smith and V. A. Engelhardt, *J. Am. Chem. Soc.*, **82**, 3838 (1962).
158. C. W. Tulloch, F. S. Fawcett, W. C. Smith, and D. D. Coffman, *J. Am. Chem. Soc.*, **82**, S39 (1960).
159. G. W. Parshall, R. Cramer, and R. E. Foster, *Inorg. Chem.*. **1**, 677 (1962).
160. S. H. Rose and B. P. Block, *J. Am. Chem. Soc.*, **87**, 2076 (1965); *J. Polymer Sci. A-1*, **4**, 573, 583 (1966).
161. G. M. Kosolapoff, *J. Am. Chem. Soc.*, **72**, 5508 (1950).
162. D. F. Peppard, G. W. Mason, and S. Lewey, *J. Inorg. Nucl. Chem.*, **27**, 2065 (1965).
163. R. H. Williams and L. A. Hamilton, *J. Am. Chem. Soc.*, **77**, 3411 (1955).

CHAPTER 4

Addition Polymers from Unsaturated Monomers

I. General Considerations

An ethylenic monomer is a substance with the general formula where

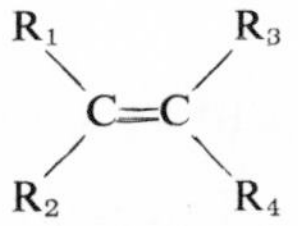

$$R_1 \diagdown \quad \diagup R_3$$
$$C=C$$
$$R_2 \diagup \quad \diagdown R_4$$

R is H or some other group. Keeping in mind the definition of polymer given in Chapter 1, there are very few tetrasubstituted monomers which gave high polymers. Two important ones are tetrafluoroethylene and chlorotrifluoroethylene. Larger groups than fluorine inhibit the growth of high polymer by known polymerization techniques. There are quite a few polymerizable monomers in which $R_1 = R_2 = H$, and R_3 and R_4 are other groups, and a few where $R_1 = R_3 = H$, with R_2 and R_4 other groups. The largest group of polymerizable vinyl compounds are those in which $R_1 = R_2 = R_3 = H$ with R_4 the only dissimilar group.

Many aspects of addition polymerization are considered in the general and specialized books and monographs in the polymer literature. Some of these sources make up the first eighteen references in the bibliography of this chapter.

1. MECHANISM

The polymerization of a typical vinyl monomer may be represented simply as follows:

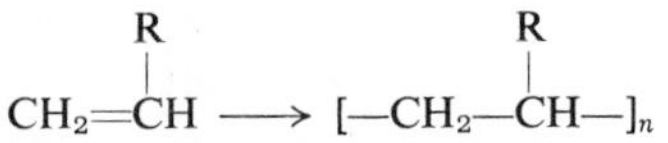

$$\underset{}{CH_2{=}\overset{\displaystyle R}{\overset{|}{C}}H} \longrightarrow [-CH_2-\overset{\displaystyle R}{\overset{|}{C}}H-]_n$$

The mechanism of vinyl polymerization is far more complex than is indicated by this oversimplified equation. This subject is treated at great length in the references listed at the end of this section, so no attempt will be made to discuss the various mechanisms rigorously. Vinyl polymerizations of all types have three basic mechanistic steps in common:

(1) *Initiation*

$$X^* + CH_2{=}CHR \longrightarrow X{-}CH_2{-}\overset{\overset{\displaystyle R}{|}}{C}H^*$$

(2) *Propagation*

$$X{-}CH_2{-}\overset{\overset{\displaystyle R}{|}}{C}H^* + CH_2{=}CHR \longrightarrow X{-}CH_2\overset{\overset{\displaystyle R}{|}}{C}H{-}CH_2\overset{\overset{\displaystyle R}{|}}{C}H^*$$

$$X{-}CH_2\overset{\overset{\displaystyle R}{|}}{C}H{-}CH_2\overset{\overset{\displaystyle R}{|}}{C}H^* + nCH_2{=}CHR \longrightarrow X(CH_2\overset{\overset{\displaystyle R}{|}}{C}H)_{n+1}CH_2\overset{\overset{\displaystyle R}{|}}{C}H^*$$

(3) *Termination*

$$X({-}CH_2\overset{\overset{\displaystyle R}{|}}{C}H{-})CH_2\overset{\overset{\displaystyle R}{|}}{C}H^* \longrightarrow \text{inactive polymer chain}$$

The details of each of these three steps are basically different for the four classes of initiators, and it is the latter that determines the character of the active center * as either a free radical (1), cation (2), anion (3), or the special ionic center of what have come to be called Ziegler–Natta or, more broadly, coordination catalysts (4,7). In the latter, chain growth takes place at a metal–carbon bond at a site that has been described as "coordinated anionic" in nature. More than a single operative mechanism for coordination catalysis, which can be homo- or heterogeneous, almost certainly exists, although a well understood, coherent picture of what is occurring at the catalyst site is just beginning to emerge (19,20). Related to the coordination class of bimetallic coordination catalysts is that represented by the Phillips-type, which is an activated chromium oxide supported on silica–alumina.

The terms initiator and catalyst have fairly distinct, if hardly precise, meanings as applied to polymerization. An initiator starts the growth of a particular chain by becoming a part of it. Growth continues at an active site in which the initiator no longer plays a role. A catalyst starts the growth of many chains, usually, and participates in the addition of each monomer; i.e., the catalyst is literally the active site or an integral part of it. Free radical polymerizations invariably require "initiators" and coordination "catalysts" almost certainly are involved in each monomer placement. Anionic processes are almost always said to use appropriate "initiators," but the situation is complicated by the fact that the anion may initiate and the cation guide the steric placement of each monomer at the active site. Cationic processes are usually said to be catalyzed; the initiation step is often begun by a cation not derived from the catalyst proper (e.g., BF_3) but from a cocatalyst (e.g., H_2O), and each catalyst proper may in this way start several chains. Many times it is simpler to overlook semantic niceties and use the terms interchangeably simply for convenience.

Few monomers are polymerizable by more than one or two initiator or catalyst categories and, when they are, it is often not with equal effectiveness in terms of rate and molecular weight. The susceptibility of a monomer to each type of initiation is determined by its structure, and, as in virtually all organic reactions, the influences are steric and electronic. Generally, the more hindered a vinyl or diene compound, the less likely it is to polymerize. Polymerization is usually enhanced by the electronic effects of substituents that provide resonance stabilization for the active center, whether radical or ion. Some groups can provide stabilization for radical and one or both ionic centers, and a monomer will thus polymerize under the influence of more than one class of initiators. Styrene, for example, polymerizes very well by radical and anionic means, and less so by cationic. Methyl methacrylate polymerizes easily by radical and anionic means, but essentially not at all cationically. Isobutylene is polymerized easily by cations, but not readily by any other means. N-Vinylcarbazole is also cationically polymerizable, and free radically as well. The degree of reactivity of a monomer can be intuitively assessed by considering the extent of resonance stabilization available to an active center; a monomer such as styrene is clearly likely to be much more reactive in free radical polymerization than vinyl chloride or vinyl acetate. An attempt to quantify reactivities of monomers is provided in the Q–e scheme developed from copolymerization studies(5).

The above considerations have been in terms of the propensity of a monomer to undergo initiation by a given mechanism. However, if subsequent propagation is not far faster than termination, polymerization will not occur in a meaningful way. For example, isobutylene is readily initiated by cations at room temperature, but termination reactions are so rapid that chain growth does not occur. Likewise, olefins such as butene-1 appear to undergo radical initiation but termination by chain transfer to monomer occurs so readily that useful chain growth is precluded. Thus, when we say that a monomer is polymerized by a certain class of initiators, we mean primarily that it is capable of an extensive propagation reaction by the mechanism involved.

The kinds of monomers polymerizable by coordination catalysts are mainly the 1-olefins and conjugated dienes; some 2-olefins have been found to polymerize by *in situ* rearrangement to the 1-olefin (21). Some functional monomers such as vinyl acetate and vinyl chloride also have been polymerized by these catalysts, but the circumstances suggest that it has usually been by dint of free radicals generated in forming bi-metallic coordination catalysts. In most cases, coordination catalysts are deactivated by excess amounts of oxygen-, nitrogen-, or sulfur-containing monomers.

Termination processes (6), wherein polymer chains cease to have an active center for continued growth, occur in characteristic ways for all four polymerization mechanisms. Some of these are shown below.

A. Free Radical Process

a. Combination of Two Radicals.

$$\sim\!CH_2\overset{\overset{\displaystyle R}{|}}{CH}\cdot \; + \; \sim\!CH_2\overset{\overset{\displaystyle R}{|}}{CH}\cdot \; \longrightarrow \; \sim\!CH_2\overset{\overset{\displaystyle R}{|}}{CH}\!-\!\overset{\overset{\displaystyle R}{|}}{CH}CH_2\sim$$

b. Disproportionation of Two Radicals.

$$\sim\!CH_2\overset{\overset{\displaystyle R}{|}}{CH}\cdot \; + \; \sim\!CH_2\overset{\overset{\displaystyle R}{|}}{CH}\cdot \; \longrightarrow \; \sim\!CH_2CH_2\!-\!R \; + \; \sim\!CH\!=\!CHR$$

c. Chain Transfer.

Shown is transfer to an added mercaptan; transfer to monomer, solvent, and dead polymer chain atoms are other possibilities.

$$\sim\!CH_2\overset{\overset{\displaystyle R}{|}}{CH}\cdot \; + \; R'SH \; \longrightarrow \; \sim\!CH_2\overset{\overset{\displaystyle R}{|}}{CH}_2 \; + \; R'S\cdot$$

$$R'S\cdot \; + \; CH_2\!=\!CHR \; \longrightarrow \; R'S\!-\!CH_2\overset{\overset{\displaystyle R}{|}}{CH}\cdot \; \longrightarrow \; \text{continued propagation}$$

Unlike a. and b., transfer reactions continue chain growth in a kinetic sense, although an individual molecular chain is dead.

B. Anionic Process

The principal mode of termination is abstraction of a relatively acidic hydrogen, usually present as an impurity in the system. If the monomer can be initiated by the resulting new anion, chain transfer can be said to have occurred. The presence of small amounts of alcohol in the anionic polymerization of formaldehyde may be such a case.

$$\sim\!CH_2O^{\ominus} \; + \; ROH \; \underset{\text{termination}}{\longrightarrow} \; \sim\!CH_2OH \; + \; RO^{\ominus}$$

$$RO^{\ominus} \; + \; CH_2O \; \underset{\text{reinitiation}}{\longrightarrow} \; RO\!-\!CH_2O^{\ominus}$$

Termination may also occur by addition of the propagating anion to any group susceptible to such attack; e.g., to an ester group, as in the intramolecular termination which occurs in the anionic polymerization of methyl methacrylate with phenyl magnesium bromide (22).

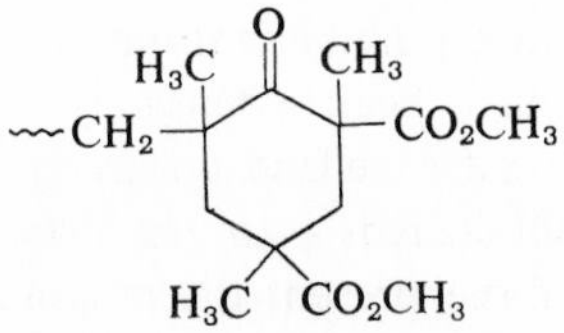

A remarkable aspect of anionic polymerization is that in the absence of built-in addition or transfer reactions, especially those due to impurities such as water, termination may not occur at all, so that the chain end remains in a "living" state when monomer is consumed. On addition of more, or different, monomer, propagation continues (23–25).

C. Cationic Process

a. Elimination.

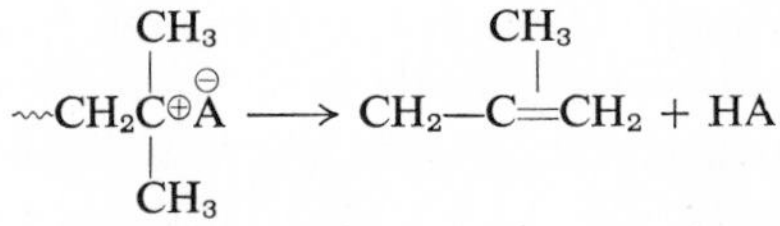

b. Chain Transfer to Monomer.
(Other transfer reactions are also possible, including that to dead polymer chain.)

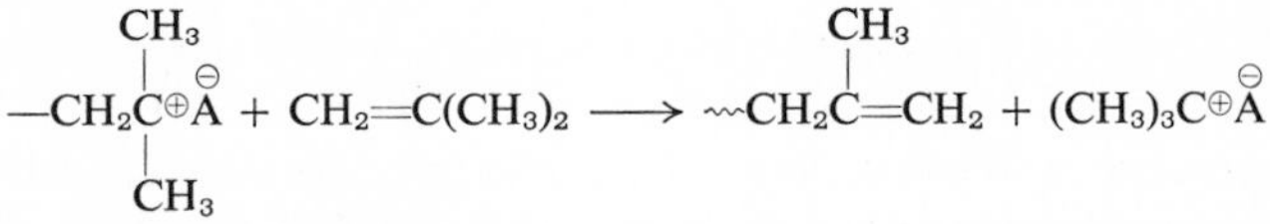

c. Reaction with Anion.

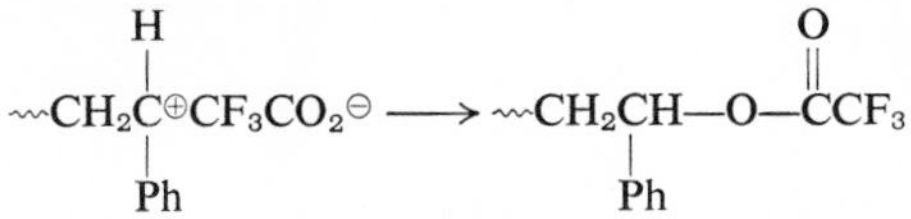

The polymerization of the cyclic ether, tetrahydrofuran by a cationic, or, possibly more correctly an oxonium, process is an example of a "living polymer" having a positively charged active chain end that does not terminate under the proper conditions (26). Tetrahydrofuran polymerization is considered in Chapter 5.

Termination processes in coordination polymerization are probably less clearly visualized than, say, the initiation and propagation steps. Evidence exists to show that in at least certain instances the growing chains are very long-lived and might be considered as "living" polymers.

The kinetics of addition polymerization by all four processes with a variety of monomers have been extensively studied. These are thoroughly discussed in some excellent books and publications and are essential to a thorough insight into the mechanisms involved. It is beyond the purpose of the present discussion to go further than the introductory treatment already accorded. The reader is referred to the sources cited in the beginning of the bibliography for a detailed approach. In the preparative examples of this chapter will be found polymerizations that embody most of the principles involved.

2. CONJUGATED DIENES

While most of the preceding section outlining the mechanisms of addition polymerization was in terms of vinyl compounds, it is well recognized that essentially the same principles apply to conjugated dienes (8-11). The major difference between the two classes is in the greater structural variation possible in diene polymers where, in the simplest case (butadiene), 1,2-, and 1,4-*cis* and 1,4-*trans* addition is possible in each monomer unit added. With more complex dienes (isoprene and 1,3-pentadiene) even more variation can occur. These possibilities are considered in this chapter in the experimental treatment of dienes.

In nonconjugated dienes, the double bonds react independently and they are therefore the addition polymer equivalent of, for example, the tricarboxylic acid–diol condensation system. The product from glycol dimethacrylate polymerization is an infusible, crosslinked resin. An exception to this principle is the nonconjugated diene which is capable of cyclopolymerization to a soluble polymer as described by Butler (27), Marvel (28), and Jones (29); examples will be found in Chapter 6.

3. COPOLYMERS

Copolymers are the result of putting together two or more vinyl or diene monomers in a macromolecule. The virtue in synthesizing a copolymer is in the modified properties that can be achieved. For example, poly(vinyl chloride) can be made more easily soluble by copolymerization with a modest amount of vinyl acetate; polyacrylonitrile can be made more dyeable by copolymerization with vinylpyridine;

and, polyisobutylene is made sulfur-vulcanizable by copolymerization with isoprene.

Copolymerization may appear to be a panacea for any adverse property, but in most cases a gain in one or more valuable properties is had only at the loss of some other property that was originally considered desirable. A reduction of brittleness by copolymerization may also be accompanied by a decrease in tensile strength, chemical resistance, surface hardness, and melting point. The synthetic polymer chemist must decide how much of a loss in one area can be tolerated to achieve a gain in another.

The effect of copolymerization on polymer properties is perhaps most readily seen in terms of its effect on crystallinity and glass temperature. Since the development of crystallinity is due to molecular symmetry and/or intermolecular attraction, it is not surprising that simple copolymerization should reduce or obliterate an ability of polymer chains to crystallize; the comonomer almost invariably reduces symmetry, and, where the comonomer is less polar or bulkier than the principal monomer, interchain forces are reduced. Similarly, the glass temperature in amorphous polymers (and crystalline, too) is modified by copolymerization, but in a different way. The general tendency is for T_g in a copolymer to lie between the T_g's of the parent homopolymers, and for fully random copolymers (defined in greater detail below) a weighted contribution of each parent is sometimes observed, according to the relationship

$$\frac{1}{T_g} = \frac{W_1}{T_{g_1}} + \frac{W_2}{T_{g_2}}$$

where T_{g_1} and T_{g_2} are glass temperatures in degrees absolute of the parent homopolymers and W_1 and W_2 are weight fractions of the corresponding monomers in the copolymer.

The problem of how to achieve copolymerization and still maintain the best of two or more worlds, so to speak, has been attacked through synthetic methods designed to prepare copolymers in four basically distinct categories. For monomers A and B, these can be described as follows:

(1) *Random*

—ABBAAABBBBBABAAB—

(2) *Alternating*

—ABABABABABABAB—

(3) *Block*

AAAAAABBBBBBBBAAAAAA

(4) *Graft*

AAAAAAAAAAAAAAAAAAAA

B	B	B	B
B	B	B	B
B	B	B	B
B	B	B	B
		B	B
		B	B

A. Random Copolymers

The preparation of random copolymers is the most straightforward. Monomer A and monomer B are mixed, and the catalyst added. Normally, A and B will polymerize at different rates, so that the composition of a copolymer isolated before polymerization is complete will depend on the relative reactivity of A versus B.

This has led to the concept of reactivity ratios (5), in which monomer pairs are compared in their reactivity toward each other. They are defined as the ratios of relative reaction rates of the monomers toward the active sites on the growing chain ends. For the monomer pair M_1 and M_2, a growing chain end can be one of two types and reaction is possible with either monomer, leading to four reaction rate constants. This is shown below for a free radical polymerization, where the reactivity ratio concept has been most applied.

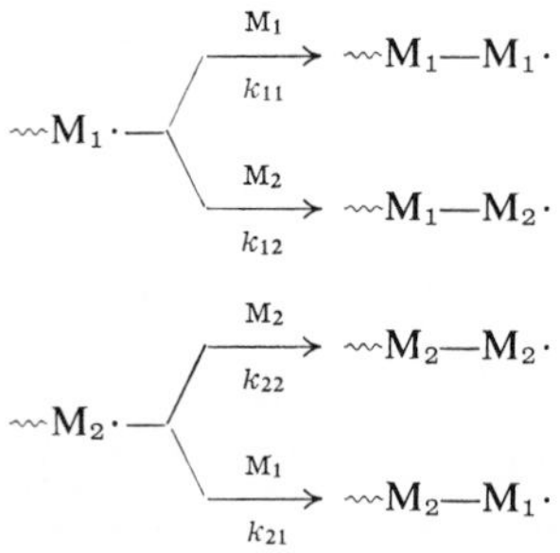

$$\sim\!\!M_1\cdot - \begin{cases} \xrightarrow[k_{11}]{M_1} \sim\!\!M_1\!\!-\!\!M_1\cdot \\ \xrightarrow[k_{12}]{M_2} \sim\!\!M_1\!\!-\!\!M_2\cdot \end{cases}$$

$$\sim\!\!M_2\cdot - \begin{cases} \xrightarrow[k_{22}]{M_2} \sim\!\!M_2\!\!-\!\!M_2\cdot \\ \xrightarrow[k_{21}]{M_1} \sim\!\!M_2\!\!-\!\!M_1\cdot \end{cases}$$

The constant k_{11} is for reaction of radical M_1 with monomer M_1, etc. The reactivity ratios, r_1 and r_2, are defined as:

$$r_1 = \frac{k_{11}}{k_{12}} \qquad r_2 = \frac{k_{22}}{k_{21}}$$

which is to say, r_1 and r_2 show the preference of a given radical toward its own monomer as compared to the second monomer. A high value for r_1 means that $M_1 \cdot$ prefers to react with M_1, while a low value means a preference for M_2. If r_1 is very high and r_2 very low for a monomer pair, it will be difficult to obtain copolymers of uniform composition by simply charging both monomers all at once; rather, a gradual addition of the more reactive monomer will be necessary. An example of this is given in the copolymerization of vinyl chloride and vinyl acetate (Preparation 156).

Several methods are known for determining $r_1 - r_2$ values and extensive compilations exist (5,30). Once obtained, they can be used with the instantaneous copolymer composition equation to estimate monomer feed composition needed to get a certain copolymer composition, when the effect of conversion level is taken into account. In one of its forms, the equation is:

$$F_1 = \frac{r_1 f_1^2 + f_1 f_2}{r_1 f_1^2 + 2 f_1 f_2 + r_2 f_2^2}$$

where F_1 is the mole fraction of M_1 in the copolymer being formed at any instant, f_1 and f_2 are mole fractions of monomers M_1 and M_2 in the feed at that instant, and r_1 and r_2 are the reactivity ratios. Knowing r_1 and r_2, F_1 (and F_2, mole fraction of M_2 in the copolymer) can be calculated for various values of f_1 and f_2. With r_1 and r_2 known and with given values of f_1 and f_2 in the initial feed, the values of F_1 and F_2 can be obtained for various levels of conversion of M_1 and M_2; this is best done by computer wherein the equation is solved at small increments of conversion and the correspondingly altered values of f_1 and f_2 at these instants.

If polymerization is allowed to go to completion from a single initial monomer feed, the copolymer will have an overall composition corresponding to the original ratio of A to B, but polymer formed toward the end will be richer in the slow component, the fast one having been consumed. At any instant, the composition of polymer being formed is necessarily different from that being formed at any other instant, as described above, except for the unique situtation of azeotropic copolymerization. The latter can occur only where r_1 and $r_2 < 1$ and $f_1 = (1 - r_2)/(2 - r_1 - r_2)$, and $F_1 = f_1$ at every instant.

Frequently a monomer that doesn't ordinarily homopolymerize will be found to copolymerize because of favorable electronic effects (see maleic anhydride with styrene, next section) or because steric restraints are less in copolymerization than homopolymerization; r_2 in such a case may be zero. On the other hand, two easily homopolymerizable monomers will occasionally copolymerize with great difficulty or not at all. Such a case is that of vinyl acetate and styrene; a small amount of styrene will essentially inhibit polymerization. Because styrene is so reactive, it rapidly captures most of the radicals generated; but, the styrene radical is too stable to add easily to the sluggishly reactive vinyl acetate. Thus, polymerization dies aborning as styrene radicals are eventually terminated at a low degree of polymerization. Butadiene inhibits vinyl chloride in the same way.

B. Alternating Copolymers

Alternating copolymers represent a special case and require that each monomer be more reactive towards the other species than towards its own kind; Such copolymers result when r_1 and r_2 are both extremely low. Thus styrene radical has a great affinity for maleic anhydride, but

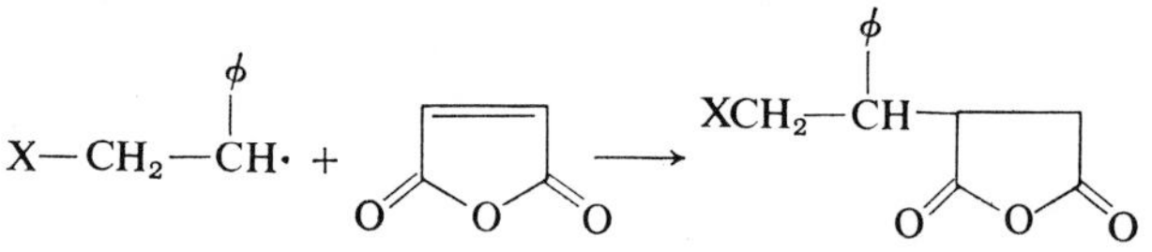

the maleic anhydride radical will not add to itself, hence a styrene molecule is added next to the growing chain; i.e., r_1 (for styrene) is very low and r_2 (for maleic anhydride) is zero.

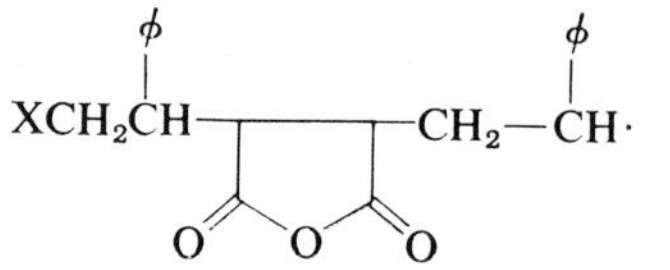

This alternation continues until the chain is terminated (5,16).

Another particularly interesting and unusual case of alternation occurs during the copolymerization of terminal olefins with sulfur dioxide (31–34a):

$$XCH_2-CH_2\cdot + SO_2 \longrightarrow XCH_2CH_2SO_2\cdot \longrightarrow$$

$$XCH_2CH_2SO_2CH_2CH_2\cdot \longrightarrow XCH_2CH_2SO_2CH_2CH_2SO_2\cdot, \text{ etc.}$$

An olefin —SO_2 complex has been suggested as an intermediate (35,36).

Another unusual "comonomer" which has been shown to alternate with styrene (37–39), 1,1,4,4-tetrafluorobutadiene (40), and others, is oxygen.

$$XCH_2-\overset{C_6H_5}{\underset{|}{CH}}\cdot + O_2 \longrightarrow XCH_2\overset{C_6H_5}{\underset{|}{CH}}-O-O- \longrightarrow X[-CH_2-\overset{C_6H_5}{\underset{|}{CH}}-O-O-]_n$$

C. Block and Graft Copolymers

The synthesis and characterization of block and graft copolymers has been reviewed (12,41,42,42a), and while special synthetic techniques have been worked out, in many cases it is difficult to prepare pure graft or block copolymers without contamination with homopolymers corresponding to both monomers. In all but a few favorable instances, removal of homopolymer by extraction or fractionation is difficult and time consuming. In practical cases, the polymer chemist must design his block or graft system so that he can live with a mixture of products and yet derive benefit from the presence of the block or graft component. A case in point is the preparation of an acrylonitrile–butadiene–styrene (ABS) polymer (Preparation No. 147), by copolymerizing styrene and acrylonitrile in the presence of polybutadiene. In this particularly complex system, the net result is a mixture of an essentially random styrene-acrylonitrile copolymer (the major constituent) and a graft of the same random copolymer to a backbone of polybutadiene; there is probably a small amount of ungrafted polybutadiene also (43).

There are practical reasons for attempting to make block and graft copolymers apart from the satisfying element of simply finding a new way to do so. They offer perhaps the best way of realizing a combination of the most desirable properties of two or more homopolymers with a minimum of loss in these properties. In the ABS case just noted, the stiffness, creep resistance, tensile strength, and chemical resistance of poly(styrene-co-acrylonitrile) are all maintained at an acceptable level, but combined with a useful part of the good impact strength and low temperature properties of polybutadiene. Likewise, when propylene is polymerized by certain coordination catalysts with intermittent admission of ethylene to the system in the absence of propylene (44), a certain amount of block copolymer is formed containing separate propylene and ethylene segments. Only a few per cent of total ethylene in block form serves to improve the impact strength over polypropylene, especially at low temperatures.

Another example is the block copolymer formed by butyl lithium-initiation of butadiene, or isoprene, which, when exhausted, is followed by addition of styrene, and again by diene (45,46). This sandwich of diene–styrene–diene blocks exhibits fully elastic behavior without the need for vulcanization and is thus a thermoplastic rubber. The preparative method used is based on the "living polymer" technique developed originally by Szwarc, which depends on the existence of a nonterminating anionic system (24,25). Examples are found in the experimental part of this chapter.

Grafting depends on creating active sites on the backbone of the substrate polymer. These may be radical in nature and originate from preirradiation of the substrate polymer, or they may occur via chain transfer to the substrate during polymerization of the grafting monomer in its presence. The efficiency of grafting is usually much greater for the former method. Oxidation of carbon atoms in the backbone of poly A can lead to hydroperoxide groups which can, on heating in the presence of monomer B, initiate polymerization of B from poly A. This has been done with polypropylene as the backbone polymer. Grafting can also occur through reaction with functional groups; e.g., the addition of living polystyrene anion to a carbonyl in poly(methyl methacrylate); the presence of acryloyl chloride units in the substrate polymer allows grafting of a condensation polymer in a low temperature system (cf. Chapter 3).

What block and graft copolymers seem to do is allow the essential homopolymer properties of each constituent to be developed. The interruption of the polymer chain by a comonomer and the consequent loss of certain properties is markedly reduced or absent; yet, the comonomer, as homopolymer, exerts its own effect on the system because its own properties are developed in the same way and are ineradicably bound into the total system by covalent linkages.

II. Free Radical Polymerization of Vinyl Monomers—
Experimental Methods

The number of examples which could be included in this section is quite large, since each of the many available monomers usually may be polymerized in a variety of ways, i.e., in bulk, suspension, emulsion, etc., and by a variety of catalysts which give free radicals. The monomers considered will be limited to those known to polymerize to high molecular weight readily, while satisfactory representative polymerization techniques will be described. No attempt will be made to consider exhaustively all methods for all monomers.

1. MONOMERS

The largest single factor in determining whether a polymerization is successful or not is the purity of the monomer used. It is absolutely essential that the material be pure. The ultimate test is successful polymerization. While the presence of small amounts of inhibiting substances may in some cases be overcome by the use of excess initiator, the only generally satisfactory, reproducible approach is to remove them.

2. Polymerization Systems (13)

Bulk polymerization is the simplest technique for converting monomer to polymer. In this method catalyst is added to undiluted monomer and this mixture is carried through the polymerization cycle. This technique is useful because of its simplicity and because it makes possible the direct preparation of castings, since the monomer–catalyst mixture will polymerize to a solid shape controlled by the shape of the polymerization vessel. This method, however, suffers from certain disadvantages. For example, polymerizations which are exothermic are liable to form local hot spots within the polymerization with consequent charring of the product. Other difficulties will be apparent during later discussion.

In order to obviate some of the difficulties encountered with bulk polymerization, solution polymerization has been used to some extent. In this technique the monomer is diluted by an inert liquid which makes control of the temperature of the reaction much simpler. This technique, if the solvent is chosen properly, will give a solution of the polymer ready for casting or spinning. However, many solvents have a deleterious effect on polymerization, since they may act as chain transfer agents, thus lowering the molecular weight of the polymer. Also, the last traces of solvents are sometimes quite difficult to remove.

Another technique which is used to compensate for the poor features of bulk polymerization is suspension polymerization. In suspension polymerization, monomer is suspended rather than dissolved in an inert liquid, usually water; the net effect is a large number of bulk polymerizations, one in each suspended monomer droplet. The initiator used must be soluble in the monomer droplets. Suspending agents such as gelatin, methyl cellulose, and other water-soluble polymers may be used to keep the monomer in a state of suspension. Mechanical agitation is required to maintain the liquid in suspension, and at the end of the polymerization the product is ordinarily obtained as a fine, granular product which is very easily filtered and handled. For polymers that are soluble in their monomer, a stop in stirring during polymerization and excessive or insufficient stirring may lead to agglomeration of the droplets when they are in a partially polymerized, tacky state. Suspension polymerization is not satisfactory for inherently tacky polymers such as elastomers, because agglomeration is virtually inevitable with such materials. An insufficiency of suspending agent will also permit agglomeration, even for polymers insoluble in their monomer, such as poly-(vinyl chloride). On finishing the polymerization, it is necessary to wash and dry the polymer thoroughly to remove traces of the suspension stabilizer and the reaction medium, usually water.

When the monomer is significantly soluble in water, initiation can take place in the aqueous phase using water-soluble initiators. An example is acrylonitrile (soluble in water to the extent of about 8%) polymerized by potassium persulfate. Initiation occurs in solution, but polymer quickly separates as a solid and continued polymerization appears to occur in the latter phase. This is often termed slurry polymerization.

The last technique to be considered is emulsion polymerization (14). In this system, water is again used as a carrier. However, an emulsifying agent such as a synthetic detergent is added. The emulsifier forms micelles which solubilize a certain quantity of monomer, the majority of which is dispersed in small droplets. The water-soluble initiator radicals penetrate monomer-rich micelles and initiate polymerization. The micelles serve as the locus of polymerization of more monomer as the latter diffuses to these sites, the monomer droplets thus acting as a reservoir for this purpose. The micelles dissipate as the polymer particles grow and continue as polymerization sites. The emulsifier then is adsorbed on the surface of these particles. Because very fine $(0.1–1.0\mu)$, stably suspended (emulsified) particles are produced, the system is well adapted for making tacky polymers, which are thus prevented from agglomerization. The kinetics of emulsion polymerization differ from that in suspension (1).

One of the big advantages of emulsion polymerization is that it gives a fluid system in which temperature control can be achieved. Rapid polymerization to very high molecular weights is easily achieved. Laboratory work-up of emulsions is usually via coagulation and filtration, which can be tedious. Commercially, emulsions of non-tacky polymers are often spray-dried, giving a fine powder with the emulsifier retained on the particles.

3. INITIATORS

There are a number of different techniques for initiating polymerization of vinyl monomers which depend upon the generation of free radicals. The simplest method is thermal polymerization in which free radicals are developed in the monomer simply by heating. About the only monomer with which this technique is satisfactory is styrene. In other cases it is necessary to add in small proportions an agent which will generate radicals *in situ*. The following compounds are popular and may be obtained commercially: benzoyl peroxide; lauroyl peroxide; *t*-butylperbenzoate; acetyl peroxide; α,α'-azodiisobutyronitrile; *t*-

butylhydroperoxide; cumene hydroperoxide; di-*t*-butyl peroxide; azodicyclohexylcarbonitrile; dimethyl-α,α-azodiisobutyrate; dicumyl peroxide; and dichlorobenzoyl peroxide. They and others differ in their half-lives in different environments and at different temperatures, resulting in differing rates of radical production and ultimately rate of polymerization and molecular weight. It is claimed occasionally that a certain initiator has inherent advantages; for example, it will give a less discolored product. However, this is something which is learned only by trial and error. These agents are generally used in bulk or suspension polymerization, where organic solubility is needed. In aqueous media, it is also possible to use certain inorganic oxidizing agents. Among those that are popular are hydrogen peroxide, sodium perborate, and various persulfates. The effectiveness of the radical catalyst can, in many cases, be enhanced greatly by the inclusion of a reducing agent, such as ferrous ion, and other modifiers. Thus the very important redox type of reduction-activated polymerization recipe contains a number of ingredients, each added for a specific purpose (10). For details on kinetics and mechanism of free radical catalyzed polymerizations, the reader should refer to a standard text on the subject.

It should be noted that the literature, in particular the patent literature, is replete with additional examples of compounds suitable for use as either sources of free radicals or as reducing agents for use in redox-type formulations. There is little point in attempting to list all of these. Only those which will actually be used in the preparation of polymer will be mentioned, and those in the appropriate place.

III. Free Radical Catalyzed Polymerization of Monosubstituted Ethylenes

The simplest olefin, ethylene, polymerizes to a high molecular weight, branched product with a melting point in the 110–135°C. range, depending on the amount of branching.

Low density polyethylene was first prepared in 1933 (15). It is ordinarily prepared in the laboratory on a small scale by free radical catalysts at high pressures and temperatures. For the laboratory preparation of high density polyethylene, a titanium-based catalyst at atmospheric pressure should be used. These experiments are described in a later section. It should be recognized that the polyethylene prepared with the titanium catalysts is of high density, with a low degree of branching. Polyethylene made at high pressure with free radicals will vary in properties from a nearly linear, high density product (47) to highly branched, low density material (7,15), depending on polymerization variables.

Higher aliphatic 1-olefins such as propylene, 1-butene, etc., do not polymerize to high molecular weight with free radicals. Catalysts based on reduced transition-metal halides (e.g., $TiCl_3$), sometimes called coordination catalysts, or the various hydrogenation type catalysts, such as reduced chromium oxide, supported on alumina are required. The most common hydrocarbon type known to polymerize with free radicals (aside from ethylene) is styrene and ring-substituted derivatives, as well as other vinyl aromatics such as vinylnaphthalene, etc. (16). Of these only polystyrene and polyvinyltoluene have achieved any technical importance.

Styrene homopolymerizes under a wide variety of conditions (17). A number of these will now be considered.

142. The Thermal Polymerization of Styrene in Bulk (48)

$$C_6H_5CH{=}CH_2 \longrightarrow [-\overset{\displaystyle C_6H_5}{\underset{\displaystyle |}{C}}H-CH_2-]_n$$

Pure styrene monomer polymerizes thermally without added initiator at a rate which increases rapidly with increasing temperature. Polymerization at room temperature may require months or years. However, at 150°C. polymerization is over in a very short time. The temperature chosen for the thermal polymerization of the styrene should be somewhere in between these extremes since, although lower temperature requires much longer period of time, it also produces much higher molecular weight.

Preparation of polystyrene with a molecular weight of about 150,000 may be carried out at 125°C. A polymer tube or beverage bottle is charged with approximately 50 g. of styrene monomer and is flushed and sealed under nitrogen. The container is immersed in a heating bath at approximately 125°C. and allowed to remain at this temperature for approximately 24 hr. Under these conditions better than 90% of the monomer will be converted to polymer. For complete conversion to polymer, it is necessary to allow the polymerization to run for 7 days or more and then finish the polymerization by heating at 150°C. for an additional 2 days. This will reduce the content of volatile material to less than 1%. However, for a volatile content of less than 10%, 24 hr. is all the time that is required at 125°C.

If polymerization is run at 102°C. for 15 hr., the conversion is about 40% and the inherent viscosity is about 1.5 (toluene, 30°C., 0.5 g./100 ml.).

Heat transfer problems can be serious if the polymerization is scaled up. The polymerization may become violent, so a larger scale is not recommended.

If desired, the polymer may be purified by first grinding to a small particle size in, for example, a Wiley mill, then dissolving in benzene. The benzene solution is poured into methyl alcohol agitated vigorously in a high speed mixer to precipitate the polymer in a finely divided condition. The solid polymer is filtered and dried in a vacuum over at 110°C.

143. Bulk Polymerization of Styrene with Peroxide Catalysis (48)

$$C_6H_5CH{=}CH_2 \longrightarrow [-\overset{\displaystyle C_6H_5}{\underset{\displaystyle |}{C}}H-CH_2-]_n$$

To 45 g. of freshly distilled styrene contained in a suitable vessel such as a polymer tube, flask, or screw-cap bottle is added 1.0 g. of benzoyl peroxide. This mixture is heated at 50°C. for approximately 3 days. At the end of this period, a solid plug of polymer is obtained which should have an inherent viscosity of about 0.4 (0.5 g./100 ml. in benzene, 25°C.). The rate of polymerization can be increased markedly by carrying out the reaction at temperatures higher than 50°C., but at sacrifice of molecular weight; by reducing the initiator concentration to one-half or less, a slower rate but substantially higher molecular weight will result at a given temperature, since rate is proportional to the square root of initiator concentration and degree of polymerization is inversely proportional thereto. With 0.25 g. of initiator, polymer conversion in 2 days is about 30%, and the inherent viscosity is about 1.0.

Polymerization mixtures of this type are suitable for preparing castings or embedding small objects in a polystyrene matrix. For example, polymerization of the mixture of styrene and benzoyl peroxide indicated above may be carried to the point where the polymerized mixture is so viscous it is difficult to pour. It may be then transferred to a mold, such as a square box, and the object to be embedded is immersed in the very viscous mixture. Polymerization is then continued at elevated temperatures until the polystyrene solidifies around the object to be imbedded. It is possible to suspend the object in the viscous mixture, if it has a tendency to sink, by use of a very fine thread or wire which may be removed when the polystyrene reaches a gel-like state. Alternatively, the casting may be built up in layers. Half of the mold is cast and hardened. The object to be embedded is laid down, the remainder of the viscous prepolymer added, and polymerization completed. Any bubbles which occur in the final casting may be removed simply by drilling a hole with a fine drill and injecting more styrene–catalyst mixture into the bubble to fill it. Polymerization is then continued to polymerize the styrene which has been added to the air pockets.

Polystyrene molds can be made very easily, again from the viscous polymerizing mixture such as described above. It is poured into the object to be reproduced and polymerization continued until the polystyrene is solid. The polymer mass will, of course, take on the outline of the surrounding vessel. Polystyrene does not adhere to glass; a coating of methyl cellulose or a silicone spray may be applied to objects which stick to polystyrene to facilitate separation.

It is not essential to use benzoyl peroxide for the polymerization of styrene in bulk; other peroxide or azo-type catalysts can be used. Techniques would be essentially the same as those described for benzoyl peroxide with the added precaution that some of the azo compounds may be more active toward producing free radicals at low temperatures.

The **polymerization of styrene in a solvent** offers little advantage (other than improved heat transfer) over the bulk polymerizations described previously, since many solvents tend to react with the growing polymer chain, limiting the molecular weight obtainable. Furthermore, rather dilute solutions must be prepared, otherwise the viscosity of the polymer solution becomes so great that manipulation becomes a problem. The principal utility of a solution method where styrene is concerned is in copolymerization with other monomers (e.g., acrylate esters and acrylic acid) to make surface coatings which can be applied directly from the solution in which they are made (see Chapter 7).

144. Emulsion Polymerization of Styrene with Persulfate (16,49)

$$C_6H_5CH{=}CH_2 \longrightarrow [{-}\overset{\displaystyle C_6H_5}{\underset{\displaystyle |}{C}H}{-}CH_2{-}]_n$$

For the simple laboratory polymerization of styrene in an emulsion, the following experiment (16, 49) is quite satisfactory. In a soda pop or beer bottle is placed 100 g. of water, 0.05 g. of potassium persulfate, 0.05 g. of sodium hydrogen phosphate, and 1.0 g. of sodium laurylsulfate. When this mixture has dissolved, 50 g. of styrene is added. Nitrogen is bubbled through the mixture to replace the air and disperse the styrene. The nitrogen tube is removed and the bottle is capped and sealed. The bottle is wrapped with some wire screen to prevent serious damage in the event the polymerization gets out of control and maintained with intermittent agitation at 70°C. for 2 hr. then at 95°C. for 2 hr. The polymer latex, so produced, is precipitated by adding alum solution and boiling of the resulting mixture. Polystyrene is separated by filtration, washed, and handled in the usual way. Instead of a bottle, a three-necked flask with stirrer, condenser, and nitrogen inlet for blanketing the mixture, is quite satisfactory.

145. Suspension Polymerization of Styrene (50)

$$C_6H_5CH{=}CH_2 \longrightarrow [{-}\overset{\displaystyle C_6H_5}{\underset{\displaystyle |}{C}H}{-}CH_2{-}]_n$$

The following ingredients are added to a 2 l. round-bottom flask equipped with a mechanical stirrer and a condenser, and maintained at a temperature of about 80°C.: 500 ml. of deaerated water, 0.1 g. sodium laurylsulfate, 1.5 g. of sodium polyacrylate, 5 g. of sodium sulfate, 150 g. of styrene, 1.5 g. of stearic acid, and 0.7 g. of benzoyl peroxide. This mixture is stirred vigorously and maintained at 80°C. for 12–24 hr. At the end of this time, the beads of polystyrene are filtered, washed with water, and dried in an oven at 60°C. in vacuum. Conversion should be complete. It is necessary that agitation be effective until the beads attain a solid consistency, otherwise the droplets will tend to fuse together. For this reason, it is generally necessary to add a small amount of a suspending agent. Gelatin or sodium polymethacrylate have been used quite extensively.

The brittleness of unmodified polystyrene constitutes a major deficiency in its performance. To correct this problem, medium and high impact polystyrenes are made by incorporating rubber into the hard polystyrene. This flexible component has the effect of increasing the ability of the composite to absorb rapidly applied stresses, as in impact.

The rubber-modified resin is usually made commercially either by mechanically blending polystyrene with the rubber (51) as on a mill or in a Banbury mixer, or by polymerizing styrene in the presence of the rubber (52) to give, at least in part, a graft of polystyrene onto the rubber. Styrene–butadiene or acrylonitrile–butadiene rubbers are often used in both the polyblend and graft types, from about 5 to 15% by weight of the hard polymer. Such materials are opaque in contrast to the very clear polystyrene. Some high styrene ($>50\%$)-butadiene copolymers are also made, but are not generally classed with the impact polystyrenes.

A variation of the high impact polystyrene resins has achieved considerable stature in recent years because of the unusual combination of stiffness, tensile strength, and impact resistance obtained. These are the ABS (acrylonitrile–butadiene–styrene) resins, which are in the category of "engineering" plastics because of the excellent resistance to creep combined with the other properties noted. As with high impact polystyrenes, ABS resins are either of the polyblend or of the graft type. The former is made by mixing rubber and hard polymer, e.g., a styrene–acrylonitrile (70/30 weight) copolymer with a butadiene–styrene (75/25 weight) copolymer, either by coagulation of a mixed latex of the two or by hot-milling the two materials. The graft resin is made by copolymerizing styrene and acrylonitrile (again, at about the 70/30 level) in a preformed latex of polybutadiene or styrene–butadiene (85/15). The final mixture is coagulated to give a mixture of free poly(styrene-co-acrylonitrile) resin and the graft of this resin onto the rubber. The compositions cited above are typical, but there is a great deal of variation possible to give a spectrum of products with different stiffness values, tensile and impact strengths, and hardnesses. α-Methylstyrene in place of styrene is said to impart greater resistance to deformation in heat (53), while replacement of the acrylonitrile by methyl methacrylate gives a transparent graft polymer instead of the conventionally opaque. In addition, blends of styrene–acrylonitrile copolymer, a hard resin, are sometimes made with a latex of styrene–acrylonitrile copolymer onto poly(butadiene) as prepared in the following sequence.

In the following examples, a latex of polybutadiene is prepared. This polymer has a relatively scrambled structure (*cis*- and *trans*-1,4-, and 1,2- units) as compared to the stereoregular polybutadienes prepared in other examples. However, the lower the temperature of polymerization, the more regular the structure of the polybutadiene, *trans*-1,4- increasing at the expense of 1,2-. The impact properties of the final polymeric composition are apparently better when the butadiene is polymerized at lower temperatures.

146. Preparation of a Polybutadiene Latex (54)

$$CH_2=CH-CH=CH_2 \longrightarrow -[CH_2-CH=CH-CH_2]-[CH_2-CH(CH=CH_2)]-$$

To an 8 oz. beverage bottle is charged 150 ml. of deaerated, distilled water, 77 g. polymerization-grade butadiene, 7.5 g. carbon tetrachloride, 2.3 g. sodium oleate (technical grade is satisfactory), and 0.4 g. potassium persulfate. About 2 g. of butadiene is allowed to boil from the bottle to remove air, the bottle is sealed with a neoprene septum and a metal cap with a hole drilled in it, and tumbled at 50°C. for 65 hr. The conversion to polymer is about 69%. The solids content can be estimated from the difference in the weight of the bottle before and after discharge of unreacted butadiene. The latex should be stripped of residual monomer by passing nitrogen through it.

147. Preparation of an ABS Polymer (54)

$$Polybutadiene + CH_2=CHPh + CH_2=CHCN \longrightarrow$$

$$[Polybutadiene]-[(CH_2CHPh)(CH_2CHCN)]- + -[(CH_2CHPh)(CH_2CHCN)]-$$

Sufficient quantity of the latex prepared in the previous example is used to give 21 g. of polybutadiene. This is charged to a beverage bottle along with 32 g. inhibitor-free styrene (twice washed with 10% aqueous sodium hydroxide, once with distilled water; drying is not essential), 16 g. acrylonitrile (inhibitor removed by passage through a silica gel column), 22 g. deaerated, distilled water, 0.7 g. sodium oleate, and 0.1 g. potassium persulfate. The bottle is then tumbled at 40°C. for 26 hr. (Since none of the monomers are a gas at the temperature used, a three-necked flask equipped with a stirrer, condenser, and nitrogen inlet may be used instead of a sealed bottle.) The latex can be coagulated by addition of a salt or alum solution, the polymer washed first in methanol to remove residual monomers, then several times in distilled water to remove inorganic impurities. The conversion of the styrene and acrylonitrile together is about 75%. The polymer can be compression molded to give opaque, tough specimens. Larger quantities than that prepared here are usually necessary for injection molding.

A wide variety of substituted styrenes has been made and polymerized. An unusual one is *p*-trimethylplumbylstyrene, which polymerizes to a clear, dense polymer which is nearly 60% by weight lead.

148. Synthesis of *p*-Trimethylleadstyrene (55)

$$Me_3PbBr + H_2C=CH-C_6H_4-MgCl \xrightarrow{THF} Me_3Pb-C_6H_4-CH=CH_2$$

In a 250 ml. three-necked flask, equipped with dropping-funnel, stirrer, and condenser, a solution of 0.10 mole of *p*-vinylphenylmagnesium chloride in 50 ml. of THF is prepared. (The THF must be distilled from $LiAlH_4$ prior to use in order to remove traces of peroxides which otherwise will cause considerable polymerization of the reaction product during distillation.) On dropwise addition of a solution of 24.9 g. (0.075 mole) of trimethyllead bromide in 75 ml. of THF, an exothermic reaction occurs. The temperature of the mixture is kept below 30°C. by cooling and, when the evolution of heat ceases, at 35°C. for 2 hr. After addition of 100 mg. of *p-tert*-butylatechol the mixture is decomposed with an ice-cold saturated solution of ammonium chloride. The organic layer is separated and the aqueous layer extracted with ether. The combined organic layers are dried over magnesium sulfate, and after the removal of the solvents, the residue is rapidly distilled *in vacuo* from a modified Claisen flask, yielding 22 g. of crude product with b.p.: 77.5°C./ 0.0003 mm.–86°C./0.01 mm. (Care should be taken when greater quantities of the crude reaction product are distilled. On attempted distillation of a 100 g. sample an explosive polymerization occurred resulting in total loss of product.) With a 30 cm. Vigreux column, this fraction is redistilled to yield about 18 g. of a slightly yellow oil with b.p. 60–61°C./0.0015 mm., n_D^{20} 1.6070, and d_4^{20} 1.7278.

149. Bulk Polymerization of *p*-Trimethylleadstyrene (55)

A mixture of 7.5 g. of *p*-trimethylleadstyrene and 6.0 mg. of 2,2'-azo-bis-isobutyronitrile (0.2 mole %) is heated at 60°C. in a Pyrex polymerization tube for 18 hr. and subsequently at 75°C. for 4 hr. (N$_2$ atmosphere). Upon breaking the glass tube a transparent, hard polymer rod is obtained. The polymer is infusible and insoluble in aromatic solvents and chloroform, but swells in these solvents after a prolonged period of time, indicating a cross-linked structure. Shaped objects can be made by polymerization in a container of a desired configuration. The high lead content suggests making radiation-shielding shapes.

Foamed polystyrene is produced either in the form of extruded boards or logs or of molded shapes derived from expandable polystyrene beads. The first of these products is made by extruding the polymer while injecting a gas into it in the extruder; as the molten polymer emerges from the extruder, the release of pressure allows the gas to expand the polymer and produces a cellular structure. The resulting product can be cut for various uses. The second method, molding of expandable beads, allows more complex articles to be made in any desired shape, in a manner related to conventional injection molding. The beads are made by polymerizing styrene in the presence of a volatile liquid such as pentane; the latter is absorbed, and when the beads are subsequently placed in a mold and heated (usually by means of steam) the softened plastic is foamed by the pentane vapor. Polystyrene pellets can also be charged with a blowing agent by immersion, as in pentane or methylene chloride, but this is generally not so satisfactory as incorporation during polymerization.

150. Preparation of a Polystyrene Foam (56)

A solution is made of 50 g. polystyrene in 100 g. of styrene monomer in a small beverage bottle previously flushed with nitrogen. Then, 10 g. of pentane and 1.3 g. of benzoyl peroxide are dissolved in the polymer solution with exclusion of air, the bottle sealed, and the mixture maintained at 40°C. for 30 days. The bottle is broken to free the solid polymer, which is ground to a fairly fine particle size. It can be expanded simply by heating with an IR lamp, but the most effective method is to fill a small perforated container with polymer to a proper level and heat the container with steam or immerse it in water at about 95°C. The amount of polymer, determined by trial and error, should be such that expansion causes the container to fill tightly, so that the pressure of the particles' expanding against each other causes them to fuse.

An interesting example of an **alternating copolymer involving vinyl monomers in which the other monomer is inorganic,** is the propylene–sulfur dioxide copolymer, obtained as follows. Polymerization probably occurs through a 1 : 1 complex of monomers, and is the exceptional case where higher α-olefins polymerize by means of free radicals. Most α-olefins (including styrene and vinyl chloride) undergo SO_2-copolymerization.

151. Alternating Copolymer of Propylene and Sulfur Dioxide (31,32,57–60)

$$CH_2{=}\overset{\overset{\displaystyle CH_3}{|}}{CH} + SO_2 \longrightarrow [-CH-\overset{\overset{\displaystyle CH_3}{|}}{CH}-SO_2-]_n$$

This experiment requires the use of high pressure equipment. To a 1 l. rocker bomb is added 0.5 g. of α,α'-azobis(α,γ-dimethylvaleronitrile). The bomb is pressure tested with nitrogen at 400 p.s.i. to detect leaks and then evacuated to less than 1 mm. for 3–4 hr. The bomb is chilled in a Dry Ice–acetone mixture and 42 g. of propylene and 240 g. of sulfur dioxide (99% purity) are distilled in. The bomb is sealed. Polymerization is allowed to proceed at 40–45°C. for 8 hr. The product, which is obtained in a yield of approximately 100 g., is removed from the bomb and washed twice with alcohol in a high speed mixer. The dry polymer is ground in a Wiley mill, or similar device, to pass through a 20 mesh screen and rewashed with alcohol. It is dried at 80°C. overnight. The yield is 96 g. of a hard white product which has an inherent viscosity of 3.3 as measured in concentrated sulfuric acid at room temperature. The product has a PMT of 300°C. At this temperature, it decomposes into monomer.

Of the **vinyl halides,**

$$\underset{\displaystyle H}{\overset{\displaystyle H}{\diagdown}}C{=}C\underset{\displaystyle H}{\overset{\displaystyle X}{\diagup}}$$

where X = F, Cl, Br, I

only vinyl fluoride and vinyl chloride (18) have given useful high polymers. Poly(vinyl fluoride), a highly crystalline moldable polymer, melts about 100°C. higher than polyethylene. With ordinary free radical catalysts, rather high temperatures and pressures are required (61–63) for the polymerization of vinyl fluoride. It can, however, be polymerized under pressure to a high molecular weight product by gamma radiation at room temperature (64).

Vinyl chloride has been known to polymerize to a useful plastic material since before World War I, and important commercial products began to appear around 1930. Although vinyl chloride is a gas, b.p. −14°C., it does not present undue problems due to excessive pressure in sealed vessels at temperatures of 40–60°C. It should nevertheless be handled with due caution when in a closed system. In the examples that will follow, experiments using both sealed beverage bottles and steel autoclaves are shown. The latter are always to be preferred, but the former are often quite convenient provided that they are handled carefully: bottles should be sealed only when the contents are frozen to −20°C. or iess; and, after polymerization, they should be vented with a hypodermic needle while properly shielded and after cooling. If polymerization has proceeded only very little or not at all, and considerable vinyl chloride remains, the bottle should be frozen before venting.

The commercial manufacture of poly(vinyl chloride) (PVC) and its copolymers has been reviewed (65). The major portion of PVC resins in the U.S. are made in a suspension polymerization; probably no more than 20% is made by emulsion methods, and only a small amount of specialty polymers are made in solution. There has been a growing interest in the commercial application of a bulk polymerization process, and several such plants are now in operation. The resulting polymer is physically much like that from suspension.

Suspension resins are of a larger particle size than the emulsion variety (50–500 μ, vs. 0.1–1.0 μ) and are usually designed to have a crenulated, porous surface for enhanced plasticizer uptake to form dry-blends for various extruding or calendering operations. Emulsion resin particles, in contrast, are usually hard spheres whose surfaces contain at least a part of the emulsifier used in the polymerization. Such resins are dispersible in plasticizers to give relatively fluid plastisols, or pastes, which can be formed and heated to gel the resin-plasticizer combination to the finished condition.

PVC is not soluble in its monomer so that it precipitates rapidly as it is formed in suspension or bulk polymerization; it is like acrylonitrile in this respect. The emulsion polymerization of vinyl chloride, while sharing many of the usual attributes of emulsion systems (e.g., water-soluble initiator, formation of a polymer latex), differs in a number of significant aspects from theory and from what is observed in emulsion systems involving polymer soluble in monomer (66). In any case, the presence of precipitated polymer in bulk (or suspension) and emulsion causes an increase in the rate of polymerization of remaining monomer (67), probably through radicals that become trapped in the surface of the solid and thereby escape some of the ordinary termination reactions. Fairly extensive chain transfer to monomer also occurs, with the result that molecular weight is not as susceptible to changes in catalyst concentration as with monomers such as styrene or methyl methacrylate, which follow more closely classical free radical polymerization kinetics. Transfer to monomer is believed to produce an unsaturated terminal group which, by allylic activation of chlorine, induces at least some of the thermal instability associated with PVC.

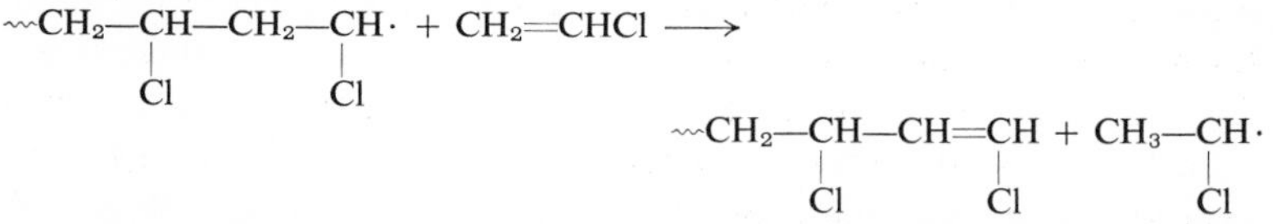

$$\sim CH_2-\underset{\underset{Cl}{|}}{CH}-CH_2-\underset{\underset{Cl}{|}}{CH}\cdot \ + \ CH_2=CHCl \longrightarrow$$

$$\sim CH_2-\underset{\underset{Cl}{|}}{CH}-CH=\underset{\underset{Cl}{|}}{CH} \ + \ CH_3-\underset{\underset{Cl}{|}}{CH}\cdot$$

Tertiary chloride, arising by branching of the main chain, may also contribute to thermal instability. The latter takes the form of successive eliminations of HCl to give a conjugated diene system, which, at the level of about seven double bonds, begins to show the characteristic yellow–brown–black color sequence of degrading PVC. Tertiary and allylic chlorides (or hydrogens) are obviously points for thermal elimination of HCl to begin, and each elimination produces another allylic system, if one considers the normal head-to-tail structure extant to a large degree in PVC. Many stabilizer systems are known to combat PVC degradation; the more widely used are either heavy metal soaps (e.g., barium and cadmium octoate) and lead salts or tin compounds, especially dialkyltin containing Sn—S bonds (e.g., $Bu_2Sn[SCH_2CO_2-C_8H_{17}]_2$). The tin compounds are a superior type and find most use in rigid PVC (i.e., no plasticizer), where the degradation problem is most severe.

152. Suspension Polymerization of Vinyl Chloride

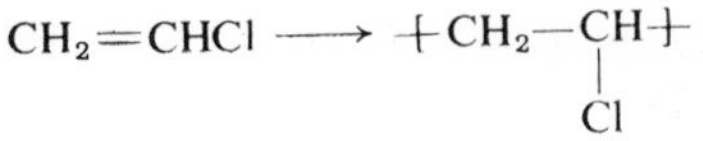

$$CH_2=CHCl \longrightarrow +CH_2-\underset{\underset{Cl}{|}}{CH}+$$

To a quart beverage bottle is added 200 ml. deaerated distilled water, 0.3 g. methyl cellulose suspending agent (e.g., Methocel MC25, Dow Chemical Co.), and 0.2 g. lauroyl peroxide. These ingredients are frozen and swept with nitrogen. An excess of liquid vinyl chloride (about 105 g.), is passed from a cylinder through a potassium hydroxide scrubber and collected in a Dry Ice-cooled, graduated cylinder mounted beneath a Dry Ice condenser. About 115 ml. is collected and added to the bottle which is allowed to warm to room temperature. When the excess of vinyl chloride has distilled (leaving 100 g. in the bottle), the bottle is sealed with a perforated steel cap, neoprene septum, and thin polyethylene liner. The bottle is agitated for 24 hr. at 50°C. (Caution: at this temperature, the bottle, which contains a pressure of 80–90 p.s.i.g., should be well shielded). After the bottle has cooled, the remaining pressure can be released by puncturing the rubber septum in the cap with a hypodermic needle point. The coarse particles of poly(vinyl chloride) are collected on a filter, washed with methanol in a blender, and dried at 50°C. in vacuum for 16 hr. This procedure should yield 80 g. of polymer with an inherent viscosity of around 1.0 (0.5 g./100 ml. solution in cyclohexanone at 30°C.).

153. Emulsion Polymerization of Vinyl Chloride

A small beverage bottle (about 220 ml. capacity) is flushed with nitrogen and charged with 0.25 g. potassium persulfate and 85 ml. of a 0.5% aqueous solution of an anionic detergent such as sodium lauryl sulfate (e.g., Duponol C). The latter should be made using deaerated water (briefly bubbled with nitrogen, or, boiled and cooled under nitrogen or carbon dioxide, e.g., by addition of Dry Ice). With maintenance of a nitrogen blanket, the contents of the bottle are frozen in Dry Ice and 27–29 g. of liquid vinyl chloride added as in the previous experiment. The monomer is allowed to evaporate until about 25 g. is left in the bottle, at which point the latter is capped with a Neoprene septum and perforated crown cap. Where no further additions to the bottle are contemplated, as in this case, it is advisable to place a thin polyethylene film under the septum to prevent any possible contamination of the system by it.

The bottle is tumbled or otherwise agitated at 50°C. for about 5–7 hr. A mobile, slightly bluish latex results. After cooling the bottle and venting what should be only a small amount of residual monomer, the emulsion can be coagulated by adding 50 ml. of concentrated sodium chloride solution. The filtered polymer is washed twice with water and once with methanol, then dried at 50°C. in vacuum. The conversion of monomer should equal or exceed 90%, and the polymer should have an inherent viscosity of around 0.9–1.0 (cyclohexanone, 0.5 g./100 ml., 30°C.). As an alternative to coagulation, which provides a moderate filtration problem, the latex can be evaporated to dryness and the polymer used as is. This conforms roughly to the common commercial practice of spray-drying PVC latexes and using the polymer with the emulsifying agent still present on the surface of the finely divided particles. The presence of the soap makes for both the poorer heat stability and electrical properties of emulsion PVC as compared to that made in suspension.

The influence of a variety of surface active agents on the emulsion polymerization of vinyl chloride has been studied by Hopff and Fakla, who related rate of polymerization, conversion, and polymer properties to emulsifier structure (68). The type used in the foregoing example was generally the most effective.

More than half the PVC used is in combination with plasticizers to impart flexibility. A variety of mechanical performance levels is possible, depending on the amount and kind of plasticizer used. Plasticizers are usually simple polyesters of some kind, and are an important part of polymer science and technology (69). One way to fabricate a sheet of clear, plasticized PVC is in the following manner:

154. A Plastisol Suitable for Coating a Film onto a Paper or Cloth Substrate (70)

To the mixing bowl is charged plasticizer equal to about 50 parts per hundred of resin, all of the stabilizer system which may include a barium–cadmium–zinc stabilizer such as Advastab BC-103A (Advance Division, Carlisle Chemical Co.), and an octyl epoxy stearate (Truflex E-68, Thompson Apex Division, Continental Oil Co.). These ingredients are premixed for 1–2 min. after which time the resin such as Trulon 900 or Geon 121 is added in increments in order to facilitate wetting. Mixing is started at a low speed and interrupted occasionally to wipe down the sides of the bowl in order to mix in all of the resin. The mixing is then continued for 15 min. at high speed after which the final portion of plasticizer (10 parts) is added and the plastisol again mixed at low speed for 5 min.

It is advisable to deaerate the plastisol thus made by placing the mixing bowl in a vacuum desiccator and drawing a vacuum of about 29 in. of mercury to remove all the entrapped air. This may take between 10 and 30 min. depending upon the plasticizer–stabilizer system used. Occasional shaking of the system may be needed to assist the breaking of the foam formed.

The final result is a heavy cream-like fluid which can then be cast or molded, etc.

155. Preparation of a Clear Flexible PVC Sheet (70)*

One hundred g. of general-purpose, high molecular weight PVC resin is weighed into a suitable mixing bowl. Forty-five g. of dioctyl phthalate, 5 g. of an epoxidized soyabean oil such as Truflex E-54, and 2 g. of a barium/cadmium stabilizer such as Mark LL (Argus Chemical Co.) are added to the resin. These ingredients are thoroughly mixed to a consistency of damp sand. This compound is poured onto a 6 in. × 12 in. two-roll plastics mill with both rolls set at 325°F. and a clearance of 0.030 in. between the rolls. The compound is fluxed and mixed for 5 min., sheeted off, and cooled.

PVC sheet of commercial quality made from general purpose resin is produced on four-roll calenders or plastics extruders.

Certain copolymeric modifications of PVC have achieved commercial significance, far and away the most important being that with vinyl acetate. The most common levels of vinyl acetate are about 5 and 15 weight per cent. The virtue of the copolymers over homo-PVC is superior performance in special applications: e.g., floor tile and phonograph records.

Vinyl chloride is more reactive than vinyl acetate, with a consequent drift in copolymer composition at high conversion if the total amount

---

* Our thanks to Jesse Edenbaum and Raymond Chartier, Thompson Apex Co., for providing this and the preceding examples.

of both monomers is mixed at the beginning of a polymerization; i.e., the initial copolymer formed is rich in vinyl chloride and that formed in the later stages of reaction is rich in vinyl acetate. The resulting compositional heterogeneity can be a drawback in many end-uses, such as solution coating. The situation is a common one for many monomer pairs and can be countered by continuous or incremental addition of the more reactive monomer. The latter method is used in the following example to prepare a copolymer with a vinyl chloride–vinyl acetate weight ratio of 85/15.

At the temperature of polymerization (60°C.) reactivity ratios of 1.68 and 0.23 have been determined for vinyl chloride and acetate, respectively. The initial charge, and number and size of vinyl chloride additions have been determined by computer solution of the instantaneous copolymer composition equation so as to maintain the copolymer being formed at any instant within the range of 13–15 weight per cent vinyl chloride content. The success of doing so depends on adding each vinyl chloride increment at the proper degree of conversion of the monomers already present. Either an analytical method must be available for determining conversion, or extent of conversion as a function of time must be known by prior experience. In the experiment that follows, vinyl chloride addition is suggested at time intervals that should correspond reasonably well to the desired conversion levels so that copolymer can be made within the composition limits stated.

For copolymers with quite low vinyl acetate content (e.g., 5%), it is usually satisfactory to charge all the monomers initially and polymerize to high conversion. Heterogeneity in such cases is necessarily of only limited consequence.

Vinyl chloride–acetate copolymers are often used at a lower molecular weight than would be realized under normal suspension conditions. To accomplish this purpose in the following instance, trichloroethylene (71) is added as a chain transfer agent.

156. Preparation of Poly(vinyl chloride-co-vinyl acetate) (85/15)(71a)*

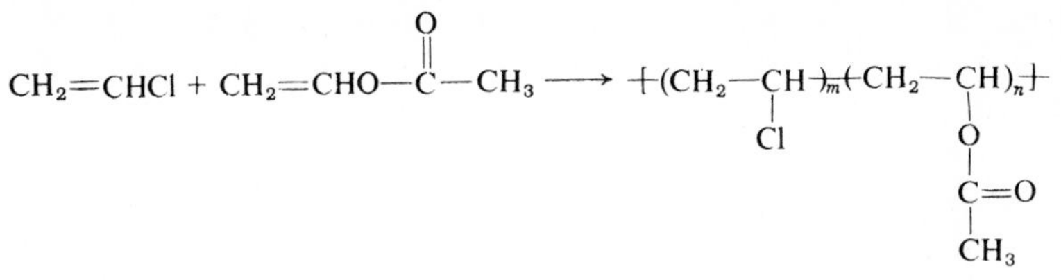

$$CH_2{=}CHCl + CH_2{=}CHO{-}\overset{\displaystyle O}{\overset{\|}{C}}{-}CH_3 \longrightarrow +(CH_2{-}\underset{\underset{Cl}{|}}{CH}{)_m}(CH_2{-}\underset{\underset{\underset{\underset{CH_3}{|}}{C{=}O}}{|}}{CH})_n+$$

* We are grateful to Dr. Franklin J. Scott, Continental Oil Co., for providing this copolymer synthesis.

To a stainless steel, stirred, 1 gal. autoclave is added 2 l. deaerated distilled water, 3.0 g. methyl cellulose (e.g., Methocel MC25, Dow Chemical Co.), 2.0 g. lauroyl peroxide, 7.0 g. trichloroethylene, 205 g. distilled vinyl acetate, and 790 g. vinyl chloride. The vinyl chloride can be conveniently added after the other ingredients are sealed in the autoclave by condensing about 840 g. of vinyl chloride into a stainless steel cylinder equipped with inlet and outlet valves. The excess vinyl chloride is then pressured into the autoclave with nitrogen. After 50 g. of vinyl chloride has been allowed to distill from the autoclave into an isopropanol–Dry Ice trap, the autoclave is resealed, heated to 60°C., and stirring is started. Subsequent additions of vinyl chloride can be made in a similar manner, i.e., by pressuring in excess liquid vinyl chloride and allowing the excess to distill. Stirring is stopped during the additions but the autoclave need not be cooled.

The timing for later monomer additions should begin from the point where the initial charge reaches 60°C. Additional decreasing increments of vinyl chloride are introduced in the following amounts:

Increment	Amount of vinyl chloride	Approximate time after preceding addition
1	90 g.	2.5 hr.*
2	75 g.	0.75
3	65 g.	0.75
4	50 g.	0.75

After the fourth increment, polymerization is allowed to proceed until an overall reaction time of 10 hr. has elapsed, at which one should obtain about 1 kg. of poly(vinyl chloride-co-vinyl acetate) which is collected on a filter, washed with methanol, and dried. This copolymer is quite uniform in composition with 13–15 weight per cent vinyl acetate and an inherent viscosity of about 0.55 (0.5% solution in cyclohexanone at 30°C.).

When vinyl chloride is polymerized by free radical initiation at considerably lower temperatures than those described in the preceding examples, a product can be obtained which shows a distinctly crystallizable character by x-ray diffraction studies of annealed samples. This is in contrast to the almost amorphous x-ray scattering shown by conventionally prepared PVC. At least a part of the enhanced crystallizability of low temperature PVC is due mainly to a more sterically regulated (primarily syndiotactic) monomer placement in the growing chain, but a substantial reduction in chain branching probably also plays a role (72–76). In any case, the properties of low temperature PVC differ in many respects from the conventional: solubility is reduced, softening and required processing temperatures are higher, tensile and modulus values are higher, and in oriented films and fibers the degree of shrinkage in boiling water is lower. However, the inherent thermal instability associated with ordinary PVC is still a factor in the

* Time after initial charge reached 60°C.

crystallizable variety; combined with the higher processing temperature required, the margin between softening and decomposition appears to be even smaller for crystallizable PVC.

The generation of free radicals at low temperatures can be accomplished, as in the following example, by use of a trialkylboron in conjunction with an oxidizing agent (e.g., hydrogen peroxide or oxygen), or by the *in situ* formation of a diacyl peroxide decomposing at the necessary low temperature (e.g., reaction of trichloroacetyl chloride and sodium peroxide at −14°C. in a suspension polymerization).

It has also been noted that when vinyl chloride is polymerized at 50°C. in the presence of an aldehyde, using a free radical initiator, a polymer of rather high crystallinity is the result (77). This was attributed to an enrichment in syndiotactic placement due to the effect of the aldehyde. It appears, however, that PVC is increasingly crystalline with decreasing molecular weight, and that the very low value of the latter when aldehyde is present is responsible for the higher crystallinity observed (78).

157. Preparation of Crystallizable Poly(vinyl chloride) (79)

A 2 l. flask or resin kettle with four necks is equipped with a stirrer, Dry Ice reflux condenser, nitrogen inlet, thermometer, and dropping funnel for catalyst addition. The vessel is purged thoroughly with nitrogen (for about 1 hr.) and cooled in Dry Ice–methanol to −40°C. Then 800 g. vinyl chloride is condensed into the reactor, taking care to remove phenol inhibitor from the monomer by distillation or passage through a suitable train (e.g., KOH pellets). Twenty g. of a 5.0% solution of tributyl borane in hexane is added over 5 min., followed by the dropwise addition of 1.5 g. of a 1% solution of hydrogen peroxide in methanol during 4 hr. (Note: Alkyl boranes should be handled with caution; ignition occurs on contact with air.) After another 30 min., 3 g. of hydroquinone in 50 ml. methanol is added to deactivate residual catalyst.

The mixture is allowed to warm to room temperature and the unreacted vinyl chloride to distill. The polymer is maintained in slurry form by adding methanol as needed to replace the liquid monomer. The polymer is finally separated by filtration, extracted with boiling methanol in a Soxhlet extractor for 6 hr., and dried under nitrogen in a vacuum oven overnight at 60°C. About 160 g. of product is obtained, having an inherent viscosity of about 1.4 in cyclohexanone (0.2 g./100 ml., 25°C.).

A portion of this polymer is then stirred slowly overnight at room temperature with 50 times its weight of tetrahydrofuran. The clear solvent is decanted from the gel portion. The latter contains primarily the crystallizable PVC, while the noncrystallizable polymer is removed by its solubility in tetrahydrofuran. The solvent is removed from the gel by thorough washing with methanol, followed by drying as before. Films can be cast from 3% solution in cyclohexanone by dissolving at 120°C. and allowing the solvent to evaporate at 70°C. in a circulating air oven for 6 hr. After drying to constant weight at 120°C./1 mm. Hg, several thicknesses of the resulting film show distinct crystallinity in x-ray diffraction.

Rigid PVC (i.e., no plasticizer) can be improved in its resistance to deformation on exposure to heat by chlorination of the polymer in such a way that 95% or more of the vinyl chloride monomer units are believed to be converted to 1,2-dichloroethylene units,—CHClCHCl—. (The latter monomer has not yet been successfully homopolymerized to a high molecular weight.) The resulting product, termed poly(vinyl dichloride) or CPVC, can have a glass temperature of over 100°C. vs. 75°C. for unmodified, rigid PVC. CPVC also appears to have a better heat stability than PVC itself.

The avoidance of 1,1-dichloroethylene monomer units in the present case is believed due to the maintenance of a sufficiently high chlorine concentration at the locus of the light-catalyzed reaction. Two factors determine the course of the reaction: dissolved chlorine content and level of photochemical activation. Moderate levels of photochemical activation can easily outstrip the ability to dissolve chlorine in the system; thus chlorine starvation must be avoided.

The starting PVC must be of a high molecular weight and have a relatively large granular form (suspension resin) with high porosity. Chloroform is used as a swelling agent and is necessary in order to obtain a superior chlorination product.

158. Chlorinated PVC (80)

$$+CH_2-CH+ \xrightarrow{Cl_2} +CH-CH+$$
$$|\phantom{CH+ \xrightarrow{Cl_2} +CH-}||$$
$$Cl\phantom{H+ \xrightarrow{Cl_2} +C}ClCl$$

To a creased, 1 l. three-necked flask equipped with a highly efficient condenser, stirrer, and a gas inlet tube extending nearly to the bottom of the flask and preferably having a fritted glass tip, is charged 160 g. of a granular high porosity PVC such as Geon 101 EP (B. F. Goodrich Co.) or Trulon 500 SP (Thompson Apex Co., a Division of Continental Oil Co.), 320 ml. of concentrated (37%) hydrochloric acid, 275 ml. distilled water, and 60 ml. chloroform. A 100 watt mercury arc lamp (A4 H 100 type) is positioned adjacent to the flask; it is preferred, however, to insert a lamp into the flask. The flask is immersed in a water bath held at a temperature of 55°C. The mixture is stirred extremely rapidly and chlorine is admitted at a rate of 1375 ml./min. as determined by a rotameter calibrated for this purpose. The reaction mixture should evidence the presence of chlorine by a greenish-yellow color throughout the addition. If this does not occur, the chlorine rate should be increased. After 7.5 hr., the reaction is stopped and the slurry filtered. The solid polymer is washed with dilute bicarbonate to neutralize the residual acid, then with water to free it of salts. The chlorine content should be about 71.9%; theoretical for poly(vinyl dichloride) is 72.3%. The glass temperature is well over 100°C., and the intrinsic viscosity is about 1.24, which is somewhat higher than the starting polymer.

159. Polymerization of Vinyl Chloride in Bulk (81)

$$CH_2=CHCl \longrightarrow [-CH_2CHCl-]_n$$

A polymer tube of approximately 150–200 ml. capacity is flushed with nitrogen and cooled in a Dry Ice–acetone mixture. Approximately 50 g. of vinyl chloride is condensed into the nitrogen filled tube from a cylinder. To the tube is now added approximately 0.15 g. of benzoyl peroxide. The tube is flushed again with nitrogen and sealed. Note that considerable pressures will develop during the polymerization process, hence the tube itself and the seal must be adequate to protect the tube against explosion. The sealed tube is now transferred to a heating bath maintained at approximately 50°C., and polymerization is allowed to proceed for approximately 24 hr. The tube is cooled to room temperature, carefully broken and the polymer plug removed. It is a slightly discolored clear, glassy solid with a molecular weight in the range 50–75,000.

Dehalogenation of poly(vinyl chloride) is another chemical transformation which can be carried out satisfactorily. It may be done with either zinc (82) or lithium aluminum hydride (83). With zinc, the product loses about 85% of the chlorine and appears to be a polymer containing cyclopropane rings with isolated halogen. Statistical calculations (84) predict that about 14% of the halogen would be isolated by reaction of adjacent groups in the formation of this type of structure. The dehydrochlorination of PVC can be carried out in a relatively controlled fashion by means of lithium chloride in DMF (87); the uncontrolled loss of HCl during thermal processing is a characteristic problem (88).

Reduction of poly(vinyl chloride) with lithium aluminum hydride

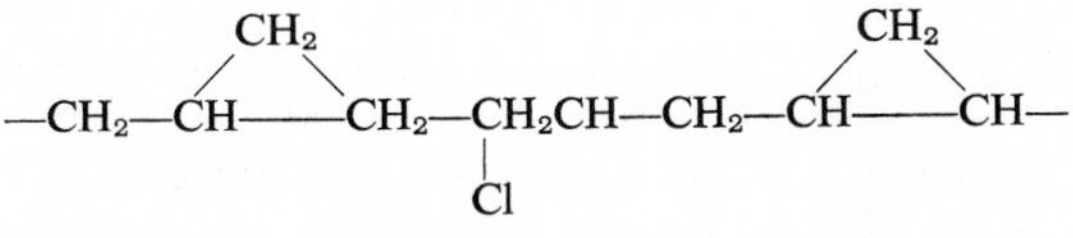

(83) gives a product which appears to be essentially chlorine free, by a typical hydride hydrogenolysis of a halide (85,86).

160. Dehalogenation of Poly(vinyl chloride) (82)

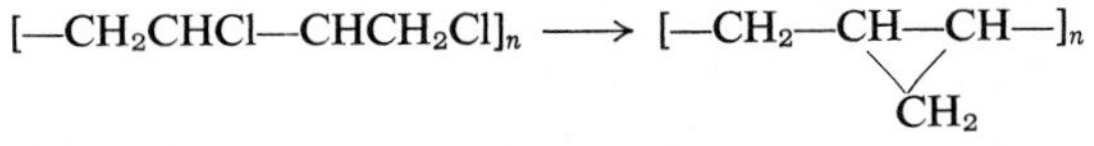

A mixture of 150 ml. of peroxide-free dioxane and 0.5 g. of poly(vinyl chloride) is refluxed with 4 g. of zinc dust which was purified by treating first with dilute hydrochloric acid, then washing with water to remove excess acid, then drying by slurrying with acetone, and filtering under nitrogen. After about 150–160 hr. refluxing, the mixture is cooled and filtered from excess zinc. The polymer may be isolated by evaporation of the dioxane or by addition of water to the filtrate. The product is a rubbery mass which is soluble in carbon tetrachloride. Solutions do not give a test for unsaturation.

161. Dehydrochlorination of Poly(vinyl chloride)* (87)

$$\begin{CD} +CH_2-\underset{\underset{Cl}{|}}{CH}+_n @>{LiCl}>{DMF}> +CH_2-\underset{\underset{Cl}{|}}{CH}+_{n-x}+CH=CH+_x \end{CD}$$

As the deyhydrohalogenated products are highly sensitive to atmospheric oxygen, it is necessary to operate under purified nitrogen or argon.

A mixture of 3 g. of PVC, 13.75 g. LiCl (previously dried under vacuum at 80°C. for 24 hr.), and 300 ml. of DMF is placed in a three-necked flask equipped with a gas inlet tube and a reflux condenser (see Fig. 4.1). The mixture is magnetically stirred and is kept at 80°C. for 8 hr. The reaction medium becomes violet-colored and the intensity of the coloration increases as the reactions proceeds. At the end of the reaction, the solution is allowed to cool under stirring and it is transferred by inert gas pressure into a dropping funnel placed above the precipitation flask. The dehydrochlorinated polymer solution is then dropwise added to about 2 l. of methanol, under vigorous stirring. When it has precipitated, the polymer has become insoluble in DMF, but it still swells in this solvent. In order to eliminate the last traces of LiCl, the polymer is allowed to settle, the supernatant liquid is removed by suction,

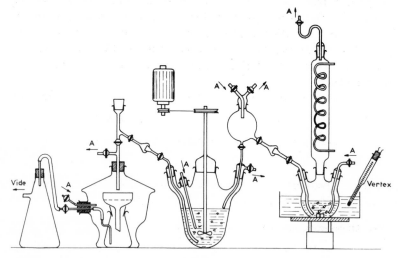

Fig. 4.1.

* We thank Professor J. Parrod, Strasbourg, for supplying the details of this example.

and one more liter of methanol is added. The suspension of polymer is then filtered under inert gas atmosphere by means of a Büchner funnel set on a suction flask, inside a two-inlet desiccator. The precipitated polymer is washed, dried under vacuum, and distributed in tubes which are sealed under high vacuum.

The chlorine content of the dehydrohalogenated polymer is about 39%, which indicates that about 50 conjugated double bonds have been created in 100 monomeric units. UV and visible spectroscopy shows a broad absorption band with a maximum near 530 mμ; this is a good evidence for very long sequences of conjugated double bonds.

By modifying the molar ratio LiCl/PVC and/or the reaction temperature, it is possible to get a whole range of polymers with different degrees of unsaturation.

162. Reduction of Poly(vinyl chloride) with Lithium Aluminum Hydride (83)

$$[CH_2CHCl]_n \longrightarrow [-CH_2CH_2-]_n$$

Tetrahydrofuran is purified by distillation from potassium hydroxide followed by refluxing over lithium aluminum hydride for 5 hr. The solvent is then distilled directly into the reaction vessel. (Do not distill to dryness!) Reaction is carried out by dissolving 13.3 g. of poly(vinyl chloride) and 13.3 g. of lithium aluminum hydride in 1 l. of tetrahydrofuran. This mixture is refluxed under nitrogen for about 150 hr. Essentially all of the halogen is removed from the polymer under these conditions. The polymer is isolated by the addition of water (Caution!), filtered, washed with dilute hydrochloric acid, water, and dried. The degree of polymerization of the product is essentially the same as the degree of polymerization of the original poly(vinyl chloride). The product has properties similar to low density polyethylene.

Acrylonitrile, the next monosubstituted ethylene to be considered, polymerizes with the greatest of ease with a wide variety of catalysts, both free radical and anionic (Chapter 4, Section VII). Solution, suspension, and emulsion techniques have been successfully employed, but the polymerization is too exothermic to make bulk polymerization satisfactory.

163. Polymerization of Acrylonitrile in a Slurry (89)

$$CH_2=CHCN \longrightarrow [CH_2-CHCN]_n$$

Commerical acrylonitrile contains an inhibitor (usually a hydroquinone derivative) which is best removed before polymerization. Immediately before use commercial acrylonitrile is passed through a column of silica gel about 24 in. long and 1 in. wide. It is maintained under a slight head of nitrogen and is collected at the bottom of the column and used immediately. If it is retained without the inhibitor, it may polymerize of its own volition.

A 500 ml. three-necked flask is equipped with a stirrer, condenser, and a nitrogen inlet and surrounded by a constant temperature bath maintained at about 40°C. Three hundred ml. of water which has previously been deaerated by boiling for 10 min. and 22 g. of purified acrylonitrile are placed in the flask and stirred gently for 10 min. to allow the mixture to come to bath temperature. The initiator is now added. It is composed of 0.3 g. of potassium persulfate dissolved in 10 ml. of water, followed after 1 min. by 0.15 g. of sodium bisulfite, also in 10 ml. of water. Almost immediately, the colorless, aqueous solution becomes somewhat opalescent and white polymer begins to precipitate. After 3 hr. the polymerization should be complete. The solid product is filtered, washed with water, and dried in a vacuum over at 60°C. overnight. The yield of polymer is 80–90%. The inherent viscosity as measured in DMF will be about 2.0 (0.5%, 25°C.).

164. Emulsion Polymerization of Acrylonitrile (90)

$$CH_2=CHCN \longrightarrow [-CH_2-\overset{\displaystyle CN}{\underset{\displaystyle |}{CH}}-]_n$$

A 500 ml. three-necked, round-bottom flask is fitted with a nitrogen inlet, a stirrer, and a reflux condenser.

The flask is thermostatted in a bath at about 35°C. and flushed for 15 min. with nitrogen. Then 120 ml. of freshly boiled distilled water is added, stirring is started, and the nitrogen flow is reduced to a very slow rate over the surface. To this flask is now added, in order, 2 g. of sodium Lorol sulfate detergent, 80 g. of acrylonitrile freed of inhibitor by the method described in the previous experiment, 0.1 g. of potassium persulfate and 0.033 g. of sodium bisulfite. Evidence that the polymerization has started is the appearance of a milkiness, usually in about 5–20 min. If the milkiness does not appear within about 1 hr., an additional amount of initiator and activator may be added. Once begun, polymerization is usually complete in 2–3 hr. However, a small additional yield may be obtained by allowing it to stand overnight. A nearly quantitative yield of polymer is obtained as a stable dispersion. The particles are nearly spherical with a diameter of approximately 0.1 μ. The polymer is isolated by pouring the dispersion into approximately 500 ml. of water, then slowly adding salt with stirring to coagulate the emulsion. The product is collected by filtration. It is washed with water and dried in air at room temperature. The molecular weight of the polymer prepared in this manner is extremely high, the inherent viscosity usually being of the order of 10.5 as measured in DMF (0.5%, 30°C.).

Polyacrylonitrile homopolymer is very resistant toward most chemical reagents. It is, however, degraded by alkali and by heat. A most interesting **transformation** occurs when an acrylonitrile fiber, such as Orlon,* is **heated** in a controlled fashion (91) at 200°C. and over. The originally white, flammable yarn or fabric turns black, and becomes fireproof without losing its identity as a fiber. The density of the polymer increases from 1.17 to 1.60, while the tensile strength of the yarn decreases, perhaps as much as 50%, though it is still equivalent or superior to

---

* Trademark for du Pont's acrylic fiber.

many commercial yarns. It has been suggested (91,92) that this product is produced by the following transformation:

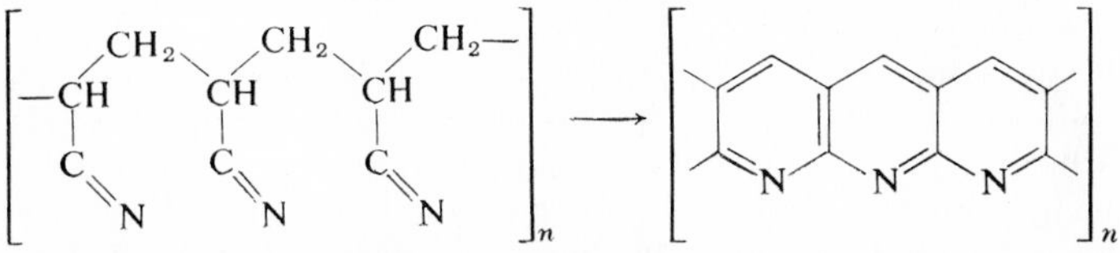

165. Thermal Condensation of Polyacrylonitrile (91,93)

For this preparation, almost any type of a forced draft oven capable of operating at temperatures in the range of 250°C. or more can be used success- fully. The condensation product may be prepared in the form of either fabric or yarn. However, it is more convenient to use a portion of fabric made, for example, from Orlon acrylic fiber. The fabric is placed in a forced draft oven and heated for a period of time suitable for converting the polyacrylonitrile to the black modification. The time varies; at 250–275°C. the time required is 4–6 hr. It should be noted that the conversion of polyacrylonitrile to the black modification is an extremely exothermic reaction, so that the material being treated should not be wadded together or compressed as this will tend to give a charred product from its own heat of reaction. It should be noted also that oxygen is necessary for the conversion. The optimum oxygen content fortu- nately is about 20%, so air is the most satisfactory medium in which to carry out this conversion. Black fabric produced as described has a remarkable resistance to fire. A sample of the fabric can be held directly in a flame. The only effect will be that the sample will glow around the edges. If left in the flame for any length of time, the fabric will lose its strength completely. However, under no conditions will it show signs of burning.

Another chemical reaction which may be carried out on **poly- acrylonitrile** is the **reaction with hydroxylamine** (94). The resulting **polyamideoxime** is formed without cleavage of the backbone, hence has the same degree of polymerization as the parent polymer. The product is film- and fiber-forming.

166. Conversion of Polyacrylonitrile to Polyacrylamideoxime (94)

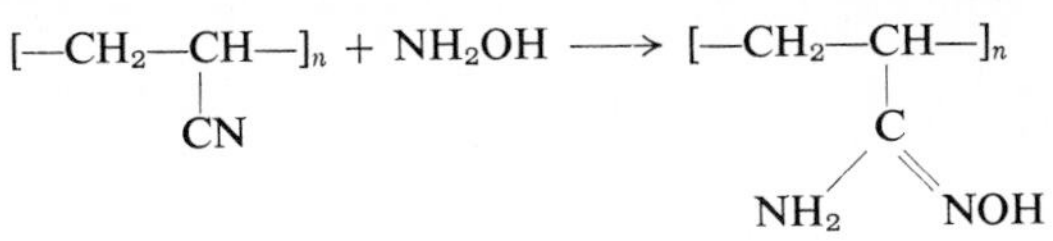

$$[-CH_2-CH-]_n + NH_2OH \longrightarrow [-CH_2-CH-]_n$$
$$\underset{CN}{|} \qquad\qquad \underset{\underset{NH_2 \quad NOH}{C}}{|}$$

A 1 l. three-necked flask containing 300 ml. of dimethylformamide and 50 g. of polyacrylonitrile is equipped with a mechanical stirrer and maintained at a temperature of 75°C. by an external water bath. Twenty g. of hydroxylamine hydrochloride and 15 g. of anhydrous pulverized sodium carbonate are added to the flask and the resulting mixture is stirred and heated for 3 hr. At the end of this time, the polymer solution is filtered, precipitated into methanol, and the product washed with methanol and dried. The nitrogen content will vary between 23 and 25%. This is not too different from the nitrogen content of pure polyacrylonitrile, suggesting that some hydrolysis of amideoxime groups has occurred. That some chemical reaction has taken place on the polymer is evidenced by the fact that although the polymer remains in solution during the reaction the precipitated and dried product no longer will dissolve in dimethyl formamide. However, it will dissolve in dilute hydrochloric acid and dilute sodium hydroxide. The dilute hydrochloric acid solution gives a deep red-to-violet color with ferric chloride, indicative of the formation of a ferric chelate of the amideoxime group.

Vinyl acetate may be polymerized by a variety of free radical catalysts. Several typical systems are given.

167. Solution Polymerization of Vinyl Acetate in Benzene

$$CH_2=CHOCOCH_3 \longrightarrow \overset{\displaystyle OCOCH_3}{[-CH_2-CH]_n}$$

A 2 l. three-necked flask, equipped with a stirrer, condenser, nitrogen inlet, and a thermometer is charged with 200 ml. of vinyl acetate and 300 ml. of dry benzene. The vinyl acetate is purified by distillation, then passed through a silica column just before use. The mixture is heated to reflux under nitrogen and about 0.2 g. of α,α'-azodiisobutyronitrile is added. Polymerization is allowed to proceed to reflux temperature for about 2 hr. and the mixture is treated with steam to remove unreacted monomer and solvents. The polymer is broken up, filtered, then dried. This polymer has an inherent viscosity in chloroform of greater than 1 (0.5% at 25°C.).

168. Emulsion Polymerization of Vinyl Acetate (95)

To a 500 ml. multi-necked flask or resin kettle equipped with stirrer, reflux condenser, dropping funnel with pressure-equalizing side arm, thermometer, and nitrogen inlet, is charged 70 ml. water, 1.5 g. polyethoxylated lauryl alcohol, 5.0 g. sodium tridecylethoxylate sulfate (the latter are available from Alcolac Chemical Corp. as Sipex L25 and EST, respectively), and 1.0 g. of a protective colloid (such as Cellosize WP-09, Union Carbide Chemicals Div.). The mixture is stirred and heated to 70°C. to effect solution as nitrogen is is bubbled through it to remove the air. The solution is then cooled to 50°C. and 0.05 g. of sodium carbonate (to act as a buffer) and 0.15 g. potassium persulfate are added. Then, 10 g. of distilled vinyl acetate is added to the flask, and the mixture is stirred and refluxed (ca. 65°C.). The polymerization begins and the temperature is raised to 80–85°C. at a rate governed by the maintenance of a mild reflux. When the temperature reaches 85°C., 90 g. of distilled vinyl acetate is added from the dropping funnel at a rate that will maintain reflux. After each fourth of the vinyl acetate in the funnel has been added, 1 ml. of a 5% potassium persulfate solution (in deaerated water) is added to the flask. When the last monomer and initiator solution has been added, the temperature is raised to 90°C. for 1 hr. The emulsion is cooled to room temperature and enough of a 5% solution of sodium carbonate is added to adjust the pH to 4.5–5.5. The creamy emulsion has a solids content of about 55%. Such a product is best used in its emulsion form, e.g., for surface coatings, rather than attempting to isolate the polymer for subsequent use.

169. Polymerization of Vinyl Acetate (96)

$$CH_2=CHOCOCH_3 \longrightarrow [-CH_2-\overset{\displaystyle OCOCH_3}{\underset{\displaystyle |}{CH}}-]_n$$

In a 3 l., three-necked flask equipped with a stirrer, an efficient condenser, and a nitrogen inlet is placed 300 g. of pure vinyl acetate, 800 ml. of water, 3 g. of commercial sodium dodecyl sulfate detergent, 3 g. of sodium dihydrogen phosphate monohydrate, and 1.5 g. of α,α'-azodiisobutyronitrile. The vessel is swept with nitrogen to remove the air and the mixture is maintained with stirring at a temperature of about 40°C. for 17 hr. The reaction mixture is then treated with steam to remove unpolymerized vinyl acetate, cooled, and the solid polymer is filtered from the aqueous phase, washed with water, and dried. The polyvinyl acetate is obtained in the form of tiny spheres or granules which are easily handled. The reaction time may be decreased by increasing the amount of catalyst.

High molecular weight poly(vinyl acetate) is a clear, glassy solid soluble in many organic solvents. It softens at a fairly low temperature and discolors above 200°C. It is amorphous.

Poly(vinyl acetate) is readily **hydrolyzed** in alcohol solution **to poly(vinyl alcohol)**, the polymer of the unknown vinyl alcohol, or acetaldehyde enol. This polymer is less readily soluble in organic media, but dissolves in water. The bulky acetoxy group has been replaced by the smaller —OH, so the polymer can now crystallize; fibers with high crystallinity and orientation can be obtained. Poly(vinyl alcohol) of various degrees of hydrolysis and of several different molecular weight ranges are available commercially.

170. Hydrolysis of Poly(vinyl Acetate) (97–100)

$$[CH_2-\overset{\displaystyle OCOCH_3}{\underset{\displaystyle |}{CH}}-]_n \longrightarrow [CH_2-\overset{\displaystyle OH}{\underset{\displaystyle |}{CH}}-]_n$$

Fifty g. of high molecular weight poly(vinyl acetate) is dissolved in about 500 ml. of boiling methanol in a 1 l. flask equipped with a condenser, with drying tube, pressure-equalizing dropping funnel, and a mechanical stirrer. All due precautions are observed to maintain anhydrous conditions. Five per cent sodium methoxide in methyl alcohol is added to the stirred refluxing polymer solution in 5–10 ml. portions at intervals of 5 min. Approximately 25–30 ml. of the solution is sufficient to catalyze the methanolysis. The reaction, once begun, proceeds rapidly with the precipitation of the polyvinyl alcohol which is insoluble in methanol. If the hydrolysis proceeds at too great a rate, the reaction may be moderated by the addition of 100–200 ml. of methanol and by external cooling. After the reaction has subsided, refluxing is continued for about 3 min. and the mixture is filtered. If the product is gel-like, it may be broken up by vigorous agitation in a Waring Blendor with cold methanol. The product is filtered and washed several times with alcohol and then dried.

Alternatively, the hydrolysis of poly(vinyl acetate) may be carried out in acidic media. For example, 30 g. of poly(vinyl acetate), 100 g. of water, and 1 g. of 95% sulfuric acid is heated and stirred for 6–8 hr. at 95°C., or until a clear solution is obtained. Steam is then passed through the solution to remove acetic acid and complete the hydrolysis. The poly(vinyl alcohol) is isolated by precipitation with concentrated salt solution or the aqueous acid solution may be used directly, for example in the preparation of poly(vinyl butyral) described below.

171. Films and Fibers of Poly(vinyl alcohol) (101,102)

The preparation of poly(vinyl alcohol) films may be carried out by dissolving polymer in solvent to a solid content of 15–20% and casting the solution on a glass plate or a polished metal surface with a doctor knife (see Chapter 2) of appropriate clearance. Poly(vinyl alcohol) is hygroscopic. Therefore, drying of the film cast from water is relatively difficult and slow. It is preferable to use a solvent such as alcohol–water (30–70) for this purpose. It is also preferable to carry out the drying of the film in a closed container in a slow stream of dry air.

It is interesting to note that poly(vinyl alcohol) film will react with iodine very much in the same manner as starch to form a sorption complex. If these films are stretched, the complex is oriented to a structure which is light polarizing. This is the basis of many of the polarizing filters now in use (108a).

Fibers of poly(vinyl alcohol) can be prepared rather simply by extrusion of aqueous solutions into precipitating baths consisting of aqueous solutions of salts in a high concentration or into an organic nonsolvent. The fiber is then further processed by stretching in the usual manner. Such fibers are sensitive to cold water and usually will dissolve in hot water. These fibers are less soluble in water when under tension than when relaxed. The following represents a typical preparation of a poly(vinyl alcohol) fiber.

A 20% solution of high molecular weight poly(vinyl alcohol) in water is prepared at a temperature of about 73°C. It is placed in a spinning apparatus such as the ones described in Chapter 2 maintained at this temperature, and extruded by a mechanical pump through a spinneret into a 40% aqueous solution of ammonium sulfate at about 50°C. The rate of extrusion should be such that the filaments are completely coagulated and capable of supporting their own weight when removed at the other end of the bath. The fibers are wound up on a mechanical windup and the yarn is washed on the bobbin in 50% acetone–water mixture. Finally, the yarn is greated with 95% acetone–H$_2$O and the yarn is then allowed to dry overnight at room temperature. The yarn is then stretched to its maximum degree at 75–100°C. and wound onto a cone.

The techniques of precipitation of poly(vinyl alcohol) solution in strong salt solutions may also be applied to the preparation of **poly-(vinyl alcohol) film.**

Thus, a 50% aqueous solution of poly(vinyl alcohol) at 75°C. to which has been added approximately 0.01 of sodium dioctylsulfosuccinate is cast on a glass plate using a doctor knife of approximately 0.004 in. clearance. The plate and film are then immersed in a saturated aqueous solution of sodium sulfate or of ammonium sulfate, maintained at a temperature of 40–50°C. The solution is allowed to coagulate for 5 min. or more, then the plate is removed and immersed in a 50% aqueous acetone solution. After 3 hr. the film is removed from the plate and washed with fresh portions of the aqueous acetone. It is finally washed with pure acetone. The product is a strong self-supporting film of poly(vinyl alcohol).

It is also possible to use organic media for the precipitation of poly(vinyl alcohol) solutions in fiber or film form. Thus, a solution of 14% by weight poly(vinyl alcohol) in water at 60°C. is extruded into a precipitating bath consisting of 94% acetone and 6% water at about 30°C. The polymer solution is precipitated in the form of a thread which is wound up at a rate sufficiently slow such that the thread, on issuing from the bath, is completely self-supporting. The yarn is then stretched approximately 5 times its former length in a mixture of 50% diethylene glycol monomethyl ether and 50% water at about 30°C. The yarn so obtained should have tenacities of better than 2 g./denier.

Poly(vinyl alcohol) may be plasticized by a number of hydroxylic materials such as ethylene glycol or glycerol. Two examples of **plasticized poly(vinyl alcohol)** given in the patent literature are as follows.

172. Preparation of Plasticized Poly(vinyl alcohol) (103)

A mixture of 100 g. of poly(vinyl alcohol), 35 g. of glycerol, 45 g. of water, and 12 g. of ammonium bromide is thoroughly mixed together, preferably by milling on a rubber mill. The resulting highly plasticized material is obtained as a rather rubbery sheet which will remain flexible for long periods of time throughout a wide temperature range.

Similarly, a plasticized composition of poly(vinyl alcohol) may be made by blending 100 g. of poly(vinyl alcohol), 45 g. of water, 10 g. of formamide, 35 g. of ethylene glycol, and 12 g. of ammonium bromide. This material again is tough and very flexible and retains its flexibility to quite low temperatures.

Poly(vinyl alcohol) with its free hydroxyl groups offers considerable latitude for **chemical transformation.** Thus acetylation converts it back to the parent poly(vinyl acetate) while, for example, butyric anhydride, will produce **poly(vinyl butyrate).**

173. Preparation of Poly(vinyl butyrate) by Esterification

$$\begin{bmatrix} -CH_2-CH- \\ | \\ OH \end{bmatrix}_n \longrightarrow \begin{bmatrix} -CH_2-CH- \\ | \\ OCOCH_2CH_2CH_3 \end{bmatrix}_n$$

Ten g. of poly(vinyl alcohol) is refluxed with a mixture of 50 ml. of pyridine and 50 ml. of butyric anhydride until a clear, homogeneous solution results. The product is precipitated by pouring into water. The solid polymer is filtered, washed thoroughly, and dried. In order to obtain a pure product, it is preferable to dissolve the polymer in a solvent such as methanol and reprecipitate by pouring into a Waring Blendor containing water agitated at a high rate of speed. The slurry is filtered and the polymer dried. It exhibits properties similar to those of poly(vinyl acetate), except that it is somewhat less brittle at lower temperatures.

Since poly(vinyl alcohol) is a 1,3 glycol, it forms **cyclic acetals** with aldehydes. For example, water insoluble fibers may be prepared by extrusion of aqueous poly(vinyl alcohol) into aqueous formaldehyde. Acetalization occurs, together with an occasional crosslink, rendering the fiber insoluble.

174. Preparation of Water Insoluble Poly(vinyl alcohol) Fibers (104)

$$\left[-CH_2CH_2-CH_2-\underset{\underset{OH}{|}}{CH}-CH_2-\underset{\underset{OH}{|}}{CH}\right]_n \longrightarrow \left[-CH_2 \cdots CH_2-\underset{\underset{-CH_2}{|}}{CH}-\right]_n$$

A 16% by weight solution of poly(vinyl alcohol) in water is prepared. The precipitating bath consists of 40% aqueous ammonium sulfate maintained at 50°C. to which has been added 10% formaldehyde (as 37% aqueous solution) and $\frac{1}{4}$ mole of sulfuric acid for every mole of ammonium sulfate. The aqueous solution of poly(vinyl alcohol) is extruded into this acidic salt solution of formaldehyde. The polymer sets up into strong fibers which should have tenacities of the order of 2–2.5 g. per denier after being removed from the spinning bath, stretched and dried.

It is obvious that other aldehydes could be substituted for the formaldehyde, giving a whole family of polymers, each with different characteristics with respect to melting point, stiffness, solubility, etc. Furthermore, acetalization may be carried out on the finished yarn, or film. For example, a film such as was made in an earlier preparation, soaked in an aqueous solution of benzaldehyde (10%) and phosphoric acid (1%) in hot ethanol will pick up a substantial weight of benzaldehyde in an acetal structure, during the course of several hours.

An important plastic which finds use in safety glass is **poly(vinyl butyral)**, made from poly(vinyl alcohol) and butyraldehyde.

175. The Preparation of Poly(vinyl butyral) (105)

A solution of 100 g. of poly(vinyl alcohol), 80 ml. of methyl alcohol, and 0.3 of sulfuric acid in 820 ml. of water is prepared by mixing the ingredients with warming in a vessel equipped with a mechanical stirrer. To the agitated

$$\left[\begin{array}{c} -CH_2-CH-CH_2-CH- \\ | \qquad\qquad | \\ OH \qquad\quad OH \end{array}\right]_n \xrightarrow{C_3H_7CHO} \left[\begin{array}{c} -CH_2 \\ O \qquad O \\ | \\ C_3H_7 \end{array}\right]_n$$

solution is added 80 g. of butyraldehyde. Three hundred g. of this solution is placed in a 2 l., three-necked flask equipped with mechanical stirrer and a condenser. Eighty g. of butyraldehyde is then added with vigorous stirring, followed by the remainder of the poly(vinyl alcohol) solution over a period of about 20 min. During this time the internal temperature should rise to about 70°C. At the conclusion of this period, 600 ml. of hot water at approximately 70°C. is added over a period of 15–20 min. The resulting mixture is agitated for an additional 10 min., then 3 g. of concentrated sulfuric acid, dissolved in 25 ml. of water, is added. The reaction mixture is allowed to stir for an additional 1 hr., then the resin is filtered and washed repeatedly with water. A product is obtained, if the agitation is satisfactory, of a particle size which is appropriate for easy handling and filtering.

The poly(vinyl butyral) prepared in this way must be washed thoroughly with dilute alkali to remove the last traces of acid which would catalyze decomposition.

The major use of poly(vinyl butyral) is in the preparation of safety glass in which a thin layer of plasticized polymer is sandwiched between two sheets of glass. The poly(vinyl butyral) has outstanding adherence to the glass. It is elastic and tough and serves admirably for this purpose.

In order to prepare a **plasticized poly(vinyl butyral)**, 100 g. of polymer is mixed with a plasticizer such as Flexol* 3GH, which is triethylene glycol di-2-ethylbutyrate. The polymer and plasticizer are blended together, with enough ethanol to form a plastic mass. This material can be spread or rolled into a sheet and the solvent allowed to evaporate. The resulting product may be dusted with talc to decrease the tackiness of the material, if it is to be stored. In order to prepare a laminate with two pieces of glass, a sheet of the butyral is washed and placed between carefully cleaned pieces of glass. The seal is effected by heating in a Carver Press or similar source of heat and pressure at temperatures of 150–175°C. and moderate pressures. For the preparation of commercial glass laminates, it is necessary to finish the process by heating at higher temperatures and pressures. Specialized equipment, however, is necessary.

Other groups reactive toward secondary hydroxyls will also transform poly(vinyl alcohol). For example, **cyanoethylation** occurs readily, without chain cleavage.

176. Cyanoethylation of Poly(vinyl alcohol) (106)

$$\left[\begin{array}{c} CH_2-CH \\ | \\ OH \end{array}\right]_n + CH_2{=}CH{-}CN \longrightarrow \left[\begin{array}{c} -CH-CH- \\ | \\ OCH_2CH_2CN \end{array}\right]_n$$

* Trademark of Union Carbide Corporation.

A slurry of 45 g. of high viscosity poly(vinyl alcohol), 265 g. of acrylonitrile, and 5 g. of a 5% aqueous solution of sodium hydroxide is placed in a 500 ml., three-necked flask fitted with a mechanical stirrer and a reflux condenser. The mixture is heated externally to reflux. After about ½ hr., the poly(vinyl alcohol) begins to go into solution and forms a gel. After another 15 min. at reflux, the external heat is discontinued and the reaction mixture is cooled and then neutralized with glacial acetic acid. The resulting viscous, light tan product, which consists of a solution of polymer in acrylonitrile, is poured into about 2 l. of diethyl ether and a taffy-like precipitate is obtained. This precipitate is dissolved in 300 ml. of acetone and again precipitated by pouring into diethyl ether. The product is then dried in a vacuum over phosphorus pentoxide. The yield is about 95 g.

Poly(vinyl acetate) from free radical polymerization differs little in tacticity regardless of the circumstances under which it is prepared; an essentially atactic placement occurs from polymerization with an azo initiator at room temperature and above as well as by triethylborane/oxygen at $-78°C$. (109). Poly(vinyl alcohol) (PVA) derived by hydrolysis of the acetate is consequently also atactic in structure, though a high level of crystallinity can be developed. Differences in properties of PVA's derived from poly(vinyl acetates) prepared in varying ways have been reported, but these differences are believed due to variances in molecular weight and chain branching rather than tacticity changes.

PVA of syndiotactic-enriched structure can be prepared from poly(vinyl trifluoroacetate) which is made by radical initiation at $-78°C$. (110). Isotactic-enriched PVA results from the cleavage of poly(vinyl t-butyl ether) made at $-78°C$. in a cationic polymerization (111,112), and from debenzylation of poly(vinyl benzyl ether) cationically polymerized at $-78°C$. (113). It has also been reported that polymerization of vinyl trimethylsilyl ether at $-78°C$. with $SnCl_4$ or Et_2AlCl as catalyst gives, after cleavage of the trimethylsilyl groups, a predominantly isotactic or syndiotactic PVA, the former in less polar solvents (toluene), the latter in polar ones (methylene chloride) (114). While the question of tacticity assignment in PVA may not yet be fully resolved, it appears that in none of these cases is the stereoregularity overwhelmingly of one type, as it is with, say, isotactic polypropylene. The vinyl trimethylsilyl ether route to both iso- and syndiotacticity may, at the present, achieve the highest levels of tactic purities. Iso-, hetero-, and syndiotactic triads of 86/10/4 and 6/40/54 have been reported (114).

There is apparently no increase in crystallinity in PVA with an increase in stereoregularity. The OH and H are evidently quite interchangeable in the crystal lattice development of this highly polar polymer. There is an influence of stereoregularity on other properties, however. Both syndio- and isotactic PVA are more water-resistant than the atactic (115).

177. Preparation of Mainly Isotactic Poly(vinyl alcohol) from Poly(vinyl t-butyl ether) (112)

$$CH_2{=}CH{-}O{-}\underset{\underset{CH_3}{|}}{\overset{\overset{CH_3}{|}}{C}}{-}CH_3 \longrightarrow \underset{I}{\{CH_2{-}CH\} \atop \overset{|}{O} \atop CH_3{-}\underset{\overset{|}{CH_3}}{\overset{|}{C}}{-}CH_3}$$

$$I + HBr \longrightarrow \{CH_2{-}\underset{\overset{|}{OH}}{CH}\} + (CH_3)_3CBr$$

A 200 ml. polymerization vessel and stirrer apparatus are baked dry at 120°C. and assembled in a stream of nitrogen to maintain dryness on cooling. To the nitrogen-purged vessel is added 100 ml. of dry toluene and a solution of 0.034 g. of distilled, boron trifluoride etherate (2.4×10^{-4} moles) in 5 ml. dry toluene. The mixture is cooled to $-87°C$. in Dry Ice–acetone and 5 g. of freshly distilled (from sodium) and previously chilled vinyl t-butyl ether (b.p. 76–78°C.) is added by syringe through a serum cap. The polymerization occurs in a homogeneous manner and is completed within an hour. The polymer is precipitated in methanol containing a small amount of aqueous ammonia, washed thoroughly in methanol, and dried in vacuum at 50°C. The polymer should show moderate crystallinity by x-ray diffraction. The intrinsic viscosity is about 0.7 in benzene at 30°C.

To prepare mainly isotactic poly(vinyl alcohol), 1 g. of the above poly(vinyl t-butyl ether) dissolved in 100 ml. of dry toluene in a 200 ml. round-bottom flask, with a gas inlet and outlet protected by a drying tube, is cooled to 0°C. and gaseous HBr passed through the solution for 15 min. The precipitated polymer is filtered, washed thoroughly with methanol containing a small amount of aqueous ammonia, and dried in vacuum at 50°C. Ether cleavage is essentially complete. The polymer has an excess of isotactic diads or triads by NMR examination of a deuterium oxide solution (111); the ratio of per cent iso-/hetero-/syndiotactic triads is about 49/38/13.

178. Preparation of Mainly Syndiotactic Poly(vinyl acetate) from Poly(vinyl trifluoroacetate) (110)

A 500 ml. three-necked round-bottom flask is fitted with a gas inlet, a stirrer, and a gas outlet protected with a drying tube. The flask is flamed under argon and a positive pressure of argon maintained. The flask is cooled to $-78°C$. and 66 g. of redistilled vinyl trifluoroacetate, b.p. 39°C. (Peninsular Chem. Research), and 18 ml. of n-heptane added. To the cold solution is added 1 ml. of tri-n-butylborane in 5 ml. of n-heptane by syringe. At 10 min. intervals, five 10 cc. portions of dry air are added also by syringe. The

$$CF_3-\overset{\overset{\displaystyle O}{\|}}{C}-OCH{=}CH_2 \longrightarrow +CH_2-CH+$$

with the repeat unit bearing:

$$
\begin{array}{c}
+CH_2-CH+ \\
\mid \\
O \\
\mid \\
C{=}O \\
\mid \\
CF_3
\end{array}
$$

I

$$I \longrightarrow +CH_2-CH+$$
$$\mid$$
$$OH$$

polymerization is allowed to continue for 16 hr. at $-78°C$. The polymerization mixture is placed in a Waring Blendor and stirred with 300 ml. of cyclohexane. The precipitated polymer is filtered, washed with 300 ml. of cyclohexane, and dried in a vacuum over at $50°C$. The dried poly(vinyl trifluoroacetate) weighs about 38 g. and has an intrinsic viscosity of about 2.2 in methyl ethyl ketone at $30°C$.

One g. of this polymer is dissolved in 10 ml. of acetone and added to 240 ml. of a $50:50$ ammonium hydroxide–methyl alcohol mixture with rapid stirring. The solution is stirred rapidly for 3 hr., filtered, washed with acetone, and dried. PVA is obtained which is free of trifluoroacetate groups as determined from IR and NMR spectra and analyses for fluorine. The percentages by NMR are $11/46/43$ for iso-/hetero-/syndiotactic triads.

Acrylic acid, its **salts, amides, esters,** and **acid chlorides** can be polymerized.

The preparation of a vinyl polymer of a high degree of reactivity is made possible by the availability of **acryloyl chloride** (116) which can be **polymerized to a polymeric acid chloride.** It has the expected high degree of sensitivity toward hydroxylic reagents and amines, and can be prepared only in anhydrous media and handled only in a dry box. Homopolymerization is not particularly easy. However, minor proportions of acryloyl chloride can be copolymerized (107) with other vinyl monomers. Crosslinking reactions such as treatment with a diamine can then be carried out to give insoluble, infusible products with improved tensile properties. These will be discussed in a later section.

179. Polymerization of Acryloyl Chloride (108)

Three ml. of freshly distilled acryloyl chloride is mixed in a polymer tube with 3 ml. pure dioxane and 50 mg. of α,α'-azodiisobutyronitrile. The tube is sealed under nitrogen and the mixture is warmed at $50°C$. for 48 hr. Evaporation of the solvent gives an 84% yield of poly(acryloyl chloride) with a molecular weight of about 36,000.

Another vinyl monomer which is highly reactive in post-polymerization reactions is vinyl chloroformate. It is easily prepared by pyrolysis of ethylene bis(chloroformate), and polymerizes readily to high polymer at low temperatures.

180. Preparation of Vinyl Chloroformate (116,117)

$$\text{ClOCOCH}_2\text{CH}_2\text{OCOCl} \xrightarrow{\Delta} \text{CH}_2\!=\!\text{CH}-\text{OCOCl}$$

Vinyl chloroformate is prepared by the pyrolysis of ethylene bis(chloroformate) according to the general method of Kung (116) as modified by Schaefgen (117). A 300 ml. standard taper round-bottom flask is attached by means of a 29/26 joint to a 12 in. 30 mm. diameter Vycor tube packed with boiling stones (Henger granules) which is heated at a controlled (thermocouple activated Pyrovane controller) temperature of 500°C. by a pair of stacked annular 300 watt heaters. The upper end of the pyrolysis tube connects through an adapter to a condenser which also is connected to the side arm of the 300 ml. flask thereby permitting condensable materials passing the pyrolysis tube to be returned to the flask. The condenser is positioned so that the condensate is returned directly to the flask. The more volatile materials, including the desired product, pass through the condenser to an air-cooled receiver followed by two traps cooled with a mixture of acetone and solid carbon dioxide. The pressure in the system is maintained at 300 mm. by use of an aspirator and a suitable pressure regulator. The flask is charged with 100 ml. of ethylene bis(chloroformate) and brought to reflux. As the starting material is consumed, more ethylene bis(chloroformate) is added to the flask through the adapter at the base of the condenser until a total of 400 ml. has been used. The pyrolysis requires about 10 hr. At the end of the reaction about 150 ml. of material including the product has been collected in the cooled traps and about 50 ml. in the receiver. The latter material is mostly ethylene bis(chloroformate) and β-chloroethylene chloroformate which can be recycled. The crude product is purified by distillation at 100 mm. pressure to free it of HCl and vinyl chloride, followed by distillation at atmospheric pressure through a spinning band column to yield 90 g., 30%, of vinyl chloroformate, b.p. 66°C. A further distillation at reduced pressure yields pure vinyl chloroformate, b.p. 30°C./150 mm.

181. Polymerization of Vinyl Chloroformate (116,117)

$$\text{CH}_2\!=\!\text{CH}-\text{OCOCl} \longrightarrow (-\text{CH}_2-\text{CH}-)_n$$
$$\qquad\qquad\qquad\qquad\qquad\quad |$$
$$\qquad\qquad\qquad\qquad\qquad \text{OCOCl}$$

Vinyl chloroformate gives low inherent viscosity, discolored polymers when subjected to conventional free radical initiated polymerization with peroxide or azo-initiators. However, at low temperatures, colorless, soluble, high molecular weight polymers are obtained. Thus, 10 ml. of vinyl chloroformate at 0°C. is mixed with 0.12 ml. of a 25% solution of tri-n-butylboron in decahydronaphthalene. Polymerization is effected in 15 min. at 0°C. to yield 82% of poly(vinyl chloroformate) of inherent viscosity of 1.03 in acetone at 0.5% concentration. Inherent viscosity of the polymer depends upon the temperature and the initiator concentration. At a temperature of $-80°C.$, a 99% yield of polymer of inherent viscosity 1.78 is obtained. At a concentration of initiator twice that cited above a 68% yield of polymer of inherent viscosity

0.35 is obtained. Films cast from a 25% solution in acetone of this polymer are quite tough and relatively insensitive to water; thus, less than 1% hydrolysis occurred after 15 min. in boiling water. Films can be drawn 4 times their initial length at 70°C. These show intermediate lateral order of high perfection and intermediate orientation by x-ray diffraction analysis. The polymer is soluble in a number of organic solvents, e.g., acetone, dimethyl-formamide, ethyl acetate, and methylene chloride. The polymer in solution may be reacted with amines, alcohols, glycols, or other compounds containing active hydrogen to form derivatives in nearly quantitative yield.

Acrylamide will undergo vinyl polymerization via free radical catalysis, to give a polymer having pendant carboxamide groups. (Cf. Chapter 3, Preparation 32, for a Michael addition-type polymerization of acrylamide.) Water-soluble polymers can be prepared in an aqueous system, as in the following example.

182. Solution Polymerization of Acrylamide (118)

$$CH_2{=}CH{-}\overset{\overset{\displaystyle O}{\|}}{C}{-}NH_2 \longrightarrow \left[\begin{array}{c} {-}CH_2{-}CH{-} \\ | \\ C{=}O \\ | \\ NH_2 \end{array}\right]_n$$

Acrylamide is Toxic. Use Care in Handling.

In a 1 l. three-necked flask equipped with stirrer, gas inlet, thermometer, and condenser are placed 51.8 g. acrylamide (Chapter 3, Preparation 32, for purification) and 414.7 g. distilled water. The acrylamide solution is stirred and heated to 68°C. under a rapid stream of carbon dioxide. Then 7.7 g. isopropyl alcohol and 0.096 g. potassium persulfate are added. The temperature of the reaction rises to 75–80°C., where it is maintained by a heating bath for 2 hr. The product is obtained in a clear, colorless solution having a very high viscosity. The polymer can be precipitated in methanol, washed well with methanol, and dried in a vacuum at 50°C. The inherent viscosity is about 1.0 (1N solution of sodium nitrate, 0.5% polymer conc., 30°C.). The relationship of intrinsic viscosity to molecular weight is

$$[\eta] = 3.73 \times 10^4 M^{0.66}$$

where M is weight average molecular weight.

The polymerization of **acrylate esters** can be carried out readily. The acrylate esters are rubbery polymers exhibiting a decreasing glass temperature with increasing chain length of the alkyl portion up to C_8, after which the T_g increases. T_g of the methyl ester is around 0°C., of the octyl, -65°C. Hexadecyl acrylate forms a polymer with a T_g of about 35°C. Consequently, acrylate polymers are best made in emulsion. The polymerization of **methyl acrylate** is typical of the preparation of the acrylate esters. An extensive series of poly(acrylate esters) has been prepared and reported in the literature (119).

183. The Polymerization of Methyl Acrylate (119)

$$CH_2=CHCO_2CH_3 \longrightarrow \left[\begin{array}{c} -CH_2-CH- \\ | \\ CO_2CH_3 \end{array} \right]_n$$

A three-necked flask is fitted with a stirrer, a reflux condenser, and a thermometer. The flask is charged with 400 ml. of water, 2 g. of Triton*720, which is an alkyl arylether sulfonate, 2-4 g. of Tergitol† paste, which is sodium 2-methyl-7-ethyldecyl-4-sulfate penetrant, and 0.01 g. of ammonium persulfate. The solution is stirred slowly and 200 g. of distilled methyl acrylate is added. Heat may be applied to the reaction vessel in order to induce polymerization. If polymerization does not start within 10 min. after refluxing has occurred, additional ammonium persulfate may be added. If excessive quantities are required the monomer is not of sufficient purity. Once initiated the polymerization usually proceeds at a rate sufficient to cause refluxing without external heating for 15- 30 min. After about 30 min., heat is applied, and the refluxing temperature is allowed to rise until it is about 95°C., at which point the polymerization may be considered to be complete. The resulting polymer emulsion is steam distilled for 15–30 min. to remove excess monomer and is run slowly into twice its volume of hot 5% sodium chloride solution. The polymer is precipitated in the form of discrete particles which are filtered and washed with hot water until free of salt. It is then air dried. The yield is quite good in all cases.

Higher alkyl acrylates may be polymerized using the identical recipe described in the previous paragraph. The properties of a whole series of such esters will be found in Ref. 119.

A number of *N*-vinyl lactams have been prepared by the reaction of acetylene with the lactam. The most important of these is *N*-vinyl pyrrolidone (120–123).

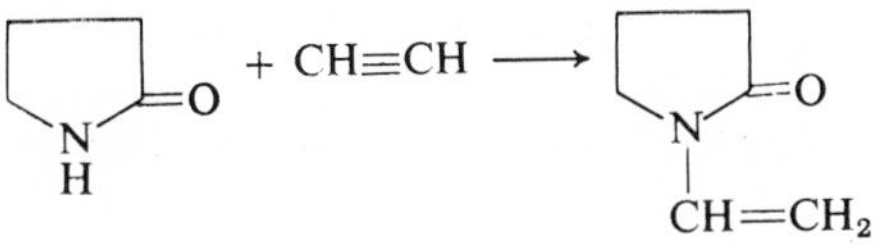

This monomer polymerizes readily with most free radical catalysts, under a variety of conditions to give a water-soluble high polymer. This material has been used successfully as a blood plasma substitute.

184. Polymerization of *N*-Vinyl Pyrrolidone (120–123)

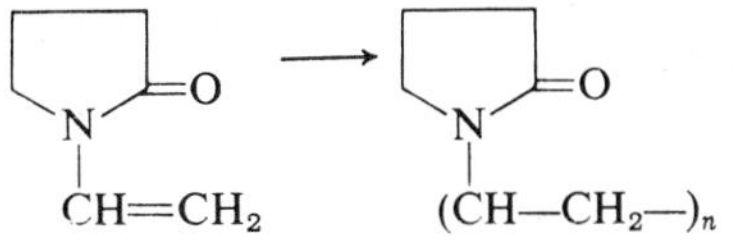

* Trademark of the Rohm & Haas Co.
† Trademark of the Union Carbide Corp.

A mixture of 30 g. of distilled *N*-vinyl pyrrolidone and a solution of 40 g. of neutral potassium sulfite in 200 ml. of water is stirred vigorously in an atmosphere of nitrogen for 24 hr. at a temperature of 35–40°C. At the end of 24 hr. the polymerization product, which is a viscous solution, is decanted into a dish and evaporated under a stream of dry air or nitrogen on a steam bath with stirring. The product, poly(vinyl pyrrolidone), is obtained in good yield in the form of a clear, horn-like solid mass mixed with potassium salts. It will dissolve in water to give a viscous solution. The polymer can be separated from the potassium salts by extraction into alcohol, or by dialysis of an aqueous solution in, for example, a cellophane bag, against running water.

Unsaturated ketones will polymerize readily with peroxide catalysts. Methyl vinyl ketone and methyl isopropenyl ketone give products which are structurally similar to poly(methyl acrylate) and poly-(methyl methacrylate):

$$\left[-CH_2-\underset{\underset{CO_2CH_3}{|}}{\overset{\overset{CH_3}{|}}{C}}- \right]_n$$

Poly(methyl methacrylate)

$$\left[-CH_2-\underset{\underset{COCH_3}{|}}{\overset{\overset{CH_3}{|}}{C}}- \right]_n$$

Poly(methyl isopropenyl ketone)

$$\left[-CH_2-\underset{\underset{CO_2CH_3}{|}}{CH}- \right]_n$$

Poly(methyl acrylate)

$$\left[-CH_2-\underset{\underset{COCH_3}{|}}{CH}- \right]_n$$

Poly(methyl vinyl ketone)

They are, however, inferior in properties to the acrylates, so have not met with wide commercialization.

185. Polymerization of Methyl Vinyl Ketone (124)

$$CH_2{=}CH-\underset{\underset{O}{\|}}{C}-CH_3 \longrightarrow \left[-CH_2-\underset{\underset{COCH_3}{|}}{CH}- \right]_n$$

In a 1 l., three-necked flask or resin kettle, equipped with a condenser, nitrogen inlet, and a mechanical stirrer is placed 100 g. of freshly distilled methyl vinyl ketone and 100 ml. of ethyl acetate. Five g. of benzoyl peroxide is then added and the mixture is stirred for 3 hr. at a temperature of 75°C. maintained by an external water bath. Approximately 95–100% of the monomer is converted to polymer. The solution in ethyl acetate may be precipitated into a nonsolvent for the polymer, such as cyclohexane, with stirring in a high speed mixer, or it may be poured out and the solvent allowed to evaporate. The product in the latter case will be a clear slab of hard colorless polymer.

Unsaturated aldehydes also polymerize readily. Acrolein is converted to a polymer readily in aqueous medium with persulfate. The product holds a mole of water, chemically bound as a hemiacetal.

186. Preparation of Polyacrolein by Redox Polymerization (141,142)

$$CH_2\!\!=\!\!CH \xrightarrow{\ H_2O\ } \cdots CH_2\!\!-\!\!CH\!\!-\!\!CH_2\!\!-\!\!CH\!\!-\cdots$$

$$\underset{HO}{\overset{CH=O}{\big|}} \qquad \underset{HO\diagdown\ \diagup O\ \diagdown\ \diagup OH}{\overset{CH\quad\ CH}{\big|}}$$

Five hundred ml. of water is placed in a 2 l. round-bottom flask equipped with stirrer, reflux condenser, dropping funnel, thermometer, and a nitrogen inlet. The water is boiled for ½ hr. under a stream of nitrogen and then cooled to 20°C. To the deaerated water is added 4.75 g. of potassium persulfate and 100 ml. of redistilled acrolein. After the monomer is dissolved a solution of 2.96 g. of silver nitrate in 60 ml. of water is added dropwise during about 10 min. to the rapidly stirred solution under nitrogen. After several minutes, the mixture thickens and the polymer precipitates. The temperature must not rise above 20°C. during the course of the polymerization. After 2¼ hr., 500 ml. of water is added and the polymer is filtered and washed twice with 500 ml. portions of water. To remove the silver salt retained in the polymer, the filter cake is dispersed in a solution of 5 g. of sodium thiosulfate in 500 ml. of water. After 1 hr., the polymer is filtered, washed several times with water, and dried in a vacuum at 20°C. This will require several days. The residual water (bound and unbound) can be determined from an elementary analysis. The unbound water can be determined by the Karl Fischer method. The yield of polymer is about 68 g. (80%).

Pendant aldehyde groups can be attached to a polymer chain by hydroformylation (oxo reaction) of the double bonds in an unsaturated polymer, such as polybutadiene or poly(butadiene-co-styrene) (142a).

$$-CH\!\!=\!\!CH- + CO + H_2 \xrightarrow{\ [CO(CO_4)]_2\ } -CH_2\!\!-\!\!\underset{\overset{|}{CHO}}{CH}-$$

High conversion to aldehyde gives a polymer with a strong tendency to gel; this can be avoided by inclusion of an agent that reacts rapidly enough to convert aldehyde to acetal, such as 2,3-butanediol and 2,2-dimethoxypropane.

High pressures (2400 p.s.i. at room temperature charge) and temperatures (125–180°C.) are required, so no examples will be included here.

Vinyl phosphorous compounds have been studied extensively, but only very limited success has been achieved in getting polymers with respectable molecular weights. An exception is the polymerization of tributylvinyl phosphonium bromide (TBVPB) by ionizing radiation or free radical polymerization (143). In contrast, triethyl-, dimethylphenyl-, and tricyclohexyl vinyl phosphonium bromide resisted polymerization entirely under conditions that led to a high conversion–high molecular weight polymer from the tributyl compound.

187. Preparation of Tributylvinylphosphonium Bromide (143)*

$$(C_4H_9)_3P + BrCH_2CH_2Br \longrightarrow [(C_4H_9)_3PCH_2CH_2Br]Br$$
$$I$$

$$I + Na_2CO_3 \longrightarrow [(C_4H_9)_3PCH{=}CH_2]Br$$

Tributylphosphine is distilled prior to use to ensure the absence of the oxide. To 300 ml. (650 g., 295 moles) of 1,2-dibromoethane in a three-necked flask equipped with a condenser ($CaCl_2$ trap), thermometer, nitrogen inlet, and mechanical stirrer was added 33 g. (0.164 mole) of tributylphosphine during a 1 hr. period at 55°C. The excess 1,2-dibromoethane is removed *in vacuo*, and the 63.7 g. residue is treated with 200 ml. of boiling chlorobenzene. (Addition of boiling chlorobenzene to the residue rather than addition of cold chlorobenzene and heating of the mixture to boiling is imperative.) The residue flask is washed immediately with several small portions of boiling chlorobenzene until quantitative transfer is made. The resultant solution is refluxed for 1 min. in the presence of a small amount of anhydrous magnesium sulfate and filtered. The filtrate, upon cooling, deposits a voluminous amount of crystals. These are collected under nitrogen and washed with ether; a yield of 45.5 g. (71.6%), m.p. $\sim 75°C$. was obtained.

A solution of 45.5 g. (0.112 mole) of the above 2-bromoethyltributyl-phosphonium bromide in 450 ml. of fresh (EWL) dioxane containing 49.2 g. (0.42 mole) of sodium carbonate is heated at reflux for 4 hr. under nitrogen. The mixture is mechanically stirred throughout. The hot solution is filtered to separate the inorganic salts. Upon cooling crystallization occurs. The crystals are collected and washed with 150 ml. of boiling dioxane. Another crop is obtained upon concentration of the mother liquor. The combined crops are dried in a vacuum oven at room temperature for 1 hr. The total yield is about 29 g. (102%), m.p. 150–152°C. The reaction can be run at seven-fold the level described and an overall yield of 55% obtained.

188. Polymerization of Tributylvinylphosphonium Bromide (TBVPB) (143)

$$CH_2{=}CHP(C_4H_9)_3 \longrightarrow [{-}CH_2{-}\overset{\displaystyle P(C_4H_9)_3}{\underset{\displaystyle |}{CH}}{-}]_n$$

Two g. of TBVPB and 0.0107 g. of azobisisobutyronitrile (1 mole per cent) are dissolved in 6 ml. of chlorobenzene and the solution put into a heavy-walled glass tube, constricted near the top. After degassing three times at $-78°C$., the tube is sealed and heated at 60°C. A phase separation is noted in 8 hr. and after one week of heating the tube is opened and the upper layer is discarded. The lower layer is dissolved in water, dialyzed for 24 hr. in Fischer dialyzing tubing to remove any residual monomer, and then the H_2O removed *in vacuo*. A 92% yield (1.84 g.) or polymer was obtained. The intrinsic viscosity measured at 30°C. in 0.3M LiBr is 0.23 dl./g., and the light scattering molecular weight is 109,500. The polymer is soluble in methyl ethyl ketone and insoluble in ether.

The intrinsic viscosity–molecular weight relationship for polymer (in 0.3M LiBr) prepared by free radical initiation, as above, is $[\eta] = 2 \times 10^{-3}$

* We wish to thank Dr. R. Rabinowitz, American Cyanamid, for providing this and the following experimental examples.

$\overline{M}_w^{0,41}$. For polymer from radiation initiation, $[\eta] = 8.0 \times 10^{-3} \ \overline{M}_w^{0,34}$. Thus, a basic difference in the two polymers exists, which may in fact be that the free radical polymers are more branched for a given molecular weight. This is the reverse of what would be expected, but in the face of the highly ionic nature of the polymer, no definite conclusions can be drawn.

1. MISCELLANEOUS MONOMERS

Conceivably, any monosubstituted ethylene, R—CH=CH_2, could give high polymer, although the monomers just considered are the most common to free radical vinyl technology. Many other monomers have been prepared and polymerized, but the polymers have not been thoroughly characterized. Table 4.1 lists those which have been studied and appear to be of some interest, particularly as comonomers to change physical or chemical properties of a given homopolymer.

Table 4.1

Name	Structure	References
Vinyl isocyanate	CH_2=CH—NCO	125–127
Nitroethylene	CH_2=CH—NO_2	128, 129
Vinyl azide	CH_2=CH—N_3	130, 131
Vinylsulfonyl fluoride	CH_2=$CHSO_2F$	132
Vinylsulfonyl chloride	CH_2=$CHSO_2Cl$	133, 134
Vinylsulfonic acid	CH_2=$CHSO_3H$	133–136
Butyl vinyl sulfone	CH_2=CH—$SO_2C_4H_9$	137
Vinyl triethoxy silane	CH_2=CH—$Si(OC_2H_5)_3$	138
Ethyl vinyl sulfoxide	CH_2=CH—SO—C_2H_5	139, 140
Ethyl vinyl sulfone	CH_2=CH—$SO_2C_2H_5$	139, 140

IV. Free Radical Polymerization of 1,1-Disubstituted Ethylenes

The number of 1,1-disubstituted ethylenes which have been successfully polymerized by free radicals is less than the number of monosubstituted ethylenes, but some very important homopolymers are found in this group. Techniques are essentially the same, and the following representative polymers will be considered: poly(methyl methacrylate) and related higher esters, poly(methyl-α-chloroacrylate), poly(α-methacrylonitrile), poly(α-chloroacrylonitrile), poly(vinylidene chloride), poly(vinylidene fluoride).

Probably the most important monomer of this group is **methyl methacrylate,** the monomer on which Lucite* and Plexiglas† as well as

---

* Trademark for du Pont's acrylic resins.

† Trademark for Rohm & Haas' acrylic resins.

numerous acrylic paints and sprays are based. It will polymerize readily to a very clear, colorless polymer. Suspension and bulk methods give representative products. Emulsion techniques may also be used (144, 145).

189. Suspension Polymerization of Methyl Methacrylate

$$CH_2{=}C\diagup\overset{\displaystyle CH_3}{\underset{\displaystyle CO_2CH_3}{}} \longrightarrow \left[-CH_2-\overset{\displaystyle CH_3}{\underset{\displaystyle CO_2CH_3}{C}}- \right]_n$$

A mixture of 200 g. of monomeric methyl methacrylate (freshly distilled) with 2.5 g. of α,α'-azodiisobutyronitrile, 40 ml. of a 5% aqueous poly(methacrylic acid) solution, 20 g. of disodium hydrogen phosphate dodecahydrate, and 400 ml. of water is placed in a 1 l., three-necked flask, mounted on a steam bath, and equipped with a nitrogen inlet, an efficient stirrer, a thermometer, and a reflux condenser. The reaction mixture is stirred vigorously and heated to boiling in a steam bath, under an atmosphere of nitrogen. The initial reflux temperature will be about 82°C. As polymerization continues, the temperature will rise to 93°C. At this temperature, polymerization is essentially complete. The granular polymeric methyl methacrylate is filtered, washed in water, and dried. The total time required for the polymerization is approximately 20 min.

Alternatively, polymerization may be carried out without added initiator. This is not a true thermal polymerization, but is initiated by adventitious impurities. Highly purified monomer will not polymerize under these conditions. In a 1 l. three-necked flask equipped with condenser and stirrer is placed 100 g. of methyl methacrylate and 200 ml. of water containing about 4 g. of poly(vinyl alcohol) dispersing agent. This mixture is stirred vigorously and heated at about 80°C. for approximately 40 min. The internal temperature begins to rise at this point and will reach a maximum of 85°C. At this point, the mixture is cooled to 60°C. by the addition of cold water to the flask. The granules of polymer are separated, washed with water, and dried at 100°C. The poly(methyl methacrylate) may be converted to molded objects.

Methyl methacrylate may be safely **bulk polymerized** under mild conditions. In this way it is possible to prepare castings by *in situ* polymerization at 40°C.

190. Bulk Polymerization of Methyl Methacrylate (96)

$$CH_2{=}\overset{\displaystyle CH_3}{\underset{\displaystyle CO_2CH_3}{C}} \longrightarrow \left[-CH_2-\overset{\displaystyle CH_3}{\underset{\displaystyle CO_2CH_3}{C}}- \right]_n$$

One hundred g. of freshly distilled monomeric methyl methacrylate is mixed with 3 g. of high molecular weight poly(methyl methacrylate) thickener, 0.007 g. of methacrylic acid, and 0.05 g. of α,α'-azodiisobutyronitrile. The viscous mixture is maintained in an oven at about 40°C., under which conditions it will polymerize in about 25–30 hr. to a clear, solid block in the shape of the polymerization vessel. For example, the viscous mixture may be poured between two glass plates which are separated by a compressible gasket. If this assembly is maintained in the oven at about 40°C., as previously described, for 25–30 hr., a clear sheet of poly(methyl methacrylate) is obtained. It may be separated from the glass retaining plates by raising the temperature to 95°C.

Poly(methyl methacrylate) has a Vicat softening temperature (see Chapter 2) of about 120°C. Its glass temperature is about 105°C. Stereoregular forms of the polymer are considered further on under "Anionic Polymerization."

Objects may be embedded in poly(methyl methacrylate) using the same techniques given for polystyrene.

If **methacrylic acid** is **esterified with higher alcohols,** polymers with lower softening points will be obtained.

191. Polymerization of *n*-Butyl Methacrylate

$$
\begin{array}{c}
\mathrm{CH_3} \\
| \\
\mathrm{CH_2}{=}\mathrm{C} \\
| \\
\mathrm{CO_2C_4H_9}
\end{array}
\longrightarrow
\left[
\begin{array}{c}
\mathrm{CH_3} \\
| \\
{-}\mathrm{CH_2}{-}\mathrm{C}{-} \\
| \\
\mathrm{CO_2C_4H_9}
\end{array}
\right]_n
$$

This monomer may be polymerized exactly as methyl methacrylate. The polymer is a solid, but the softening point is now 30°C. (144,145).

192. Polymerization of *n*-Amyl Methacrylate

$$
\begin{array}{c}
\mathrm{CH_3} \\
| \\
\mathrm{CH_2}{=}\mathrm{C} \\
| \\
\mathrm{CO_2C_5H_{11}}
\end{array}
\longrightarrow
\left[
\begin{array}{c}
\mathrm{CH_3} \\
| \\
{-}\mathrm{CH_2}{-}\mathrm{C}{-} \\
| \\
\mathrm{CO_2C_5H_{11}}
\end{array}
\right]_n
$$

This monomer may be polymerized exactly as in the preceding examples. Poly(*n*-amyl methacrylate) is an elastomer, with a softening point below room temperature (144,145).

193. Polymerization of Glycol Dimethacrylate

$$
\left[
\begin{array}{c}
\mathrm{CH_3} \\
{}^{/} \\
\mathrm{CH_2}{=}\mathrm{C} \quad\quad \mathrm{O} \\
{}^{\backslash} \quad {}^{\|} \\
\mathrm{C} \\
{}^{\backslash} \\
\mathrm{OCH_2}{-}
\end{array}
\right]_2
\longrightarrow \text{3-Dimensional network polymer}
$$

Glycol dimethacrylate is purified before use by distillation at 84°C./1 mm. It may be polymerized exactly as the above methacrylate esters. The product is, however, completely insoluble and infusible. This monomer is used in dental fillings, of the type which are polymerized *in situ*.

194. Preparation of a Copolymer of Acryloyl Chloride and Methyl Methacrylate (107)

$$\underset{\underset{\text{Cl}}{\diagdown}}{\overset{\overset{\text{O}}{\diagup}}{\text{CH}_2\!\!=\!\!\text{CH}\!-\!\text{C}}} \; + \; \underset{\underset{\text{CO}_2\text{CH}_3}{\diagdown}}{\overset{\overset{\text{O}}{\diagup}}{\text{CH}_2\!\!=\!\!\text{CH}\!-\!\text{C}}} \quad \longrightarrow \quad \text{Copolymer}$$

A mixture of 50 g. of freshly distilled methyl methacrylate and 50 g. of acryloyl chloride is placed in a thoroughly dried polymer tube under an atmosphere of dry nitrogen. To this mixture is added 0.2 g. of α,α'-azobis-(α,γ-dimethylvaleronitrile). The tube containing this mixture is fitted with an ordinary capillary inlet reaching beneath the surface of the monomer and is further protected with a drying tube on the outlet. The mixture is heated in a water bath at approximately 50°C. while a slow stream of nitrogen is passed through the capillary. The material becomes quite viscous after 1 hr. and the capillary is raised to just above the surface of the polymerizing mass. Heating is continued for a total of 3–4 hr., at the end of which time the contents of the polymer tube has set to a hard, clear, colorless solid. The copolymer is isolated in nearly quantitative yield by breaking the glass tube in a nitrogen filled dry box in order to prevent hydrolysis of the acid chloride. The inherent viscosity of polymers made in this manner will lie in the range of 1–2.4 (0.5%; methylene chloride).

195. Preparation of Crosslinked Products from Acryloyl Chloride Copolymers (107)

A solution of the acryloyl chloride copolymer prepared above is made at approximately 10% concentration in anhydrous methylene chloride or a closely related unreactive solvent. A film is dry-cast (Chapter 2) on a glass plate under an atmosphere of nitrogen in a dry box. It is advisable to use a casting knife of approximately 30 ml. clearance since the solution is relatively dilute. The film is removed from the glass plate and a portion of it is soaked in a 15–20% aqueous solution of ethylene diamine for approximately 10 min. The film is then washed carefully with water and dried. The effect wrought by the crosslinking with diamine is quite marked. The uncrosslinked film is not form stable and is likely to be tacky and difficult to handle. The crosslinked material shows a considerable increase in form stability as well as improved tensile properties.

Similar experiments may be carried out on fibers by wet spinning solutions of acryloyl chloride copolymers into a precipitating bath containing a cross-linking agent such as ethylene diamine.

The **nitrile of α-methacrylic acid, methacrylonitrile,** may also be polymerized by free radicals. The product softens lower than poly-acrylonitrile, hence can be molded, although it tends to discolor on molding.

196. Polymerization of Methacrylonitrile (146)

A mixture of 100 g. of freshly distilled methacrylonitrile, 300 ml. of water, 0.5 g. of Duponol* ME detergent, and 0.5 g. of potassium persulfate is placed

* Trademark for du Pont's surface active agent.

$$CH_2=C \begin{matrix} CN \\ \\ CH_3 \end{matrix} \longrightarrow \left[\begin{matrix} CN \\ | \\ -CH_2-C- \\ | \\ CH_3 \end{matrix} \right]_n$$

in a sealed glass tube or in a stainless steel bomb. This mixture is maintained at 50°C. for 24 hr.; it is either stirred or tumbled in order to agitate the contents of the reaction vessel. At the end of 24 hr., the temperature is raised to 85°C. for an additional 4 hr. At the end of this period, a 90% yield of a stable, white polymer latex is obtained. The polymer may be coagulated by the usual techniques. It may be frozen or it may be precipitated by the addition of an electrolyte. The dried polymer is colorless when prepared in the described manner and can be injection molded or formed into film at temperatures of 135–155°C. and pressures of 1500–4000 p.s.i.

Methyl α-chloroacrylate and **α-chloroacrylonitrile** both polymerize readily. The products are higher melting, but are less stable thermally, than the methyl analogs.

197. Preparation of Methyl α-Chloroacrylate (147)

$$ClCH_2CHCl-CO_2CH_3 \longrightarrow CH_2=CClCO_2CH_3$$

Caution. Methyl α-chloroacrylate is a potent lachrymator.

Methyl α,β-dichloropropionate is prepared by the addition of chlorine to methyl acrylate. One hundred g. of methyl α,β-dichloropropionate is mixed with 35 g. of concentrated sulfuric acid to give a clear solution. This solution is heated cautiously in a distillation set-up without fractionation at a temperature ranging from 80 to 150°C. During the course of this heating, hydrogen chloride is evolved and methyl α-chloroacrylate distills. The product is washed with dilute alkali, then with water, and dried. It is fractionated through an efficient column, b.p. 57–59°C./55 mm.

This monomer polymerizes with greater ease than methyl methacrylate.

198. Polymerization of Methyl α-Chloroacrylate

$$CH_2=C \begin{matrix} Cl \\ | \\ | \\ CO_2CH_3 \end{matrix} \longrightarrow \left[\begin{matrix} Cl \\ | \\ -CH_2-C- \\ | \\ CO_2CH_3 \end{matrix} \right]_n$$

This monomer may be polymerized exactly as methyl methacrylate (see Preparations 190 and 191). The polymer tends to form discolored castings, but is more resistant to scratching and has a softening temperature about 40°C. higher than the corresponding methacrylate polymer.

199. Preparation of Trichloropropionitrile (148)

$$CH_2=CH-CN + Cl_2 \longrightarrow ClCH_2-CCl_2CN$$

A 1 l., three-necked flask equipped with a stirrer, a condenser, and a gas inlet tube and cooled externally by an ice-water bath is charged with 265 g. of acrylonitrile containing a small amount of polymerization inhibitor such as hydroquinone. Chlorine gas is bubbled slowly into the acrylonitrile with external cooling until a total of 419 g. of chlorine is absorbed. This chlorinated product is distilled at 30 mm. to give 560 g. of a product boiling at 70–75°C. This material may be purified by redistillation; b.p. 80–81°C./63 mm. However, the once distilled material is satisfactory for the next experiment.

200. Preparation of α-Chloroacrylonitrile (149,151)

$$ClCH_2CCl_2CN \xrightarrow{Mg} CH_2{=}CClCN$$

A dehalogenating agent is prepared as follows in a three-necked flask equipped with a stirrer and a condenser. In the flask is placed 29 g. of metallic magnesium together with 51 g. of iodine dissolved in 350 ml. of butyl ether containing 0.5–1 g. of hydroquinone. After the iodine color disappears, the flask containing the agent is heated in an oil bath at 150°C. while 99 g. of α,α,β-trichloropropionitrile is added dropwise over 30–45 min. During the entire operation the mixture is stirred vigorously. An exothermic reaction takes place with the removal by distillation of the lower boiling products together with the butyl ether. Stirring and heating is continued after the addition of the trichloropropionitrile is complete, until approximately 250 ml. of distillate has been obtained. This distillate is shaken with mercury to remove free iodine and is then fractionated. Approximately 20 g. of α-chloroacrylonitrile with a boiling point of 85–88°C. is obtained. Prior to polymerization the α-chloroacrylonitrile should be freshly redistilled. The refractive index is reported to be 1.4205 at 32°C.

201. Polymerization of α-Chloroacrylonitrile (150,151)

$$CH_2{=}\underset{\underset{CN}{|}}{\overset{\overset{Cl}{|}}{C}} \longrightarrow \left[-CH_2-\underset{\underset{CN}{|}}{\overset{\overset{Cl}{|}}{C}}- \right]_n$$

A mixture of 109 g. of freshly distilled chloroacrylonitrile, 300 g. of deaerated distilled water, 1 g. of ammonium persulfate, 2.0 g. of sodium metabisulfite, 0.6 g. of edible-grade gelatin, and 0.72 g. of sodium phosphate is placed in a three-necked flask equipped with stirrer and condenser. The mixture is stirred at 55°C. for about 24 hr.

The suspension is cooled to room temperature and the polymer, which is present as a fine, white powder, is filtered to give about 100 g. of poly-α-chloroacrylonitrile.

Copolymers of α-chloroacrylonitrile with diethylmaleate, vinyl chloride, ethyl acrylate, methyl methacrylate, styrene, etc., may be prepared. The homopolymer may be made into a viscous solution (37) suitable for spinning or casting by dissolving in a solvent comprised of 40 parts of nitromethane, 1.2 parts of water, and 12 parts of phenol.

Vinylidene chloride is a low boiling (32°C.) liquid which polymerizes readily. Bulk polymerization may be carried out at 40–50°C. in sealed tubes, but should not be done on a large scale, since the polymerization may get out of control if efficient dissipation of heat is not possible. It is best polymerized in an emulsion. The polymer may be molded, but the molding temperature (ca. 200°C.) is rather high and some decomposition occurs. Vinylidene chloride is found most frequently in copolymers. Some are described in a later section.

Caution! Vinylidene chloride monomer tends to form peroxides and phosgene in contact with air, giving a mixture which may explode on heating (152). Anyone planning to work with this monomer should acquaint himself fully with the hazards (153).

202. Polymerization of Vinylidene Chloride (154)

$$CH_2{=}CCl_2 \longrightarrow [-CH_2-CCl_2-]_n$$

In a 1 l., three-necked flask equipped with a nitrogen inlet, a condenser, and a stirrer is placed 100 g. of pure vinylidene chloride, 300 ml. of an aqueous solution containing 3 g. of ammonium persulfate, 1 g. of sodium hydroxide, 1.5 g. of sodium thiosulfate, and 3 g. of a detergent, such as sodium Lorol sulfate. The air in the reaction vessel is displaced by nitrogen and the temperature is maintained at 30°C. with stirring. After about 6 hr., polymerization is essentially complete and a polymer emulsion is obtained. This is removed from the reaction vessel and the polymer is precipitated by the addition of 100–150 ml. of saturated salt solution with stirring. The easily filterable, finely divided white powder is removed, washed with water, and dried. The yield is approximately 85 g. T_m is about 160°C.

In view of the low boiling point of vinylidene chloride (32°C.) a nitrogen sweep should not be used. Instead, the reaction vessel should be kept under a slight positive pressure of nitrogen. If desired, pressure bottles can be used for the polymerization.

203. Copolymer of Vinyl Chloride and Vinylidene Chloride (155,156)

$$CH_2{=}CHCl + CH_2{=}CCl_2 \longrightarrow Copolymer$$

A buffered hydrogen peroxide catalyst is prepared by mixing 500 ml. of water, 4 g. of soap or other dispersing agent, 3 g. of 30% hydrogen peroxide, and 0.5 g. of acid ammonium phosphate. This buffer is mixed in a 1 l. stainless steel, stirred autoclave with 42 g. vinylidene chloride and 126 g. of vinyl chloride measured from a pressure cylinder. The sealed vessel containing the vinyl chloride–vinylidene chloride mixture is heated and agitated at 48°C. for about 20 hr. Polymerization is complete at the end of this period and the resulting emulsion of copolymer is coagulated by the addition of salt. The precipitated polymer is filtered, washed with dilute alkali, and then with copious quantities of water. The copolymer so obtained contains about 25% by weight of vinylidene chloride and 75% of vinyl chloride. It is satisfactory for molding. It is also soluble in most organic solvents, for example, butyl acetate, benzene, and acetone. Solutions of the polymer may be used for casting film.

Vinylidene fluoride may also be polymerized to a crystalline polymer of outstanding thermal stability and chemical resistance. Although it is easier to fabricate than its fully fluorinated counterpart, polytetrafluoroethylene, it does not equal the latter in its upper temperature use range. Polymerization of vinylidene fluoride must be done under rather high pressure conditions, although with di-*t*-butyl peroxide this need is kept to a minimum. Still, an autoclave and all due precautions in its use are required.

204. Polymerization of Vinylidene Fluoride (157)

$$CH_2=CH_2 \longrightarrow \{CH_2-CF_2\}$$

A 300 ml. stainless steel autoclave is charged with 100 ml. of deionized and deoxygenated water and 0.8 g. of di-*t*-butyl peroxide. The autoclave is evacuated, cooled in liquid nitrogen, and then charged with 35 g. of vinylidene fluoride by gaseous transfer *in vacuo*. The autoclave is then sealed and placed in an electrical heating jacket mounted in a shaking apparatus and held at 122–124°C. for $18\frac{1}{2}$ hr. A maximum pressure of about 800 p.s.i. is reached after the first 2 hr. of heating and the pressure then decreases as the polymerization proceeds.

After the reaction period, the autoclave is cooled, vented, and opened. The contents consist of precipitated poly(vinylidene fluoride) suspended in a liquid phase having a pH of 2.5. The polymer is vacuum-filtered and washed on the filter funnel with methanol, then washed ten times with distilled water, and given a final wash with methanol. It is then dried in a vacuum oven at 102°C. The washed, dried polymer weighs 29 g., representing an 83% conversion of the monomer to polymer. The polymer, which melts at 160–165°C. has a high molecular weight as indicated by its plasticity number of 3020. The "plasticity number" is an empirical index indicating relative molecular weight of vinylidene fluoride polymers. Because of the difficulty of obtaining a true solution of the polymer, absolute molecular weight determinations have not been possible to obtain. The plasticity number is the area in square millimeters of a plaque made by placing 0.5 g. of polymer powder piled in a cone between the platens of a Carver press heated at 225°C. The platens are brought together to compress the powder under slight pressure (less than 50 p.s.i.) between the heated platens and the powder is preheated in this manner at 225°C. for 30 sec. A pressure of 2500 p.s.i. is then applied for 60 sec. at platen temperature of 225°C. The greater the area of the plaque so produced, the lower the molecular weight of the polymer, and conversely. Thus, comparison of different preparations of the polymer is possible.

The polymer likewise has excellent thermal stability. It does not decompose when heated to 320°C. and shows substantially no discoloration when exposed in a circulating air oven for 100 hr. at 200°C. It has good low temperature properties as shown in a test in which the polymer is flexed 180°C. over a $\frac{1}{8}$ in. mandrel at −70°C. without breaking.

V. The Free Radical Polymerization of Other Di-, Tri-, and Tetrasubstituted Olefins

In sharp contrast to the number of mono- and 1,1-disubstituted olefins known to homopolymerize by a free radical mechanism, there are only very few **1,2-disubstituted olefins** which give high polymer. It is interesting to note that most of the 1,2-disubstituted olefins which polymerize well (including those which polymerize by other mechanisms, cf. acenaphthylene) are unsaturated 5-membered cyclic compounds.

An interesting 1,2-olefin is **vinylene carbonate,** first reported in the literature by Newman and Addor (158,159). It is prepared by chlorination of ethylene carbonate, followed by dehydrohalogenation. Polymerization is carried out with benzoyl peroxide or an azo catalyst (160).

It is essential that the monomer be very pure if high molecular weight polymer is to be obtained. A thermal treatment has been claimed (161), but treatment with sodium borohydride is preferred.

205. Preparation of Chloroethylene Carbonate (160)

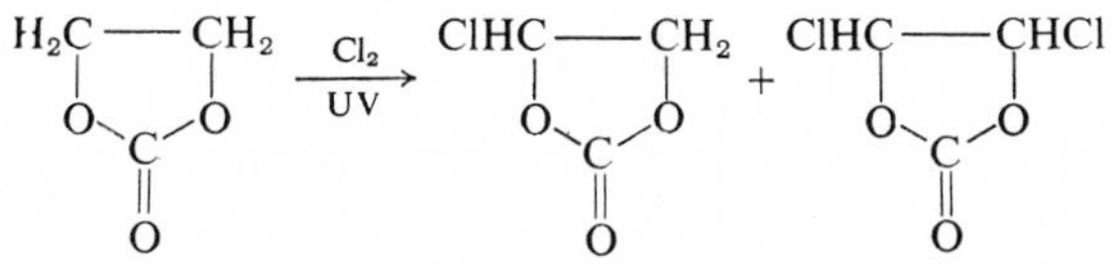

Ethylene carbonate, 500 g. (5.7 moles), and carbon tetrachloride, 1 l., are mixed in a 2 l. three-necked flask equipped with an UV lamp in a quartz jacket immersed in the flask, a gas inlet tube, and an efficient condenser. The two-phase system is heated by use of a heating mantle until refluxing occurs. The heat is then turned off, the UV lamp turned on, and chlorine from a cylinder is introduced at a rate sufficient to maintain vigorous refluxing. The ethylene carbonate-rich phase gradually disappears and a homogeneous solution forms. Chlorination is continued beyond this point until the total weight of chlorine added is about 600 g. (8.5 moles). This requires 3–5 hr. The product is isolated by fractional distillation through an efficient column. After removal of the solvent and a low-boiling solid impurity, 1,2-dichloroethylene carbonate, 114 g. (13%), b.p. 91°C. at 30 mm., n_D^{25} 1.4606, and chloroethylene carbonate, 420–475 g. (60–68%), b.p. 102°C. at 8 mm., n_D^{25} 1.4525, are isolated.

206. Preparation of Vinylene Carbonate (160)

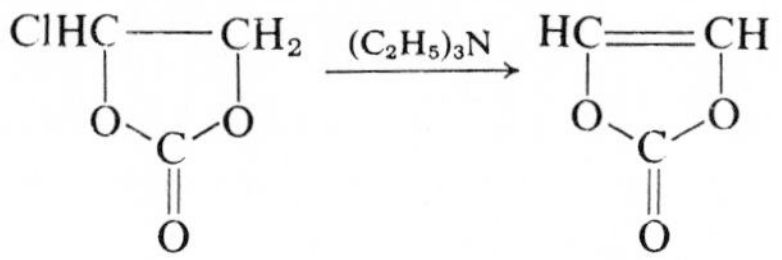

The chloroethylene carbonate from the preceding preparation, 450 g. (3.65 moles), 450 ml. of anhydrous ether and 4 g. of di-*tert*-butyl-*p*-cresol to prevent adventitious polymerization of the monomer, are added to a 2 l. three-necked flask equipped with a precision-ground stirrer, dropping funnel, and reflux condenser to which a drying tube filled with Drierite* is attached.

* Trademark for W. A. Hammond Drierite Company's desiccant drying solids, liquids, and gases.

Triethylamine, 560 ml. (4.1 moles), is added slowly over about 4 hr. to the stirred refluxing solution (a temperature of about 45°C. should be maintained). Gentle refluxing is maintained for 2 days. A copious precipitate of amine salt forms and the color of the solution becomes dark brown. The precipitate is collected and washed 4 times, each time with 400 ml. of a mixture of 50/50 vol. % benzene and ether. The second and third washings are carried out by slurrying the solid precipitate with the solvent mixture in a beaker. The filtrate and washings are combined and most of the ether and some of the benzene are removed by simple distillation. Distillation of the remainder of the solution at reduced pressure through an efficient column yields 200–230 g. (63–73%) of vinylene carbonate, b.p. 74°C. at 30 mm. This material rapidly colors (brown) on standing. It is further purified by refluxing for 1 hr. over 1.5% by weight sodium borohydride and then distilling. A second treatment with sodium borohydride is recommended to obtain a color-stable product, n_D^{25}, 1.4185; m.p. 20.5°C.

207. Polymerization of Vinylene Carbonate (160)

$$\underset{\substack{O\diagdown_{\substack{C}}\diagup O\\ \|\\ O}}{HC=\!\!=\!\!CH} \xrightarrow{\text{AIBN}} \underset{\substack{O\diagdown_{\substack{C}}\diagup O\\ \|\\ O}}{(-HC=\!\!=\!\!CH-)_n}$$

A thick-walled test tube is necked down near the top and, after cooling, 0.01 g. of azobiisobutyronitrile (AIBN) is introduced. By use of a hypodermic syringe, 5 ml. of the sodium borohydride-treated vinylene carbonate is added. The tube is cooled in ice water to freeze the monomer and evacuated through a stopcock to 1 mm. pressure. The stopcock is closed and the monomer is then degassed by melting and refreezing. The evacuation and degassing procedure is then repeated, after which the system is sealed *in vacuo*. The sealed tube is placed in a bath thermostated at 60–65°C. Polymerization takes place slowly to give a clear solid resin in 18–72 hr. The tube is broken and the tough plug of polymer is dissolved in 50 ml. of N,N-dimethylformamide (DMF) at room temperature and reprecipitated as a white fibrous solid by adding this solution slowly with stirring to 200 ml. of methanol. The polymer is collected by filtration and washed repeatedly by slurrying with methanol until the filtrate is nearly clear. The yield of polymer is 3.7–5.6 g. (57–87%); the inherent viscosity at 30°C. of a 0.5% solution of polymer in N,N-dimethylformamide is 2.0–3.5.

Vinylene carbonate polymer can be hydrolyzed to polyhydroxymethylene, a very intractable polymer. Hydrolysis is best carried out on a finished product, e.g., a cast film of poly(vinylene carbonate) to give an orientable film of polyhydroxymethylene.

208. Preparation of Polyhydroxymethylene (160)

Poly(vinylene carbonate) is dissolved in DMF to form a 10% solution. This is cast as a 10 ml. film on a glass plate by use of a doctor knife. After drying overnight at room temperature, the clear film is removed from the plate and

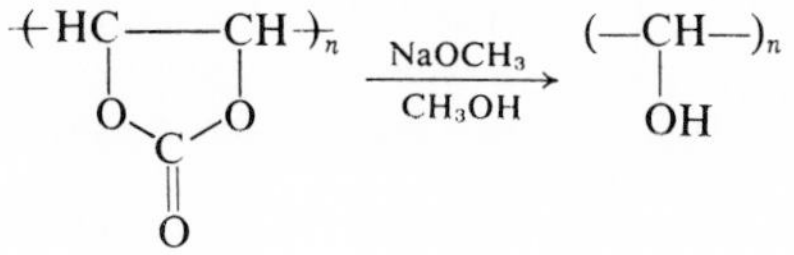

$$\left(HC\!\!-\!\!-\!\!-\!\!CH\right)_n \quad \xrightarrow[\text{CH}_3\text{OH}]{\text{NaOCH}_3} \quad \left(-CH-\right)_n$$

hydrolyzed by suspending it in a 1% sodium methoxide solution in methanol in a covered beaker. Hydrolysis to clear, but crinkled, films of polyhydroxymethylene is complete after 24 hr. at 50–60°C. or after 3–5 days at room temperature. The progress of hydrolysis may be followed conveniently by noting the disappearance of the carbonyl bond at 5.5 μ in the IR spectrum.

The films of polyhydroxymethylene are stiff and brittle when thoroughly dry, but become limper and tougher in moist air. They are insoluble even in boiling water and retain a moderate amount of strength when wet. The wet film can be cut into narrow strips (about 5 mm. wide), and these can be oriented by drawing them quickly over a rod heated at 200°C. Such films are quite strong and very stiff.

Surprisingly, the rather highly hindered phenyl vinylene carbonate can be polymerized in bulk to a respectable molecular weight. The homopolymer has a high T_g, 213°C. by DTA.

The glass transition temperatures of vinyl polymers are significantly raised by incorporation of low percentages of this monomer. Thus, a copolymer of methyl methacrylate containing 1.2 mole % of phenyl vinylene carbonate has a glass transition temperature of 124°C., and incorporation of 12.5 mole % of the carbonate into polystyrene raises the T_g to 129°C. (values for methyl methacrylate and styrene homopolymers are about 105°C. and 95°C., respectively).

209. Preparation of Phenyl Vinylene Carbonate (162)*

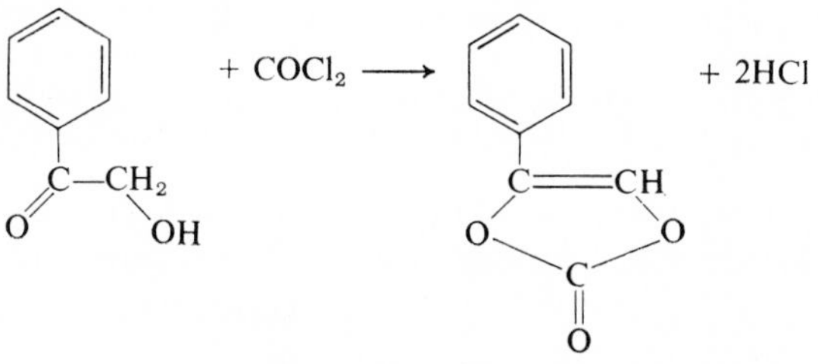

$$+ \text{COCl}_2 \longrightarrow \qquad + 2\text{HCl}$$

2-Hydroxyacetophenone (55.0 g., 0.404 mole) and 200 g. of dry, redistilled dioxane are charged into a 500 ml., three-necked reaction flask equipped with a stirrer, a Dry Ice condenser, and an inlet tube connected to a phosgene source. To the condenser is connected a series of traps composed of four 1 l. Erlenmeyer flasks arranged in the following manner: flasks 1 and 3 are used as back-up traps and flasks 2 and 4 contained 300 ml. toluene and 300 ml. ammonia respectively.

* We are indebted to Dr. R. S. Forgione, American Cyanamid, for supplying this and the following experiment.

Phosgene gas (100 g., 1 mole) is bubbled into the reaction mixture for 3 hr. at 10°C. The reaction vessel is maintained under a slight nitrogen pressure (to prevent back-up) at room temperature 18 hr. The mixture is then heated to 40°C. and more phosgene (25 g.) added in about 30 min. The remaining phosgene and hydrogen chloride are flushed with a strong flow of nitrogen for 2 hr. The crude crystalline product which is obtained after the solvent is evaporated under vacuum is dissolved in ether. Hexane is added to the cloud point and cooling to about 10°C. affords about 48 g. of light-yellow crystals. Recrystallization from benzene–hexane mixture yields about 24 g. (30% yield) of white needles, m.p. 81–82°C.

Preparation of this compound by the chlorination-dehydrochlorination of phenylethylene carbonate according to Morris (161a) affords low yields ($\sim 10\%$) of monomer which does not polymerize readily. This is apparently due to trace impurities which cannot be eliminated easily.

210. Preparation of Poly(phenyl vinylene carbonate) (162)

Nine-tenths of a gram of freshly recrystallized phenyl vinylene carbonate is added to a polymerization tube containing 50 mg. of t-butyl-perbenzoate. The tube is degassed and sealed under nitrogen and the mixture heated at 92°C. for 4 days. The resulting clear amber plug is dissolved in dimethylformamide and the solution poured into 1 l. of methanol, giving about 0.48 g. (53%) of poly(phenyl vinylene carbonate). Its intrinsic viscosity in DMF at 30°C. is about 0.14 dl./g. The product softens at about 300°C. and its glass transition temperature (by differential thermal analysis) is 213°C. It is soluble in dioxane and chloroform; evaporation of a solution of the latter produces a transparent brittle film.

A sample with an intrinsic viscosity of 0.16 dl./g. was found to have a weight average molecular weight of 13,000 (a DP of 80) by light scattering.

Other 1,2-disubstituted monomers of a similar structure will, in some cases, polymerize or at least copolymerize. These include N-substituted maleimides (130,163,164), and maleic anhydride (165). In addition, the noncyclic maleonitrile will form copolymers (87).

Tetrasubstituted monomers known to polymerize satisfactorily include **chlorotrifluoroethylene(I)** (129,166,167) and **tetrafluoroethylene (II)** (168–170).

(I)   (II)

These compounds polymerize only under pressure and are very dangerous to handle; therefore, the polymerizations should not be attempted except by those experienced in the handling of these materials. Both polymers are available commercially. Teflon is du Pont's trademark for its fluorocarbon resins, including tetrafluoroethylene polymers, and Kel-F is the trademark of Minnesota Mining and Manufacturing Co.'s polychlorotrifluoroethylene resin.

VI. Cationic Polymerization of Vinyl Compounds

Cationic polymerization of vinyl compounds is not nearly so applicable as is free radical polymerization. The growing chain has a terminal carbonium ion together with its counter ion and polymerization is ordinarily much more rapid and vigorous. Cationic polymerizations are usually initiated at low temperatures in order to suppress undesirable chain-terminating side reactions. The choice of solvent, catalyst concentration, cocatalyst, etc., is extremely important. It is, of course, essential that the solvent, if used, should be almost completely unreactive. The theoretical implications of general cationic catalysis are discussed at length in the literature (2).

The following experimental examples illustrate some of the different types of techniques used in the polymerization of several vinyl compounds. It will be noted that the procedures are quite different from those used in the polymerization of vinyl monomers by typical free radical recipes.

One of the few monomers which responds satisfactorily to cationic as well as to free radical catalysis is **styrene,** although it is admittedly difficult to get a product of as high molecular weight with cationic catalysis as is possible with free radical.

Substitution of styrene with an α-methyl group gives a monomer which will polymerize readily with typical cationic catalysts. Again, it is necessary to operate at very low temperatures in order to obtain high molecular weight. It appears that, in general, for cationic catalysis to occur, a cocatalyst is necessary which is capable of generating a proton or carbonium ion by reaction with what is customarily designated as the catalyst. The simplest cocatalyst is water, which is often adventitiously present. For example, with boron trifluoride,

$$BF_3 + H_2O \longrightarrow H^\oplus + \overset{\ominus}{B}F_3OH$$

water provides a proton as the initiating fragment. The unavoidable presence of small quantities of water almost certainly provides the cocatalyst for the next preparative example, which is a convenient cationic polymerization of α-methylstyrene.

211. Preparation of Cationic Polymerization of Methylstyrene (171)

Toluene is dried over calcium hydride and used directly. α-Methylstyrene is purified by first washing with 5% aqueous sodium hydroxide twice, with distilled water three times, then dried over calcium hydride. It should be distilled before use (b.p. 52°C./10 mm.), taking a heart cut. To a dry, nitrogen-flushed, 8 oz. beverage bottle is charged 50 ml. of toluene and 10 ml. α-methylstyrene, using a nitrogen sweep during addition. The bottle is closed with a rubber septum and crown cap with a hole for catalyst addition. The bottle is immersed in Dry Ice–acetone.

Boron trifluoride gas is flushed through a 1 ft. length of Tygon tubing attached directly to a cylinder of the gas; the end of the tubing should be vented through a hypodermic needle to assure high gas velocity at the exit and no possible back-up of air. When the tubing is thoroughly flushed, a dry hypodermic syringe is inserted through the tubing, and 10 ml. of BF_3 is withdrawn; it is injected directly into the bottle whose contents are at $-78°C$. The bottle is swirled gently and cooling is maintained. Polymerization occurs very quickly, but the bottle is allowed to stand at $-78°C$. for 5 hr. The contents are poured with stirring into about 400 ml. methanol in a blender, filtered, washed 3 times with methanol in the blender and dried at 60°C. in vacuum. About 7 g. of polymer is obtained which softens around 175–200°C. The inherent viscosity in toluene (0.1 g./100 ml., toluene, 25°C.) should be 0.85–1.0.

Probably the most important monomer which is polymerized commercially by a cationic catalyst is **isobutylene** (172). It polymerizes very easily at low temperatures to high molecular weight polymers which are relatively soft and rubbery. Isobutylene is not affected by free radical type catalysts. However, the cationic polymerization of carefully purified monomer may occur with almost explosive violence, hence it is ordinarily necessary to moderate this reaction by using very low boiling diluents such as ethyl or methyl chloride or ethylene. The following represents a typical technique for polymerizing isobutylene with a cationic catalyst.

212. Polymerization of Isobutylene with Cationic Catalyst

$$CH_2=C{\overset{CH_3}{\underset{CH_3}{}}} \longrightarrow \left[-CH_2-C{\overset{CH_3}{\underset{CH_3}{}}}-\right]_n$$

A mixture of 10 g. of isobutylene with approximately 5 g. of anhydrous Dry Ice is stirred at $-80°C$. and approximately 10 ml. of boron fluoride gas is introduced via syringe. (See Cationic Polymerization of α-Methylstyrene.) Polymerization is initiated almost at once and polymer is produced, the heat of reaction being dissipated by the Dry Ice present in the reaction vessel. The product is a high molecular weight, clear, nontacky, elastomeric material. Use of this technique requires Dry Ice from which all excess moisture is absent, since gross moisture will inhibit the activity of the catalyst (173). Taking the center from a large piece of Dry Ice should be satisfactory.

Another method (174) of dissipating heat and moderating violence of the polymerization is to use a low-boiling diluent. For example, a mixture of 20 parts of pure isobutylene and 80 parts of ethane (b.p. $-88°$C.) or ethylene (b.p. $-104°$C.) is cooled in a liquid nitrogen bath ($-196°$C.) and treated with 0.2 parts of boron fluoride gas. Polymerization occurs rapidly and the product is of high molecular weight. The mixture of polymer and solvents is allowed to warm to room temperature and is dried in a vacuum oven at 50°C. The product is a chunk of clear, rubber-like plastic.

Two other monomers which polymerize with Lewis acids are *N*-**vinyl carbazole** and **acenaphthylene.** The following techniques illustrate preparation of polymers from these monomers.

213. The Polymerization of *N*-Vinyl Carbazole (175,176)

$$CH=CH_2 \qquad -CH_2-CH- \Big]_n$$

Fifty g. of freshly distilled *N*-vinyl carbazole and 150 ml. of methylene chloride in a 1 l., three-necked flask equipped with a stirrer, an inlet tube, and an outlet tube is cooled in a Dry Ice bath to $-60°$C. with exclusion of atmospheric moisture by means of suitably placed drying tubes. The solution is stirred rapidly and 0.1 ml. of boron fluoride etherate solution is added by means of a hypodermic syringe through the inlet tube which may be capped by a piece of thin rubber sheeting, or a serum type stopper (Chapter 2). Polymerization is initiated almost immediately and the temperature of the reaction mixture rises. After approximately 5 min., the gel-like reaction mixture is treated with 1 ml. of concentrated aqueous ammonia to neutralize the catalyst present and the polymeric solution is coagulated by stirring with methyl alcohol in a high speed mixer. The polymer is filtered and is obtained as a white mass in a yield of about 80–85%.

It is possible to carry out this experiment at room temperature or even at higher temperatures, but lower molecular weight polymer is always obtained. Other solvents may be used such as toluene, carbon tetrachloride, etc., but they are all inferior to methylene chloride in that lower molecular weight products are invariably obtained.

The polymerization of *N*-vinyl carbazole will take place under a wide variety of conditions. For example, highly purified monomer may be heated in the absence of catalyst at temperatures of 85–120°C. to give a nearly colorless clear product similar in appearance to polystyrene. Again it must be emphasized that it is essential for the monomer to be very pure, otherwise high molecular weight material will not be obtained. The monomer should be distilled, or recrystallized from a suitable solvent such as methyl alcohol or cyclohexane. Poly(vinyl carbazole) can be molded at temperatures of 210–270°C. to sheets which are clear and stiff. The polymer is soluble in chloroform, trichloroethylene, aromatic hydrocarbons, etc. The polymer has excellent electrical properties, but has not found widespread use in this field mainly because of the high cost of the monomer.

214. Polymerization of Acenaphthylene (177)

A solution of about 9 g. of the hydrocarbon dissolved in ether at $-50°C$. is treated briefly with a slow stream of boron trifluoride gas. The solution is then allowed to warm to 25°C. After 4 hr., the precipitated polymer is removed by filtration, dissolved in benzene, and reprecipitated with methyl alcohol. The polymer has a molecular weight in the range of 183,000–341,000.

Alternatively, polymerization may be carried out by treating a solution of 50 g. of acenaphthylene in 140 ml. of chlorobenzene maintained at -50 to $-20°C$. with a very slow stream of boron trifluoride gas for about 30 min. The polymer is obtained from the chlorobenzene by precipitation with alcohol. It is dissolved in benzene and reprecipitated with methanol. The yield is approximately 37 g. of very high molecular weight material.

Polymerization at a higher temperature is also possible (179): a solution of 1 g. acenaphthylene in 10 ml. dry benzene is placed in a dry test tube under exclusion of moisture but not necessarily of air. It is kept at 40°C. and injected with 0.15 ml. redistilled boron trifluoride diethyl etherate (b.p. 125–126°C.). After several hours the darkened solution is poured into methanol; the recovered polymer is purified as above. It has an intrinsic viscosity of about 1.25 in benzene.

Acenaphthylene can be recrystallized several times from enthanol to improve its purity. From some sources, the original state is sufficient for acceptable polymerization.

Acenaphthylene can also be thermally polymerized in bulk by heating slightly above its melting point (e.g., 95°C.; the m.p. is 92.5°C.) for several hours (178). Fractionation of polymer prepared in this way has given the following intrinsic viscosity–molecular weight relationship for benzene at 25°C., and is believed to be valid over the molecular weight range of 20,000–1,000,000:

$$[\eta] = 3.04 \times 10^{-2} M^{0.594}$$

Another group of vinyl compounds which is usually susceptible as a class to cationic polymerization is the vinyl ethers. Vinyl isobutyl ether has probably been more closely examined than any other member of the family, a fact owing in large measure to its early stereoregular polymerization using boron trifluoride etherate at low temperature and the subsequent question of the mechanism of occurrence and the physical state in which it takes place (180–187). Much of the mechanistic controversy centered on whether a heterogeneous surface was necessary for the stereoregular polymerization, since Schildknecht's original discovery of this phenomenon involved polymerization at the interface of the catalyst droplet and the monomer solution in a slow, proliferous fashion. Yet, it was not certain whether polymerization occurred in a truly heterogeneous system or in a homogeneous solution. It was finally shown that stereoregular polymer (at least, relatively so) could indeed form in a homogeneous solution (181,186), and even in the heterogeneous system, the polymerization occurs in a homogeneous phase.

Polymerization with boron trifluoride etherate in the manner necessary to give relatively crystalline polymer occurs slowly. In contrast, boron trifluoride gas at low temperature in propane solvent causes polymerization to occur literally in a flash, and rubbery, amorphous polymer results. The crystalline polymer prepared in the former method has an isotactic chain structure. The concept and terminology of tacticity was developed initially around the crystalline polyolefins and later was extended in a fruitful manner to other polymer classes including the poly(vinyl ethers) particularly isotactic poly(vinyl isobutyl ether), despite the fact that the latter had been prepared well before the stereoregular polymerization of olefins (180).

215. Preparation of a Relatively Crystalline, Isotactic Poly(vinyl isobutyl ether)

$$CH_2{=}CH{-}O{-}CH_2CH(CH_3)_2 \longrightarrow \{CH_2{-}CH\}$$

$$\begin{array}{c} | \\ O \\ | \\ CH_2 \\ | \\ CH(CH_3)_2 \end{array}$$

The following procedure (186) involves essentially anhydrous conditions and the polymerization is fully homogeneous through its initial stage (i.e., about 35% conversion); it then enters a clear, gel-like condition. The reaction is optically clear at all times. Polymer isolated at low conversion is slightly less stereoregular than that which has proceeded through the clear gel phase.

Materials are readied as follows: Toluene is distilled from calcium hydride. n-Hexane is shaken successively with acidic and alkaline potassium permanganate solutions, then washed with water, and finally distilled from calcium hydride. Isobutyl vinyl ether is shaken 3 times with 5% aqueous potassium hydroxide, and dried by fractional distillation from sodium. At least 10% of forerun and tails are discarded when using commercial vinyl ether. In order to achieve a homogeneous polymerization, the boron trifluoride etherate catalyst should also be distilled from calcium hydride; inhomogeneity due to boron trifluoride hydrate present in the catalyst, which may be insoluble in the polymerization medium, is thus avoided.

A convenient reaction vessel (250 ml. capacity) is the three-necked elongated flask shown in Fig. 4.2, equipped with a stirrer and a rubber serum cap stopper. It is flamed out under nitrogen. Nitrogen inlet and outlet can be achieved with insertion of hypodermic needles through the serum caps. It is charged, after cooling to room temperature, with a 90 ml. of a 33/67 vol. % mixture of n-hexane and toluene, and 2.85 g. isobutyl vinyl ether (0.0285 mole). The mixture is cooled to $-78°$C. in Dry Ice–acetone, and 0.051 g. boron trifluoride etherate (3.6×10^{-4} moles) in a standard solution in about 10 ml. hexane–toluene, previously chilled in Dry Ice–acetone, is added by syringe. The mixture remains stirrable to about 35% conversion, where it gels and stirring is virtually impossible. (Prior to gelation at least, molecular weight increases with conversion, indicating a relatively slow propagation step.) After 90 min., the mixture is scooped into 400 ml. isopropanol in a blender and washed thoroughly 3 times with 300 ml. portions of isopropanol. It is dried at 50°C. in a nitrogen stream under vacuum to give upwards of 80% conversion. The inherent viscosity in toluene (0.1 g./100 ml.) at 25°C. is 1.0 or more.

An alternate procedure involving heterogeneous catalyst droplets requires no care to maintain anaerobic and anhydrous conditions, although monomer purity is important and use of distilled boron trifluoride etherate is desirable. A stirred reaction flask can be used, but stirring is not essential, and in fact a simple open flask can be used. The vessel is immersed in Dry Ice–acetone and 40 ml. of propane is condensed in, followed by 10 ml. of vinyl isobutyl ether. Three drops of catalyst ($BF_3 \cdot Et_2O$) is added. The polymerization occurs around the insoluble droplets of catalyst. After about 30 min., 3 more drops of catalyst is added, and reaction allowed to proceed for 90 min. Growth of polymer washed in methanol to remove catalyst and monomer, and dried in a

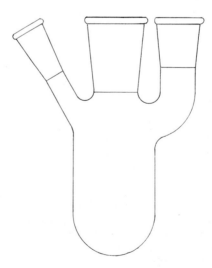

Fig. 4.2. Elongated flask for exothermic polymerizations.

current of nitrogen in a vacuum oven at 50°C. to give about 6 g. of polymer with an inherent viscosity of about 1.5 (toluene, as above).

The crystalline melting point of polymers prepared in each of the foregoing procedures is 90°C. or more, and usually is over a fair range, indicating the presence of some noncrystallizable polymer. The residue from extraction of the polymer with heptane, benzene, and tetrahydrofuran can have a T_m as high as 165°C.

216. Preparation of Amorphous Poly(vinyl isobutyl ether)

Liquid propane (30 ml.) is condensed into an open three-necked flask cooled in Dry Ice–acetone and containing 10 g. pure vinyl isobutyl ether and in which is suspended a thermometer. The mixture is allowed to warm up $-60°C$. and a stream of BF_3 gas is passed rapidly through the mixture. Reaction occurs almost instantaneously and propane gas evolves rapidly from the heat of reaction. The white, rubbery solid is thrown all over, and possibly out of, the flask. The remaining propane is evaporated. The polymer should have an inherent viscosity of at least 1.0 (toluene, 0.1 g./100 ml., 25°C.). The propane gas boiled out during the flash polymerization constitutes a flammability hazard, so the reaction should be conducted in a good hood.

Crystalline poly(vinyl ethers) can be made at or near room temperature using certain complex metal sulfate catalysts (188). The following method is effective with ethyl-, isobutyl-, and isopropyl vinyl ethers, as well as n-butyl. The mechanism of polymerization over catalysts such as that used below is not clear. It is very likely not a conventionally cationic process. Since the catalyst is insoluble, it may act in a manner similar to heterogeneous coordinated anionic (Ziegler-Natta) catalysts.

217. Preparation of a Relatively Crystalline Poly(vinyl n-butyl ether) (188)

The catalyst (189) is prepared by dissolving 10 g. of aluminum sulfate octadecahydrate $(Al_2(SO_4)_3 \cdot 18H_2O)$ in a minimum of water and 3.3 g. concentrated sulfuric acid is added. The mixture is evaporated to dryness and the residue is heated in an oven at 170°C. for 4 hr. The complex salt has the approximate composition $Al_2(SO_4)_3 \cdot 3H_2SO_4 \cdot 7H_2O$. It is protected from moisture since it is quite hygroscopic and unstable to water. A suspension of the catalyst in dry Decalin or mineral oil is made at 2% concentration by rolling the components in a bottle with dry porcelain spheres to a fine state of subdivision.

Vinyl n-butyl ether is washed with water, dried over potassium hydroxide pellets, and distilled from calcium hydride or sodium wire. A mixture of 10 ml. vinyl n-butyl ether and 60 ml. dry n-pentane is charged to a small beverage bottle previously baked dry and flushed with nitrogen. It is sealed with a rubber septum and crown cap with a hole and 0.2 ml. of the 2% catalyst suspension is added by dry syringe. The bottle is tumbled at 35°C. for at least 12 hr. (A magnetic stirring bar can be placed in the bottle and stirring achieved by a magnetic stirrer placed under a heating bath in which the bottle stands.) The polymer is precipitated into methanol containing a small amount of phenyl-β-naphthylamine. The polymer is dried at 40°C. in vacuum. The conversion is about 80% and the polymer has an inherent viscosity of about 4(0.1 g./100 ml. benzene at 30°C.). The fraction which is insoluble in methyl ethyl ketone is crystalline and has a T_m of 68–69°C.

One of the most remarkable developments in synthetic polymer chemistry has been the observation of asymmetric selection, i.e., the more favored polymerization of one optical antipode from a racemic mixture of *d*- and *l*-isomers. The polymerization of *d,l*-propylene oxide by a catalyst made up of diethyl zinc and either D- or L-diethyl glutamate is an example, each ester producing a predominant polymerization of one of the oxide enantiomers and hence a polymer with optical activity (190,194). The stereoregular polymerization of optically pure *d*- or *l*-propylene oxide to a crystalline optically active polymer is also known, but is a different phenomenon.

Racemic α-olefins with an asymmetric carbon adjacent to the double bond have also been selectively polymerized with coordination catalysts using zinc alkyls having an asymmetric component, giving polymers of about 15% optical purity (191). In the olefin case, optical activity is due to an excess of monomers with one asymmetric side chain carbon over the other.

Related to asymmetric selection is the generation of an optically active polymer from a monomer having no asymmetric center. 1,3-pentadiene, whose polymerization to various polytactic species is described in this chapter, has been converted to polymers showing optical activity by means of coordination catalysts where either constituent contains asymmetric groupings, e.g., (+) tris (2-methylbutyl) aluminum or (−) titanium tetramenthoxide (192). Optical activity in these polymers results from a difference in the immediately adjacent groups of a main-chain carbon atom, rather than a side-chain carbon.

The following experiment, the polymerization of benzofuran to a polymer having optical activity, is a case of a monomer which is not asymmetric in the sense of having optical antipodes, but an optical asymmetry is generated in the backbone chain by formation of the *threo*- or *erythro*diisotactic polymer. There is no internal compensation of the truly asymmetric carbons formed. Polymerization is cationic in nature, evidently, with an asymmetric counterion contributing to stereoselective monomer placement. Benzofuran is also of interest as an example of a polymerizable cyclic vinyl ether. The field of optically active addition polymers has been fully reviewed by Pino (193) and of optically active polymers generally by Schulz and Kaiser (194).

218. Preparation of an Optically Active Polybenzofuran (195,196)

(a) erythro-diisotactic   (b) threo-diisotactic

The above formulas portray in Fischer projection the two possible optically active forms of polybenzofuran. It is not known which is formed in the ensuing example. It is certain that the polymer obtained is not optically pure, so that units with asymmetric carbons are in a majority, but are not exclusive.

Benzofuran is fractionated at 60–70 mm. until a chromatographically pure material is obtained. Toluene is washed with concentrated sulfuric acid, then with water, percolated through an active alumina column, distilled, refluxed over sodium for 20 hr., and finally distilled directly into the reaction vessel as needed. Aluminum chloride is sublimed under nitrogen and collected in vials which are flame-sealed. The amount of aluminum chloride used is always in excess of the β-phenylalanine component, and is not severely critical. β-Phenylalanine of either optical persuasion is recrystallized several times from water and thoroughly dried at 60°C. under vacuum. (+) β-Phenylalanine produces a polymer with (+) rotation; the reverse is true for the (−) amino-acid. The pure β-phenylalanine is also sealed into vials. Aluminum chloride and aminoacid vials are placed in a reaction vessel which has been flamed dry and purged with nitrogen and is fixed for receiving toluene via distillation, and a siphon for transfer of the catalyst solution to the polymerization reactor. The vessel is held under a high vacuum for several hours before toluene is distilled in. About 100 ml. of toluene is used for catalyst component quantities of about 0.067 g. (+) or (−) β-phenylalanine (0.405 mmole) and 0.324 g. aluminum chloride (2.43 mmoles). The reactor can be basically a pear-shaped flask; a Trubore stirrer shaft in the center neck can be used to crush the thin-walled vial seals, then used without stirring blade to agitate the contents. After the glass vials are broken, the reactants are stirred at 20°C. for 1 hr., and the excess aluminum chloride then allowed to settle until a clear supernatant solution results (about 3 hr.).

The clear solution containing the active catalyst has an aluminum chloride/β-phenylalanine mole ratio of about 3. It is siphoned with care into the reaction vessel, which can be a 500 ml. Erlenmeyer or round-bottom flask fixed with a thermometer and addition funnel, and having a magnetic stirring bar. This flask and funnel can be connected by a pressure-equalizing tube on the funnel; in this way the system can be effectively closed. A three-way stopcock on the pressure-equalizing sidearm is convenient for applying vacuum for siphoning the catalyst solution. The assembly is, of course, thoroughly dried and flushed with nitrogen. The dropping funnel is modified by a surrounding jacket in which will be placed Dry Ice–acetone coolant. The funnel can be filled initially in a dry box before final assembly of the system. The funnel contains a solution of 4 g. benzofuran in 100 ml. dry toluene, which is cooled to $-75°C$. The catalyst solution is also cooled to $-75°C$. and the monomer solution is added with stirring. The polymer formed in the early stages of polymerization has a higher optical rotation (benzene solution, ca. 0.25%, sodium line, room temperature) than that formed later, due, it is believed, to termination reactions that tend to racemize the counterion. Hence, the sooner the reaction is terminated, the greater the specific rotation of the product. Samples can be withdrawn and quenched in methanol at intervals and the decrease in rotation noted. For convenience, the entire reaction can be terminated in about 30 min. to give about 3 g. of polymer, after thorough washing in methanol and drying. The intrinsic viscosity is about 1.0 (in toluene, 30°C.) and $[\alpha]_D$ is about $\pm 50°C$., depending on which isomer of β-phenylalanine was used. The polymer resists racemization in decalin solution at 200°C. over several hours. The optical purity of the polymer is not known. Because the polymer is amorphous, a crystallographic determination of its exact steric structure has not been possible.

α- and β-Naphthofuran (197) have also been converted to optically active polymers under conditions similar to those given here. Polymers from both monomers have shown crystallinity on annealing, but films of the crystalline polymers could not be oriented, and x-ray fiber diagrams could not be obtained for structure analysis.

VII. Anionic Polymerization of Vinyl Compounds

One of the most scientifically rewarding areas of addition polymerization is that of anionic initiation. The number of anionically polymerizable monomers is not great, but a detailed study has been made in some instances. The subject has been reviewed generally (198) and in some of its specific areas (199–201).

Polymerizations by free alkali metals are included in this category, since a free radical propagation is apparently not involved, as witness the ready polymerization of **α-methylstyrene** by metallic potassium. The initiator is probably

$$C_6H_5-\underset{\underset{K}{|}}{\overset{\overset{CH_3}{|}}{C}}-CH_2CH_2-\underset{\underset{K}{|}}{\overset{\overset{CH_3}{|}}{C}}-C_6H_5$$

219. Polymerization of α-Methylstyrene by Metallic Potassium (202)

$$C_6H_5-\overset{\overset{CH_3}{|}}{C}=CH_2 \longrightarrow \left[-CH_2-\underset{\underset{CH_3}{|}}{\overset{\overset{C_6H_5}{|}}{C}}-\right]_n$$

In a glass wall polymer tube of at least 150 ml. content are placed 72.5 g. of freshly distilled α-methylstyrene together with about 2 g. of metallic potassium (**Danger**!) in the form of wire or pellets. The mixture is sealed under vacuum and agitated at 15°C. for about 12 hr. An induction period of about 7 hr. is noted followed by a polymerization period of about 5 hr. The reaction mixture is removed from the tube and the viscous liquid is separated from metallic potassium by filtration. Unpolymerized α-methylstyrene is removed from the mixture by heating at 190°C./1 mm., or by blowing with steam, after removal of the potassium. The product remaining in the flask consists of about 35–40 g. of polymeric α-methylstyrene, with an inherent viscosity of about 0.7–0.8 as measured in toluene (0.5%, 25°C.).

α-Methylstyrene may be polymerized using similar conditions with metallic sodium, metallic lithium or alloys of the alkali metals. The reaction with metallic sodium is considerably slower than with potassium, while lithium is intermediate.

Catalysts for the anionic polymerization of vinyls are ordinarily salts of very weak bases. The classic example is the **polymerization of methacrylonitrile by Grignard reagents, or triphenylmethyl sodium,** as described by Beaman (203).

220. Polymerization of Methacrylonitrile with Sodium in Liquid Ammonia (203)

$$CH_2{=}C \overset{\displaystyle CN}{\underset{\displaystyle CH_3}{<}} \longrightarrow \left[-CH_2{-}\underset{\displaystyle CH_3}{\overset{\displaystyle CN}{C}}{-} \right]_n$$

A 500 ml. round-bottom, three-necked flask, equipped with a Dry Ice condenser, a stirrer, and a gas inlet is cooled in a Dry Ice bath, and about 100 ml. of anhydrous liquid ammonia is condensed into the flask. Approximately 0.4 g. of metallic sodium is now introduced into the liquid ammonia and allowed to dissolve to give the intense blue solution characteristic of sodium dissolved in liquid ammonia. To this solution, maintained at −75°C., is added 15 g. of freshly distilled α-methacrylonitrile. The blue color is discharged almost instantaneously. After approximately 15 min., 2 g. of solid ammonium chloride is added to decompose any organometallic compounds present and the ammonia is allowed to evaporate. The residual solid polymer is washed with water to remove inorganic salts, filtered, and dried. The yield of polymer is quantitative, the inherent viscosity in the neighborhood of 0.8 as measured in dimethylformamide solution (0.5%, 25°C.).

Methacrylonitrile can also be polymerized to a crystalline, predominantly isotactic polymer at room temperature and higher (e.g., 70°C.) by the action of catalysts such as diethylmagnesium, di-(piperamido)magnesium (206), and other complex organometallic compounds (204,205).

221. Stereospecific Polymerization of Methacrylonitrile (206)*

$$CH_2{=}\overset{\overset{\displaystyle CH_3}{|}}{C}{-}CN \longrightarrow \left[\begin{array}{c} CH_2 \\ \diagdown \quad \diagup \\ C \\ \diagup \quad \diagdown \\ CN \qquad CH_3 \end{array}\right]$$

Catalyst preparation (diethylmagnesium)

$$2EtMgBr \rightleftharpoons Et_2Mg + MgBr_2$$

$$Et_2Mg + Et_3Al \longrightarrow Mg(AlEt_4)_2$$

A 1 l. three-necked flask equipped with a sealed mechanical stirrer, a reflux condenser, and a pressure-equalized dropping funnel, is arranged for carrying out a reaction in an atmosphere of nitrogen by fitting into the top of the condenser a T-tube attached to a low-pressure supply of nitrogen and to a mercury bubbler. In the flask is placed 50 g. (2.05 gram atoms) of fine magnesium turnings and 250 ml. of absolute ether which is freshly distilled over CaH_2 and under nitrogen immediately before use. After the vessel is purged with nitrogen the Grignard reaction is started in the usual way by introducing 5 ml. of a solution of 250 g. (175 ml., 2.3 moles) of ethyl bromide in 250 ml. of freshly distilled absolute ether. The reaction, which starts at once, is maintained by gradually adding the remainder of ethyl bromide–ether solution. When the spontaneous reaction subsides, the mixture is heated gently under reflux with stirring for about 30 min. After the preparation of ethylmagnesium bromide is complete, the flask is cooled and then 193 g. of anhydrous dioxane is introduced dropwise through a dropping funnel with stirring under nitrogen atmosphere. A white precipitate is formed by introducing the dioxane to the Grignard solution. After the precipitate has settled down, the supernatant transparent liquid is withdrawn by a syringe and is transferred into another vessel which has been flushed with dry nitrogen gas. To the residual precipitate is added about 200 ml. of absolute ether with stirring, then is allowed to stand several hours. Supernatant liquid is again withdrawn by a syringe and added to the ether solution previously transferred in the same fashion. This procedure is repeated several times. The sum of the ethereal solutions is then concentrated under nitrogen until the white crystals of diethylmagnesium–dioxane complex is formed. After almost all the ether is removed, the vessel is connected to the vacuum pump to remove all traces of ether, then it is gradually warmed up to about 100°C. in order to remove the complexed dioxane at 3 mm. Hg. To remove the complexed dioxane completely from diethylmagnesium, over 10 hr. are necessary under these conditions. After this procedure is over, nitrogen gas is introduced to the vessel to atmospheric pressure and the vessel is placed in a dry box filled with nitrogen. The crystals of diethylmagnesium are pulverized into uniform and finely divided form under nitrogen. The yield of diethylmagnesium is about 70%.

---

* We are grateful to Dr. Yosushi Joh, Mitsubishi Rayon Co., for making available this synthesis in full detail prior to publication.

Diethylmagnesium (0.12 mole) is placed in a vessel which has been purged with dry nitrogen gas; then, 30 ml. of dry toluene is introduced. To this suspension, 0.2 mole of AlEt$_3$ is added dropwise at room temperature. The mixture is warmed to and held at 70°C. for 30 min. with occasional shaking. After 30 min., almost all the Et$_2$Mg dissolves in the solvent. After cooling, the supernatant liquid is withdrawn by a syringe and transferred into another nitrogen flushed vessel.

The precipitate, which is composed of unreacted Et$_2$Mg and decomposition products derived from trace contaminants in the solvent, is washed several times with toluene and the clear, supernatant liquid is added to the supernatant liquid removed previously; the total volume should be 100 ml. Thus, this gives a catalyst solution of Mg[AlEt$_4$]$_2$ with a concentration of 0.001 mole/ml. Concentration of the catalyst can be checked by analysis for Al or Mg, which should have the indicated ratio of the two.

Polymerization:

The reaction vessel is a 300 ml. three-necked flask equipped with a mechanical stirrer, reflux condenser, and inlet and outlet tube for nitrogen gas. One neck of the flask is covered with rubber serum bottle cap. After the flask is flushed with dry nitrogen gas, 270 ml. of anisole, which has been distilled over CaH$_2$ immediately before use, is introduced with syringe through the serum cap. An amount of the catalyst solution calculated to give 0.5 g. Mg[AlEt$_4$]$_2$ is then added under nitrogen. After the solution is maintained at constant temperature of 70°C., the polymerization is started by injecting 30 ml. of purified methacrylonitrile. On addition of the monomer the simultaneous appearance of a deep-red color which remains during the polymerization is observed. A positive nitrogen pressure is maintained during the polymerization. After 2 hr. crude polymer is isolated by pouring the reaction product into 1000 ml. of methanol containing small amount (usually 2–3%) of hydrochloric acid, and then allowing the mixture to stand at room temperature overnight. Precipitated white polymer is collected, filtered, washed several times with methanol and dried *in vacuo*. Thus, 10.9 g. of polymethacrylonitrile is obtained. When the polymer is extracted with acetone in a Soxhlet extractor for 24 hr., 79.7% of the polymer is isolated as an insoluble fraction which gives a typical crystalline x-ray diagram. The intrinsic viscosity of the crystalline polymer can be measured in dichloroacetic acid at 30°C. The acetone-insoluble fraction obtained by this procedure has an intrinsic viscosity of about 4.7. If one wishes to isolate a higher crystalline fraction, the following procedure is recommended: 1 g. of the acetone-insoluble fraction of the polymer is placed in a flask and 100 ml. of dimethylformamide (or dimethylsulfoxide) is introduced. The flask is then warmed up to 70°C. with stirring. After 2 hr. the polymer is extremely swollen. The swollen polymer can be isolated by centrifuge. The white precipitate which is obtained by addition of methanol to the swollen polymer is washed with a sufficient amount of methanol, dried, and weighed; 0.7 g. of highly crystalline material can be isolated. The dimethylformamide soluble part can be also isolated by concentration of the solution followed by precipitating with methanol. This fraction gives an x-ray diagram of low crystallinity. Films can be cast at room temperature from trifluoroacetic acid; these can be oriented at 90°C. after removing residual solvent by immersion in boiling water for

2 hr. The intrinsic viscosity–molecular weight relationship determined for the acetone-insoluble polymer in Cl_2CHCO_2H is:

$$[\eta] = 2.27 \times 10^{-4} M^{0.75}$$

In the anionic polymerization of styrene the reactive chain propagating species, $[R—CH_2—CHPh]^{\ominus}M^{\oplus}$ is a substituted benzyl anion which is stable indefinitely in an inert environment. The macromolecular anions have been called "living polymers" because they will resume chain growth in the presence of additional monomer (207). If an anionically polymerizable monomer other than styrene is added, block copolymers may be formed. Reaction with reagents such as CO_2 or SO_2 will give, after hydrolysis, macromolecular acids.

In the butyllithium initiated polymerization of styrene, each mole of butyllithium generates one chain-propagating anion. Polymer molecular weight therefore is determined only by the quantities of monomer and initiator, according to the equation

$$M = \frac{\text{grams monomer}}{\text{moles of initiator}}$$

Polymers with predetermined molecular weights thus may be prepared by adjusting the quantities of monomer and initiator, providing that initiation is very rapid with respect to propagation.

Since in any homopolymerization all macromolecular anions have equivalent reactivities, chain growth and chain length (molecular weight) distribution is governed by probability considerations. Theory (210) shows that the idealized polymer will have chain lengths which conform to a Poisson distribution, as given by the formula

$$X_{(P)} = \frac{n^{P-1}e^{-n}}{(P-1)!}$$

where n is the number of moles of monomer consumed per active chain end, P is the number of monomer units in a given chain, and $X_{(P)}$ is the mole fraction of the chains containing P monomer units. Polymers having a Poisson molecular weight distribution have a M_w/M_n of unity.

Any reactive impurities such as protonic compounds, carbonyl compounds, halogen compounds, oxidizing agents, etc., can kill some of the growing chains, thereby broadening the molecular weight distribution. Elegant vacuum system techniques have been developed to attain the scrupulous purities necessary to prepare polymers having M_w/M_n approximating 1 (207,211,212). But by working in an inert atmosphere one can make quite good polymers using standard glassware (212,213). The key to the latter procedure is that the deleterious impurities are removed from the polymerization medium and from the monomer by titration before polymerization (under conditions where polymerization is slow) with the reactive anion which constitutes the initiator. Because initiation by BuLi in benzene occurs more slowly than propagation, the molecular weight distribution tends to be broader than when initiation is faster than propagation. However, the problem is minimized when quite high molecular weight polymer is synthesized and when part of the initiation process occurs with only a small amount of monomer present, both of which conditions prevail in the present case.

222. Polystyrene of Predetermined Molecular Weight and Narrow Molecular Weight Distribution by Anionic Polymerization with Butyllithium (171)*

The benzene purification system is illustrated in Fig. 4.3. The argon scrubber A and the solvent reservoir B are assembled ahead of time, and flushed with argon. Dry benzene (about 150 and 1500 ml. respectively), 1.6M butyllithium (20 ml. to each) and styrene (2 ml. to each) are then added, and the exit of B is stoppered until reaction flask C is attached. During several hours both solutions gradually attain the characteristic yellow-orange-to-red color of the R—CH$_2$CHPh$^-$ anion. All subsequent operations are performed with a stream of argon moving through the system. One l. flask C (necks and outlets shown schematically) is attached via the condenser (at 2). C is also fitted with a Teflon-covered stirring bar, a thermometer (at 3) a 125 ml. graduated addition funnel with a Teflon stopcock (at 4), a serum cap (at 6), and an exit tube (at 7) leading to a mineral oil U bubbler, D C and the addition funnel are flamed and cooled under argon; the addition funnel is then sealed with a serum cap (at 5). The tube connecting the exit 7 to D must be arranged so that any condensing vapors will not drain back into C. About 600 ml. benzene is distilled from B to C. During the latter stages of the distillation, 125 ml. benzene is transferred from C to the addition funnel with a 100 ml. syringe having a 6 in. needle (via caps at 6 and 5). When the distillation is finished, B is brought to room temperature, removed from the

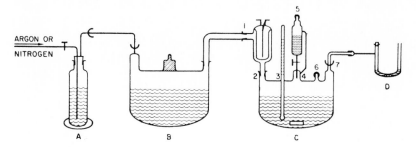

Fig. 4.3. Apparatus for solvent purification and distillation.

* Our thanks are due Dr. D. B. Miller, Stanford Research Institute, for this preparation.

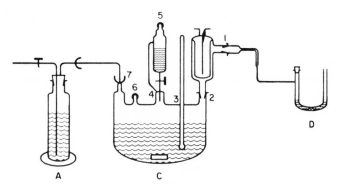

Fig. 4.4. Apparatus for monomer polymerization.

system, stoppered, and set aside for future use so long as the anion survives. C is quickly reattached to the argon supply at 7 and exit bubbler D is attached at 1 (Fig. 4.4).

The initiator solution is prepared by adding 0.81 ml. 1.6M butyllithium and 0.4 ml. styrene to the addition funnel with syringes, giving an initiator concentration of about 0.01 meq. per ml. Warming with a heat gun will hasten the formation of the orange-red anion. The benzene in C is heated to reflux and titrated with the initiator solution until a yellow color persists. The refluxing and titration should continue for about 2 hr. and may consume 10–30 ml. initiator solution. After reactor C is cooled to 5–10°C. addition of 50 g. styrene (freshly distilled from calcium hydride) with a syringe via serum cap at 6 dissipates the yellow color. Impurities in the monomer are titrated at 5–10°C. by adding initiator until a yellow color persists for 0.5 hr. (This will consume about 10 ml. initiator). After C is brought to 50°C. with a warm water bath, 5.0 ml. initiator is added. In 5 min. a 3–5°C. exotherm will be observed; within 30 min. the solution will be quite viscous and after 1 hr. stirring is difficult. The temperature is kept at about 50°C. for 6 hr. with a heat lamp, then polymerization is terminated by adding a few drops of isopropanol. The polymer is precipitated by slowly adding the viscous solution to 2–3 l. methanol stirring in a 1 gal. Waring Blendor (or in 4 batches using a 1 l. blender). Conversion is quantitative. The intrinsic viscosity in benzene at 25°C. is about 2.8, corresponding to a molecular weight of about 10^6. The M_W/M_n ratio is 1.3 or less. If 50 ml. initiator is used, polymerization may be so fast that cooling is necessary. The resulting polymer has a molecular weight of about 10^5 and as M_W/M_n ratio of < 1.1.

Another effective type of catalyst for anionic polymerization is **sodium naphthalene,** or **sodium benzophenone,**

$$\text{Na}^+ {}_{(-)}$$

, and

$$\begin{array}{c} C_6H_5 \\ | \\ C\!-\!O^{(-)} \\ | \\ C_6H_5 \end{array}$$

which are ion-radicals, but appear to initiate anionic polymerization (23–25,207) as follows:

$$\begin{array}{c} C_6H_5 \\ \diagdown \\ \cdot C\!\!-\!\!\bar{O} \;+\; CH_2\!\!=\!\!C \\ \diagup \qquad\qquad\quad\diagdown \\ C_6H_5 \qquad\qquad\quad Y \end{array} \xrightarrow{} \phi_2CO \;+\; \cdot CH_2\!\!-\!\!C \qquad (-)$$

The radicals dimerize and the chain grows anionically in both directions, until terminated. Catalysts of this type will polymerize **styrene** and **acrylonitrile** to high molecular weight products, provided adequate precautions are taken to maintain purity of reagents.

223. Preparation of Lithium and Sodium Naphthalene Catalysts (208,209)

Lithium naphthalene catalyst is prepared in the following manner. A three-necked reaction flask of suitable size is equipped with a gas inlet, a stirrer, a stopper, and a means for allowing the inert gas to exit, which is protected by a drying tube. The flask is flamed out under nitrogen, or better, argon, and 50 ml. of tetrahydrofuran, purified by distillation from lithium aluminum hydride, is added followed by 15 g. of resublimed naphthalene. To this solution at room temperature is added 1.5 g. of metallic lithium in small pieces, or as a lithium dispersion. The reaction begins almost at once as evidenced by the appearance of the dark greenish-black color of lithium naphthalene. The reaction proceeds so rapidly that it is exothermic and becomes warm to the touch, and if lithium dispersion is used external cooling may be necessary. After 2 hr. of stirring, the reaction is considered to be complete. A 3 ml. aliquot may be withdrawn at this point and quenched in methanol. The titer is then determined with standard hydrochloric acid. The solution should ordinarily contain approximately 1.6 milliequivalents of base/ml. when prepared in the above manner.

Sodium naphthalene is prepared in an identical manner to the lithium naphthalene described in the preceding paragraph. Again the solution is standardized by titration of a quenched sample with dilute hydrochloric acid.

224. Anionic Polymerization of Styrene with a Sodium–Naphthalene Initiator (23–25,207)

$$C_6H_5CH\!\!=\!\!CH_2 \xrightarrow{} \underset{\displaystyle \overset{|}{C_6H_5}}{(-\overset{}{C}H\!\!-\!\!CH_2)_m} \underset{\displaystyle \overset{|}{C_6H_5}}{(CH_2\!\!-\!\!\overset{}{C}H-)_n}$$

In order to successfully polymerize styrene to high molecular weight polymer with an anionic initiator, it is necessary that all liquid reagents be distilled and maintained under nitrogen until required. The nitrogen used in flushing the equipment under which the reagents are to be stored should be previously purified by passing through silica gel. All solid reagents used should be dried in desiccators for at least one week. All glass equipment should be flamed out under dry nitrogen after assembly and immediately prior to use. All reaction vessels should be maintained under a positive nitrogen pressure.

A 100 ml., three-necked flask fitted with a stirrer, a nitrogen inlet, and a side arm for the introduction of reagents is assembled. To the flask is added 10 ml. of styrene, 50 ml. of glycol dimethyl ether purified by stirring with sodium dispersion for several hours, followed by distillation at atmospheric pressure under nitrogen. This solution is cooled to $-70°C$. by an external Dry Ice bath and 50 mg. of sodium naphthalene catalyst is added. The polymerization proceeds very rapidly and the solution assumes a bright-red color, due to the styrene anion. This color persists for long periods of time, presumably indefinitely if reactive agents are excluded. The polymerization is quenched by the addition of some alcohol which causes immediate disappearance of the color. The mixture is allowed to warm to room temperature and the polymer is filtered, mixed with alcohol, and dried. The yield is quantitative; the inherent viscosity will run between 1.0 and 1.5 in toluene at 0.5% concentration.

225. Preparation of a Polystyrene with Carboxyl Ends (23–25,207,214)

$$C_6H_5CH{=}CH_2 \longrightarrow HO_2C(\overset{\overset{\displaystyle C_6H_5}{|}}{-}CH{-}CH_2)_m(CH_2{-}\overset{\overset{\displaystyle C_6H_5}{|}}{C}H{-})_nCO_2H$$

Polymerization is carried out in a three-necked reaction vessel, preferably a creased flask of the type originated by Morton and coworkers (256). This flask is equipped with a nitrogen flush, a stirrer, a stopper, and a means for the nitrogen to escape. The flask is flamed under nitrogen prior to addition of the reagents. To the flask is now added 250 ml. of purified tetrahydrofuran. In order to make certain that the tetrahydrofuran is completely free of impurity, a few drops of the lithium naphthalene catalyst is added until the greenish black color of the organometallic reagent persists. At this point, a quantity of solution containing 21.9 milliequivalents of catalyst is added. The flask is then immersed in a Dry Ice bath and cooled until a temperature of about $-77°C$. is reached. At this point, 150 milliequivalents (13.6 g.) of styrene is added via a hypodermic syringe inserted through a serum type rubber stopper (Chapter 2) in one of the necks of the flask. The green-black color of the lithium naphthalene catalyst is completely changed to the dark red color of the benzyl anion. The relatively nonviscous solution is allowed to come to room temperature when 35 g. of dry, solid carbon dioxide is quickly added. The dark-red solution immediately becomes colorless and considerably more viscous. After the solid carbon dioxide has all evaporated, dilute hydrochloric acid is added to liberate the macrodicarboxylic acid. The mixture is precipitated with methanol and the solid filtered and washed repeatedly with water and alcohol until free of salts and mineral acid. The solid is dried overnight in an $80°C$. oven. The yield is approximately 90%. On the basis of the suggested ratio of ingredients, the degree of polymerization should be approximately 30. Experimentally, the value will not differ from this calculated figure appreciably. If a higher or lower degree of polymerization is desired, this may be obtained by varying the ratio of lithium naphthalene to monomeric styrene in the initial charge.

Again it should be stressed that in experiments of this type it is essential to maintain all glass equipment and all reagents absolutely free of impurities which might tend to either inactivate the catalyst or act as chain terminators. When due precaution is taken, no problems are encountered in preparing living polystyrene molecules which can be terminated with carboxyl groups in the manner indicated above. It is possible to vary the molecular weight of the material obtained over a fairly wide range. The difunctionality of the resulting product is almost theoretical.

Acrylonitrile may be polymerized in essentially the same manner as described above for styrene with sodium naphthalene or sodium benzophenone. With acrylonitrile, it is convenient to use dimethylformamide as a reaction medium, in which case the polymer obtained remains in solution and may be used directly for further applications. A variation on this anionic polymerization technique uses a salt of a somewhat stronger (but still very weak) acid, namely, **sodium cyanide.** This salt in dimethylformamide at very low temperatures acts as a very efficient anionic chain initiator for the polymerization of acrylonitrile.

226. Anionic Polymerization of Acrylonitrile (215)

$$CH_2{=}CHCN \longrightarrow [-CH_2-\overset{\displaystyle CN}{\underset{\displaystyle |}{CH}}-]_n$$

A 250 ml., three-necked, round-bottom flask is fitted with a stirrer, an inlet tube for the introduction of nitrogen, and an outlet tube. As in the previous experiments, the nitrogen must be dried by passing it through silica gel and the equipment should be flamed out under nitrogen immediately prior to use. In the flask is placed 60 ml. of freshly distilled dimethylformamide and 10 ml. of acrylonitrile recently distilled under nitrogen. The flask with its contents is immersed in a cooling bath consisting of Dry Ice and alcohol, and the temperature is lowered to about $-50°C$. The initiator, 2 ml. of a saturated solution of anhydrous sodium cyanide in dry dimethylformamide, is rapidly introduced by means of a hypodermic syringe inserted in a serum type rubber stopper. Sodium cyanide can be dried by storing in a vacuum desiccator over silica gel for several days prior to use. A saturated solution of this salt in dimethylformamide contains somewhat less than 1 g. of cyanide in 100 g. of dimethylformamide.

Within a few seconds of adding the initiator, the temperature of the reaction mixture will rise rapidly and the solution may become so viscous it may climb up the stirrer shaft. The contents of the flask is allowed to stir for about 30 min. in the cooling bath. At the end of this reaction time, 5 ml. of 3% sulfuric acid in dimethylformamide is added to destroy unreacted initiator and to adjust the acidity of the mixture to a value of pH of 7 or less. The polymer may be isolated by precipitation in water, or the solution may be used directly for other purposes. The yield is quantitative; the inherent viscosity measured in dimethylformamide is 2–3 (0.5%, 30°C.).

Poly(methyl methacrylate) has been prepared in basically three stereoregular forms (216). Type I is highly syndiotactic and can be obtained from free radical initiation at low temperatures (e.g., $-40°C.$) and by anionic catalysis in ether solvents. Type II is highly isotactic and is prepared with an anionic catalyst (fluorenyllithium or Grignard reagent) in a hydrocarbon solvent at $-60°C$. Type III is a stereoblock composition of iso- and syndiotactic segments and is the product from low temperature anionic polymerization in ether toluene mixtures. All three are crystallizable, the isotactic being the most readily so. There are distinct differences in T_m and T_g values, which are listed below along with the latter value for conventional poly(methyl methacrylate). It is interesting to note that even the conventional polymer has considerable syndiotactic stereoregularity, and that a truly statistically random polymer may not be known as yet.

	T_g	T_m	Density
Type I Syndiotactic	115	200	1.19
Type II Isotactic	45	160	1.22
Type III Stereoblock	60–95	170–190	1.20–1.22
Conventional	104	—	1.188

Stereoregular acrylate polymers have also been characterized. Isotactic and syndiotactic (217,218) forms of poly(isopropyl acrylate) have been prepared by initiation with Grignard-in-ether at $-70°C$.

227. Preparation of Isotactic Poly(methyl methacrylate) (219)

9-Fluoroenyllithium is prepared as a $0.22M$ suspension by refluxing a slight molar excess of recrystallized fluorene (10.4 g., 0.062 mole) with butyllithium (3.52 g., 0.055 mole) in enough toluene (dried over calcium hydride) to give 250 ml. total solvent when that used in adding the butyllithium is included. Butyllithium should be used from a fresh bottle of commercial material in hexane or similar solvent, and is added by syringe to the fluorene in a 500 ml. three-necked flask equipped with condenser, nitrogen inlet, and serum cap closure. The apparatus should be flamed out and cooled under dry, oxygen-free nitrogen. The product separates as a bright-orange, finely divided solid.

Methyl methacrylate is freed of inhibitor by low pressure distillation and stored at $-20°C.$ under nitrogen.

A solution of 50.0 g. (0.5 mole) of methyl methacrylate in 750 ml. of anhydrous toluene is placed in a 1 l., three-necked flask equipped with a mechanical stirrer, thermometer, and inlet and outlet tubes for nitrogen gas. One neck of the flask is covered by a rubber serum cap. The flask is flushed with dry nitrogen, and the contents cooled to $-60°C$. A 30 ml. portion of the $0.22M$ suspension of 9-fluorenyllithium in toluene is added by means of a hypodermic syringe inserted through the rubber cap.

The temperature of the reaction mixture is maintained at $-40 \pm 6°C$. for 1 hr.; during this period the solution becomes extremely viscous.

A small amount of methanol is added, and the reaction mixture is permitted to warm to room temperature. The polymer is precipitated by pouring the solution into 7 l. of vigorously agitated methanol. The swollen solid which separates is dried and dissolved in 800 ml. of acetone, and the solution filtered. Precipitation of the polymer by pouring into 7 l. of water produces, after drying, about 41 g. (83%) of poly(methyl methacrylate).

A 5% solution of this polymer in di-n-propyl ketone, prepared at reflux temperature, is cooled to 30°C. and held at that temperature for 48 hr. Centrifugation of the mixture and removal of the supernatant liquid produces a fraction amounting to 32% of the original polymer. This material displays the crystalline x-ray diffraction characteristics typical of type II poly(methyl methacrylate). The intrinsic viscosity is determined in chloroform at 25°C., and the viscosity average molecular weight from the equation:

$$[\eta] = 4.8 \times 10^{-5} \overline{M}_v^{0.80}$$

An arbitrary IR parameter, the J value, is used to characterize stereoregularity. A clear, uniform film is cast on a silver chloride plate from a 3–5% solution of the polymer in benzene. The thickness (about 10 μ) should be such that the air-dried film transmits between 2 and 15% of the IR radiation at the intense band near $8.0 \pm 0.2 \mu$. The plate bearing the film is heated at 135°C. for 45 min. to remove the last traces of benzene; no peaked absorption at 14.8 μ should remain.

The spectrum of the film is scanned at 5–15.5 μ in a Perkin-Elmer Model 21 recording IR spectrometer at standard scanning conditions. A 100% transmission line is drawn between 5.4 and 14.5 μ, and the absorbances at 6.75, 7.2, and 10.1 μ are calculated by use of this base line. The absorbance at 9.3 μ is determined, a line connecting the points of minimum absorbance on either side of the 9.3 μ maximum being used as a base line.

Two subparameters, J_1 and J_2, are calculated from these absorbances by means of the equations

$$J_1 = [179A_{9.3}/A_{10.1}] + 27$$
$$J_2 = [81.4A_{6.75}/A_{7.20}] - 43$$

The J value is the arithmetic average of J_1 and J_2. The lower the J value, the higher the isotacticity; high J values mean high syndiotacticity. In the present case, the J value of the polymer should be about 30–35, indicative of high isotacticity.

228. Preparation of Syndiotactic Poly(methyl methacrylate) (219)

Tetrahydrofuran is dried by refluxing 24 hr. over calcium hydride, then 500 ml. is distilled into, or otherwise transferred under anhydrous, anaerobic conditions to, a dry 1 l. reaction apparatus as described in the previous experiment, in which is already placed 1.66 g. (0.01 mole) recrystallized fluorene. Then, enough fresh butyllithium solution (hexane or similar solvent) to provide 0.0097 mole of active agent is transferred by dry syringe and the mixture stirred under nitrogen for an hour, when metallation of the fluorene should be complete. The mixture is cooled to $-70°C$. in Dry Ice–acetone and 83 g. of previously chilled ($-20°C$. at least), purified, dry (see prior preparation) methyl methacrylate is added by syringe. The polymerization is continued for 6 hr. to give a viscous solution, which, after addition of a few ml. of methanol and warming to room temperature, is poured with stirring into about 5 l. petroleum ether. The filtered polymer is redissolved in benzene, centrifuged to remove insoluble material, reprecipitated into petroleum ether, filtered and washed well with methanol in a blender to give nearly 100% conversion of poly(methyl methacrylate) having a J value of about 117 (see previous preparation), indicative of a syndiotactic character. The viscosity average molecular weight is about 16,000. Swelling with n-propyl ketone or annealing at 100–130°C. may be necessary to effect crystallization.

See Sandler + Karo Vol I p. 466.

Extremely Hazardous.

Vinylidene cyanide, $CH_2\!=\!C(CN)_2$, has been studied extensively (e.g., 220–222). It polymerizes readily by an anionic mechanism, but the polymer is easily depolymerized. It is more useful in copolymers.

229. Preparation of Di(acetyl cyanide) (222)

$$2KCN + 2(CH_3CO)_2O \longrightarrow CH_3COO\!-\!\underset{\underset{CN}{|}}{\overset{\overset{CN}{|}}{C}}\!-\!CH_3 + 2CH_3CO_2K$$

In a 2 l., three-necked flask equipped with a stirrer, condenser, and dropping funnel and cooled with a water bath is placed 500 ml. of benzene and 100 g. of potassium cyanide. (**Poison!**) To this stirred mixture is added 150 g. of acetic anhydride over a period of approximately $\frac{1}{2}$ hr. Any excessive increase in temperature is moderated with the water bath. The mixture is stirred for approximately 5 hr. at the reflux temperature after addition of acetic anhydride is completed. The cooled reaction mixture is filtered and distilled. The product obtained at 100–110°C. at 10 mm. should have a melting point of approximately 69°C. If it is lower than this, the product should be recrystallized from carbon tetrachloride. The over-all yield of di(acetyl cyanide) is about 60%.

230. Preparation of Vinylidene Cyanide (221)

Do not inhale!

$$CH_3COO\!-\!\underset{\underset{CN}{|}}{\overset{\overset{CN}{|}}{C}}\!-\!CH_3 \overset{\Delta}{\longrightarrow} CH_2\!=\!C(CN)_2$$

An apparatus for pyrolyzing di(acetyl cyanide) is made as follows. A tube of $^{85}\!/_{15}$ brass, 3 ft. long, $\frac{5}{8}$ in. inside diameter is wrapped with resistance wire and jacketed with asbestos. It is equipped with a side thermocouple well and is packed with a tight roll of brass window screen. Both ends of the tube are wound with four turns of small copper tubing through which water is circulated to prevent rubber-stopper connections from softening. The tube may be used either vertically or at a slight incline from the horizontal. The tube is maintained at a temperature of 600–650°C. A 125 ml. distilling flask is connected to the inlet (top) of the tube and the outlet (bottom) is connected to a 250 ml. suction flask connected in turn to a vacuum source. Eighty g. of diacetylcyanide is placed in the distilling flask and 2 g. of phosphorus pentoxide is placed in the suction flask. The system is evacuated to 10 mm. The receiving flask is cooled with a Dry Ice–acetone bath and the distilling flask is heated at 100°C. The diacetyl cyanide distills smoothly through the pyrolysis tube in approximately 1 hr. The pyrolysis product is allowed to warm to room temperature out of contact with moisture. Seventy-two g. of light-yellow liquid is obtained which is approximately 40% vinylidene cyanide.

The pyrolysis product is purified by distilling through a 6 in. Vigreux column at 15 mm. pressure. The fraction boiling at 54–57°C. is about 70% pure vinylidene cyanide. This fraction diluted with $\frac{1}{2}$ its weight of dry chloroform is cooled slowly to $-30°C$. with stirring. The filtrate is removed by suction with a filter stick and the crystals remaining are washed with cold ($-30°C$.) dry toluene in a quantity equal to the weight of chloroform used originally. The washed, recrystallized vinylidene cyanide is distilled rapidly to yield 18 g. of pure monomer melting at 9°C.

231. Preparation of Alternating Copolymer from Vinylidene Cyanide and Vinyl Benzoate (222)

$$CH_2{=}C(CN)_2 + CH_2{=}\overset{\displaystyle OCO\phi}{\overset{|}{C}H} \longrightarrow Copolymer$$

A mixture of 174 ml. of benzene, 20 g. of pure vinylidene cyanide, and 38 g. of pure vinyl benzoate is treated with 0.06 g. of o,o'-dichlorobenzoylperoxide in a sealed tube. The mixture is maintained for 17 hr. at about 43°C. At the end of this time the copolymer is removed by filtration.

The composition of the polymer so obtained is virtually independent of the ratio of vinylidene cyanide to vinyl benzoate in the original charge. Analysis of polymer made over a wide range of composition shows that the product is always essentially a 1 : 1 alternating copolymer. The copolymer is soluble in dimethylformamide and solutions of polymer in this solvent can be spun to fibers which have shown excellent properties.

VIII. Stereoregular Polymerization of Olefins

It was stated earlier that among the olefins, only ethylene and styrene can be readily polymerized by radicals, the former most commonly at high pressure and temperature. It has been found that catalysts composed of transition metal compounds, especially halides, and organometallic compounds will polymerize ethylene and higher α-olefins to high molecular weight, usually crystalline polymers.

These catalysts (7,223–227), now known popularly as Ziegler-Natta or coordination catalysts, polymerize olefins at room temperature and

atmospheric pressure, hence are admirably suited to small scale operations in laboratory glassware. The polymers are generally very high in
molecular weight, sometimes too high for suitable fabrication. In this
case it may be possible to thermally crack the polymer to an equally
crystalline, but lower molecular weight material.

With higher olefins, such as propylene, these catalysts usually give
high melting products which have a stereoregular structure (228–230).
In normal polymerization of a substituted olefin, a new asymmetric
center is produced as each monomer unit is added, but there is no
control of the configuration of each succeeding center.

$$\underset{\sim}{CH_2}-\underset{\underset{R}{|}}{CH}\cdot \; + \; CH_2{=}\underset{\underset{R}{|}}{CH} \; \longrightarrow \; -CH_2-\underset{\underset{R}{|}}{\overset{*}{CH}}-CH_2-\underset{\underset{R}{|}}{\overset{*}{CH}}\sim$$

The result is a completely random configuration of the chain.

These configurations may be visualized by imagining the carbon–
carbon polymer chain laid out on a plane in the extended zigzag con-
formation. If the substituents from the monosubstituted vinyl monomer
are arranged at random above and below the plane of the carbon chain,
the polymer lacks stereochemical regularity and is called *atactic*:

The coordination catalysts give a stereoregular chain. If the substituents all fall on one side of the plane, the polymer is said to be
isotactic:

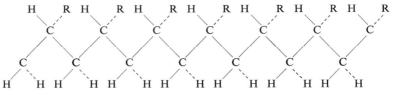

Finally, if the substituents fall alternately above and below the plane of
the chain, the polymer is designated *syndiotactic*:

The stereoregularity permits the chains to crystallize in most cases, hence the properties of the polymers differ markedly from the random counterpart. Thus, free radical polystyrene is clear, noncrystalline, and low melting, while stereoregular polystyrene is hazy like nylon, crystallizable, and high melting. The nature of R also affects the melting point markedly; the bulkier it is the higher melting the polymer (231,232). The preparation of some selected polymers follows.

The stereoregular polymers have been discussed extensively by Natta (228–230) and others (7).

232. Preparation of Lithium Aluminum Tetradecyl (223–225)

$$LiAlH_4 + C_8H_{17}CH=CH_2 \longrightarrow LiAl(C_{10}H_{21})_4$$

A mixture of tetrahydronaphthalene (700 ml.), 1-decene (150 ml.) and lithium aluminum hydride (7.6 g.) is heated with stirring to 135°C. A mildly exothermic reaction occurs and the temperature is allowed to rise to about 180°C. It is maintained at this temperature for about 2 hr., then cooled. The originally clear liquid containing lumps of white hydride has become a solution in which is suspended a gray-black flocculent solid. The flask is transferred to a nitrogen-filled dry box and filtered while still warm through a Celite pad. The filtered solution is stored and the pyrophoric residue on the funnel destroyed at once with isopropanol. For standardization, a 5.0 ml. aliquot of the solution is removed, dissolved in some alcohol, then 200 ml. of water is added. The resulting mixture is titrated potentiometrically to pH 7 with standard acid. Under these conditions, only the lithium is titrated, and normality = molarity. This preparation should have concentrations of around $0.2M$. It is necessary to prevent contact of oxygen and moisture with the lithium aluminum tetradecyl solution. Otherwise, no problems should be encountered during storage.

233. Preparation of Titanium Tetrachloride Solution

A commercial product is distilled at 136.5°C. after removal of an appreciable forecut. A stock solution is made up in cyclohexane in 500 ml. batches as needed. A convenient concentration which should be sought for is about $0.5M$. The exact concentration is determined gravimetrically.

234. Preparation of Catalyst and Polymerization: General Procedure (223–225,231)

In general, measured amounts of the catalyst components (titanium tetrachloride and lithium aluminum tetradecyl) are mixed in some inert solvent, usually cyclohexane. Stirring is rapid during mixing and during polymerization. The major cause of trouble in polymerizations is oxygen which is excluded during all phases of the polymerization and catalyst preparation. Also, water and other electron-rich substances must be excluded, since they also inactivate the catalyst.

In the actual experiments listed, the volumes and concentrations used are taken directly from the literature. It is obvious that other concentrations could be used, the volumes of the component solutions being adjusted accordingly.

If aluminum triisobutyl or triethyl are on hand, it may be advantageous to use these materials. However, it should be recognized that they are very dangerous reagents. A catalyst is then prepared as follows.

A 1 l., three-necked flask equipped with stirrer, a nitrogen inlet, a thermometer, a dropping funnel, and a condenser is flushed with nitrogen and maintained with an atmosphere of nitrogen throughout the entire preparation. One hundred ml. of decahydronaphthalene is introduced into the reaction flask and heat is applied through a heating mantle. To the decahydronaphthalene is added in succession 6 ml. of $1M$ titanium tetrachloride, and 2 ml. of $1M$ triisobutylaluminum, both solutions having previously been made up in decahydronaphthalene. Addition of the aluminum alkyl causes precipitation of a brownish black product. The temperature of the flask is then increased as rapidly as possible to 180–185°C. and maintained at this temperature for 40 min. The color of the suspended complex changes to a deep violet which is quite intense. The solution is now cooled and 400 ml. of cyclohexane is added followed by 12 ml. of $1M$ aluminum triisobutyl solution. The violet color becomes at once a deep purplish black.

All of the polymers described below are prepared in essentially the same manner. A three-necked flask or a resin kettle is equipped with a stirrer, a nitrogen inlet, and a simple outlet. A catalyst suspension is prepared in the flask by mixing appropriate amounts of the catalyst components under nitrogen with or without additional solvent. Monomer is then added and the polymerization is allowed to proceed. The polymer is isolated by addition of alcohol followed by filtration. It is purified by washing in a high speed home mixer with additional quantities of alcohol, then freed of organic solvents in an appropriate manner, usually either with steam or with dry nitrogen at 100–120°C.

235. Preparation of Linear Polyethylene (47,223–225)

$$CH_2{=}CH_2 \longrightarrow [-CH_2-CH_2-]_n$$

A three-necked, 4 l. resin kettle is equipped with a stirrer, a gas inlet tube, and an outlet consisting of a simple glass tube 24 in. long, protected with a drying tube. The kettle is flushed with nitrogen and a catalyst suspension is prepared in the following manner. Two l. of cyclohexane is added to the kettle followed by 200 ml. of a $0.2M$ solution of lithium aluminum tetradecyl as previously made. The mixture is cooled externally in a water-ice bath and 0.029 mole of titanium tetrachloride is added as a cyclohexane solution. The mixture immediately becomes brownish black and is now an active catalyst for the polymerization of ethylene. A cylinder of ethylene is attached to the gas inlet tube through a safety trap. Ethylene is bubbled through the vigorously stirred catalyst suspension, and polyethylene begins to separate with the evolution of some heat. The polymerization may be continued as long as desired until the solution becomes unstirrable. The slurry of polymer and solvent containing catalyst is poured into a large excess of isopropyl alcohol with vigorous stirring and the finely divided, precipitated polymer is isolated by filtration. The product is usually obtained as a white powder which can be molded to clear, tough films or extruded to tough fibers. The product has a crystalline m.p. in the range of 130°C.

As an alternative to the metal alkyl used above, some of the commercially available aluminum alkyls may be used, as triisobutyl- or triethylaluminum and aluminum sesquichloride. For the above experiment, 8 ml. of triethyl-aluminum (0.060 mole) and 4 ml. titanium tetrachloride (0.036 mole) may be used in about 2 l. of total solvent.

The ethylene gas stream can be purified if necessary by passing it through an aluminum alkyl solution prior to introducing it to the polymerization flask.

When $TiCl_4$ is reduced by aluminum alkyls as in Experiment 235, the $TiCl_3$ produced is present in primarily its β form, which is brown in color. It is capable of polymerizing propylene but a very large part of the resulting polymer will be the amorphous, atactic variety. In order to maximize the generation of crystalline, isotactic polypropylene, the reduction of $TiCl_4$ should be carried out at 185–200°C., where γ-$TiCl_3$ is formed. This variety of $TiCl_3$ is capable of a much higher degree of stereoregulation as is α-$TiCl_3$, which results from reduction of $TiCl_4$ with hydrogen or aluminum at high temperatures. The α- and γ-$TiCl_3$ are purple in color, and normally contain aluminum chloride when produced, in their respective cases, from aluminum or aluminum alkyl reduction steps (233).

The activating aluminum alkyl used to form the bimetallic coordina-tion catalyst system is also influential in the isotactic stereoregulation of the propagation step (233a). Trialkylaluminum compounds decrease in effectiveness with increasing alkyl chain length. Dialkylaluminum monohalides are distinctly more stereoregulating than the correspond-ing trialkylaluminum, and the monohalides themselves induce higher isotacticity increasingly in the order -Cl, -Br, -I (233). A host of modi-fied catalysts are known which are capable of polymerizing propylene with considerable stereoregulating effectiveness, and a veritable torrent of patent literature exists on the subject (234). The catalysts shown in the following examples are illustrative and are convenient for labora-tory work. The second example, using an activated α-$TiCl_3$ from aluminum reduction in conjunction with Et_2AlCl, is highly effective for the polymerization of most α-olefins to highly isotactic polymers.

236. Preparation of Isotactic Polypropylene

$$CH_2=CHCH_3 \longrightarrow [-CH_2-\overset{\overset{\displaystyle CH_3}{\displaystyle |}}{CH}-]_n$$

Polypropylene may be polymerized over either the catalyst prepared in the previous experiment or over a catalyst prepared as follows. In a 4 l., three-necked resin kettle equipped with a stirrer, gas inlet, and an outlet consisting of a simple glass tube 24 in. long protected with a drying tube, is placed 500 ml. of decahydronaphthalene. The flask is swept with nitrogen and heated moderately with a heating mantle. To the decahydronaphthalene is added, in succession, 30 ml. of 1.0 molar titanium tetrachloride and 10 ml. of 1.0 molar triisobutylaluminum, both the latter solutions in decahydronaphthalene.

Addition of the aluminum alkyl causes precipitation of a brownish black product. The temperature of the flask is then increased as rapidly as possible to about 185°C. and maintained at this temperature for 40 min. The color of the suspended complex changes to a deep violet. This suspension is now cooled and 2000 ml. of cyclohexane is added, followed by 60 ml. of 1.0 molar aluminum triisobutyl solution. The purplish-black suspension is now an effective catalyst for the polymerization of gaseous propylene. The propylene is bubbled through the catalyst suspension as in the previous experiment and the slurry of polypropylene is precipitated into isopropyl alcohol, filtered, washed, and dried. Isotactic polypropylene can be pressed to clear, tough films and molded to other objects. The crystalline m.p. is about 165°C. The yield is determined by the length of time the propylene is bubbled into the catalyst.

237. Preparation of Isotactic Polypropylene over a Preformed $TiCl_3$ Catalyst

Diethylaluminum chloride can be obtained commercially or it can be easily prepared by mixing in a dry box 33.5 g. triethylaluminum (0.29 mole) and 19.0 g. sublimed aluminum chloride (0.14 mole) in 60 ml. dry n-heptane in a septum-capped beverage bottle. The reaction occurs with little evolution of heat as the aluminum chloride dissolves via reaction. The solution will contain about 3.8 mmoles Et_2AlCl per ml. α-Titanium trichloride can be obtained from Stauffer Chemical Co. as the AA grade, which contains one-third mole of $AlCl_3$ per mole $TiCl_3$. It is obtained from high temperature reduction of $TiCl_4$ with aluminum.

To a 200 ml. beverage bottle, baked dry at 115°C. and cooled under nitrogen, is added 100 ml. dry n-heptane, 0.24 g. diethylaluminum chloride (2 mmoles), conveniently in n-heptane solution, and 0.198 g. (1 mmole) titanium trichloride AA (see above). The latter can be added as a slurry in cyclohexane or n-heptane by ordinary syringe technique if the needle is not less than 18 gauge. Propylene is pressured into the bottle at 40 p.s.i. The polymerization can then be carried out under continuous propylene pressure of 40 p.s.i. if the bottle is heated in an upright position in a shaker assembly. Alternatively, the monomer can be charged only to its limit of saturation, about 6–7 g./100 ml. at 40 p.s.i. The bottle is then tumbled at 70°C. for at least 4 hr.

In either case, the bottle is cooled, carefully vented with a hypodermic, and 20 ml. isopropanol added to deactivate the catalyst. The mixture is slurried in a blender with 600 ml. isopropanol containing some HCl. The polymer is filtered and washed additionally with methanol, then dried at 60°C. under nitrogen in a vacuum oven overnight. If propylene was charged only initially, about 6 g. of polymer should be obtained; if charged continuously, at least 25 g. should be had. A sample of polymer is subjected to continuous extraction with n-heptane in a vapor-jacketed Soxhlet (Kumagawa) extractor for 10 hr.; a ceramic thimble is advantageous. At least 90% of the polymer should be insoluble in boiling n-heptane in this manner, and 94% is quite within reach. This is the isotactic index value. The soluble, amorphous polymer can be recovered from the heptane extract. The crystalline, isotactic polymer has a T_m of about 165°C., though values of 170°C. are sometimes reported. The inherent viscosity should be 2.5–3.5 (0.1 g./100 ml. in Decalin, 130°C.).

Essentially the same product can be obtained by running the polymerization in a stirred flask or resin kettle; propylene is passed into the catalyst-solvent slurry as in the polyethylene case.

A useful intrinsic viscosity–molecular weight relationship for polypropylene is (235):

$$[\eta] = 1.10 \times 10^{-4} M_v^{0.80}$$

It should not be out of place at this point to remark that isotactic polypropylene in a way stands as an introduction to the enormous contributions of Professor Guilio Natta to polymer science. The *Journal of Polymer Science*, in an issue dedicated entirely to him (**51**, 383 (1961)), called him "The Father of Stereoregular Polymers," which is no less than the truth, and the reader is commended to the brief biography to be found there. To no one's surprise, he and Professor Ziegler shared the Nobel Prize in chemistry in 1963. Professor Natta's Nobel award address was published in *Science* (**147**, 261 (1965)). While the phenomenon of polymer stereoregularity had early been predicted to be a matter of importance in controlling physical properties, and while a few synthetic examples were recognized or believed to exist, it was not until Professor Natta's work that the vast scientific richness of the field was realized in fact. The numerous examples of preparations of stereoregulated polymers in this book are only representative of the full harvest; many are derived directly from Professor Natta's work, but those that are not are often not far removed in lineage.

Polypropylene having mainly a syndiotactic placement of monomers has been prepared thus far only at quite low temperatures with certain coordination catalyst components, e.g., VCl_4 and $i\text{-}Bu_2AlCl$ with anisole added (236–238). The resulting polymer is of a relatively lower molecular weight than obtained customarily with isotactic polypropylene and is also less crystalline, due in all likelihood to a stereoblock structure with the syndio-structure dominant but not exclusive. The syndiotactic polymer is not even remotely of commercial importance yet, nor is it likely to be. The need to prepare and examine it, in this, the age of stereoregulation, undoubtedly constituted a kind of chemical equivalent of the Mt. Everest syndrome.

238. Preparation of Primarily Syndiotactic Polypropylene (236)

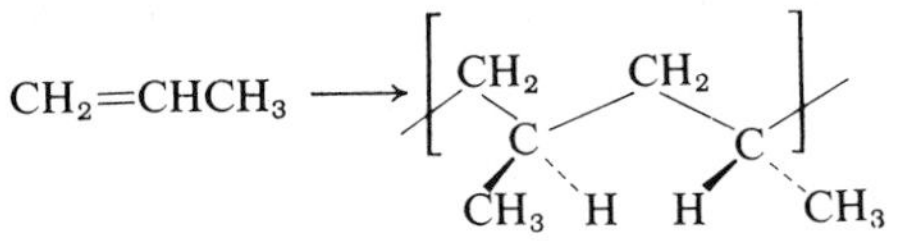

A 250 ml. flask with stirrer, Dry Ice condenser, nitrogen inlet, and serum cap, and a means for adding propylene below the Dry Ice condenser, is baked dry and assembled in a stream of nitrogen. In a stream of nitrogen, the flask is charged with 100 ml. of dry toluene and cooled to $-78°C$. in a Dry Ice–methanol bath. There are introduced in sequence by syringe: 0.108 g. anisole (10^{-3} moles) in 5 ml. toluene, 0.193 g. VCl_4 (10^{-3} moles) as a solution in toluene, and 0.885 g. i-Bu_2AlCl (5×10^{-3} moles), also as a solution in toluene. Then 80 g. of high purity propylene (b.p., $-48°C$.) is added, and, after initially mixing the components, the polymerization is allowed to proceed for 24 hr. without stirring. The polymerization can also be executed in a septum-capped beverage bottle immersed at $-78°C$. and agitated occasionally by hand.

The slightly viscous, purple mixture is poured into excess methanol containing a small amount of HCl. The precipitated polymer is washed repeatedly with methanol and dried in vacuum at $60°C$. to give about 1 g. of product with an intrinsic viscosity of 1.1 dl/g. (tetralin, $135°C$.). The T_m of syndiotactic polypropylene varies with steric purity, but for practical purposes is about $131°C$., although it has been estimated (238) that the ultimate T_m for syndio- is $166°C$. For the isotactic polypropylene, the ultimate T_m is estimated in the range $188–200°C$., although the usual practically observed value is around $165°C$. Thus, the syndiotactic polymer appears destined to melt substantially lower than the isotactic variety at comparable levels of crystalline development.

239. Preparation of Poly(4-methyl-1-pentene) (231)

$$CH_2{=}CH{-}CH_2\overset{\overset{\displaystyle CH_3}{|}}{\underset{\underset{\displaystyle CH_3}{}}{CH}} \longrightarrow [{-}CH_2{-}\overset{\overset{\displaystyle CH_2{-}CH(CH_3)_2}{|}}{CH}{-}]_n$$

A three-necked, 4 l. resin kettle is equipped with a stirrer, nitrogen inlet, and an outlet consisting of a simple glass tube 24 in. long. The kettle is flushed with nitrogen and a catalyst suspension is prepared in the following manner. Two l. of cyclohexane is added to the kettle followed by 200 ml. of a $0.20M$ solution of lithium aluminum tetradecyl as previously made. The mixture is cooled in a water bath and 33 ml. of a 0.87 molar titanium tetrachloride solution in cyclohexane is added. The mixture immediately becomes brownish black and is now an active catalyst for the polymerization of an α-olefin. To the catalyst suspension is now added 450 g. of distilled, dry 4-methyl-1-pentene, which may be obtained commercially. The mixture warms up moderately and rapidly becomes viscous. Polymerization may be allowed to proceed for 12 hr. It is essentially complete in a much shorter time and the reaction may be worked up after 2 hr. if it is desired, although the yield may be diminished by a few per cent. Since the polymerization is mildly exothermic, a certain amount of monomer may be lost by distillation and entrainment from the reaction vessel. This may be trapped in a condenser system if desired.

After a 12 hr. period the polymerization is essentially complete and the reaction mixture has the appearance of a solid, blackish-brown lump of rubber. This mass of polymer which is swollen by the cyclohexane present, is cut up into convenient sized lumps with scissors or a knife and then cut up very finely in a high-speed cutter, such as a household blender, with isopropyl alcohol. The color of the original polymer is discharged immediately on contact with the alcohol and the resulting product is isolated by filtration as a pure, white, rather granular product. The polymer may be washed repeatedly with alcohol and then dried either in a vacuum oven at pressures less than 1 mm. and temperatures of 100°C. for 8 hr. or by treatment with a rapid stream of live steam or nitrogen at 100°C. with vigorous agitation. The yield of dry polymer is about 250 g. and the inherent viscosity will be 4–6, measured at 130°C. on 1 0.1% solution in decahydronaphthalene. The extremely high molecular weight product may be fabricated directly to a clear tough film by pressing at temperatures in excess of 250°C. It also may be extruded from a spinning cell in the form of a continuous filament which may be after-drawn on a hot pin at 100–150°C. The polymer shows a crystalline melting point of about 240°C. as measured on a polarizing microscope.

4-Methyl-1-pentene may also be polymerized over a catalyst prepared as above from aluminum triisobutyl. To this catalyst solution is added 100 ml. of 4-methyl-1-pentene. The mixture is stirred for a period of 90–100 min., at which time the mixture is so thick that it wraps around the stirrer blade and breaks away from the walls of the vessel. The polymer is isolated then dried in a vacuum oven at 50°C. by methods previously described. Polymer prepared in this manner is essentially the same as prepared in the previous experiments. Yields will be of the order of 65–80%. The inherent viscosity is 2–4 (0.1% in decahydronaphthalene at 130°C.).

The Et_2AlCl–$TiCl_3$ catalyst system (the later component preformed) used for polymerizing propylene also works well in this instance. In fact, such a catalyst gives a distinctly lower amount of boiling-heptane extractables (amorphous polymer) than any of the others. Poly(4-methyl-1-pentane) with as high as 98% heptane-insoluble content can be realized. The polymerization rate is slower with Et_2AlCl–$TiCl_3$ than with the others, however.

If the polymer obtained is too high in molecular weight for the desired use, the molecular weight may be conveniently lowered by a cracking process.

240. Thermal Cracking of Poly(4-methyl-1-pentene) (239)

One hundred g. of finely divided poly(4-methyl-1-pentene) prepared as in the previous experiment is freed of low molecular weight atactic polymer by extraction at room temperature with 500 ml. of petroleum ether followed by 500 ml. of cyclohexane. The extracted polymer is dried, then preferably molded into a solid object such as a circular plug, and placed in a glass tube. It is heated at approximately 280°C. in a high vacuum for 8 hr. Polymer with an inherent viscosity of 4–6 should be reduced to polymer with a viscosity between 1.2 and 1.9. The viscosity of the polymer may be checked at the end of this heating period and if it is desired to lower it further, an additional heating period may be carried out.

241. Polymerization of 3-Methyl-1-butene (231)

$$CH_2{=}CH{-}\underset{\underset{CH_3}{|}}{CH}{-}CH_3 \longrightarrow [{-}\underset{\underset{\underset{\underset{CH_3\;\;\;CH_3}{\diagdown\;\diagup}}{CH}}{|}}{CH_2}{-}CH{-}]_n$$

A catalyst suspension is prepared as in the preceding experiment by mixing in a 4 l. resin kettle under nitrogen 250 ml. of 0.19 molar lithium aluminum tetradecyl and 40 ml. of 1.08 molar titanium tetrachloride in 1 l. of cyclohexane. One hundred ml. of 3-methyl-1-butene, b.p. 20°C., is collected in an ice bath and added to the mixture. After 20 hr. the polymer is isolated by filtration and washed with alcohol. Only 13.8 g., approximately 22%, is isolated in this manner. The inherent viscosity cannot be determined since the product is incompletely soluble in decahydronaphthalene. The crystalline melting point (310°C.) is much higher than that of poly(4-methyl-1-pentene) and it is necessary to go to temperatures above 310°C. in order to fabricate the polymer into a clear, transparent film. Strips of this film can be oriented by stretching at temperatures of the order of 250–300°C. or fibers may be drawn from the melt at 310°C. Oriented film strips or fibers show extremely high crystallinity and very high orientation. The crystalline melting point is of the order of 310°C.

Once again, the Et_2AlCl–$TiCl_3$ catalyst (see poly(4-methyl-1-pentene) preparation for comments) gives a higher content of stereoregular polymer.

242. Poly(4-methyl-1-hexene) (231)

$$CH_2{=}CH{-}CH_2{-}\underset{\underset{CH_2CH_3}{\diagdown}}{\overset{\overset{CH_3}{\diagup}}{CH}} \longrightarrow \underset{\underset{\underset{[{-}CH_2{-}CH{-}]_n}{}}{\overset{\overset{\overset{\overset{CH_3CH_2\;\;\;CH_3}{\diagdown\;\diagup}}{CH}}{|}}{CH_2}}}{}$$

In order to illustrate further the effect of structure of the olefin on the properties of the resulting polymer, 4-methyl-1-hexene, b.p. 86.5°C., is made from *sec*-butyl magnesium chloride and allyl chloride (47) and is polymerized in a manner similar to that described in the previous experiments. The polymer is a hard solid quite similar in appearance to poly(4-methyl-1-pentene). It may be pressed to film or extruded to fiber. It may be stretched over a hot pin to get a highly oriented crystalline sample. However, the crystalline melting point is only 160°C. This illustrates the effect of breaking up the symmetry of the branch on the side chain.

243. Preparation of 4-Phenyl-1-Butene (240,241)

$$C_6H_5CH_2MgCl + BrCH_2CH{=}CH_2 \longrightarrow C_6H_5CH_2CH_2CH{=}CH_2$$

A Grignard reagent is prepared from 172 g. of benzyl chloride and 33 g. of magnesium metal turnings in the usual way. To this solution is added over a period of 2 hr. a solution of 170 g. of allyl bromide dilute with 600 ml. of ether. The mixture is allowed to stir overnight, then it is cautiously hydrolyzed with water and the ether layer is separated and distilled. 4-Phenyl-1-butene is obtained in a yield of approximately 130 g. (72%) with a boiling point of 86–87°C./35 mm. The product is distilled through a precision fractionating column prior to use.

244. Polymerization of 4-Phenylbutene-1 (231,242)

$$C_6H_5CH_2CH_2CH{=}CH_2 \longrightarrow [-CH_2-\overset{\displaystyle CH_2CH_2C_6H_5}{\underset{\displaystyle |}{CH}}-]_n$$

A catalyst suspension is prepared by mixing 100 ml. of $0.18M$ lithium aluminum tetradecyl, 15 ml. of 1.08 molar titanium tetrachloride, and 180 ml. of dry cyclohexane. To this suspension is added 50 ml. of 4-phenyl-1-butene. Polymerization is quite rapid and after 1 hr. the mixture is very viscous. The polymer may be isolated at this point or polymerization may be allowed to proceed for several hours, in which case the yield will be slightly increased. The polymer is isolated by pouring the very viscous solution into isopropyl alcohol which is being agitated rapidly in a high speed mixer. The polymer is isolated and dried by heating in a stream of steam for 1 hr. The yield is approximately 24 g.; the inherent viscosity is in the range of 3–4 (0.1%, in decahydronaphthalene at 130°C.). The polymer can be pressed to clear, very tough film at 200°C. Strips of film may be drawn at 125°C. over a hot surface. The oriented crystalline polymer shows a crystalline melting point of 160°C.

The stereoregular polymerization of styrene and other vinylaromatics exhibits some peculiarities not seen in the polymerization of ethylene and vinylalkanes. For example, high conversions are best attained in solvent which dissolve or swell the polymer. Benzene is the preferred solvent; cyclohexane is suitable for styrene but not for 4-vinylbiphenyl. With vinylaromatics, $Et_3Al–TiCl_3$ is the preferred catalyst system. The $Et_2AlCl–TiCl_3$ system gives both lower conversion and poorer stereoregularity. Perhaps this is because the stereoregular polymerization with the latter catalyst is so slow that cationic polymerization leading to atactic polymers becomes important. Frequently isotactic polystyrene contains a toluene-insoluble fraction (243). There are indications that the proportion of toluene-insoluble polymer depends on the particular batch of $TiCl_3$ which is used. The cause of the toluene insolubility is not definitely established. It has been found, however, that polymerization in the presence of vinyl chloride (a molecular weight regulator) decreases the toluene insolubility (too much vinyl chloride greatly lowers conversion and isotaxy), and that controlled pyrolysis of the polymer (300°C.) also decreases toluene insolubility.

245. Preparation of Isotactic Polystyrene (171)*

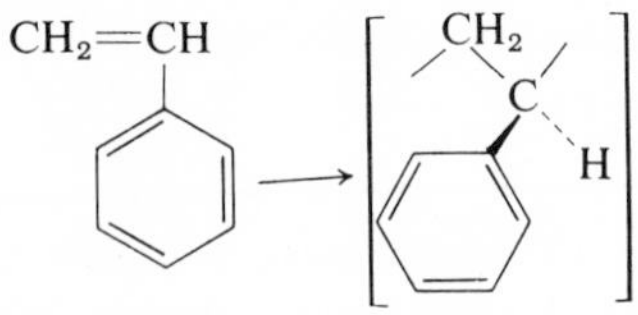

$$CH_2{=}CH \longrightarrow \left[\begin{array}{c} CH_2 \\ C{\cdots}H \end{array} \right]$$

An argon-flushed pop bottle containing 50 ml. dry benzene and a Teflon-covered stirring bar is capped with a Buna N septum. Then, 0.41 ml. (3 mmoles) triethylaluminum and 3 ml. ($\sim$1.8 mmoles) of a "$1M$ suspension" of TiCl$_3$ AA in cyclohexane are transferred to the bottle with syringes (18 ga. needle, 5 ml. syringe for the TiCl$_3$) in an inert atmosphere. Finally, 5 g. styrene is introduced with a syringe and the bottle is agitated at 60°C. by placing it in a water bath on a hot plate with a magnetic stirrer. After 20 hr. the thick, black mass is transferred to a blender and washed twice with isopropanol. If not yet colorless the polymer is washed additionally once or twice with 2-butanone and dried *in vacuo* at 80–100°C. Conversion is 95%.

Continuous extraction with 2-butanone removes the polymer (about 5%) which has low stereoregularity. Continuous extraction of the butanone in-soluble (isotactic) polymer with toluene gives a toluene insoluble fraction A (about 10% of the total polymer) and a toluene soluble fraction, B. The latter fraction is precipitated with methanol. Films of A and B may be pressed at 250°C.; after annealing for 30 min. at 180°C. both give the characteristic IR spectrum of crystalline polystyrene (244). The polymer melts at about 230°C. Although the isolated polymer, B, is readily redissolved in toluene only upon heating to near reflux, the polymer remains dissolved when the solution returns to room temperature. The inherent viscosity (0.1 g./100 ml. in toluene at 30°C.) is 1.6.

In CDCl$_3$ isotactic polystyrene displays broad NMR signals for the benzylic and methylenic protons at 7.96 and 8.54τ, respectively, while the corresponding signals for the atactic polymer are at 8.17 and 8.59τ.

Isotactic co-polyhydrocarbons can be made, as in the following example.

246. Random Copolymer of 4-Methyl-1-pentene and 1-Hexene (245)

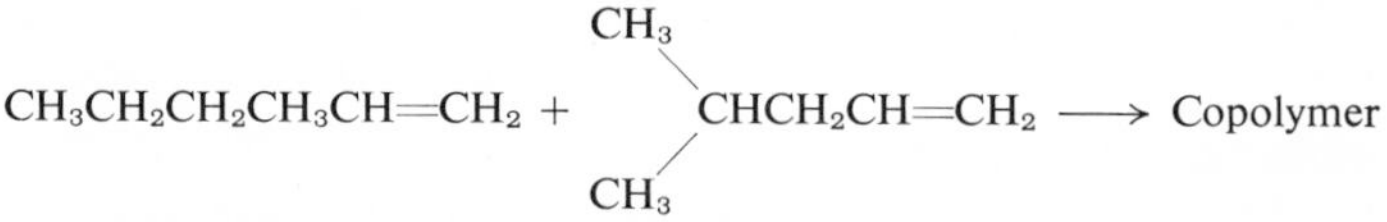

$$CH_3CH_2CH_2CH_3CH{=}CH_2 + \begin{array}{c} CH_3 \\ CHCH_2CH{=}CH_2 \\ CH_3 \end{array} \longrightarrow Copolymer$$

In order to illustrate the effects of copolymerization on the properties of poly-α-olefins, the following experiments can be performed. A mixture of 40 ml. of 4-methyl-1-pentene and 10 ml. of 1-hexene is polymerized for 3 hr. as in Section VIII. The polymer is isolated by precipitation in alcohol followed

* Dr. D. B. Miller, Stanford Research Institute, was kind enough to provide this example and much of the foregoing commentary.

by filtration. The inherent viscosity is approximately 2.5–3.5 as measured in cyclohexane (0.5%) at room temperature. This polymer may be pressed to clear film at about 120°C. It may be drawn and oriented at 125°C. These strips show a crystalline melting point of approximately 195°C. The interesting thing about this copolymer is that it is readily soluble in cyclohexane to give a very viscous but true solution in contrast to poly(4-methyl-1-pentene), which forms with cyclohexane a swollen, gel-like mass. The added 1-hexene has changed the solubility characteristics quite markedly.

The commercially most significant olefin copolymer is that from ethylene and propylene. When prepared so as to minimize long blocks of either monomer, and by a catalyst that is not favorable to highly isotactic placement of consecutive propylene units when they do occur, the polymer is completely amorphous, has a low T_g, and has many useful elastomeric properties. It can be vulcanized with peroxides, but it is generally the custom to prepare a terpolymer with a diene so that unsaturation is introduced to allow sulfur vulcanization. Dicyclopentadiene is frequently used to make the terpolymer (EPT), because its double bonds are of unequal reactivity; one of them does not readily enter into copolymerization.

247. Preparation of an Elastomeric Terpolymer of Ethylene, Propylene, and Dicyclopentadiene (246)*

This procedure describes the preparation of a terpolymer containing 68.8 mole % (56.5 wt. %) ethylene (E), 29.3 mole % (36.1 wt. %) propylene (P), and 1.9 mole % (7.4 wt. %) dicyclopentadiene (D).

The procedure is analogous to that described elsewhere (5) for the preparation of EP copolymer containing 30 mole % P, except that D is also added initially and in many increments (or continuously) during the polymerization. To prepare a terpolymer of uniform composition, all three monomer concentrations in solution must be kept constant at a precalculated ratio throughout the polymerization. This requirement is fulfilled by using monomer reactivity ratios to calculate the initial monomer concentrations, and then supplying each monomer during the polymerization at a rate corresponding to its rate of consumption, under conditions of sufficient agitation and constant temperature.

* We are very grateful to Dr. Carl Lukach and the Hercules Powder Co. for making available this extensively detailed preparation.

The procedure involves a relatively slow rate of catalyst addition, and therefore of polymerization, to facilitate equilibration of gas and liquid phases, and to minimize the temperature rise.

Apparatus

The apparatus used is a jacketed, 1 l. resin kettle equipped with condenser, thermometer, gas inlet tube, and paddle stirrer (with glass shaft and Teflon half-moon blade) mounted from an air-driven motor (*electric motors should not be used in the immediate vicinity of the reactor because of the possibility of a gas leak*). One neck of the reactor is provided with a rubber stopule so that injections can be made with a hypodermic syringe.

The gas inlet tube, projecting into the reactor about 1 in. above the stirrer blade, is connected to an exterior monomer inlet line containing two sets of flowmeters for ethylene and two sets for propylene. Each set consists of one 06-150/13 and one 08-150/13 Fischer-Porter flowmeter (steel ball) connected in parallel through top and bottom stopcocks so as to provide a total flow rate range of at least 1500 cm.^{3}/min. (0–300 cm.^{3}/min. with the 08-, and higher flow rates with the 06-flowmeter). Each set is connected to the appropriate monomer cylinder. The inlet line is also provided with a manometer, T-tube, and stopcock between the row of 8 flowmeters and the reactor, for introducing nitrogen, or evacuating (aspirator) the reactor.

The excess gas exits from the reactor through the condenser. A two-way stopcock is connected to the top of the condenser for removing gas aliquots for analysis, if desired. The exit gas passes through two bottle traps, the last containing glass wool to trap any solvent mist carried by the gas, and then through an 06-150/13 flowmeter (to measure the exit gas flow rate) before being vented into the hood.

Hot water is circulated through the outer jacket of the resin kettle. A temperature regulating device is used for adjusting the water temperature. A manually operated needle valve is also provided for introducing cold water into the constant-temperature stream to control any exothermic heat rise and maintain a constant temperature.

Both catalyst components (ethyl aluminum sesquichloride and VCl$_4$) are best added separately and continuously at a constant Al/V ratio. Either motor-driven syringe drivers, microbellows pumps, or Hershberg dropping funnels can be used for this purpose, with the catalyst components being pumped directly into the reactor slightly above the liquid level via stainless steel, small-diameter tubing. It is convenient to provide the catalyst pump system with a timer (such as a Flex-O-Pulse Timer, Eagle Signal Corp., Moline, Ill.) so that the motor on-off cycle can be adjusted to control the rate of delivery.

Procedure

The flowmeters are calibrated at several settings with their intended monomers, either ethylene or propylene, by timing the rise of a soap bubble in a graduated column attached to the flowmeter. A nonlinear plot of flow rate versus flowmeter setting is prepared for each flowmeter.

After shutting the appropriate stopcocks, the reactor (exclusive of monomer inlet line or off-gas line) is alternately evacuated and filled with nitrogen twice, while hot water (50°C.) is circulated through the outer jacket of the resin kettle. Pure grade Phillips *n*-heptane (500 ml., previously dried by being passed through a column of Linde Type 4A molecular sieves) is added via stainless steel tubing from a pop bottle under nitrogen pressure (10 p.s.i.g.), or by syringe. The apparatus is again evacuated and then filled with nitrogen to atmospheric pressure. The temperature is adjusted so that the heptane is at 50°C. After the stopcocks are opened, the heptane is saturated with a mixture of E and P containing 68 mole % P fed at a total gas rate of 700 cm.^{3}/min. from one set of E and one set of P flowmeters. When the exit gas flow rate becomes constant, this saturating stream is reduced to 300 cm.^{3}/min., and *kept at this flow rate throughout the polymerization* without changing its composition. Thus, before polymerization occurs, the inlet and exit gas flow rate will each be 300 cm.^{3}/min. and the gas composition will be 68 mole % P and 32 mole % E.

Dicyclopentadiene (0.137 g.; 1.04 mmoles) and 1.0 ml. of 0.5N ethyl–aluminum sesquichloride (0.5 mmole Al) are added directly to the saturated heptane by syringe. The syringe driver is turned on to feed heptane solutions of both ethyl–aluminum sesquichloride (0.30N in Al) and VCl$_4$ (0.06N in V) at a rate of 0.09 ml./min. Shortly after the VCl$_4$ addition begins, the start of polymerization is heralded by a decrease in the exit gas flow rate to below 300 cm.^{3}/min.

At this point, a second monomer stream containing 30 mole % P, controlled by the second set of E and P flowmeters, is also opened and fed at whatever rate is necessary to bring the total exit gas flow rate back to 300 cm.^{3}/min. and keep it there. This second monomer input stream therefore supplies E and P of the composition desired in the product, at a rate corresponding to their rate of consumption. The rate of addition of this 30% C$_3$ monomer stream is adjusted throughout the run so that the exit gas flowrate remains constant. While this is being done, the first monomer input stream is also feeding a 68% P composition at a constant rate of 300 cm.^{3}/min.

Dicyclopentadiene must also be added during the run so as to keep its concentration in solution constant at the initial value. This objective is best accomplished by basing the D addition rate upon the rate of consumption of either E, P, or both, as measured by the appropriate flowmeter of the second monomer input stream. In the present example, 0.105 g. of D is added, as 0.29 ml. of a 1 : 2 D : heptane solution (vol./vol.), for every 700 cm.^{3} of E (or alternatively every 300 cm.^{3} of P) consumed throughout the run. This amount corresponds to 0.08 mmole of D/1.21 mmoles of P consumed. The addition of D is easily programmed in this way with the help of the flowmeter calibration charts prepared previously.

Manipulation of the addition rate of E, P, and D is continued for 75 min., during which time the solution becomes viscous but remains clear and free from any gel or precipitate. During this period, the catalyst syringe driver adds 6.75 ml. of 0.3M ethylaluminum sesquichloride (2.03 mmoles Al) and 6.75 ml. of 0.06M VCl$_4$ (0.41 mmole V), while 1.21 g. (9.15 mmoles) of D is added in 12 equal increments (as the D heptane solution). The rate of reaction of E and P (as measured by the second input stream flowmeters) gradually increases for 20 min. and then remains essentially constant at a total EP rate of 155 cm.^{3}/min. Periodic gas chromatographic analysis of both the exit gas and the reaction mixture indicate that the exit gas composition remains at 66–68 mole % P and the D concentration remains essentially constant throughout the terpolymerization.

The terpolymerization is stopped after 75 min. by discontinuing catalyst addition and *slowly* adding 5 ml. of *n*-butanol to the reaction mixture. After the initial reaction of the butanol and aluminum alkyl subsides, the monomer inlet stream is replaced with nitrogen, which is bubbled through the reaction mixture for 30 min.

The reaction mixture is cooled and washed from the reactor with heptane. It is then washed with three 500 ml. portions of water (preferably hot). The organic layer is then poured into a shallow Pyrex baking dish which is placed in a nearly-closed hood overnight. The product (17 g.; 27.2 g./l. per hr.; 41.4 g. per mmole of V) is obtained as a clear film easily peeled from the baking dish. Its reduced specific viscosity (Decalin, 0.1%, 135°C.) is 1.8 and it contains 7–9 wt. % dicyclopentadiene linkages by IR analysis.

The terpolymerization may be run for a longer time but polymerization to a higher product concentration becomes progressively more difficult since equilibrium with the gas phase suffers severely at high solution viscosities.

Calculations

In the preparation of any terpolymer composition, the ideal copolymerization equation is assumed to apply for any pair of monomers, i.e.,

$$\frac{dm_1/dt}{dm_2/dt} = r_{12} \frac{M_1}{M_2}$$

where *m* refers to copolymer composition, *M* to monomer composition, and r_{12} is the reactivity ratio of monomer 1 with respect to monomer 2.

The relationship between P and D is then given by:

$$\frac{dm_D/dt}{dm_P/dt} = r_{DP} \frac{M_D}{M_P}$$

where: M_D is the concentration of D in solution, M_P is the concentration of P in solution, r_{DP} is the reactivity ratio of D with respect to P, dm_D/dt is the rate of consumption of D, and dm_P/dt is the rate of consumption of P.

The mole % of D and P desired in the product can be used for the left side of the equation. For example, in the present case, for 500 ml. solvent and 50°C.,

$dm_D/dt = 1.93$
$dm_P/dt = 29.3$
$r_{DP} = 6.0$
$M_P = 94.4$ mmoles (3.97 g.) at 0.554 atm. of P (based upon a P solubility value of 2.1 g./100 g. of heptane at 1 atm. and 50°C., and a vapor pressure value of heptane at 50°C. of 141 mm.).

With these values, M_D is calculated from the equation to be 1.04 mmoles (0.137 g.) for 500 ml. of solvent. This is the amount of D added initially, and determines the D concentration to be kept constant throughout the polymerization. The addition rate used for D is based upon the rate of consumption of P; it is calculated so that the mole ratio of D added to P consumed is 1.93 to 29.3.

Similarly for E and P, the relationship is:

$$\frac{dm_E/dt}{dm_P/dt} = r_{EP} \frac{M_E}{M_P}$$

and $r_{EP} = 17$–20 (1). Knowing two reactivity ratios, a third can be calculated from:

$$r_{ED} = \frac{r_{EP}}{r_{DP}}$$

thus enabling the use of any combination of the three monomers in heptane at 50°C. with an ethylaluminum sesquichloride–VCl_4 catalyst system. The reactivity ratio values will be different if any drastic departures from these specific conditions are used, especially with a different catalyst system. The solubility of ethylene and propylene will also change with different solvents.

Possible Procedure Variations

(a) A 1 l. round-bottom flask immersed in a thermostat can be used in place of a resin kettle. The stirrer must be able to create a rapidly renewed suspension of gas bubbles. With ordinary laboratory stirrers, this is possible only with a relatively shallow depth of liquid. Adequate interior baffling or a creased flask is desirable.

(b) The constant off-gas stream of 68 mole % P provides a convenient source of gas for analysis, serves to purge inert gases, and helps to correct minor errors in the feed ratio of P to E. If the quality of feed gas is good and control is adequate, the off-gas stream can be dispensed with during polymerization. Even so, the system must be first presaturated with the appropriate monomer composition (68 mole % P), and a different monomer composition (30 mole % P) must be fed during the run.

(c) The elaborate system of flowmeters used was set up so that terpolymer of any composition could be prepared. If only the composition of this example is desired, it would be more convenient to provide two sources of mixed gases, of compositions 68 mole % P for presaturation, and 30 mole % P for feeding during the run. The proper rate of addition of D could then be calculated from the pressure drop of the container holding the 30 mole % P mixture.

(d) The molecular weight of the product decreases as its propylene content increases. The catalyst requirement is also higher at higher propylene content. Both effects can be counteracted by operation at a lower temperature. As the temperature is lowered, the same gas compositions may be used for presaturation and running, but higher initial concentrations of D will be needed.

(e) Diethylaluminum chloride may be used instead of ethylaluminum sesquichloride. The VCl_4 may also be replaced with either $VOCl_3$ or a vanadium ester such as triethyl orthovanadate, but a slightly higher Al/V ratio should be used, and reactivity ratios may be slightly different.

Procedure at High Pressure—For terpolymerizations at higher pressures, a modified Sutherland reactor (5,246a) can be used. The solvent is saturated with the proper E and P composition (in this case, 68 mole % P) at the higher pressure. During the terpolymerization, the total pressure is held constant by automatic feed of an EP mixture of the composition desired in the product (in this case, 30 mole % P). The diene is added initially and this initial concentration is kept constant by adding D during the run at a rate dependent upon the rate of consumption of E or P, as measured by the pressure drop in the container holding the feed mixture. Both M_P and M_E will have different values at higher pressures in the calculations used for determining the proper M_D.

IX. Acetylene Polymers

Acetylene and simple monofunctional derivatives are polymerized to black, highly conjugated, and intractable polymers. However, when a sufficiently bulky side group is introduced, complete conjugation is prevented, and soluble products of yellow color are obtained. Thus, polymerization of 4-methyl-1-hexyne gives a high polymer with UV maxima at 230 and 325 mμ (247–249).

248. Preparation of Iron-tris-Acetylacetonate (250)

$$FeCl_3 + CH_3COCH_2COCH_3 \longrightarrow Fe\left[\begin{array}{c} CH_3 \\ | \\ O=C \\ \diagdown \\ \diagup \quad\quad CH \\ O-C \\ | \\ CH_3 \end{array}\right]_3$$

To a solution of 67.6 g. (0.25 mole) of $FeCl_3 \cdot 6H_2O$ in 250 ml. of water is added a solution of 75 g. of acetylacetone (0.75 mole) in 150 ml. methanol, with stirring. To the mixture is added 0.75 mole of sodium acetate in 200 ml. of water, and the product is heated briefly on a hot plate, cooled to room temperature, and then refrigerated several hours. The product is filtered, recrystallized from methanol–water mixture, and dried thoroughly; m.p. 178–183°C.

249. Preparation of Polymerization of Racemic 4-Methyl-1-hexyne (247)

$$\begin{array}{c} CH_3 \\ \diagdown \quad CH_2CH_3 \\ CH \\ | \\ CH_2 \\ | \\ C\equiv CH \end{array} \longrightarrow \begin{array}{c} CH_3 \\ \diagdown \quad CH_2CH_3 \\ CH \\ | \\ CH_2 \\ | \\ [-C=CH-]_n \end{array}$$

4-Methyl-1-hexyne is made from the corresponding olefin by adding bromine and treating with sodium amide in mineral oil at 160°C. (248,249). $\eta_D^{25} = 1.4055$, b.p. 91–92°C.

Polymerization is carried out in a 100 ml. pear-shaped flask equipped with nitrogen inlet, stirrer, condenser, and thermometer. Into the reaction vessel under nitrogen is introduced 0.735 g. of iron acetylacetonate, 3 ml. isooctane, and 1.238 g. of aluminum triisobutyl. The mixture is heated and stirred at 70°C. for 15 min. At this point, 42 ml. of isooctane and 5.00 g. of 4-methyl-1-hexyne are added at room temperature, and the mixture warmed 3 hr. at 30–35°C., then left to stand 45 hr. at room temperature. The polymerization is interrupted by the addition of diethyl ether to dissolve the polymer, and dilute hydrochloric acid to kill the catalyst. The organic layer is treated with $NaHCO_3$ solution, washed with water and evaporated to yield 4.65 g. of polymer. This product is extracted with boiling acetone, to give 4.50 g. of acetone-insoluble product, intrinsic viscosity 2.7–3.5 dl./g. at 30°C.

in toluene. The polymer has a UV spectrum with $\lambda_{max.} = 230$ (log $E = 3.43$) and $\lambda_{max.} = 325$ (log $E = 3.45$), and is amorphous at room temperature.

X. Diene Polymers and Copolymers

The preparation of diene polymers and copolymers is an important technology which has occupied the attention of many scientists since before World War I. These polymers are, in general, elastomers and have gone far toward supplementing and, perhaps, ultimately supplanting natural rubber.

The volume of published work in this field is very large and has been well summarized in many excellent books (9,10,13,14,251,251a) and papers. Briefly, dienes will polymerize by a variety of techniques and with a variety of catalysts. With butadiene, the resulting polymerization may give the following structural units:

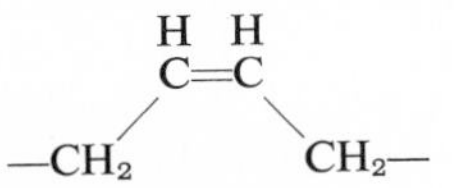

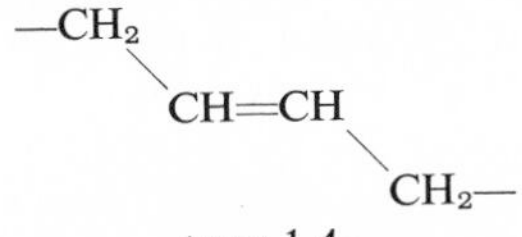

Ordinarily, the free radical homopolymer will contain varying amounts of these structural units making it actually a copolymer. The proportion of units will vary with the technique or catalyst used.

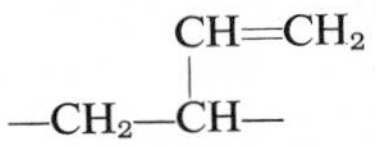

Isoprene, 2-methylbutadiene, gives both 1,2- and 3,4-polymers because of its unsymmetrical structure, as well as *cis*- and *trans*-1,4. On the other hand, chloroprene, which is basically similar, appears to give only *trans*-1,4 polymerization with free radicals. 2,3-Dichlorobutadiene polymerizes similarly. Interestingly, the product from this monomer is a hard plastic, and not an elastomer. The following experiments are illustrative of the preparation of diene polymers and copolymers.

Butadiene may be homopolymerized conveniently in a variety of ways. One of the more interesting techniques is that using the "**Alfin**" **catalyst,** discovered by Morton and co-workers (252–254). This is an organometallic system composed of a mixture of a metal alkyl, an alkali halide, and an alkali metal alkoxide. The rate of polymerization and the molecular weight of the product are very sensitive to changes in the alkyl group of the organometallic and the alkoxide.*

* Freshly purified styrene may be polymerized by the "Alfin" catalyst essentially as is butadiene. The product obtained is of high molecular weight and has been reported to contain a crystalline fraction (255).

250. Preparation of "Alfin" Catalysts

$$2Na + C_5H_{11}Cl \longrightarrow C_5H_{11}Na + NaCl$$

$$NaCl + C_5H_{11}Na + 0.25(CH_3)_2CHOH \longrightarrow$$

$$0.75\ C_5H_{11}Na + 0.25(CH_3)_2CHONa + NaCl \xrightarrow{CH_2=CHCH_3}$$

$$0.75\ CH_2{=}CH{-}CH_2Na + 0.25(CH_3)_2CHONa + NaCl$$

In order to prepare this catalyst successfully, it is necessary to use high speed stirring apparatus essentially as described by Professor Morton (256, 257).

Amylsodium. In a 1 l., four-necked flask attached to a high speed stirrer capable of at least 10,000 r.p.m., are placed 500 ml. of dry decane and 23.5 g. of metallic sodium. This mixture is heated to 105°C. and stirred vigorously for 2 min. The flask is cooled with stirring, then the sodium sand is allowed to settle. This mixture is now cooled to $-20°C.$. and 62.5 g. of freshly distilled amyl chloride is added from a dropping funnel. After the addition of approximately 10–15 ml. of amyl chloride, the reaction mixture is stirred vigorously until a dark-purple color develops indicating initiation of reaction. The remaining amyl chloride is now added over a period of 1 hr., maintaining the temperature at $-20°C.$ The mixture is now allowed to warm to room temperature and stirred for an additional 30 min.

Amylsodium–Sodium Isopropoxide Catalyst. To 1 mole of amylsodium prepared as in the preceding paragraph is added 12.5 g. of isopropanol at room temperature with stirring.

Allylsodium–Sodium Isopropoxide Catalyst. The combination of amylsodium–sodium isopropoxide prepared in the preceding paragraph is cooled to $-20°C.$ and stirred vigorously. Propylene gas is bubbled in at $-20°C.$ until the amylsodium is completely converted to allylsodium. The propylene is then bubbled through the suspension for an additional 3 hr. to ensure completion of the reaction. The dark-bluish purple suspension may be stored under nitrogen for future use.

251. Polymerization of Butadiene by an Alfin Catalyst

$$CH_2{=}CH{-}CH{=}CH_2 \longrightarrow (C_4H_6)_n$$

A flask equipped with high speed stirring, such as was used in the preparation of the organometallic catalyst, is charged with 250 ml. of anhydrous pentane, and 20 ml. of the catalyst suspension is added by means of a hypodermic syringe or other anaerobic method of transfer. The catalyst suspension is stirred rapidly, and 30 ml. of high purity butadiene in 30 ml. of cold pentane is added rapidly to the well-stirred mixture. Polymerization is allowed to proceed for approximately 2 hr. when dilute hydrochloric is added to quench the reaction and phenyl β-naphthylamine (approximately 4% by weight of the polymer expected) is added. The polymer is now isolated by evaporation of the pentane and the residue is placed in a vacuum oven at 40°C. The resulting polybutadiene should be obtained in a yield of about 60% with an inherent viscosity of about 9 as measured in pentane (0.1, 25°C.).

Ordinarily, polymers prepared with the Alfin catalyst are only partially soluble in pentane. The solubility may be, however, as high as 98% with the combination of alcohol and olefin used above in the preparation of the catalyst. The highest viscosity polymer is obtained when the catalyst is prepared as described in the preceding paragraph from isopropanol and propylene. The viscosity decreases with the use of higher olefins and higher alcohols. For example, using 2-heptanol and 2-pentene in place of isopropanol and propylene ordinarily gives a polymer with viscosities below 3, at a much slower rate than the preceding example. As is the case with all organometallic catalyzed polymerizations, both catalyst and monomer must be handled under anhydrous conditions.

Polymerization is usually very rapid, and it is allowed to go for 2 hr. only to ensure completion and to allow for possible subnormal activity of the catalyst. The great speed of the polymerization can be demonstrated quite effectively. A few milliliters of active catalyst suspension is mixed in a cork-stoppered pop-bottle with 30 ml. of butadiene and 150 ml. of pentane. The contents will come swelling out of the bottle after 2–3 min. in spectacular fashion.

Butadiene also can be **polymerized in a typical emulsion system,** such as described earlier for vinyl monomers, or in a GR-S type system as in Preparation 257. It can be polymerized with **metallic sodium,** the following procedure being typical (258).

252. The Sodium-Catalyzed Polymerization of Butadiene (258)

$$CH_2=CH-CH=CH_2 \longrightarrow (C_4H_6)_n$$

The reaction vessel used in this polymerization is a simple 4 oz. screw-cap bottle which has been provided with a heavy rubber disk covered with a heavy tin foil disk underneath the screw-cap. The bottle is flushed with gaseous butadiene and a volume of sodium dispersion in xylene or toluene containing about 0.15 g. of sodium is added to the bottle. Ten ml. of dry toluene is now added, followed by 60–70 g. of butadiene which has been condensed in an ice-salt bath. The mixture is allowed to boil gently for a short time in order to completely expel the air from the reaction vessel, then the cap plus the rubber gasket and heavy tin foil disk is placed on top of the bottle and the vessel is sealed. The bottle is maintained in a thermostatted bath and tumbled by a mechanical device at a temperature of approximately 50°C. As polymerization proceeds the contents of the bottle become viscous and eventually become solid. After 24 hr. the polymer can be isolated as follows.

Benzene containing 10% alcohol and a trace of phenyl-β-naphthylamine antioxidant is added to the cooled bottle. The mixture is removed and added to a large excess of benzene to give a homogeneous dispersion. Polymer is precipitated with methanol as a rubbery mass and pressed free of liquid, then mixed with about 2% of its weight of antioxidant. Drying is accomplished by placing in a circulating air oven at 70–80°C. for 6–8 hr.

Butadiene also will polymerize readily with organotitanium catalysts and with lithium and lithium alkyls, as is described subsequently for isoprene.

Polybutadienes prepared by the Alfin, emulsion, sodium, and stereo-specific techniques differ in average isomer content. The percentages also vary within a given type, depending on temperature of polymerization and the other factors. For example, emulsion polybutadiene runs about 80% total *cis* and *trans* 1,4 addition; Alfin polymer is about 70%, sodium polymer only 25–30% (220,259), and polybutadiene from stereoregulating catalysts can be almost 100% *cis*- or *trans*-1,4, or iso- or syndiotactic-1,2. An example of emulsion polybutadiene was given earlier (Preparation No. 146) as part of an ABS synthesis.

A very effective catalyst for polymerization of butadiene to a highly *cis*-1,4 structure involves a cobalt salt with an alkylaluminum halide. Both diethylaluminum chloride and ethylaluminum sesquichloride are effective with cobalt octoate, but the former aluminum alkyl requires water for activation. No polymerization occurs in an anhydrous system; about 10–15 mole % water based on aluminum gives optimum *cis*-1,4 levels. The sesquihalide, in contrast, requires no water.

253. Polybutadiene with a High *cis*-1,4 Content with an Aluminum Alkyl-cobalt Octoate Catalyst (260)

$$CH_2\!=\!CH\!-\!CH\!=\!CH_2 \longrightarrow \begin{array}{c} +CH_2 \qquad CH_2+ \\ \diagdown \quad \diagup \\ C\!=\!C \\ \diagup \quad \diagdown \\ H \qquad\quad H \end{array}$$

To a previously oven-dried and nitrogen-flushed beverage bottle of about 1 qt. capacity is charged 450 ml. of thiophene-free benzene which has been purified as described below. Slightly in excess of 50 g. of polymerization-grade butadiene is condensed into the bottle and enough allowed to boil out to expel residual air and to give a final weight of about 50 g. monomer. The bottle is closed with a Neoprene gasket and a metal crown cap with a hole for hypodermic insertion.

Then, 10 mmoles of ethylaluminum sesquichloride (calculated as $Et_{1.5}AlCl_{1.5}$) and 0.02 mmoles of cobalt octoate are added through the septum by syringe. The aluminum alkyl can be conveniently added as 10 ml. of a $1M$ solution in benzene and the cobalt salt as 1 ml. of a $0.02M$ solution in benzene.

The very small quantities of catalyst used requires that a highly purified system be used. The benzene should be distilled initially and the first 20% discarded, the subsequent distillate passed through a silica gel column, and finally stored over calcium hydride. Higher amounts of catalyst may be required if sufficient purity is not maintained.

The polymerization is conducted by rotating the bottle in a 5°C. bath for 2 hr., in which time conversion should exceed 90%. The polymer is coagulated by pouring the solution into excess isopropanol containing phenyl-β-naphthylamine. The solid is leached for 24 hr. in fresh isopropanol-antioxidant, blotted dry, and covered with a pentane solution of antioxidant. The swelled polymer is dried in vacuum at 50°C. under nitrogen. The final product should have a cis-1,4 content of 95–98% by IR (British Pat. 592,477, December 6, 1957, to Montecatini). Other IR methods have been used, but the film technique of this reference has been commonly used for comparison with polybutadiene prepared and reported in early work. The inherent viscosity is 3–4 in benzene (0.5 g./100 ml.) at 25°C.

High cis-1,4-polybutadiene can also be prepared using a catalyst based on an aluminum alkyl and titanium tetraiodide. The titanium chlorides do not have a cis-1,4 stereodirecting capacity equal to that of the iodides. The following example uses TiI_4 in conjunction with tetrabutyltitanate and triisobutylaluminum. The vast differences in coordination catalyst action as a function of relatively minor changes in composition is illustrated by the fact that the latter two components alone give a polybutadiene high in 1,2-units. It is evident from the patent literature on the subject that titanium tetraiodide is the key to the cis-1,4 polymer when a catalyst based on aluminum and titanium is used.

254. Polybutadiene with a High cis-1,4 Content Using an Aluminum Alkyltitanium Iodide Catalyst (261)

$$CH_2{=}CH{-}CH{=}CH_2 \longrightarrow \ \begin{matrix} (CH_2 & CH_2) \\ \diagdown\ \ \diagup \\ C{=}C \\ \diagup\ \ \diagdown \\ H\ \ \ \ H \end{matrix}$$

A solution is made up in a small beverage bottle consisting of 100 ml. toluene (dried over and distilled from calcium hydride), and 2.93 mmoles of both tetra-n-butyl titanate (1.00 g.) and titanium tetraiodide (1.63 g.). The bottle is capped with a neoprene septum and shaken to achieve good mixing. Titanium tetraiodide is slow to dissolve. It should be ground to a fine particle size to speed its solution, but grinding should be done with care (e.g., in a good, nitrogen-flushed dry box).

A dry beverage bottle of about 1 qt. capacity is charged with 500 ml. dry toluene, then flushed thoroughly with nitrogen, capped as above, and pressured with nitrogen to about 10 lb. Then 2.2 mmoles of triisobutylaluminum is added, conveniently as 10 ml. of a 0.22M solution in toluene. (The bottle is prepressured with nitrogen to preclude entry of air during subsequent charging. This step is not essential but is a useful precaution against contamination. If it is employed, great care must be exercised in adding catalysts from a syringe to prevent the plunger and contents from being forced out of the syringe.) Then, 0.26 mmole of titanium tetraiodide and tetra-n-butyl titanate is added as 9.3 ml. of the mixture made as described, after which 50 g. of polymerization grade butadiene is carefully pressured into the cooled bottle through the septum.

The bottle is tumbled for 17 hr. at 5°C., after which 0.5 ml. of a solution of 2,2′-methylene bis(4-methyl-6-t-butylphenol) (52 g. in 4 l. toluene and 100 ml.

isopropanol) is added and thoroughly mixed in. The contents of the bottle is then poured into 1 l. isopropanol and stirred vigorously. The polymer is treated with a phenyl-β-naphthyl amine solution in pentane as in the preceding example and dried under nitrogen in vacuum at 50°C. The conversion is 85–90%, and the inherent viscosity is about 3.5 (benzene, 25°C., 0.5 g./100 ml.). The cis-1,4 content is about 96%, trans-1,4 is 0.7%, and the remaining 3.3% is 1,2. These values are determined by IR examination of a 25% solution of the polymer in carbon disulfide (262).

A polybutadiene with only a somewhat lower cis-1,4 content than the above (e.g., 87%) can be prepared by using titanium tetrachloride in place of the tetrabutyl titanate. A mole ratio of components such as 15:1:1 for triisobutylaluminum: titanium tetraiodide: titanium tetrachloride (263).

Polybutadiene with a high degree of trans-1,4 enchainment is a crystalline polymer which can be made with trialkylaluminum–titanium (264) or vanadium (265) halide catalysts, or a mixture of the two transition metal halides (266). At least 95% trans-1,4 structure can be made to prevail. A catalyst derived from lithium aluminum hydride and titanium tetraiodide (mole ratio 0.86/1.31) in benzene produces a polymer with only 78–86% trans-1,4-structure (267); this polymer displays useful elastomeric properties. The trans-1,4 polymer can also be made in a water emulsion by means of rhodium chloride and related salts and their complexes (267a). Molecular weights are modest, as indicated by intrinsic viscosity (e.g., 0.4).

255. Preparation of trans-1,4-Polybutadiene (266)*

$$CH_2{=}CH{-}CH{=}CH_2 \longrightarrow \left[\begin{array}{c} H \\ | \\ C \\ \diagup \diagdown \\ CH_2 \quad\; CH_2 \\ \diagdown \diagup \\ C \\ | \\ H \end{array} \right]$$

In this example, the monomer is bubbled at atmospheric pressure through the catalyst–solvent mixture rather than being added all at once to either a bottle or an autoclave which is then sealed. If the catalyst is sufficiently active, loss of butadiene is not significant in the present case. Solvent and monomer are conveniently dried over Linde Molecular Sieves No. 4, which may also be used to dry the nitrogen used to protect the system during the operation. The system must also be kept oxygen-free.

A 500 ml. three-necked flask is equipped with a stirrer, gas inlet reaching below the liquid level in the flask, and a gas outlet through a condenser and drying tube. One inlet is glass stoppered. The flask assembly is flamed out in a stream of nitrogen and cooled while being purged; the glass stopper is

* We wish to thank Dr. Jack Laskey, Uniroyal Corp., for making the details of this preparation available to us.

removed and replaced by a serum cap for catalyst addition. To the flask is charged 300 ml. dry benzene, 0.227 g. titanium tetrachloride (1.2 mmoles), 0.058 g. vanadium tetrachloride (0.3 mmole) and 0.063 g. aluminum triethyl (0.55 mmole). The mixture is stirred and heated to reflux for 1 hr. The transition metal halides are both reduced to primarily the trivalent state and are coprecipitated, a fact which appears to enhance their activity. If this reduction of the halides with aluminum triethyl is carried out at 170°C. in a higher boiling solvent or in an autoclave, an even more highly active catalyst results, though its stereoregulating capacity is not very changed. The aluminum chloride formed in the reduction in either case is believed to be present in the crystal lattice of the transition metal trihalides and is not washed out during polymerization. Reduction at 80°C. forms β-TiCl$_3$ while the γ-isomer forms at 170°C. (268).

When the mixture has cooled, 0.513 g. additional aluminum triethyl (4.5 mmole) is added to activate the trihalides. The advantage of the two-step catalyst preparation (i.e., reduction and activation) is that reduction of titanium and vanadium to valence states lower than three is avoided, thus minimizing the number of differing catalyst sites. An Al/(Ti + V) mole ratio of slightly more than 1/3 is maintained in the reduction, and 3/1 in the activation.

Butadiene (high purity polymerization grade) is then passed through the stirred solvent–catalyst with the temperature maintained at 60°C. by means of a heating bath. The initial rate of polymerization should be upwards of 18 g./hr. After 1 hr., the mixture is poured into about 1.5 l. of methanol containing 1% phenyl-β-naphthylamine. The polymer is washed at least 3 times in a blender with methanol containing the antioxidant and dried under a nitrogen stream in a vacuum oven at 50°C. The polymer is judged to be greater than 95% of the trans-1,4 type, by IR (band at 10.36 μ, a solution of 10 g./l. in CS$_2$:CCl$_4$, 1 : 1). It has a crystalline melting point of around 146°C. using a polarizing microscope. This represents a second crystalline modification; the first is stable up to 75°C., going over to the second, higher melting, form at that temperature.

Butadiene can be polymerized in an essentially complete 1,2-enchainment and syndiotactic placement of the pendant vinyl group by using a cobalt salt complexed with pyridine in conjunction with aluminum triethyl (269). Other catalysts are known, e.g., aluminum triethyl-titanium tetrabutoxide and vanadium or molybdenum acetylacetonates with metal alkyls (270), but in general do not give quite as stereospecific a synthesis.

It is interesting to note that diethylaluminum chloride in place of aluminum triethyl will produce, in the system of the following example, a polybutadiene of 96% cis-1,4 content. Mixtures of the two aluminum alkyls will generate highly syndiotactic 1,2-polymer with an Et$_3$Al/Et$_2$AlCl mole ratio as low as 0.84; at an intermediate ratio of 1.0, the crystallinity of the polymer is higher than with Et$_3$Al alone. At ratios lower than 0.84, cis-1,4 content increases abruptly.

256. Preparation of Syndiotactic 1,2-Polybutadiene (269)*

$$CH_2{=}CH{-}CH{=}CH_2 \longrightarrow$$

A 1 qt., dry, nitrogen-flushed beverage bottle sealed with a rubber septum and cap arrangement for addition of components by syringe provides a convenient reaction vessel. A stainless steel stirred autoclave can be used to advantage, if available.

To the vessel is added, in order, 400 ml. benzene (distilled from calcium hydride or, better, K–Na alloy), 9.72 mg. (7.48 $\times$ 10^{-5} moles) cobalt(II) chloride, and 0.0118 g. (1.49 $\times$ 10^{-4} mole) dry, distilled pyridine. The objective is to form the soluble $CoCl_2 \cdot 2C_5H_5N$ complex, and the vessel should be closed and agitated for 1–2 hr. Then, somewhat more than 40 g. of polymerization grade subsequently allowed to distill out. The vessel is closed and 1.57 g. (1.33 $\times$ 10^{-2} mole) of aluminum triethyl is added. An Al/Co mole ratio anywhere between 0.3 and 600 will produce highly syndiotactic polymer. The polymerization is conducted at 16°C. and the mixture should be at this temperature when the final component is added. If catalyst components are added in benzene solution, the final amount of benzene should be 400 ml. As an alternative to the above, the $CoCl_2 \cdot 2C_5H_5N$ complex can be prepared by mixing 0.2 g. anhydrous $CoCl_2$ and 1.5 ml. dry pyridine in 180 ml. dry benzene under nitrogen and with exclusion of moisture and stirring for 3–4 hr. A solution containing about 0.17–0.18 g./l. of $CoCl_2$ is obtained, the requisite amount of which is used in preparing the polymerization catalyst solution.

After 15 hr., about 50 ml. of methanol is added to terminate the polymerization. The finely divided, white powder, which separates during reaction, is filtered and washed thoroughly in a blender with methanol, then dried at room temperature in vacuum to give about 9 g. of polymer. The polymer should be protected by a nitrogen blanket throughout these operations. If the polymer is successively extracted in a jacketed Soxhlet with boiling acetone, ether, and benzene, about 3% of the crude polymer is removed. The residue is judged to be about 85% crystalline and to be 98% or more of a syndiotactic configuration, as judged by x-ray diffraction and IR, respectively, the latter by a band at 660 cm^{-1}. The polymer should be protected by addition of an antioxidant in the manner shown for previous polybutadiene if it is desired to handle the polymer in air for any operations. T_m for the syndiotactic-1,2 polymer is about 156°C. The insolubility of the polymer makes intrinsic viscosity determination difficult.

Copolymers of butadiene have shown much usefulness in technical applications. Thus important copolymers with styrene and acrylonitrile, have been developed.

* We are grateful to Dr. Ermanno Susa, Montecatini, for his helpful comments on this experiment.

Copolymers of styrene with butadiene were the basis of the synthetic rubbers made in large amounts during World War II. They were prepared using the so-called "Mutual," or "**GR-S**" recipe, which was chosen for its simplicity and reproducibility. The butadiene units in GR-S made at 50°C. are about 60% *trans*-1,4, 20% *cis*-1,4, and 20% 1,2. *Trans*-1,4 content increases at a lower temperature.

257. Preparation of GR-S Rubber (14)

$$CH_2{=}CH{-}CH{=}CH_2 + \phi CH{=}CH_2 \longrightarrow Copolymer$$

Table 4.2 gives a recipe for "Mutual" or "GR-S" rubber in its simplest form.

Table 4.2

Constituent	Quantity, parts
Butadiene	75
Styrene	25
Commercial dodecyl mercaptan	0.5
Potassium persulfate	0.3
Soap flakes	5
Water (freshly boiled)	180

The mixture given in Table 4.2 is polymerized at 50°C. The conversion is approximately 6% per hour, and the polymerization is ordinarily short-stopped after about 75% conversion, that is, after about 12 hr. of polymerization.

Polymerization may be carried out in 4 oz. screw-cap bottles mechanically tumbled end-over-end in a constant temperature bath. Bottles larger than 4 oz. should not be used since the reaction is exothermic and might get out of control if the heat cannot be dissipated rapidly. It should be borne in mind that all traces of air must be kept out of the system. That is, the water used should be boiled to deaerate it, while the reaction vessel should be flushed by allowing a small amount of the butadiene to boil out before capping.

After approximately 12 hr., the polymerization is short-stopped by adding about 0.2 g. hydroquinone and the polymer latex so obtained is poured into a beaker of suitable size, and steam is passed through it to remove unreacted butadiene and styrene. To this stripped latex is now added an antioxidant such as phenyl-β-naphthylamine and the latex is coagulated. This may be done by first adding sodium chloride solution which causes partial coagulation ("creaming") of the mixture. Coagulation is then completed by the addition of dilute sulfuric acid which converts the dispersing salts to the free acids. The product is obtained in the form of crumbs, which are filtered, washed well with water, and dried.

The following polymerization of 2,3-dimethylbutadiene is also done in an emulsion system, using a "peroxamine" catalyst; the latter generally involves a hydroperoxide–polyamine couple, and permits radical formation and initiation at low temperature (10).

258. Preparation of Poly(2,3-dimethylbutadiene) (271)

$$CH_2{=}C{-}C{=}CH_2 \quad \overset{H_3C \quad CH_3}{\underset{}{}} \longrightarrow \quad {\Big[}{+}CH_2{-}C{=}C{-}CH_2{\Big]}{-}$$

A 4 oz. bottle with a perforated screw-cap and a butyl- or nitrile rubber septum (extracted in sodium hydroxide solution) is charged with 36 ml. distilled, deaerated water, 20 g. 2,3-dimethylbutadiene, 1 g. KOSR soap, 0.2 g. potassium chloride (latex viscosity depressant at high conversions), 0.08 g. potassium phosphate, 0.08 g. tetraethylenepentamine, and 0.04 g. diisopropylbenzenemonohydroperoxide. The bottle is flushed with nitrogen, capped, and tumbled in a bath at 15°C. The conversion rate is about 15%/hr. After 2 hr., a booster charge of initiator (monoperoxide and tetramine) is added to prevent dying out of the rate. After 4 hr., the conversion is about 60%, and the polymer can be coagulated with a salt solution, washed with isopropanol containing some phenyl-β-naphthylamine, and dried at 50°C. in a vacuum oven under nitrogen. The intrinsic viscosity in benzene (25°C.) is at least 0.7, corresponding to a number average molecular weight of around 70,000. The polymer contains about 13% 1,2-enchainment, the remainder being an undetermined mixture of *cis*- and *trans*-1,4.

The monomer for this experiment can be obtained commercially (Borden Co., Monomer-Polymer Div.), and fractionally distilled; the portion with b.p. 68.5–69.0°C./760 mm. is used. The tetramine (Union Carbide) is distilled at reduced pressure and a heart cut used. The peroxide is available from Hercules Chemical Co. as about 60% active; the amount specified above is for 100% active peroxide. KOSR soap flakes are a potassium salt of mixed fatty acids (stearic, palmitic, oleic) from the Office of Synthetic Rubber.

Copolymers of butadiene and acrylonitrile achieved considerable importance in Germany as the oil resistant Buna-N, and later in the United States under a variety of names. The following procedure is typical.

259. Preparation of Nitrile Rubber (10)

$$CH_2{=}CHCN + CH_2{=}CH{-}CH{=}CH_2 \longrightarrow Copolymer$$

A recipe very similar to the GR-S recipe for styrene butadiene is quite satisfactory for the preparation of a nitrile rubber. The following ingredients (Table 4.3) are handled essentially in the manner described in Preparation 257.

The mixture given in Table 4.3 may be polymerized in capped bottles such as described in the previous preparations. The solutions are made up in the following manner. The soap and stearic acid are dissolved in about 50 parts of water at 50°C. The sodium pyrophosphate, potassium chloride, and ferric sulfate are dissolved in about 5 parts of water. The excess water is first placed in the reactor followed by the soap solution, the ferric pyrophosphate solution, the acrylonitrile, the mercaptan, the butadiene, and finally, the hydrogen

Table 4.3

Constituent	Quantity, grams
Butadiene	75
Acrylonitrile	25
Soap flakes	4.5
Stearic acid	0.6
tert-Dodecyl mercaptan	0.5
Potassium chloride	0.3
Sodium pyrophosphate	0.1
Ferric sulfate (anhydrous basis)	0.02
Hydrogen peroxide (20% solution) (anhydrous basis)	0.35
Water (freshly distilled)	180

peroxide. The reactor is sealed and maintained with mild agitation at a temperature of 30°C. About 90% conversion is obtained in 24 hr. As in the previous preparations, the latex is discharged, steamed to boil off excess monomer, and stabilized by adding 2 parts of phenyl-β-naphthylamine antioxidant. The latex is coagulated by the addition of 0.5 parts of sodium alkyl benzene sulfonate, followed by 40 parts of saturated sodium chloride solution. The mixture is then acidified with 0.25% sulfuric acid to a pH of about 3, with vigorous stirring. The basicity is returned to pH 11 with 5% sodium hydroxide, the rubber filtered, washed repeatedly with water, and dried at 60°C. It may be pressed into sheets by passing through a rubber mill.

The relative proportion of acrylonitrile is important in determining the properties of the resulting nitrile rubber. At 5% or below, the polymer will swell badly in the presence of oil. At 15% acrylonitrile, the resistance to oil is fair, at 25% it is fairly good, while at 35–40% the resistance to oil is very high. At the same time, however, the low temperature flexibility becomes poorer (i.e., T_g is increased). If the per cent of acrylonitrile is increased to 50–60%, the nature of the polymer will change. It is no longer the rubber-like material; it becomes a leathery plastic which has very high resistance to aromatics. As the percentage of acrylonitrile is increased beyond the 60% range, the properties approach those of pure polyacrylonitrile.

Sulfur dioxide adds to polybutadiene, polyisoprene; and natural rubber to give an insoluble, more or less intractable, polymer of high sulfur content. Presumably the reaction involves a radical initiated addition of SO_2 to the double bonds with the formation of 5 or 6 membered sulfone rings along the chain. The amount of SO_2 addition depends on the type of polymer used. 1,2-Vinyl structures which interrupt the sequence of butene units interfere with SO_2 addition. Emulsion polybutadienes which always possess 1,2-vinyl content in excess of 15% are less satisfactory for the reaction than all cis or all trans polymers prepared with coordination type catalysts.

260. Preparation of Polysulfones by the Interaction of SO_2 and Polybutadiene (272,273)

$$+CH_2-CH=CH-CH_2\xrightarrow{}_n + SO_2 \longrightarrow \left(\begin{array}{c} H_2C-\!\!\!-\!\!\!-CH_2 \\ | \quad\quad | \\ -CH \quad\quad CH- \\ \diagdown \quad \diagup \\ SO_2 \end{array} \right)_n$$

Eight g. of polybutadiene is cut into small pieces and dissolved in 50 ml. of toluene with the aid of an air-powered or spark-proof stirrer in a 400 ml. tall form beaker. When solution is complete it is diluted with an additional 50 ml. of toluene containing 1.0 ml. tertiary butyl hydroperoxide. To the solution is quickly added 50 ml. of a saturated solution of sulfur dioxide in absolute alcohol. Immediately after addition of the SO_2 solution, stirring is stopped; the reaction has set up to a semisolid mass. The contents of the beaker is mixed with 500 ml. of water and heated on a steam bath in a well ventilated hood to drive off organic solvents and excess SO_2. The remaining polymer–water slurry is neutralized with sodium bicarbonate and the polymer is filtered and washed thoroughly with water. After drying at 60°C. in a vacuum oven a white insoluble powder is obtained which has a sulfur content of approximately 20–22%.

Instead of powdered polymer, shaped articles can be prepared. For example, tough films can be made by casting the catalyzed polybutadiene solution on a glass plate with the aid of a doctor knife. Immediately after casting, the plate containing the film is placed in a box filled with SO_2 gas. After remaining in the SO_2 atmosphere for one minute the glass plate containing the film is removed. The film is stripped from the plate, neutralized in dilute sodium bicarbonate solution, and boiled in water. Strips of this film can be drawn in boiling water about two times, and are tough, and very stiff.

The alternating copolymerization of olefins and SO_2 is well known, and an example will be found earlier in this chapter. Conjugated diolefins react with SO_2 to give cyclic structures, while conjugated diene polymers give a heterocyclic structure (see previous example). An unusual reaction of a nonconjugated cyclic diolefin with SO_2 has recently been described by Frazer and O'Neill: One mole of cyclooctadiene copolymerizes with two moles of SO_2 to give a polymer with an —SO_2—link between the hydrocarbon rings, and another—SO_2—group bridging the ring.

261. Preparation of Copolymer of *cis,cis*-1,5-Cyclooctadiene and Sulfur Dioxide (274)

In a round-bottom flask equipped with a thermometer, a magnetic stirrer and a Dry Ice-cooled reflux condenser are placed 10.8 g. (0.1 mole) of 1,5-cyclooctadiene, b.p. 67–69/46–49 mm. and 150 ml. of redistilled tetramethylene sulfone. The flask is cooled to −70°C. in Dry Ice–acetone and 16.0 g.

$$
\begin{array}{c}
\text{H}_2\text{C}\underline{\hspace{1em}}\text{CH}_2 \\
\mid \qquad \mid \\
\text{HC} \qquad \text{CH} \\
\diagdown \qquad \diagdown \\
\text{HC} \qquad \text{CH} \\
\mid \qquad \mid \\
\text{H}_2\text{C}\underline{\hspace{1em}}\text{CH}_2
\end{array}
+ 2\text{SO}_2
\xrightarrow[\text{Catalyst}]{\text{Peroxide}}
\left[
\begin{array}{c}
\text{H}_2\text{C}\underline{\hspace{1em}}\text{CH}_2 \\
\mid \qquad \mid \\
\text{CH} \qquad \text{CH}\underline{\hspace{0.5em}}\text{SO}_2 \\
\diagdown \qquad \diagup \\
\text{HC} \qquad \text{CH}\underline{\hspace{0.5em}}\text{SO}_2\underline{\hspace{0.5em}} \\
\mid \qquad \mid \\
\text{H}_2\text{C}\underline{\hspace{1em}}\text{CH}_2
\end{array}
\right]_m
$$

(0.25 mole) of liquid sulfur dioxide is added. To the mixture at $-70°$C. are added 5 drops of ascaridole and 5 drops of concentrated hydrochloric acid. Note that ascaridole is much more effective than other catalysts.

The Dry Ice bath is removed and the reaction is permitted to proceed with stirring for a period of 16 hr. at a temperature of 25°C. The solution is poured into 150–200 ml. of stirred methanol in a Waring Blendor under a hood. The precipitated polymer is filtered through a Büchner funnel and returned twice to the Blendor with similar amounts of methanol.

The polymer is dried overnight in a vacuum oven with a nitrogen purge at 90°C. and 21 g. (89%) of white amorphous powder is obtained with η_{inh} of about 2.0 m-dimethyl sulfoxide and containing the theoretical amount of sulfur. The polymer does not melt but decomposes with gas evolution at temperatures over 250°C.

Like butadiene, **isoprene** may be polymerized by a variety of techniques. High molecular weight polyisoprene has been obtained in a typical emulsion polymerization at 50°C., with metallic sodium, and with organometallic catalysts similar to those described for polymerization of butadiene. Since natural rubber is a polyisoprene, it is not surprising that chemists have directed their attention to the synthesis of polyisoprene of the same chemical configuration as the natural product. The two principal types of naturally occurring polyisoprene are hevea, which is about 97.8% cis-1,4 and 2.2% of 3,4-polyisoprene, and balata, which is about 98.7% trans-1,4 and about 1.3% 3,4-polyisoprene. The synthetic polyisoprenes made in an emulsion system have approximately 12–14% of 1,2 product, while those made with sodium have between 50 and 55% 1,2 addition, the remainder being mainly trans-1,4 addition product, with some cis. It has been found that polymerization of isoprene with organotitanium compounds, with lithium alkyls, or with lithium aluminum alkyls produces a polyisoprene which is essentially identical to the cis-1,4-polyisoprene of Hevea rubber. Furthermore, although metallic sodium in a finely divided condition gives a product containing very large percentages of 1,2 addition, it has been found that finely divided lithium metal will give essentially the same results as the organometallic derivatives. The following preparations are typical of the polymerization of isoprene with this type of catalyst. In all these polymerizations it must be recognized that success depends on a number of factors, the most important of which is purity of the monomer and absence of contaminants such as moisture or air in the system.

262. Preparation of the Catalysts

The organotitanium type catalyst is prepared as described in the previous section on coordination catalysis (Section VIII). The butyllithium may be purchased as a commercial product dissolved in pentane, or synthesized. Finely divided metallic lithium may also be obtained commercially and is much more satisfactory than any product which may be made in the laboratory with ordinary equipment.

263. Polymerization of Isoprene with n-Butyllithium (275,276)

$$CH_2{=}CH{-}\overset{\overset{\textstyle CH_3}{|}}{C}{=}CH_2 \longrightarrow (C_5H_8)_n$$

The butyllithium solution is standardized by hydrolysis and titration of lithium hydroxide with standard acid. The concentration is adjusted with n-pentane to 1.0 molar. The polymerization is carried out very simply by adding 84 ml. of pure isoprene, 180 ml. of petroleum ether, or n-pentane, and 3.0 ml. of the butyllithium solution to a round-bottom flask which should be dried thoroughly and flushed with an inert gas, preferably helium or argon. All transfers should be made under absolutely anaerobic and anhydrous conditions. The flask is stoppered and placed in a water bath at 30°C. Polymerization time is approximately 18 hr. At the end of this period, the flask is removed from the water bath and the contents poured into methanol which contains about 3% based on weight of polymer of an antioxidant such as phenyl-β-naphthylamine. The polymer is coagulated, filtered, washed thoroughly with methyl alcohol, and dried in a vacuum at 50°C. Polymer made in this way is approximately 77.4% cis-1,4, 13.0% trans-1,4, and about 9.5% 3,4.

264. Polymerization of Isoprene over Finely Divided Lithium (277)

$$CH_2{=}CH{-}\overset{\overset{\textstyle CH_3}{|}}{C}{=}CH_2 \longrightarrow (C_5H_8)_n$$

Polymerization of isoprene over finely divided lithium is most conveniently carried out in the laboratory according to the following technique. To purify isoprene, it is refluxed over metallic sodium for 4 hr., then distilled, passed through a silica column, and used immediately. It is kept out of contact with air or moisture. The silica column should be freed of air before use by passing a stream of oxygen-free helium through the column. Absolutely dry glass bottles sealed with aluminum-lined crown caps are charged with 100 ml. of isoprene. To the isoprene contained in the crown-capped bottles is added 0.1 g. of lithium as a 35% dispersion in vaseline or petroleum oil. The cap is placed on the bottle loosely and the bottle and contents are brought to a vigorous boil. Approximately 10% of the total isoprene is allowed to boil out in order to completely free the reaction vessel of traces of oxygen and moisture. The bottle is now rapidly sealed and placed in a constant temperature bath at 30–40°C. It is allowed to remain at this temperature either agitated or unagitated until the content have been converted to a solid chunk of polymer. This may require 30 min. to 3 days, depending on the purity of the ingredients. The unagitated polymerization is somewhat slower. However, it is also safer, since polymerization is exothermic and may become dangerous if not properly controlled.

When polymerization is deemed to be complete, the cooled bottle is broken and the solid chunk of polymer is removed and soaked in isopropanol containing a trace of acetic acid to remove the catalyst and a small amount of a suitable antioxidant such as phenyl-β-naphthylamine. Infrared examination of the polymer should indicate that it is of the order of 98% cis-1,4 structure, the remainder being 3,4. The product may be milled and compounded exactly as is natural rubber.

265. Polymerization of Isoprene over a Titanium-Based Catalyst (278–280)

$$CH_2{=}CH{-}\overset{\overset{\displaystyle CH_3}{\displaystyle |}}{C}{=}CH_2 \longrightarrow (C_5H_8)_n$$

Petroleum ether is purified by treating with concentrated sulfuric acid until no further discoloration is observed. It is then washed with water, dried by passing through an alumina column, and distilled from metallic sodium. The isoprene is distilled, then refluxed immediately prior to use with sodium, and passed through a silica column as described in the previous preparation. The catalyst is prepared by mixing equimolar quantities of triisobutyl aluminum and titanium tetrachloride. In view of the hazardous nature of triisobutyl aluminum, all possible care must be taken in handling this material and the experimenter should be completely familiar with all the safety hazards inherent in triisobutyl aluminum. If desired, lithium aluminum tetraalkyls may be used advantageously in place of the triioisobutyl aluminum (279). It is convenient to prepare a 1 molar solution of either alkyl compound in anhydrous, olefin-free heptane to be used as needed. All monomers, solvents, and catalyst components are kept absolutely free of moisture and air and are stored in an inert atmosphere. The bottles are conveniently capped with a self-sealing stopper of the type used on serum bottles (see Chapter 2). A measured amount may be removed by use of a hypodermic syringe.

A mixture of 75 ml. of petroleum ether and 25 ml. of isoprene is placed in a beverage bottle and heated to vigorous boiling in a hot water bath. A quantity of petroleum ether is distilled from the bottle sufficiently to ensure the absence of all moisture and air from the polymerization vessel. Two ml. of the 1 molar triisobutyl aluminum is now added under inert atmosphere, and the bottles are stoppered with a serum-type rubber stopper through which can be inserted a hypodermic syringe. Bottles containing the monomer plus alkyl aluminum are cooled to the desired polymerization temperature and an amount of titanium tetrachloride equivalent in moles to the aluminum alkyl used is added from a hypodermic syringe. The titanium tetrachloride may be added either as undiluted catalyst or as a premixed 1 molar solution in heptane. Polymerization is quite rapid and the mixture of catalyst and monomer rapidly becomes sufficiently viscous to disperse the catalyst particles making stirring unnecessary. However, stirring or shaking during the first part of the polymerization cycle is recommended.

Polymerization is allowed to proceed for approximately 24 hr. when the polymer is isolated and soaked in alcohol for 24 hr. to destroy the catalyst components. It is then mixed with an antioxidant, milled, or otherwise treated as in previous experiments.

In order to obtain polymer with a low gel content in high yield with a high inherent viscosity, it is necessary to have the molar ratio of trialkylaluminum to titanium tetrachloride at about 1:1. It may be desirable to have a very slight excess of alkylaluminum since this appears to minimize the production of gel.

The temperature at which the polymerization is run is also important in determining the molecular weight of the resulting polymer and, to a lesser extent, the micro-structure of the polymer. Temperatures between 5 and 25°C. appear to be most suitable for this purpose. Above about 25°C. the molecular weights obtained are too low to be useful. Polymer prepared at 25°C. is approximately 96% cis-1,4 and 4% 3,4 polyisoprene. No trans-1,4 structure is observed if the polymer is made according to the instructions previously given.

2,3-Dimethylbutadiene gives a polymer by free radical initiation having about 13% 1,2-addition and the remainder an undetermined mixture of cis- and trans-1,4 (see Preparation 258). However, with an Al/Ti catalyst similar to that in the previous example, an essentially cis-1,4-polymer is produced as a crystalline powder with T_m of about 189°C. (281). Conditions are: i-Bu$_3$Al/TiCl$_4$ mole ratio 1:1; 0.06 mole of total catalyst/mole of monomer; monomer/solvent (benzene) of 1/6; temperature, 25°C.; time, 72 hr.; conversion, about 25°C.; inherent viscosity, about 0.7 (0.2 g./100 ml., tetralin at 100°C., with antioxidant).

Aluminum trialkyls and vanadium tri- and tetrachlorides are capable of converting isoprene and butadiene to trans-1,4 polymers. It has been reported that VCl$_4$ is more efficient than VCl$_3$ in converting butadiene to the trans polymer (282); but the reverse appears to be true for the preparation of trans-1,4-polyisoprene (283). This is another example of monomer–catalyst variation which affects the overall effectiveness of catalysis (efficiency defined as g. polymer/g. catalyst component) rather than altering the structural features of the polymer.

In the following example, the efficiency of VCl$_3$ for isoprene polymerization is enhanced further by supporting it on an inert carrier such as titanium dioxide, kaolite, or magnesium oxide. Mixed Ti/V halides have also been used to prepare the trans-1,4 polymer (266).

trans-1,4-Polyisoprene is a natural polymer bearing the common name of balata or gutta-percha, a tough, crystalline thermoplastic finding use in golf ball covers (284). Its laboratory synthesis is as remarkable, though not so commercially significant, as that of its cis counterpart, remarked previously.

266. Preparation of *trans*-1,4-Polyisoprene (283)

All operations should be carried out with equipment that has been baked dry (120°C.) and cooled under nitrogen. Handling and transfers of catalyst components should be done in a dry and oxygen-free atmosphere.

A sample of kaolin (Continental Clay, R. T. Vanderbilt Co., about 10 m^2/g. surface area) is thoroughly dried by heating at 125°C. for 15 hr. After cooling under nitrogen, 8.0 g. is added to 70 ml. benzene, which has been dried over sodium or Linde 4A Molecular Sieves, in a 250 ml., three-necked flask with stirrer, condenser, and inert gas inlet. Then, 1.5 ml. vanadium tetrachloride (2.72 g.) is added, conveniently as a solution in 10–15 ml. dry benzene. The mixture is refluxed for 3 hr. with stirring, care being taken to blanket the reaction with nitrogen throughout, including mixing, cooling, and workup. The tetrachloride decomposes smoothly to the trichloride and chlorine, the former depositing on the surface of the kaolin. Vanadium trichloride is formed in 80–90% yield, and amounts to about 18–19 % of the carrier. The solid is filtered in a dry box, washed well with dry benzene, and dried at 1 mm. in a vacuum oven under nitrogen for 24 hr.

To a 1 qt. beverage bottle flushed with nitrogen is added 300 ml. dry benzene, 0.78 g. of the VCl$_3$-on-kaolin (containing about 0.14 g. VCl$_3$, 0.98 mmole), 0.2 ml. tetra-2-ethylbutyl titanate (0.44 mmole) in 10 ml. dry benzene, 2.3 ml. aluminum triisobutyl (8.9 mmoles) in 10 ml. dry benzene, and 200 g. (300 ml.) polymerization grade isoprene which has been distilled from sodium and stored under nitrogen, is quickly added. The mixture is heated at 50°C. for 6 hr. with agitation. An equivalent amount of tetraisopropyl titanate may be used, it should be mentioned, in place of the 2-ethylbutyl titanate ester described.

The mixture is cooled and poured into 2 l. of methanol containing 3 g. of an antioxidant such as 2,6-di-*t*-butyl-4-methylphenol. The polymer is filtered, washed repeatedly with methanol and antioxidant, and dried at 40°C. in a vacuum oven under a nitrogen stream. About 90 g. of *trans*-1,4-polyisoprene having a dilatometric melting point of 56 and 62°C., representing the phase changes of two crystalline modifications.

The resulting polymer has some gel content, preventing full solubility and thus solution viscosity determination. If it is milled for only a few minutes at 240°C., it is rendered completely soluble in benzene and will have an intrinsic viscosity of three or more at 30°C. In this respect, it is much higher in molecular weight than natural balata (intrinsic viscosity, 1.0 or less).

267. Preparation of 3,4-Polyisoprene (270)

In a suitable stirred flask or beverage bottle, taking customary precautions to exclude air and moisture, is placed 100 ml. toluene (distilled from calcium hydride or, better, sodium hydride), 1.25 g. (10.92 mmoles) aluminum triethyl,

$$CH_2\!=\!\underset{\underset{CH_3}{|}}{C}\!-\!CH\!=\!CH_2 \longrightarrow \underset{\underset{\underset{CH_2}{\|}}{\overset{|}{C\!-\!CH_3}}}{(CH_2\!-\!CH)}$$

and 0.50 ml. (0.517 g., 1.82 mmoles) tetra-*n*-propyl titanate (distilled before use). The catalyst is aged 12 min. at 18°C. An Al/Ti mole ratio of 6 gives a maximum conversion. Then, 30 ml. polymerization grade isoprene is added. Polymerization is continued with stirring or agitation for 8 hr. at 24°C. The polymer is poured into excess methanol and washed thoroughly with methanol in a blender, then dried at room temperature under nitrogen. An antioxidant such as phenyl-β-naphthylamine is added to the polymer via the last methanol wash. About 10 g. of added polymer is obtained which cannot be crystallized. Infrared indicates that the polymer is around 95% 3,4-; the remainder is *cis*-1,4. If the polymerization is carried out at -10°C., the product is about 99%, 3,4- and is completely amorphous. The failure to crystallize despite the high 3,4- content is believed to mean that the polymer is nonstereoregular (i.e., is atactic at the unsymmetrical carbon of each chemical repeat unit). The intrinsic viscosity is about 2.5 dl./g. in toluene at 25°C.

All the uses for polyisobutylene itself are somewhat limited by the fact that it is, even at high molecular weight, a relatively soft, plastic material. It was found by workers at Standard Oil (New Jersey) that **copolymerization of** a small amount of **a diene with isobutylene** gives a product which can be crosslinked (vulcanized) to a very useful product known as **butyl rubber** and used extensively in tires and inner tubes.

268. Preparation of an Isobutylene–Isoprene Copolymer by Cationic Catalysis (285,286).

$$CH_2\!=\!CH\!-\!\underset{\underset{CH_3}{|}}{C}\!=\!CH_2 + CH_2\!=\!C\overset{\diagup CH_3}{\diagdown CH_3} \longrightarrow Copolymer$$

Pure isobutylene (100 ml.) and 1.5 ml. of pure isoprene are placed in a 1 l., three-necked flask equipped with a mechanical stirrer, a gas inlet tube, and a Dry Ice condenser. Approximately 300 ml. of methyl chloride is now added from a cylinder and the mixture is cooled to about -100°C. by means of a sludge of alcohol in liquid nitrogen. The solution of isobutylene and isoprene is stirred gently and successive 1 ml. portions of a solution of 0.2 g. of anhydrous aluminum chloride in 40 ml. of methyl chloride are added. As each portion is poured into the solution, an insoluble mass of copolymer is produced which floats in the cold solution. Catalyst may be added until conversion of the isobutylene–isoprene to copolymer is about 50%. Higher conversions give improper monomer balance to the copolymer because of the different reactivity of the monomers. The polymerization mixture is quenched by the addition of a small amount of isopropyl alcohol previously cooled to -100°C.

and the mixture is then allowed to warm to room temperature. The lumps of rubbery copolymer are removed, washed with alcohol, dried in a vacuum oven, and converted to sheet products by conventional techniques.

Certain highly substituted butadienes, e.g., 2,5-dimethyl-2,4-hexadine (1,1,4,4-tetramethylbutadiene) polymerize like isobutylene, i.e., at low temperature with Lewis acids. The product is completely 1,4-*trans*.

269. Preparation of Cationic Polymerization of Tetramethylbutadiene(2,5-dimethyl-2,4-Hexadiene) (287)

$$
\begin{array}{c}
CH_3 \\
\diagdown \\
C=CH-CH=C \\
\diagup \\
CH_3
\end{array}
\quad
\begin{array}{c}
CH_3 \\
\diagup \\
\diagdown \\
CH_3
\end{array}
\quad
\xrightarrow[\text{BF}_3]{-80^\circ \text{C.}}
\quad
\left[
\begin{array}{c}
CH_3 \\
| \\
-C-CH=CH-C- \\
| \\
CH_3
\end{array}
\quad
\begin{array}{c}
CH_3 \\
| \\
\\
| \\
CH_3
\end{array}
\right]_n
$$

2,5-Dimethyl-2,4-hexadiene (Benzol Products Company, 237 South Street, Newark, N.J.) is best purified by bulk recrystallization, followed by distillation. The monomer melts at 14°C., and boils at 133°C. (760 mm.). A sample with $n_D^{23°C.}$ 1.4760 and purity by gas chromatography of 99.4% should be used. Polymerization proceeds readily at temperatures well below 0°C. with cationic initiators such as boron trifluoride and antimony pentafluoride. Hydrocarbons and halogenated hydrocarbons are useful solvents for polymerization.

In a typical polymerization, 750 ml. of dry petroleum ether in a 2 l., four-necked, round-bottom flask fitted with a thermometer, stirrer, dropping funnel, drying tube, and gas inlet is cooled to −70°C. in a solid carbon dioxide-cooled bath. A gentle stream of BF_3 is introduced for a few seconds, until a slight excess escapes through the drying tube. A solution of 75 g. of the diene in 75 ml. of petroleum ether is added to the stirred solution over a period of about 4 min. The temperature increases spontaneously to −50°C. and the reaction mixture turns to a yellow slush. The addition of 100 ml. of denatured alcohol followed by 500 ml. of acetone yields 54 g. (72%) of a white, filterable, finely divided solid product. The inherent viscosity should be about 1.4 (0.5 g./100 ml. of decahydronaphthalene at 130°C.).

The polymer is soluble in high boiling solvents such as decahydronaphthalene, xylene, and chlorobenzene, but only at temperatures above about 120°C. Ten to twenty per cent solutions are obtainable above this temperature, but the polymer precipitates below this temperature. The crystalline melting point is 263–265°C., as measured on the hot stage microscope by the disappearance of birefringence in polarized light. The polymer depolymerized rapidly to monomer on heating above its melting point, and at appreciable rates in solution at lower temperatures. X-ray diffraction shows that the polymer possesses very high crystallinity. X-ray diagrams show less than 10% amorphous scatter.

Because of the very high crystallinity, only brittle films can be obtained by conventional solution-casting or melt-pressing methods. However, tough films can be made by polymerizing the monomer in thin films. The inside wall of a test tube or flask is coated at room temperature with monomer, with or without solvent, and exposed briefly under anhydrous conditions to gaseous

BF$_3$, after cooling in a bath to $-78°C$. Tough, orientable, transparent film forms rapidly, which is identical to the above-described polymer in x-ray spacings, IR absorption spectrum, and crystalline melting point.

Chloroprene (CH$_2$=C—CH=CH$_2$) with a Cl substituent on the central carbon, is a monomer which duplicates in many ways the over-all geometry of isoprene; however, the polymer differs in many respects. This monomer is the basis for the neoprenes which have been successfully commercialized by the du Pont Co. in a variety of forms.

Chloroprene is synthesized by addition of hydrogen chloride to monovinyl acetylene. The vinyl acetylene is prepared by dimerization of acetylene, **an operation which is not recommended for anyone not familiar with the hazards of acetylene chemistry,** or by the dehydrohalogenation of 1,4-dichloro-2-butene (288). Chloroprene itself is relatively stable, and may be obtained commercially as a 50% solution in toluene. When pure, it will polymerize spontaneously in about 10 days to a high molecular weight, clear, tough product, the so-called "μ" polymer described by Carothers and co-workers (288a). Polychloroprene shows a structural dependence on polymerization temperature. The typical product (289) is composed mainly of *trans*- and *cis*-1,4 units, with the latter not in excess of 20%. There are about 10–15% of the 1,4-units present in head-to-head, tail-to-tail enchainment along with the dominant head-to-tail structure. Essentially pure *trans*-1,4 polymer results from free radical polymerization at $-30°C$. The *cis*-1,4 polymer has been prepared by polymerization of 2-(tributyltin)-1,3-butadiene followed by chlorinolysis of the substituent (290).

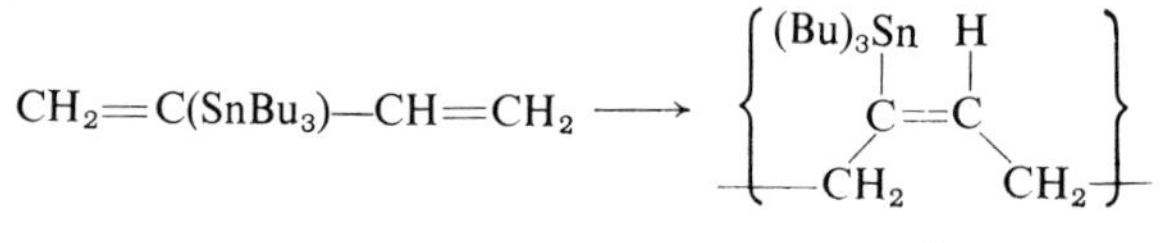

$$CH_2=C(SnBu_3)-CH=CH_2 \longrightarrow \left\{ \begin{array}{c} (Bu)_3Sn \quad H \\ | \qquad | \\ C=C \\ / \qquad \backslash \\ -CH_2 \qquad CH_2- \end{array} \right\}$$

I

Never try to polymerize chloroprene with an organotitanium catalyst; a violent explosion may result.

270. Polymerization of Chloroprene in an Emulsion (291)

$$CH_2=CH-\underset{\underset{Cl}{|}}{C}=CH_2 \longrightarrow [-CH_2-CH=\underset{\underset{Cl}{|}}{C}-CH_2-]_n$$

Emulsion polymerization of chloroprene may be carried out satisfactorily according to the following procedure. One hundred g. of freshly distilled chloroprene is emulsified in 150 ml. of water containing 4 g. of wood resin,

0.6 g. of sulfur, 0.8 g. of sodium hydroxide, 0.5 g. of potassium persulfate and 0.7 g. of the sodium salts of naphthalene sulfonic acid–formaldehyde condensation product, or other emulsifier. The progress of the polymerization is followed by means of specific gravity changes (292). The density of the emulsion increases with time and polymerization may be considered complete when the specific gravity is between 1.068 and 1.070. The polymer now may be precipitated by acidification with 2 ml. of dilute acetic acid or the emulsion may be allowed to age in the presence of tetraethylthiuram disulfide. During this ageing period, the polymer properties will improve to a more desirable level as a result of the action of the disulfide or sulfur linkages in the polymer (293) yielding a more soluble, plastic product. The coagulated polymer prepared by either method is filtered, washed thoroughly with water, and air dried at 120°C. The polymer is then compounded for the specific purpose for which it is desired.

An interesting halogenated diene polymer which is a hard, tough, material and not an elastomer, is prepared by persulfate initiated polymerization of **2,3-dichlorobutadiene.** This polymer may be made by the methods described by Kuhn who has defined specialized conditions claimed to be necessary to produce a polymer which can be molded and shaped.

271. Preparation of 1,2,3,4-Tetrachlorobutane (294)

$$CH_2{=}CH{-}CH{=}CH_2 + 2Cl_2 \longrightarrow CH_2ClCHClCHClCH_2Cl$$

In a 2 l., three-necked flask equipped with a stirrer, a gas inlet tube, and a condenser is placed 600 ml. of chloroform. Butadiene (54 g.) and chlorine (140 g.) are passed into the chloroform from cylinders over a period of 45 min. The reaction vessel is maintained at a low temperature by means of an ice–salt bath. When all of the chlorine and butadiene is introduced, the resulting solution is fractionally distilled at atmospheric pressure. The fraction coming over between 209 and 220°C. is taken as 1,2,3,4-tetrachlorobutane of sufficient purity for the next stage.

272. Preparation of 2,3-Dichlorobutadiene-1,3 (294)

$$ClCH_2CHClCHClCH_2Cl \xrightarrow{\text{KOH}} {=}CClCCl{=}CH_2$$

Ninety-four g. of tetrachlorobutane prepared as above is dissolved in 32 g. of methanol. This mixture is introduced with agitation into 219 g. of 27% potassium hydroxide in methanol. This addition is carried out with the temperature being maintained at 10–15°C. throughout. Approximately 1 hr. should be required. The temperature is now allowed to rise to 25°C. and stirring is continued for an additional 2 hr. The reaction mass is then filtered and the filtrate is poured into 4 l. of distilled water. A lemon-colored oil separates which is removed and dried over calcium chloride, best in the presence of an inhibitor such as hydroquinone. When dried, the product is distilled at a pressure of approximately 80 mm., the product boiling in the range of 45–50°C. The monomer polymerizes very readily and should not be stored for any length of time. It should be used directly in one of the following recipes, after an additional distillation.

273. Polymerization of 2,3-Dichlorobutadiene (294)

$$CH_2=CClCCl=CH_2 \longrightarrow [-CH_2CCl=CCl-CH_2-]_n$$

A mixture of 330 ml. of freshly boiled distilled water, 100 g. of dichloro-butadiene, 1 g. of alkyl sodium sulfonate detergent, 0.02 g. of potassium per-sulfate, and 0.02 g. of thiophenol is sealed in a bottle under anaerobic conditions and agitated at 30–40°C. for 24–48 hr. The resulting polymer latex is coagulated by the addition of methyl alcohol and the precipitate is filtered, washed with water, and dried. This polymer should have an inherent viscosity of approximately 1.0 measured on a 0.5% solution in o-dichlorobenzene at 110°C. The polymer can be extruded at temperatures of the order of 200–250°C. into filaments or may be pressed to clear, tough film. Both film and fibers can be stretched and oriented; the resulting products have a high crystallinity.

Polymerization of 1,3-pentadiene to give 1,4 enchainment brings another structural element into consideration beyond that found in dienes such as butadiene and isoprene. It is possible for isotactic, syndiotactic, and atactic cis-1,4 and $trans$-1,4 polymers to be formed from 1,3-pentadiene and, in fact, three of these stereoregular polymers have been isolated: $trans$-1,4-isotactic (295), cis-1,4-isotactic (296,297), and cis-1,4-syndiotactic (298). In addition, 1,2-syndiotactic has also been prepared (299).

274. Preparation of Predominantly cis-1,4-Syndiotactic Poly-1,3-Pentadiene (300)

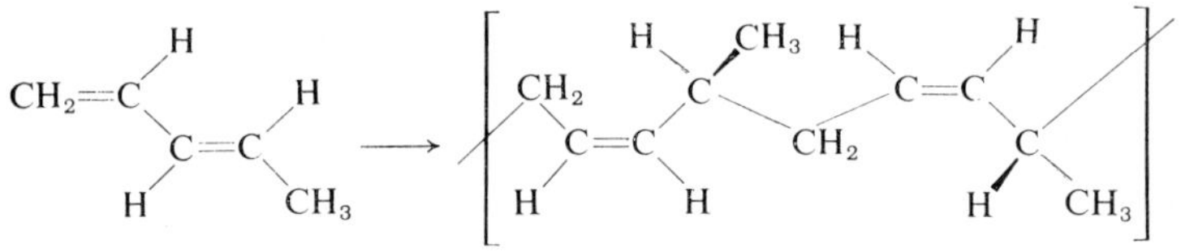

1,3-Pentadiene has been available from Houdry Process Corp. as a crude mixture which includes cyclopentene, cyclopentadiene, and isoprene. The $trans$ isomer has been obtained from this by making the cyclic sulfone and decomposing it after isolation and purification (297,301,302). Purity of 98–99% $trans$-1,3 can be achieved. cis-1,3 was gotten from the crude mixture in 99% purity by preparative gas chromatography. 1,3-Pentadiene isomer mixture with some 1,4-pentadiene has been prepared by pyrolysis of 2,4-diacetoxypentane (302); the sulfone method is well suited to isolation of the $trans$ isomer.

Only the $trans$ isomer of 1,3-pentadiene is polymerized by the catalyst of this example. The cis isomer is evidently unaffected when a mixture of cis and $trans$ is used; the former has little influence on the stereoregularity of the polymer when present in less than 30% of the total monomer.

Solvent and monomer are purified by distillation from calcium hydride or, better, from Na–K alloy, and are stored under nitrogen. The small quantities of catalyst components should be added as benzene solutions. The total amount of benzene added as solvent and for catalyst solutions should be 350 ml. Glassware is baked at 110°C. and cooled in a stream of nitrogen. A beverage bottle closed with rubber septum and cap with holes for syringe admission is convenient for this polymerization. Because the monomer is a liquid at room temperature, a flask method is also applicable, as described.

To a 500 ml. round-bottom flask equipped with stirrer, condenser, and drying tube, nitrogen inlet, and serum cap, is charged, in order, 350 ml. benzene (total, as noted above) 1.31×10^{-2} g. $(5.1 \times 10^{-5}$ mole) cobalt diacetylacetonate, 2.14 g. $(2.55 \times 10^{-2}$ mole) dry, distilled thiophene, 3.18 g. $(2.55 \times 10^{-2}$ mole) ethyl aluminum dichloride, and finally, after a few minutes, 28 g. of *trans*-1,3-pentadiene (99%; if an isomer mixture is used, the amount added should contain 28 g. of *trans* isomer). The Al/Co mole ratio is 500, and that for thiophene/Al is 1. The thiophene modifies the inclination toward cationic polymerization inherent in EtAlCl$_2$. Similar results can be achieved by using pyridine in a mole ratio of 1.88 to aluminum. The temperature is maintained at 20°C. and the mixture is stirred for 24 hr. A slight head of nitrogen is maintained through component addition and polymerization. Because the monomer boils at 42°C., some loss through the condenser may occur if nitrogen is swept over the system too vigorously.

The polymer can be precipitated in its entirety by pouring the polymerization mixture into a large excess of methanol containing some HCl; the crude polymer is washed repeatedly with methanol and dried at room temperature under nitrogen in vacuum. (The last methanol wash should contain about 0.5% of phenyl-β-naphthylamine, and the polymer should be wet with residual methanol before drying.) However, handling of the polymer should be under nitrogen as far as possible to avoid the possibility of oxidation. About 20 g. of polymer is obtained which, by IR analysis, is about 77% *cis*-1,4 and 23% *trans*-1,4. By redissolving in benzene and precipitating into methyl ethyl ketone, the insoluble fraction can be brought to about 84/16 *cis/trans*-1,4. The intrinsic viscosity is about 2.5 (toluene, 30°C.), and this fraction is crystalline by x-ray diffraction after annealing 4 hr. at 35°C. The MEK-insoluble polymer is also largely syndiotactic, as determined by x-ray diffraction. The T_m of the more highly stereoregulated and annealed fraction is about 52–53°C.

275. Preparation of Predominantly *cis*-1,4-Isotactic Poly(1,3-pentadiene) (300)

This polymerization is conducted in essentially the same way as the previous example. Again, a septum-closed beverage bottle tumbled or shaken in a temperature bath is a convenient method, or the stirred flask approach may be taken, with the risk of some monomer loss by its volatility. Purity of reagents and exclusion of air and moisture from the system is again of importance.

A total of 100 ml. benzene or toluene is used as reaction solvent, including that used in adding catalyst components. There are then added 0.544 g. (1.6×10^{-3} moles) tetra-*n*-butyl titanate (Stauffer Chemical, distilled before use) 0.912 g. (8.0×10^{-3} moles) aluminum triethyl, and after a few minutes 15 g. *trans*-1,3-pentadiene. *Cis* isomer or a mixture of *cis* and *trans* will undergo polymerization but a less isotactic stereoregulated structure results; from a 50:50 mixture the polymer is completely amorphous. *Cis* isomer is isomerized under the conditions of the polymerization and it is possible that only the *trans* is polymerized. The decrease in stereoregularity is possibly due to the influence of the nonpolymerizable *cis* diolefin on the action of the coordination catalyst, a phenomenon observed in other systems.

The polymerization mixture is maintained at 0°C. for 35 hr., then it is poured into methanol containing a small amount of HCl. The precipitated polymer is worked up as in the previous example. About 6 g. of product is obtained which is about 80/14/6 in *cis*-1,4/*trans*-1,4/3,4 enchainment, and is amorphous. Dissolution in benzene and reprecipitation in methyl ethyl ketone produces an insoluble polymer (about 30–40% of the original) with a higher level of crystallinity and as much as 85% *cis*-1,4 enchainment, the remainder being *trans*-1,4 (10%) and 3,4 (5%). This MEK-insoluble fraction is crystalline by x-ray diffraction after annealing 4 hr. at 35°C. and an isotactic structure is indicated. The T_m is about 44°C. The intrinsic viscosity (toluene, 30°C.) is about 5.

Allene is the simplest of possible dienes in structure, but several structural variants are possible when it is polymerized. With bimetallic coordination catalysts, the polymer contains varying amounts of vinylidene-, vinyl-, and *cis*-unsaturation (303). The propagating species can be considered as an anion (in an admitted oversimplification) and the mechanism leading to the structural units visualized as follows:

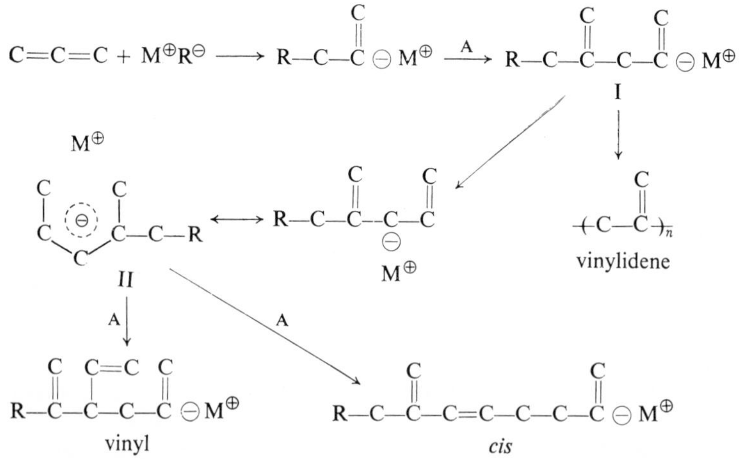

The relative amounts of each vary polymerization conditions: increasing monomer concentration will result in an increase of vinylidene units because addition of allene to the carbanion I will tend to occur before hydride shift to carbanion II. Polymerization at low pressure reduces vinyl content markedly, Heterogeneous polymerization and low polymer solubility or swelling will favor vinyl formation, and vigorous agitation will decrease it, because of their effect on monomer concentration at the growing sites. Polymers as prepared can range from amorphous to crystalline, depending on reaction conditions but both types are soluble in halogenated hydrocarbons in particular. High crystallinity can evidently be induced by film casting or pressing, to give rather brittle films. T_m is about 122°C. (303).

276. Preparation of Polyallene (303)

$$CH_2=C=CH_2 \longrightarrow +CH_2-\overset{\overset{\displaystyle CH_2}{\|}}{C}+(CH=CHCH_2)+\overset{\overset{\displaystyle CH=CH_2}{|}}{CH}+$$

To a 1 l. three-necked flask, previously baked 24 hr. at 140°C. and cooled under nitrogen, and equipped with a stirrer, thermometer, and a gas inlet and outlet, is added 500 ml. of benzene (distilled from calcium hydride) under nitrogen. The solvent is then saturated with allene that has preferably been distilled and passed through a silica gel column. Pure allene is essential to successful polymerization. Then, 0.05 ml. VOCl$_3$ is added, causing a dark-red color. Addition of 2.5 ml. of 2.2M triisobutylaluminum in cyclohexane changes the color to a cherry red. Allene is then bubbled through the solution and the polymerization is conducted at 30°C. until the gelled or precipitated polymer prevents easy stirring and monomer uptake is difficult. Cooling may be required. Then, 50 ml. ethanol is added and the mass slurried into excess ethanol. The filtered polymer is washed repeatedly in a home blender with 10% ethanolic HCl, ethanol, water, and acetone; the last wash should contain an antioxidant such as 2,2'-methylenebis(4-methyl-6-t-butylphenol). The polymer is dried under nitrogen in vacuum at 50°C. It should have an inherent viscosity in bromobenzene (0.5 g./100 ml., with an antioxidant present) of about 2. The yield is about 15 g. There are three crystalline forms of poly-allene, two of which are metastable. The T_m value of 122°C. mentioned earlier is from an x-ray melting point on a stable crystalline form.

Allene can also be polymerized to a crystalline polyallene, having the majority of the vinylidene units CH$_2$—C(=CH$_2$) in its structure as a 2$_1$ helix, using a pi-allylnickel bromide catalyst (304). The bimetallic coordination catalyst apparently can give a spectrum of polymers, of which the polymer from the pi-allylnickel bromide catalyst is probably one (305).

It has been possible to polymerize conjugated trienes with bimetallic coordination catalysts to give polymers with primarily 1,6-enchainment and, consequently, a conjugated diene in the chemical repeat unit of the polymer (306). Other mixed enchainments (e.g., 1,4- and 1,6-) can also be induced with substantial resultant changes in the character of the polymer. Examples are 1,3,5-hexatriene, 1,3,5-heptatriene and 2,4,6-octatriene. Generally, a Lewis base is used to restrain the activity of the catalyst toward secondary reactions on the polymeric diene.

277. Preparation of *trans*-1,3,5-Hexatriene (306)

$$CH_2-CH=CH-CH=CH-CH_2OH \longrightarrow CH_2=CH-CH=CH-CH=CH_2$$

A procedure similar to that reported by Woods and Schwartzman (307) is used to prepare hexatriene. A 350 g. portion of 2,4-hexadiene-1-ol (sorbyl alcohol) is dropped into a 2.5 × 50 cm. Pyrex column packed with 8–14 mesh Alcoa alumina at such a rate as to maintain the temperature at 260–280°C. The crude products are swept with nitrogen at a pressure of 5–10 mm. into two traps cooled with Dry Ice. The crude product is separated from water and the hexatriene separated from the major impurity (cyclohexadiene) by crystallization and filtration at −50°C. The hexatriene thus obtained is refined by two recrystallizations from methanol, at −50 and −25°C. The product is extracted thoroughly with water, dried with calcium sulfate, and distilled at 130 mm. (b.p. 33–34°C.) from calcium hydride. A yield of 149 g. (52%) of *trans*-1,3,5-hexatriene is to be expected; b.p. 80°C., m.p. −11.5°C. The product should be 99.8% pure, determined by chromatographing over a β,β-oxydipropionitrile column at 30°C. Hexatriene is stored at −15°C. over calcium hydride.

278. Amorphous 1,6-Polyhexatriene (306)

$$CH_2=CH-CH=CH-CH=CH_2 \longrightarrow (CH_2-CH=CH-CH=CH-CH_2)$$
trans, trans, and *cis-trans*

The glassware used is first flamed out and cooled under nitrogen. Syringes are oven-dried, and solvents are stored over calcium hydride. A solution of 0.17 g. (0.4 mmole) of tetraphenyl titanate and 0.02 ml. (0.2 mmole) of vanadyl trichloride in 55 ml. of chlorobenzene is cooled to −25°C. in a 100 ml. flask equipped with stirrer and blanketed with nitrogen. A 3 ml. portion (3.0 mmoles) of a $1M$ solution of diethylaluminum chloride in heptane, to which a molar equivalent of anisole has been added, is injected into the flask. Hexatriene (5 ml., 0.045 mole) is added, and the solution is stirred at −25°C. for 24 hr. This viscous solution is carefully poured into cold, acidified ethanol (3% HCl) to precipitate a white polymer and inactivate the catalyst. The polymer is washed well with cold acidified ethanol and absolute ethanol and dissolved in benzene. Small amounts of residual alcohol can be removed by partial evaporation of benzene or with calcium hydride. Removal of small amounts of insoluble material is accomplished by centrifugation. In order to preserve the soluble nature of the triene polymers, it is necessary to purify them in this manner, since solid, dry polymer almost always becomes cross-linked. The polymer can be stored for considerable periods of time as a benzene solution. The yield of polymer (determined by evaporating the benzene from an aliquot of the polymer solution and weighing the residue) is about 2.7 g.; 78%. η_{inh} (0.5% in benzene at 30°C.) is 0.61. Clear, flexible films can be cast from benzene solution. The IR spectrum is indicative of

1,6-enchainment, along with a minor amount of 1,2-polymer. Strong absorption bands are noted at 3010, 2925, 2852, 985, and 970 cm.$^{-1}$, moderate bands at 1445 and 1425 cm.$^{-1}$, and weak bands at 947 and 910 cm.$^{-1}$.

279. Crystalline 1,6-Polyhexatriene (306)

$$CH_2=CH-CH=CH-CH=CH_2 \longrightarrow +CH_2-CH=CH-CH=CH-CH_2+$$
trans, trans

The initial comments in the preceding example should be noted first. A solution of 0.05 ml. (0.5 mmole) of vanadyl trichloride in 60 ml. of chlorobenzene in a 100 ml. flask is stirred at $-30°C$. under a slight flow of nitrogen. A 2 ml. portion (2.0 mmoles) of a $1M$ solution of triisobutylaluminum in cyclohexane is added, followed by 5 ml. (0.045 mole) of hexatriene. It is essential that the monomer be at least 98% pure. The solution is stirred 2.5 hr. at $-30°C$., after which time the flask is choked with a slurry of swollen polymer. The catalyst is inactivated and the polymer precipitated by the addition of cold acidified (3% HCl) ethanol. The polymer is collected by filtration and washed well in a Waring Blendor, first with cold acidified ethanol and then with cold ethanol.

The polymer is dried superficially by pressing between filter paper. It can be immediately melt-pressed in a Carver press at 110°C. for 30 sec., followed by water quenching. Very thin films (less than 1 ml.) are smooth, flexible, tough, and slightly hazy, while thicker films are opaque. The IR spectrum displays strong absorption bands at 3010, 2925, 28252, 1445, and 985 cm.$^{-1}$, indicating nearly exclusive *trans,trans*-conjugated diene structure resulting from a 1,6-mode of polymerization. An x-ray goniometer trace should show two sharp peaks at $2\theta = 21.6$ and $23.3°C$., which completely disappear upon melting at 250°C. and do not reappear upon cooling.

The polytrienes of the preceding examples can be modified by addition of a dienophile to the conjugated double bond units in a typical Diels-Alder reaction (308). Maleic anhydride, sulfur dioxide, tetracyanoethylene, 1,2-dicyano-1,2-di(trifluoromethyl)ethylene, and dimethyl acetylenedicarboxylate are active dienophiles, though the degree of acceptance by the diene ranges from only about 10% of theory for sulfur dioxide to greater than 75% for the acetylene dicarboxylate. Models suggest that the build-up of successive cyclohexene rings along the chain imposes a great deal of steric strain, such that reaction of more than every other diene unit would appear difficult. It was also clear that *trans-trans* diene units in the polymer chain underwent reaction much more readily than *cis-trans* dienes, in keeping with observations on conventional diene compounds.

The Diels-Alder reaction of the dienophilic double bonds of polyesters made from maleic anhydride has been demonstrated with monomeric dienes (309).

280. Modification of 1,6-Polyhexatriene via Diels-Alder Reactions with Dienophiles (308)

$$-(CH_2-CH=CH-CH=CH-CH_2)- + (NC)_2C=C(CN)_2 \longrightarrow$$

A solution of 2.0 g. (0.025 equiv.) of amorphous 1,6-polyhexatriene from Preparation 278, in 25 ml. of benzene is treated with a solution of 3.2 g. (0.02 mole) of tetracyanoethylene in 15 ml. of tetrahydrofuran. After 4 hr., the original red color of the solution has changed to a pale yellow-green. Methanol is added to precipitate a quantity of white polymer, which is washed well with methanol and dried at room temperature under vacuum. A 3 g. yield of colorless polymer is obtained which is insoluble in benzene, but completely soluble in tetrahydrofuran. The polymer has an η_{inh} (0.5% in THF at 30°C.) of 0.52. Clear films can be cast from tetrahydrofuran solution. The IR spectrum should show that much of the *trans,trans*-diene absorption band at 985 cm.$^{-1}$ has been removed, while the *cis,trans*-diene shoulder at 970 cm.$^{-1}$ is virtually unchanged. A relatively weak cyano absorption band appears at 2220 cm.$^{-1}$. A nitrogen analysis of about 18.2% indicates approximately 45% of the theoretical diene content has been reacted with TCNE.

A similar reaction is possible with maleic anhydride by stirring 1.6 g. (0.02 mole) of the dienic polymer with 2.0 g. (0.02 mole) maleic anhydride for three days at room temperature in toluene solution. After precipitation in ether and resolution in tetrahydrofuran, clear films can be cast which, in IR, appear to have lost 55–60% of the original *trans-trans* content.

REFERENCES

The first eighteen references are books which treat the polymerization of vinyl compounds in a broader sense than in this chapter:

1. C. H. Bamford, W. G. Barb, A. D. Jenkins, and P. F. Onyon, *The Kinetics of Vinyl Polymerization by Radical Mechanisms*, Academic Press, New York, 1958.
2. P. A. Plesch, Ed., *Chemistry of Cationic Polymerization*, Macmillan, New York, 1963.
3. F. W. Billmeyer, Jr., *Textbook of Polymer Science*, Interscience, New York, 1962.
4. N. G. Gaylord and H. F. Mark, *Linear and Stereospecific Addition Polymers*, Interscience, New York, 1959.
5. G. Ham, Ed., *Copolymerization*, Interscience, New York, 1964.
6. P. J. Flory, *Principles of Polymer Chemistry*, Cornell University Press, Ithaca, New York, 1953.
7. R. A. V. Raff and K. W. Doak, Eds., *Crystalline Olefin Polymers*, Parts 1 and 2, Interscience, New York, 1964; H. V. Boenig, *Polyolefins: Structure and Properties*, American Elsevier, New York, 1966.
8. J. K. Stille, *Introduction to Polymer Chemistry*, Wiley, New York, 1962.
9. F. Marchionna, *Butalistic Polymers*, Reinhold, New York, 1946.

10. G. S. Whitby, Ed., *Synthetic Rubber*, Wiley, New York, 1954.
11. H. Mark, Ed., *Collected Papers of Wallace H. Carothers on High Polymeric Substances*, Interscience, New York, 1940.
12. W. J. Burlant and A. S. Hoffman, *Block and Graft Copolymers*, Reinhold, New York, 1960.
13. C. E. Schildknecht, *Polymer Processes*, Interscience, New York, 1956.
14. F. A. Bovey, I. M. Kolthoff, A. I. Medalia, and E. J. Meehan, *Emulsion Polymerization*, Interscience, New York, 1955.
15. A. Renfrew and P. Morgan, Eds., *Polythene: The Technology and Uses of Ethylene Polymers*, Interscience, New York, 1960.
16. C. E. Schildknecht, *Vinyl and Related Polymers*, Wiley, New York, 1952.
17. R. H. Boundy and R. F. Boyer, Eds., *Styrene, Its Polymers, Copolymers and Derivatives*, Reinhold, New York, 1952.
18. H. Kainer, *Polyvinylchlorid und Vinyl Chlorid-Mischpolymerisate*, Springer-Verlag, Berlin/New York, 1965; W. S. Penn, *PVC Technology*, MacLaren, London, 1962; F. Chevassus and R. Broutelles (C. J. R. Eichhorn and E. E Sarmiento, Transl.), *Stabilization of Polyvinyl Chloride*, Edward Arnold, London, 1963.
19. P. Cossee, *Tetrahedron Letters*, **17**, 12 (1960); *J. Catal.*, **3**, 80 (1964).
20. L. A. M. Rodriguez, H. M. van Looy, and J. A. Gabant, *J. Polymer Sci. A-1*, **8**, 1905, 1917, 1927, 1951, 1971 (1966).
21. A. Shimizo, T. Otsu, and M. Imoto, *J. Polymer Sci. B*, **3**, 1031 (1965).
22. W. E. Goode, F. H. Owens, and W. L. Myers, *J. Polymer Sci.*, **47**, 75 (1960).
23. H. Brody, M. Ladacki, R. Milkovich, and M. Szwarc, *J. Polymer Sci.*, **25**, 221 (1957).
24. M. Szwarc, *Nature*, **178**, 1168 (1956).
25. M. Szwarc, M. Levy, and R. Milkovich, *J. Am. Chem. Soc.*, **78**, 2656 (1956).
26. M. P. Dreyfuss and P. Dreyfuss, *J. Polymer Sci. A-1*, **4**, 2179 (1966).
27. G. B. Butler and R. J. Angelo, *J. Am. Chem. Soc.*, **79**, 3128 (1957).
28. C. S. Marvel and R. D. Vest, *J. Am. Chem. Soc.*, **79**, 5771 (1957).
29. J. F. Jones, *J. Poly. Sci.*, **33**, 7, 15, 513 (1958).
30. Y. Yamashita, T. Tsuda, M. Okada, and S. Iwatsuki, *J. Polymer Sci. A-1*, **4**, 2121 (1966).
31. A. H. Frazer, private communication.
32. F. J. Glavis, L. L. Ryden, and C. S. Marvel, *J. Am. Chem. Soc.*, **59**, 707 (1937).
33. M. Hunt and C. S. Marvel, *J. Am. Chem. Soc.*, **57**, 1691 (1935).
34. L. L. Ryden and C. S. Marvel, *J. Am. Chem. Soc.*, **57**, 2311 (1935).
34a. N. L. Zutty, C. W. Wilson III, G. H. Potter, D. C. Priest, and C. J. Whitworth, *J. Polymer Sci. -A*, **3**, 2781 (1965).
35. W. G. Barb, *J. Am. Chem. Soc.*, **75**, 224 (1953).
36. F. S. Dainton and K. J. Ivin, *Proc. Roy. Soc. (London)* A212, **66** (1952).
37. R. M. Elotson and G. D. Jones, *J. Am. Chem. Soc.*, **76**, 210 (1950).
38. F. R. Mayo and A. A. Miller, *J. Am. Chem. Soc.*, **78**, 1023 (1956).
39. A. A. Miller and F. R. Mayo, *J. Am. Chem. Soc.*, **78**, 1017 (1956).
40. R. E. Putnam and W. H. Sharkey, *J. Polymer Sci. A-1*, **4**, 2289 (1966).
41. R. J. Ceresa, *Block and Graft Copolymers*, Butterworths, London, 1962.
42. P. W. Allen, Ed., *Techniques of Polymer Characterization*, Academic Press, New York, 1959.
42a. G. Smets and R. Hart, *Advan. Polymer Sci.*, **2**, 173 (1960).
43. B. D. Gesner, *J. Polymer Sci. A*, **3**, 3825 (1965).

44. G. Bier, *Angew. Chem.*, **73**, (6), 186 (1961).
45. M. A. Luftglass, W. R. Hendricks, G. Holden, and J. T. Bailey, *Tech. Papers, Vol. 12, Soc. Plastics Engrs. 22nd ANTEC, Montreal*, March 7, 1966, p. XIV-6.
46. British Pat. 1,000,090, (to Shell Intern. Res.) Aug. 4, (1965).
47. A. W. Larchar and D. C. Pease, U.S. Pat. 2,816,883 (Dec. 17, 1957).
48. Dow Chemical Company, Product Bulletin, *The Polymerization of Styrene*.
49. I. M. Kolthoff and W. J. Dale, *J. Am. Chem. Soc.*, **69**, 442 (1947).
50. J. R. Hiltner and W. F. Bartoe, U.S. Pat. 2,264,376 (Dec. 2, 1941).
51. L. E. Daly, U.S. Pat. 2,439,202 (to U.S. Rubber) (April 6, 1948).
52. J. L. Amos, J. L. McCurdy, and O. R. McIntire, U.S. Pat. 2,694,692 (to Dow Chemical) (November 16, 1954).
53. W. C. Calvert, U.S. Pat. 2,908,661 (to Borg-Warner) (October 13, 1959).
54. G. H. Fremon and W. N. Stoops, U.S. Pat. 3,168,593 (to Union Carbide) (February 2, 1965).
55. J. G. Noltes, H. A. Budding, and G. J. M. van der Kerk, *Rec. Trav. Chim.*, **79**, 1076 (1960).
56. F. Stasny and K. Buchholz, U.S. Pat. 2,744,291 (to Badische Anilin und Soda Fabrik) (May 8, 1956).
57. F. L. Ramp, *Polymer Preprints*, **7** (2), 582 (1966), Polymer Div., Am. Chem. Soc., September Meeting, New York.
58. R. E. Cook, F. S. Dainton, and K. J. Ivin, *J. Polymer Sci.*, **29**, 549 (1958).
59. M. Hunt and C. S. Marvel, *J. Am. Chem. Soc.*, **57**, 1691 (1935).
60. L. L. Ryden and C. S. Marvel, *J. Am. Chem. Soc.*, **57**, 2311 (1935).
61. D. D. Coffman and T. A. Ford, U.S. Pat. 2,419,008 (April 15, 1947).
62. D. D. Coffman and T. A. Ford, U.S. Pat. 2,419,009 (April 15, 1947).
63. D. D. Coffman and T. A. Ford, U.S. Pat. 2,419,010 (April 15, 1947).
64. P. J. Manno, *Nucleonics*, **22** (2), 49; **22** (6), 64; **22** (9), 72 (1964).
65. J. T. Barr, in *Manufacture of Plastics*, Vol. 1, W. M. Smith, Ed., Reinhold, New York (1964).
66. E. Peggion, F. Testa, and G. Talamini, *Makromol. Chem.*, **71**, 173 (1964).
67. G. Talamini, *J. Polymer Sci. A-2*, **4**, 535 (1966).
68. H. Hopff and I. Fakla, *Makromol. Chem.*, **88**, 54 (1965).
69. E. H. Immergut, in *Plasticization and Plasticizer Processes*, N. Platzer, Ed., *Adv. in Chem. 48*, Amer. Chem. Soc., 1965.
70. J. Edenbaum and R. Chartier, private communication.
71. L. Fishbein and B. F. Crowe, U.S. Pat. 3,172,877 (to Air Reduction Co., Inc.) (March 9, 1965).
71a. F. J. Scott, private communication.
72. W. C. Tincher, *Makromol. Chem.*, **85**, 20 (1965).
73. S. Enomoto, M. Asahina, and S. Satoh, *J. Polymer Sci. A-1*, **4**, 1373 (1966).
74. Y. Abe, M. Tasumi, T. Shimanouchi, and S. Satoh, *J. Polymer Sci. A-1*, **4**, 1413 (1966).
75. A. Nakajima, H. Hamada, and S. Hayashi, *Makromol. Chem.*, **95**, 40 (1966).
76. A. Nakajima and K. Kato, *Makromol. Chem.*, **95**, 52 (1966).
77. I. Rosen, in *Macromolecular Syntheses*, C. G. Overberger, Ed., Vol. 1, Wiley, New York, 1963, p. 55.
78. O. C. Bockman, *J. Polymer Sci. A*, **3**, 3399 (1965).
79. R. A. Isaksen and E. H. Merz, U.S. Pat. 2,984,593 (to Monsanto) (May 16, 1961); British Pat. 975,861 (to Rhone-Poulenc) (November 18, 1964).

80. M. L. Dannis and F. L. Ramp, U.S. Pat. 2,996,489 (to B. F. Goodrich Co.) (August 15, 1961); Australian Pat. 241,363 (November 22, 1962).
81. E. Jenckel, H. Eckmanns-Mettegang, and B. Rumbach, *Makromol. Chem.*, **4**, 15 (1949).
82. C. S. Marvel, J. H. Sample, and M. F. Roy, *J. Am. Chem. Soc.*, **61**, 3241 (1939).
83. J. D. Cotman, Jr., *J. Am. Chem. Soc.*, **77**, 2791 (1955).
84. P. J. Flory, *J. Am. Chem. Soc.*, **61**, 1518 (1939).
85. J. E. Johnson, R. H. Blizzard, and H. W. Carhart, *J. Am. Chem. Soc.*, **70**, 3664 (1948).
86. R. F. Nystrom and W. G. Brown, *J. Am. Chem. Soc.*, **70**, 3739 (1948).
87. J. P. Roth, P. Remp, and J. Parrod, *J. Polymer Sci. C*, **4**, 1347 (1964).
88. D. E. Winkler, *J. Polymer Sci.*, **35**, 3 (1959).
89. V. E. Shashoua, private communication.
90. R. G. Beaman, private communication.
91. W. G. Vosburgh, private communication.
92. N. Grassie and I. C. McNeill, *J. Polymer Sci.*, **39**, 211 (1959).
93. R. C. Houtz, *Textile Res. J.*, **20**, 796 (1950).
94. British Pat. 786,960 (Nov. 27, 1957).
95. *Emulsion Polymerization I*, Alcolac Chemical Corp.
96. M. Hunt, U.S. Pat. 2,471,959 (May 31, 1949).
97. W. O. Herrmann and W. Haehnel, *Ber.*, **60**, 1658 (1927).
98. W. O. Herrmann and W. Haehnel, U.S. Pat. 1,672,156 (June 5, 1928).
99. W. O. Herrmann and W. Haehnel, U.S. Pat. 2,109,883 (May 1, 1938).
100. L. M. Minsk, W. J. Priest, and W. O. Kenyon, *J. Am. Chem. Soc.*, **63**, 2715 (1941).
101. R. C. Houtz, U.S. Pat. 2,388,325 (Nov. 6, 1945).
102. D. L. Wilson, U.S. Pat. 2,399,970 (May 11, 1946).
103. C. Dangelmajar, U.S. Pat. 2,246,915 (June 24, 1941).
104. G. Kranzlein and H. Reis, Ger. Pat. 765,265 (Jan. 1, 1954).
105. G. S. Stamatoff, U.S. Pat. 2,400,957 (May 18, 1946).
106. R. C. Houtz, U.S. Pat. 2,341,553 (Feb. 15, 1944).
107. L. A. R. Hall, W. J. Belanger, W. Kirk, Jr., and Y. Sundstrom, *J. Appl. Polymer Soc.*, **2**, 246 (1959).
108. R. C. Schulz, P. Elyer, and W. Kern, *Chimia*, **13**, 235 (1959).
108a. E. A. Land and C. D. West, *Colloid Chemistry*, Vol. 6, Reinhold, New York, 1946, p. 160.
109. H. N. Friedlander, H. E. Harris, and J. G. Pritchard, *J. Polymer Sci. A-1*, **4**, 649 (1966).
110. H. E. Harris, J. F. Kenney, G. W. Willcockson, R. Chiang, and H. N. Friedlander, *J. Polymer Sci. A-1*, **4**, 665 (1966).
111. W. C. Tincher, *Makromol. Chem.*, **85**, 46 (1965).
112. S. Okamura, T. Kodama, and T. Higashimura, *Makromol. Chem.*, **53**, 180 (1962).
113. S. Murahashi, H. Yuki, T. Sano, U. Yonemura, H. Tadokoro, and V. Chatani, *J. Polymer Sci.*, **62**, 877 (1962).
114. S. Murahashi, S. Nozakura, and M. Sumi, *J. Polymer Sci. B*, **3**, 245 (1965); *ibid.*, **4**, 65 (1966); *ibid.*, **4**, 59 (1966).
115. J. F. Kenney and G. W. Willcockson, *J. Polymer Sci. A-1*, **4**, 679 (1966).
116. F. E. Kung, U.S. Pat. 2,377,085 (May 29, 1945).

117. J. R. Schaefgen, U.S. Pat. 3,118,862 (to du Pont) (January 21, 1964).

118. *American Cyanamid Co. New Prod. Bull.*, Coll. Vol. III.

119. W. C. Mast and C. H. Fisher, *Ind. Eng. Chem.*, **41**, 790 (1949).

120. H. Fikentscher and K. Herrle, *Modern Plastics*, **23**, 157 (1945).

121. W. Reppe and C. Schuster, U.S. Pat. 2,265,450 (Dec. 9, 1941).

122. C. Schuster, R. Sauerbier, and H. Fikentscher, U.S. Pat. 2,335,454 (Nov. 30, 1943).

123. J. H. Werntz, U.S. Pat. 2,497,705 (Feb. 14, 1950).

124. R. F. Conaway, U.S. Pat. 2,008,577 (Aug. 3, 1937).

125. D. D. Coffman, U.S. Pat. 2,326,287 (Aug. 10, 1943).

126. D. D. Coffman, U.S. Pat. 2,334,476 (Nov. 16, 1943).

127. Y. Iwakura et al., *Chem. High Polymers (Japan)*, **13**, 390 (1956).

128. H. Wieland and E. Sakellarios, *Ber.*, **52**, 898 (1919).

129. G. D. Jones, *J. Org. Chem.*, **9**, 500 (1944).

130. W. E. Hanford, U.S. Pat. 2,396,785 (March 19, 1946).

131. R. H. Wiley and J. Moffat, *J. Org. Chem.*, **22**, 995 (1957).

132. R. M. Hedrick, U.S. Pat. 2,653,973 (Sept. 29, 1953).

133. G. D. Jones and C. E. Barnes, U.S. Pat. 2,515,714 (July 18, 1950).

134. H. R. Snyder, H. V. Anderson, and D. D. Hallad, *J. Am. Chem. Soc.*, **73**, 3258 (1951).

135. V. U. Alderman and W. E. Hanford, U.S. Pat. 2,348,705 (May 16, 1944).

136. W. Heuer, Ger. Pat. 724,889 (Sept. 9, 1942).

137. C. G. Overberger, D. E. Baldwin, and H. P. Gregor, *J. Am. Chem. Soc.*, **72**, 4864 (1950).

138. R. Y. Mixer and D. L. Bailey, *J. Polymer Sci.*, **18**, 573 (1955).

139. D. L. Schoene, U.S. Pat. 2,474,808 (July 5, 1949).

140. H. Ufer, U.S. Pat. 2,163,180 (June 20, 1939).

141. R. C. Schulz, C. H. Cherdron, and W. Kern, *Makromol. Chem.*, **24**, 141 (1957).

142. E. E. Ryder and P. Pezzaglia, *J. Polymer Sci. A*, **3**, 3459 (1965).

142a. F. L. Ramp, E. J. DeWitt, and L. E. Trepasso, *J. Polymer Sci. A-1*, **4**, 2267 (1966).

143. R. Rabinowitz and R. Marcus, *J. Polymer Sci. A*, **3**, 2063 (1965); R. Rabinowitz, A. C. Henry, and R. Marcus, *ibid.*, *-A*, **3**, 2055 (1965).

144. J. W. C. Crawford, *J. Soc. Chem. Ind.* (Trans.), **68**, 201 (1949).

145. D. E. Strain, R. G. Kennelly, and H. R. Dittmar, *Ind. Eng. Chem.*, **31**, 382 (1939).

146. Shell Development Company, Report S-9976, June 25, 1947.

147. M. A. Pollach, U.S. Pat. 2,870,193 (Jan. 20, 1959).

148. J. G. Lichty, U.S. Pat. 2,231,838 (Feb. 11, 1941).

149. British Pat. 741,239 (Nov. 30, 1955).

150. British Pat. 741,236 (Nov. 30, 1955).

151. N. Grassie and E. M. Grant, *J. Polymer Sci. A-1*, **4**, 1821 (1966).

152. R. C. Reinhardt, *Chem. Eng. News*, **25**, 2136 (1947).

153. Dow Chemical Company, Product Bulletin, *Handling Precautions for Vinylidene Chloride Monomer*.

154. British Pat. 570,711 (July 19, 1945).

155. R. M. Wiley, U.S. Pat. 2,160,931 (June 6, 1939).

156. R. M. Wiley, U.S. Pat. 2,183,602 (Dec. 19, 1939).

157. M. Hauptscheien, U.S. Pat. 3,193,539 (to Pennsalt) (July 6, 1965).

158. M. S. Newman and R. W. Addor, *J. Am. Chem. Soc.*, **75**, 1263 (1953).

159. M. S. Newman and R. W. Addor, *J. Am. Chem. Soc.*, **77**, 3789 (1955).
160. N. D. Field and J. R. Schaefgen, *J. Polymer Sci.*, **58**, 533 (1962).
161. R. M. Thomas, U.S. Pat. 2,873,230 (Feb. 10, 1959).
161a. L. R. Morris and D. J. Hubbard, *J. Org. Chem.*, **27**, 1451 (1962).
162. P. S. Forgione, in press.
163. H. W. Arnold, M. M. Brubaker, and G. L. Dorough, U.S. Pat. 2,301,356 (Nov. 10, 1942).
164. British Pat. 505,120 (May 5, 1939).
165. J. L. Lang, W. A. Pavelich, and H. D. Clarey, *Polymer Preprints*, **2** (2), 36 (1961), Polymer Div., Am. Chem. Soc., September 1961; G. H. Potter and N. L. Zutty, U.S. pat. 3,280,080 (to Union Carbide) (October 18, 1966).
166. French Pat. 922,429 (July 9, 1947).
167. F. Scholoffer and O. Scherer, Ger. Pat. 677,071 (June 17, 1939).
168. R. M. Joyce, U.S. Pat. 2,394,243 (Feb. 5, 1946).
169. R. J. Plunkett, U.S. Pat. 2,230,654 (Feb. 4, 1941).
170. F. P. Reding, *J. Polymer Sci.*, **21**, 547 (1956).
171. D. B. Miller, private communication.
172. J. P. Kennedy and R. M. Thomas, *J. Polymer Sci.*, **55**, 311 (1961).
173. A. J. Morway and F. L. Miller, U.S. Pat. 2,243,470 (May 27, 1941).
174. M. Müller-Cunradi and M. Otto, U.S. Pat. 2,203,873 (June 11, 1940).
175. W. Repp, E. Keysner, and E. Dorrer, U.S. Pat. 2,072,465 (March 2, 1937).
176. D. E. Sargeant, U.S. Pat. 2,560,251 (July 10, 1951).
177. H. F. Miller and R. G. Flowers, U.S. Pat. 2,445,181 (July 13, 1948).
178. J. Springer, K. Ueberreiter, and R. Wenzel, *Makromol. Chem.*, **96**, 122 (1966).
179. M. Imoto and K. Takemoto, *J. Polymer Sci.*, **15**, 271 (1955).
180. C. E. Schildknecht, A. O. Zoss, and C. McKinley, *Ind. Eng. Chem.* **39**, 180 (1947).
181. S. Okamura, T. Higashimura, and H. Yamamoto, *J. Polymer Sci.*, **33**, 510 (1958).
182. S. Okamura, T. Higashimura, and I. Sakurada, *J. Polymer Sci.*, **39**, 507 (1959).
183. S. Okamura, T. Higashimura, T. Yonezawa, and K. Fukui, *J. Polymer Sci.*, **39**, 487 (1959).
184. D. J. Cram and K. R. Kopecky, *J. Am. Chem. Soc.*, **81**, 2748 (1959).
185. A. D. Ketley, *J. Polymer Sci.*, **62**, 581 (1962).
186. G. J. Blake and A. M. Carlson, *J. Polymer Sci. A-1*, **4**, 1813 (1966).
187. G. Natta, G. Dall 'Asta, G. Mazzanti, U. Giannini, and S. Cesca, *Angew. Chem.*, **71**, 205 (1959).
188. J. Lal and J. E. McGrath, *J. Polymer Sci. -A*, **2**, 3369 (1964).
189. S. A. Moseley, U.S. Pat. 2,549,921 (to Union Carbide) (April 24, 1951).
190. J. Furukawa, T. Saegusa, S. Yasui, and S. Akutsu, *Makromol. Chem.*, **94**, 74 (1965).
191. P. Pino, F. Ciardelli, and G. P. Lorenzi, *Makromol. Chem.*, **70**, 182 (1964); P. Pino, F. Ciardelli, and G. Montagnoli, *Symp. Macromol. Chem.*, Prague, 1965, Preprints, p. 428.
192. G. Natta, P. Pino, and S. Valenti, *Makromol. Chem.*, **67**, 225 (1963).
193. P. Pino, *Adv. Polymer Sci.*, **4**, 393 (1966).
194. R. C. Schulz and E. Kaiser, *Advan. Polymer Sci.*, **4**, 236 (1965).
195. M. Farina and G. Bresson, *Makromol. Chem.*, **61**, 79 (1963); Y. Takeda, V. Hayakawa, T. Fueno, and J. Furukawa, *ibid.*, **83**, 234 (1965).

196. G. Natta and M. Farina, *Tetrahedron Letters*, **1963**, 603.
197. G. Bresson, M. Farina, and G. Natta, *Makromol. Chem.*, **93**, 283 (1966).
198. J. E. Mulvaney, C. G. Overberger, and A. M. Schiller, *Advan. Polymer Sci.*, 3, 106 (1961).
199. S. Bywater, *ibid.*, **4**, 66 (1965).
200. M. Roha, *ibid.*, **4**, 353 (1965).
201. M. Szwarc, *ibid.*, **2**, 173 (1960).
202. T. E. Werkema, U.S. Pat. 2,658,058 (Nov. 3, 1953).
203. R. G. Beaman, *J. Am. Chem. Soc.*, **70**, 3115 (1948).
204. A. L. Serge, F. Ciampelli, and G. Dall 'Asta, *J. Polymer Sci. B*, **4**, 633 (1966).
205. K. Ishigure, Y. Tabata, and K. Oshima, *J. Polymer Sci. B*, **4**, 669 (1966).
206. Y. Joh, T. Yoshihara, Y. Kotake, F. Ide, and K. Nakatsuka, *J. Polymer Sci. B*, **3**, 933 (1965); **4**, 673 (1966).
207. R. Waack, A. Rembaum, J. D. Coombes, and M. Szwarc, *J. Am. Chem. Soc.*, **79**, 2026 (1957).
208. N. D. Scott, U.S. Pat. 2,181,771 (Nov. 28, 1939).
209. N. D. Scott, J. F. Walker, and V. L. Hansley, *J. Am. Chem. Soc.*, **58**, 2442 (1936).
210. P. J. Flory, *J. Am. Chem. Soc.*, **62**, 1561 (1940).
211. M. Morton, R. Milkovich, D. B. McIntyre, and L. J. Bradley, *J. Polymer Sci. A*, *1*, 443 (1963).
212. F. Wenger and Shiao-Ping S. Yen, *Makromol. Chem.*, **43**, 1 (1961).
213. D. P. Wyman and T. G Fox, *Tech. Doc. Rept. No. ASD-TDR-62-1110* (January, 1963).
214. S. L. Jung, private communication.
215. E. F. Evans, A. Goodman, and L. D. Grandine, private communication.
216. L. S. Luskin and R. J. Meyers, *Encyclopedia of Polymer Science and Technology*, Vol. 1, Interscience, New York, 1964, p. 290 ff.
217. W. E. Goode, R. P. Fellmann, and F. H. Owens, *Macromolecular Syntheses*, Vol. 1, C. G. Overberger, Ed., Wiley, New York, 1963, p. 25.
218. C. F. Ryan and J. J. Gormley, *ibid.*, p. 30.
219. W. E. Goode, F. H. Owens, R. P. Fellmann, W. H. Snyder, and J. E. Moore, *J. Polymer Sci.*, **46**, 317 (1960); D. L. Glusker, E. Stiles, and B. Yoncoskie, *ibid.*, **49**, 297 (1961).
220. A. E. Ardis, U.S. Pat. 2,615,865 (Oct. 28, 1952).
221. A. E. Ardis, S. T. Averill, H. Gilbert, F. F. Miller, R. F. Schmidt, F. D. Stewart, and H. L. Trumball, *J. Am. Chem. Soc.*, **72**, 1305 (1950).
222. H. Gilbert and F. F. Miller, U.S. Pat. 2,615,867 (Oct. 28, 1952).
223. A. W. Anderson et al., U.S. Pat. 2,721,189 (Oct. 18, 1955).
224. A. W. Anderson, N. G. Merckling, and P. H. Settlage, U.S. Pat. 2,799,668 (July 16, 1957).
225. British Pat. 777,538 (June 26, 1957).
226. K. Ziegler and H. Martin, *Makromol. Chem.*, **18/19**, 186 (1956).
227. K. Ziegler, E. Holzlcamp, H. Breil, and H. Martin, *Angew. Chem.*, **67**, 426, 541 (1955).
228. G. Natta, *J. Polymer Sci.*, **16**, 143 (1955).
229. G. Natta, *Angew. Chem.*, **68**, 393 (1956).
230. G. Natta, P. Pino, P. Corradini, F. Danusso, E. Manteca, G. Mazzanti, and G. Moragli, *J. Am. Chem. Soc.*, **77**, 1708 (1955).

231. T. W. Campbell and A. C. Haven, Jr., *J. Appli. Polymer Sci.*, **1**, 79 (1959).
232. F. P. Reding, *J. Polymer. Sci.*, **21**, 547 (1956).
233. G. Natta, I. Pasquon, A. Zambelli, and G. Gatti, *J. Polymer Sci.*, **51**, 383 (1961); G. Natta, P. Corradini, and G. Allegra, *ibid.*, p. 387.
233a. A. K. Ingberman, I. J. Levine, and R. J. Turbett, *J. Polymer Sci. A-1*, **4**, 2781 (1966).
234. F. W. Breuer, L. E. Geipel, and A. B. Loebel, in *Crystalline Olefin Polymers*, Part I, R. A. V. Raff and K. W. Doak, Eds., Interscience, New York, 1965.
235. J. L. Jezl, T. L. Kelley, H. M. Khelghatian, and E. M. Honeycutt, in *Manufacture of Plastics*, Vol. 1, W. M. Smith, Ed., Reinhold, New York, 1964.
236. A. Zambelli, G. Natta, and I. Pasquon, *J. Polymer Sci. C*, **4**, 411 (1963).
237. G. Natta, A. Zambelli, G. Lanzi, I. Pasquon, and E. R. Magnaschi, *Makromol. Chem.*, **81**, 161 (1965).
238. J. Boor, Jr. and E. A. Youngman, *J. Polymer Sci. A-1*, **4**, 1861 (1966).
239. T. W. Campbell, U.S. Pat. 2,842,532 (July 8, 1958).
240. H. Gilman and B. McGlumphey, *Bull. Soc. Chim. Belg.*, **43**, 1326 (1928).
241. C. N. Riiber, *Ber.*, **44**, 2392 (1911).
242. W. N. Baxter, U.S. Pat. 2,842,531 (July 8, 1959).
243. F. Ang, *J. Polymer Sci.*, **25**, 126 (1957).
244. H. Tadokoro, N. Nishiyama, S. Nozakura, and S. Murahashi, *J. Polymer Sci.*, **36**, 553 (1959).
245. T. W. Campbell, Italian Pat. 579,572 (July 16, 1958).
246. C. A. Lukach, private communication.
246a. J. D. Sutherland and J. P. McKenzie, *Ind. Eng. Chem.*, **48**, 17 (1956).
247. F. Ciardelli, E. Bennedetti, and O. Pieroni, *Makromol. Chem.*, in press.
248. M. Bourgel, *Ann. Chim. France*, **3**, 191, 325 (1925).
249. L. Lardicci, C. Botteghi, and E. Bennedetti, *J. Org. Chem.*, **31**, 1534 (1966).
250. R. G. Charles and M. A. Paulikowski, *J. Phys. Chem.*, **62**, 440 (1958).
251. M. Morton, Ed., *Introduction to Rubber Technology*, Reinhold, New York, 1959.
251a. J. P. Kennedy and E. Tornqvist, Eds., *The Polymer Chemistry of Synthetic Elastomers*, Interscience, New York, in press.
252. A. A. Morton, *Ind. Eng. Chem.*, **42**, 1488 (1950).
253. A. A. Morton, F. H. Bolton, F. W. Collins, and E. F. Cluff, *Ind. Eng. Chem.*, **44**, 2876 (1952).
254. A. A. Morton, R. L. Letsinger, and E. E. Magat, *J. Am. Chem. Soc.*, **69**, 950 (1947).
255. J. L. R. Williams, J. Van Den Berghe, K. R. Dunham, and W. J. Dulmage, *J. Am. Chem. Soc.*, **79**, 1716 (1957).
256. A. A. Morton, B. Darling, and J. Davidson, *Ind. Eng. Chem. Anal. Ed.*, **14**, 734 (1942).
257. A. A. Morton, D. M. Knott, *Ind. Eng. Chem. (Anal. Ed.)*, **13**, 649 (1941).
258. C. S. Marvel, W. J. Bailey, and G. E. Inskeep, *J. Polymer Sci.*, **1**, 275 (1946).
259. J. D. D'Ianni, *Ind. Eng. Chem.*, **40**, 253 (1948).
260. M. Gippin, *Ind. Eng. Chem. Prod. Res. Develop.*, **4**, 160 (1965).
261. R. C. Farrar and F. E. Naylor, U.S. Pat. 3,223,692 (to Phillips Petroleum) (December 14, 1965).
262. R. S. Silas, J. Yates, and V. Thornton, *Anal. Chem.*, **31**, 529 (1959).
263. F. E. Naylor and J. R. Hooten, U.S. Pat. 3,205,212 (to Phillips Petroleum) (September 7, 1965).

264. N. G. Gaylord, T. K. Kwei, and H. F. Mark, *J. Polymer Sci.*, **42**, 417 (1960).
265. G. Natta, L. Porri, and A. Carbonaro, *Rend. Accad. Nazl. Lincei*, **31**, 189 (1961).
266. G. J. van Amerongen, in *Adv. in Chem.*, **52**, B. L. Johnson and M. Goodman, Eds., Am. Chem. Soc., 1966, p. 11.
267. R. P. Zelinski and D. R. Smith, U.S. Pat. 3,050,513 (to Phillips Petroleum Company) (August 21, 1962).
267a. R. E. Rinehart, *ACS Polymer Div. Preprints*, **7** (2), 556 (1966).
268. G. Natta, I. Pasquon, A. Zambelli, and G. Gatti, *J. Polymer Sci.*, **51**, 383 (1961).
269. E. Susa, *J. Polymer Sci. C*, **4**, 399 (1964).
270. G. Natta, L. Porri, and A. Carbonaro, *Makromol. Chem.*, **77**, 126 (1964).
271. M. Morton and W. E. Gibbs, *J. Polymer Sci. -A*, **1**, 2679 (1963).
272. G. E. Rumscheidt and J. M. Goppel, U.S. Pat. 2,622,962 (December 23, 1953).
273. H. M. G. Williams, British Pat. 694,890 (July 29, 1953).
274. A. H. Frazer and W. P. O'Neill, *J. Am. Chem. Soc.*, **85**, 2613 (1963).
275. German Pat. 1,040, 795 (Oct. 9, 1958).
276. German Pat. 1,040,796 (Oct. 9, 1958).
277. F. W. Stavely et al., *Ind. Eng. Chem.*, **48**, 778 (1956).
278. H. E. Adams, R. S. Stearns, W. A. Smith, and J. L. Binder, *Ind. Eng. Chem.*, **50**, 1507 (1958).
279. British Pat. 776,326 (June 5, 1957).
280. S. E. Horne, J. P. Kiehl, J. J. Shipman, V. L. Folt, C. F. Gibbs, E. A. Wilson, E. B. Newton, and M. A. Reinhart, *Ind. Eng. Chem.*, **48**, 784 (1956).
281. T. F. Yen, *J. Polymer Sci.*, **35**, 533 (1959).
282. G. Natta, L. Porri, and A. Mazzei, *Chim. Ind.*, **41**, 116 (1959).
283. J. S. Lasky, H. K. Garner, and R. H. Ewart, *Ind. Eng. Chem. Prod. Res. Develop.*, **1**, 82 (1962).
284. E. G. Kent and F. B. Swinney, *Ind. Eng. Chem. Prod. Res. Develop.*, **5**, 134 (1966).
285. J. D. Calfie et al., U.S. Pat. 2,431,461 (Nov. 25, 1947).
286. R. M. Thomas and W. J. Sparks, U.S. Pat. 2,356,128 (Aug. 22, 1944).
287. F. B. Moody, *ACS Polymer Div. Preprints*, **2**, 285 (1961).
288. G. F. Hennion, C. C. Price, and T. F. McKeon, Jr., *Org. Syn.*, **1958**, 70.
288a. W. H. Carothers, I. Williams, A. M. Collins, and J. E. Kirby, *J. Am. Chem. Soc.*, **53**, 4203 (1931).
289. R. C. Ferguson, *Anal. Chem.*, **36**, 2204 (1964); *J. Polymer Sci. A.*, **2**, 4735 (1964).
290. C. A. Aufdermarsh, Jr. and R. Pariser, *J. Polymer Sci. A.*, **2**, 4727 (1964).
291. H. W. Walker and W. E. Mochel, *Proc. Rubber Technol. Conf. 2nd*, 69–78 (1948).
292. R. S. Barrows and G. W. Scott, *Ind. Eng. Chem.*, **40**, 2193 (1948).
293. W. E. Mochel and J. H. Peterson, *J. Am. Chem. Soc.*, **71**, 1426 (1949).
294. L. B. Hunt, Canadian Pat. 525,592 (May 29, 1956).
295. G. Natta, L. Porri, P. Corradini, and F. Ciampelli, *J. Polymer Sci.*, **51**, 463 (1961).
296. G. Natta, L. G. Stoppa, G. Allegra, and F. Ciampelli, *J. Polymer Sci. B*, **1**, 67 (1963).
297. G. Natta, L. Porri, A. Carbonaro, G. Stoppa, *Makromol. Chem.*, **77**, 114 (1964).

298. G. Natta, L. Porri, L. Carbonaro, F. Ciampelli, and G. Allegra, *Makromol. Chem.*, **51**, 229 (1962).
299. G. Natta, L. Porri, and G. Sovarzi, *European Polymer J.*, **1**, 81 (1965).
300. G. Natta and L. Porri, *Adv. in Chemistry*, **52**, *Elastomer Stereospecific Polymerization*, American Chemical Society, 1966, p. 24.
301. D. Craig, *J. Am. Chem. Soc.*, **65**, 1006 (1943).
302. R. L. Frank, R. D. Emmek, and R. S. Johnson, *ibid.*, **69**, 2313 (1947).
303. W. P. Baker, Jr., *J. Polymer Sci. A*, **1**, 655 (1963).
304. S. Otsuka, *J. Am. Chem. Soc.*, **87**, 3017 (1965).
305. W. P. Baker, Jr., private communication.
306. V. L. Bell, *J. Polymer Sci. A*, **2**, 5291 (1964).
307. G. F. Woods and L. H. Schwartzman, *J. Am. Chem. Soc.*, **70**, 3394 (1948).
308. V. L. Bell, *J. Polymer Sci. A*, **2**, 5305 (1964).
309. H. Batzer and H. Reblin, *Makromol. Chem.*, **44–46**, 179 (1961).

CHAPTER 5

Ring Opening Polymerizations

I. General Discussion

It is possible in many instances to go directly from a heterocyclic monomer to a linear high polymer by a process of ring opening polymerization. The polymers are condensation-type, although no small molecule is eliminated and no hydrogen transfer is involved. However, ring opening polymerizations may be catalyzed by reagents which typically polymerize vinyl monomers. Most of these are cationic and anionic. Only a few examples of free radical initiation have been reported, and these are not well illustrated.

Although there are many heterocycles which give polymer by ring-opening polymerization, only those which have given polymers fitting the conditions given in Chapter 1 will be considered.

II. Cyclic Amides

An interesting feature regarding ring-opening polymerization, in general, is the relationship between ring size and polymerizability. Caprolactam, a seven-membered ring, polymerizes readily at high temperatures with anionic initiators. Butyrolactam, a five-membered ring, and valerolactam, a six-membered ring, polymerize anionically also. However, *low* temperatures are required. Above 60–80°C., polymer will revert to monomer in the presence of the catalyst. The relationship between polymerizability of cyclic amides and configurational strain in the ring has been studied extensively by H. K. Hall, Jr. (1–5), who has examined polycyclic and bridged monomers as well as the simpler systems. The reader is referred to his papers for a thorough treatment of the subject.

The anionic fast polymerization of caprolactam to 6-nylon

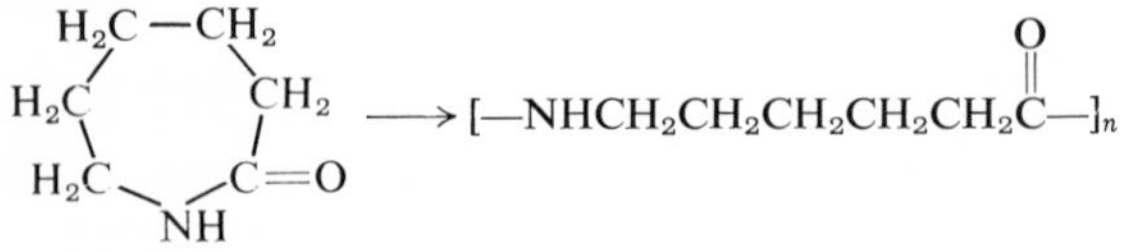

$$
\begin{array}{c}
H_2C-CH_2 \\
H_2C \qquad CH_2 \\
H_2C \qquad C=O \\
NH
\end{array}
\longrightarrow [-NHCH_2CH_2CH_2CH_2CH_2\overset{\overset{\displaystyle O}{\|}}{C}-]_n
$$

goes very rapidly at elevated temperatures to a polymer with very high viscosity. If this polymer is maintained at an elevated temperature, the viscosity drops and levels off at a much lower value. Since degradation of the polymer chain does not appear to be a contributing factor, a change in the molecular weight distribution appears to be the most likely explanation and has been demonstrated recently (6).

281. Fast Polymerization of ε-Caprolactam to 6-Nylon with Anionic Catalyst (7,8)

Caprolactam is purified before use by recrystallizing twice from cyclohexane. It is then stored in a vacuum desiccator at room temperature over phosphoric anhydride for 48 hr., preferably at pressures below 0.1 mm. After this treatment, the water content should be below 0.15% as determined by Karl Fischer titration.

A suitable quantity of caprolactam, usually about 25 g., is melted under nitrogen in a polymer tube having a nitrogen capillary inlet, at temperatures of approximately 80–100°C. To the molten caprolactam is added a quantity of sodium dispersion in xylene corresponding to 0.04–0.08% of sodium based on caprolactam. The mixture of caprolactam and the sodium salt of caprolactam that results may be maintained in the molten condition for many hours without loss of activity. In order to polymerize this mixture, it is brought to a temperature of 255–265°C. under nitrogen by a vapor bath as rapidly as possible. From the time of transfer to the high temperature vapor bath to the completion of polymerization will require approximately 5 min. The course of the polymerization may be judged by observing the rate of rise of nitrogen bubbles issuing from a capillary in the bottom of the liquid. As polymerization begins, the rate of rise will diminish abruptly and the liquid will take on the consistency of an extremely thick honey. Polymerization will be complete after 6 min. and the polymer should have an inherent viscosity of about 2.5 as measured in formic acid at 0.5% concentration. If the polymer is maintained at the elevated temperature for longer than 6 min., the molecular weight distribution will alter and the viscosity will drop off. It should level off at an inherent viscosity of about 1.0 after several hours.

This experiment may be carried out using other alkaline catalysts. For example, lithium, potassium, lithium hydride, sodium hydride, or lithium aluminum hydride may be used in place of the sodium dispersion. However, metallic sodium dispersion is the most convenient additive to carry out the reaction.

The polycaproamide or 6-nylon which is produced according to the above directions is obtained as a tough, horny plug with a melting point of about 215°C. It may be fabricated to a tough film by pressing in a laboratory press at temperatures in excess of 215°C. or it may be extruded from a spinneret in the form of a filament. Both filament and film may be stretched over a hot plate to give highly oriented crystalline products which are very tough.

The toughness of the polymer may be illustrated very dramatically by removing the capillary from the viscous mass of polymer after approximately 5 min. of polymerization time, and before cooling. The viscous mass will be pulled up out of the hot zone and will cool rapidly. It is possible to draw a long and very strong fiber directly on the tip of the capillary.

282. Polymerization of Caprolactam with Water Catalyst (9,10)

The water catalyzed polymerization of caprolactam does not involve hydrolysis of the caprolactam to the amino acid followed by a typical polycondensation reaction. The polymer grows by reaction of the chain end with additional cyclic monomer (10) in a manner similar to that noted below for the polymerization of carboanhydrides.

The polymerization of caprolactam is carried out in two stages as follows. In a polymer tube is placed 56 g. of purified caprolactam. Purification of the caprolactam may best be carried out by recrystallization from cyclohexane. To the purified caprolactam is now added 1 ml. of water and the tube is sealed under nitrogen (see Chapter 2, Section 3). The polymer tube is heated to 250°C. and maintained at this temperature for about 6 hr. The tube is now cooled, opened cautiously, and reheated under a stream of nitrogen to about 250–255°C. During the warm-up period, most of the water added as catalyst will be flushed out of the system. The polymerization is allowed to proceed under nitrogen for about 2 hr. At the end of this period the polymer is obtained as an extremely viscous melt which will cool to a tough, horny plug.

Continued heating of the melt will continue to raise the viscosity. In actual industrial practice, it is possible to obtain polymer of too high a melt viscosity for satisfactory fabrication. To obviate this difficulty, small amounts of acetic acid may be added to the original polymerization mixture, to act as a chain terminator, or molecular weight control agent.

It has been noted (11) that the polymerization of cyclic lactams such as butyrolactam and caprolactam is very effectively catalyzed by trace quantities of N-acyl lactams. The following experiment will illustrate the **effect of an acetyl lactam on the polymerization of caprolactam** itself.

283. Polymerization of Caprolactam Catalyzed by N-Acetyl Caprolactam

In a glass polymer tube is placed 25 g. of caprolactam which is then melted in a steam bath under nitrogen. To the molten caprolactam is added 0.6 g. of sodium hydride which is allowed to dissolve to give the N-sodio derivative. This mixture may be maintained at 139°C. in a boiling xylene vapor bath for several hours, but no polymer is produced. To the molten caprolactam containing the sodium derivative is now added 0.33 g. of N-acetyl caprolactam at

139°C. The tube is shaken to mix the contents which solidify rapidly. After 30 min. the tube is cooled and broken, the polymer is ground up in, for example, a Wiley mill. The ground product is extracted with hot water and dried to give high molecular weight 6-nylon in yields of the order of 80% and an inherent viscosity of the order of 1.0 as measured in *m*-cresol. Note that the polymerization described here is below the melting point of the polymer, hence on polymerization the caprolactam goes directly from the liquid to the solid polymetric state.

284. Low Temperature Polymerization of α-Piperidone to 5-Nylon (12)*

$$\text{(structure: piperidone ring with NH and =O)} \xrightarrow{\text{MAlEt}_4} (\text{NH—CH}_2\text{CH}_2\text{CH}_2\text{CH}_2\overset{\overset{\displaystyle O}{\displaystyle \|}}{\text{C}}-)_n$$

with N-acetyl-α-piperidone (ring, N—COCH₃, =O) shown below the arrow.

A. Preparation of MAlEt₄ (M = Li, Na, or K)

$$3M + 4\text{AlEt}_3 \longrightarrow 3\text{MAlEt}_4 + \text{Al}$$

Alkali metal (dispersed form is preferable) and a slight excess of AlEt₃ are allowed to react in a small volume of toluene under reflux in an atmosphere of dry nitrogen. In the course of reaction, metallic aluminum gradually separates. After about 6 hr., the residual alkali metal and aluminum are separated from the solution. LiAlEt₄ and NaAlEt₄ are soluble in boiling toluene, but crystallize in plate forms at room temperature. These crystalline products can be purified by recrystallization from toluene. KAlEt₄ forms a viscous red-brown solution in toluene, but separates into two phases by adding *n*-hexane. This product can be purified by repeated washing with *n*-hexane.

A tetrahydrofuran solution containing 0.5–2.0 moles/l., of MAlEt₄ is used as catalyst for polymerization. The concentration of MAlEt₄ is determined by back-titration (indicator, phenolphthalein) or gasometry after hydrolyzing by 5% hydrochloric acid–tetrahydrofuran (1:1 v/v).

B. Polymerization

α-Piperidone is purified by repeated vacuum distillation under dry nitrogen atmosphere, b.p. 112.4°C./5 mm. Hg, 138°C./10 mm. Hg, 196°C./115 mm. Hg, m.p. 40°C. Water content is less than 0.010 wt. %, by Karl Fischer method.

All the operations are done under a dry nitrogen atmosphere. Polymerization is carried out conveniently in an apparatus having two separate compartments. In one, 2.0 ml. (2.0 mmole) of α-piperidone is treated with the tetrahydrofuran solution of 0.44 mmole of MAlEt₄ at 40°C.–50°C. It is essential to keep the reaction temperature in this range. After the evolution of gaseous ethane has ceased, tetrahydrofuran is removed as completely as possible under reduced pressure. In the other compartment 0.080 g. (0.57 mmole) of N-acetyl-α-piperidone (from piperidone and acetic anhydride) is charged. After the contents of both compartments reach 45°C., they are

---

* We wish to thank Professor Hiyasa Tani for details of this preparation.

mixed together. After a specified time, the polymerization is terminated by adding water or methanol. The catalyst is removed by washing with 5% hydrochloric acid. The polymer is washed thoroughly with water and methanol, and is dried at 70°C. under reduced pressure. Reduced viscosity of polymer η_{sp}/c is measured in m-cresol (concentration, 0.5 g. polymer/100 ml. m-cresol) at 30°C. In order to reach high molecular weight, quite long times are required, as shown in the table:

Polymerization time (days)	1	5	10	25	30
Yield of polymer (%)	18	21	31	43	50
η_{sp}/c	0.16	0.25	0.40	0.79	0.91
m.p. of polymer (°C.)	253	259	264	267	—

The polymer having reduced viscosity > 0.8 forms a film by casting its formic acid solution.

285. Low Temperature Polymerization of γ-Butyrolactam to 4-Nylon (1,2,4,13)

$$\text{(structure)} \longrightarrow [NH-CH_2CH_2CH_2\overset{\overset{\displaystyle O}{\|}}{C}-]_n$$

Five hundred g. of freshly distilled γ-butyrolactam is placed in a 1 l., three-necked round-bottom flask under dry nitrogen. It is absolutely essential to protect the freshly distilled lactam from moisture, since it is extremely hygroscopic and the absorption of any moisture will interfere with the polymerization. The flask is heated by means of a heating mantle to approximately 80°C. when 5 g. of metallic potassium (**Danger**) weighed under dry hexane is then added over a period of about 1 hr. Approximately 100 ml. of monomer is now distilled from the flask under vacuum to remove by-products of the reaction of the potassium with the pyrollidone. The flask, which now contains approximately 400 g. of lactam and several grams of catalytic potassium butyrolactam, is allowed to cool to room temperature, still under nitrogen and protected from moisture. Polymerization begins when the contents of the flask reach approximately 50°C. The flask is allowed to stand for 12 hr., then the polymer cake is removed and broken up. The polymer cake should be a solid lump which is very hard and difficult to break up. It is frequently necessary to use a hack saw to reduce the chunk into pieces that can be cut further to a size that will permit easy washing and eventual fabrication. (If the polymerization is less successful at this point, a monomer–polymer slurry will result, which can be filtered directly for recovery of monomer. This polymer, washed thoroughly with water and dried, may still have a high molecular weight for fabrication, but will be obtained in a diminished yield.) The washed polymer cake is dried in a vacuum at 70°C. The yield should be in the range of 300–320 g. The polymer should have an inherent viscosity measured in m-cresol (0.5% concentration) of 1.2–1.8. It is soluble in formic acid and very viscous solutions in this solvent can be cast to tough films or spun into fibers, according to the techniques described in Chapter 2. The polymer is quite crystalline and has a crystalline melting point of 265°C., a value close to 6–6 nylon.

The polymerizability of butyrolactam is very much a function of its purity. A common variation to the above method is to use an activator such as N-acetylpyrrolidone at roughly one fourth the molar concentration of potassium salt for absolutely pure monomer. It is probable that use of an activator is essential. In the above example, it is possible that trace amounts of butyrolactone are present which react with some of the potassium salt to give the corresponding N-acyl lactam which functions as an activator. The next example shows the use of an activator.

286. Preparation of 4-Nylon (1)

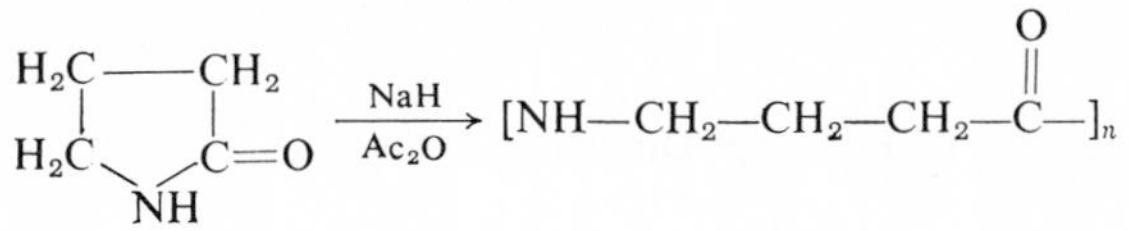

$$\text{H}_2\text{C}\text{---}\text{CH}_2 \qquad \xrightarrow[\text{Ac}_2\text{O}]{\text{NaH}} \qquad [\text{NH}\text{---}\text{CH}_2\text{---}\text{CH}_2\text{---}\text{CH}_2\text{---}\overset{\displaystyle \overset{\text{O}}{\|}}{\text{C}}\text{---}]_n$$

Acetic anhydride, 0.10 g., is added to a solution of 0.13 g. of sodium hydride dispersion (54% in mineral oil) in 6.5 g. of pyrrolidone contained in a polymer tube and blanketed with dry nitrogen. An exothermic reaction ensues, leading to the rapid formation of a hard white plug of polymer. This is broken into small pieces with a knife and hammer and extracted with water and acetone to give 5.7 g. (88%) of poly-γ-butyramide, $\eta_{inh} = 0.88$ in m-cresol (0.5 g./100 ml., 30°C.).

The reaction should not be run this way on much larger scale. The exothermic nature will lead to excessive temperature rises which will cause the polymerization to get out of control.

β-Lactams have only recently been converted to polymers. The parent β-lactam is difficult to synthesize, but has been reported (14) in very low yield (0.8%). It has a melting point of 73–74°C., and is reported to be converted to a "viscous material" at 180°C. More recently, **β,β-disubstituted β-lactams** have been reported via the following route (15):

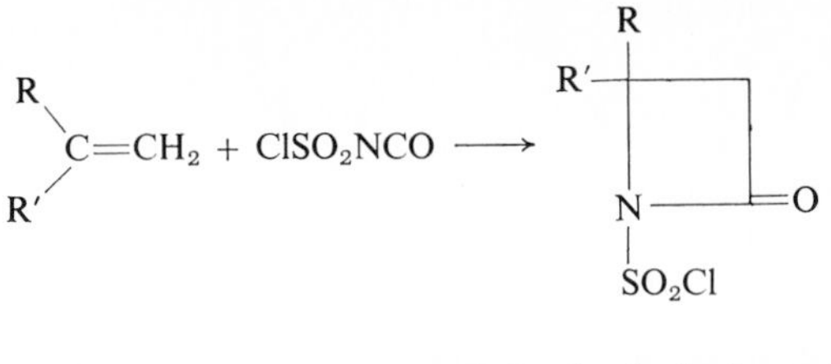

$$\overset{\text{R}}{\underset{\text{R}'}{}}\text{C}\text{=}\text{CH}_2 + \text{ClSO}_2\text{NCO} \longrightarrow$$

The N-sulfonyl chlorides are converted by hydrolysis under weakly acidic conditions to the lactams. The polymerization of monomers of this type has been studied extensively (15).

The α,α-disubstituted lactams have been synthesized (16) by the following reaction:

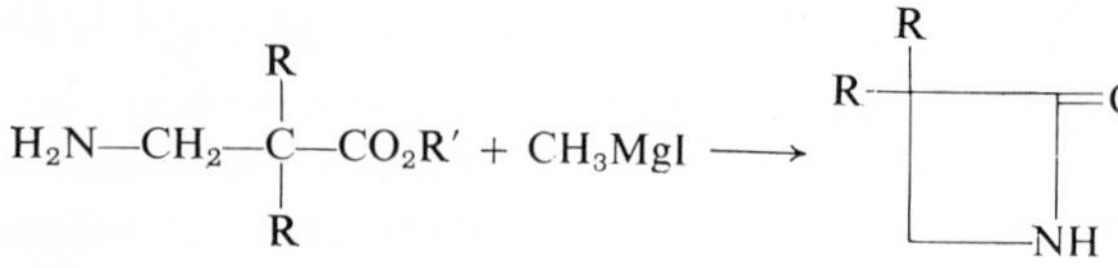

$$H_2N-CH_2-\underset{\underset{R}{|}}{\overset{\overset{R}{|}}{C}}-CO_2R' + CH_3MgI \longrightarrow$$

(ring structure: R, R substituents on carbon, C=O, NH)

The β,β-disubstituted lactams yield higher melting, less tractable polymers, and the monomers present some synthetic problems for laboratory scale operation.

The following laboratory preparation of a α,α-substituted β-lactam is due to Testa (16).

287. Preparation of Ethyl α,α-Diethyl β-Aminopropionate (16)

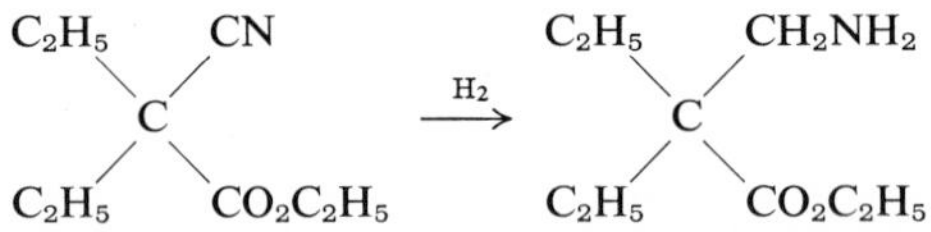

$$\underset{C_2H_5}{\overset{C_2H_5}{\diagdown}}C\underset{CO_2C_2H_5}{\overset{CN}{\diagup}} \quad \overset{H_2}{\longrightarrow} \quad \underset{C_2H_5}{\overset{C_2H_5}{\diagdown}}C\underset{CO_2C_2H_5}{\overset{CH_2NH_2}{\diagup}}$$

A solution of 150 g. ethyl α,α-diethyl cyanoacetate in 300 ml. of absolute alcohol is hydrogenated at 80°C. and 600 p.s.i. over 100 g. Raney nickel. After about 3 hr., hydrogenation should be complete. The catalyst is filtered (usual precautions against fire!) and the alcohol removed in a vacuum. The residual oil is treated with water, and HCl added until the solution is acid. The solution is extracted with ether, and the aqueous phase is separated, treated with a little charcoal, and filtered. The aqueous filtrate is made alkaline with saturated sodium carbonate, and the aminoester extracted with ether. The ether solution is washed with water, dried, and distilled. The aminoester is obtained as an oil in about 115–120 g., b.p. 85–95°C./8 mm. It is sufficiently pure for the next step.

The α,α-diethyl cyanoacetic ester is prepared in two steps by conventional means from cyanoacetic ester and ethyl bromide. A variety of other disubstituted products has been described, but the diethyl is one of the more convenient to work with.

288. Preparation of α,α-Diethyl-β-Propiolactam (16)

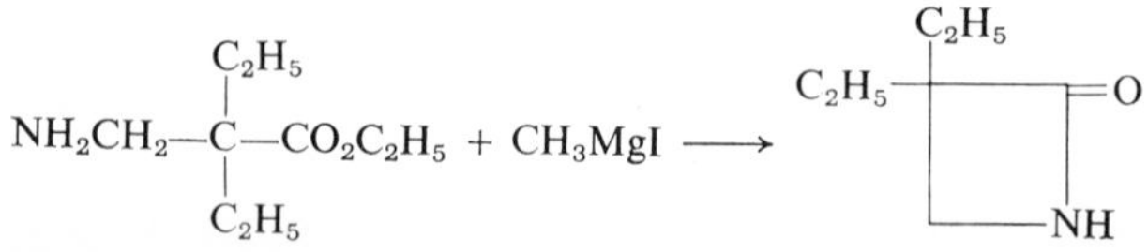

$$NH_2CH_2-\underset{\underset{C_2H_5}{|}}{\overset{\overset{C_2H_5}{|}}{C}}-CO_2C_2H_5 + CH_3MgI \longrightarrow$$

(ring structure: C_2H_5, C_2H_5 substituents on carbon, C=O, NH)

In a 2 l., three-necked round-bottom flask equipped with stirrer, efficient reflux condenser, thermometer, nitrogen inlet, and dropping funnel is placed 0.5 mole of methyl magnesium bromide (commercial product, or synthesized *in situ*) in about 300 ml. of ether. The solution is cooled to 0–5°C., and

25 g. of ethyl α,α-diethyl-β-amino propionate in 200 ml. anhydrous ether is added with stirring over a period of about 40 min. Temperature should be kept at 0–5°C. during addition. The mixture is then refluxed, cooled to 0°C., and treated dropwise with 100 ml. of 5% aqueous ammonium chloride. It is warmed to room temperature, stirred for about 15 min., then the ether solution is separated. The aqueous phase is extracted with 5–50 ml. portions of ether. The combined ether extracts are washed with 10% sodium thiosulfate, dilute hydrochloric acid, and water. The ether solution is dried (Na_2SO_4), the ether stripped and the oil distilled. The yield is about 18 g. (90% or better), b.p. 91–96/0.8 mm.

289. Polymerization of α,α-Diethyl-β-Propiolactam (17,18)

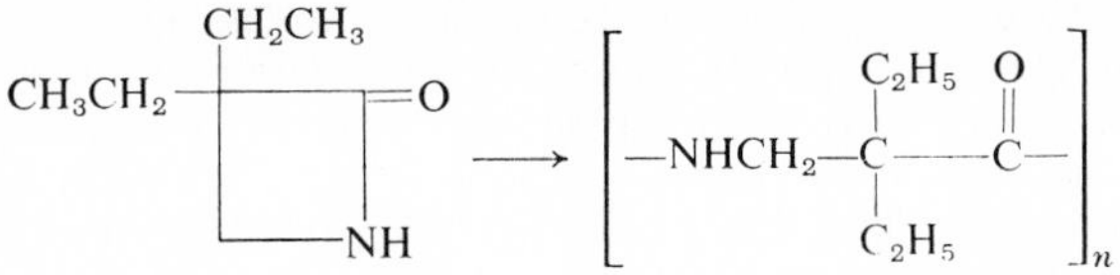

A solution of 25 g. of the lactam is dissolved in 150 ml. of dimethyl sulfoxide in a 250 ml. three-necked flask with nitrogen inlet and stirrer and thermometer. The flask and all ingredients must be very dry. To insure completely anhydrous conditions, some of the solvent may be distilled away in vacuum; however, some monomer may be lost. To the solution of monomer is added 1 g. potassium pyrrolidone and 3 mg. of oxalyl dipyrrolidone at room temperature. Polymerization is exothermic and the temperature is kept at 20–25°C. with a cooling bath. After 2–3 hr., the gel-like product is mixed with 300 ml. acetic acid. The product is filtered, washed with water, and dried. It is obtained as a fine white powder, with an inherent viscosity of 1–2 measured in concentrated sulfuric acid (0.5 g./100 ml., 30°C.). The polymer melts about 200°C., and can be pressed into tough films.

Unsymmetrical β-lactams can be synthesized in optically active form (19). Polymerization of the antipodes has not been reported.

The ring-opening polymerization of **propiosultam** (20,21) has been carried out using a base catalyst and an N-sulfonyl derivative of the monomer, in a manner, and presumably by a mechanism, very similar to that postulated for lactams. Very little is known about the polymerization mechanisms of sultams, in contrast to the lactams. The polypropiosultam, a sulfonamide analog of 3-nylon, melts at 257–260°C., with degradation.

290. Preparation of Propiosultam (20)

$$CH_3\overset{O}{\overset{\|}{C}}-SH + CH_2=CHCH_2Cl \longrightarrow CH_3\overset{O}{\overset{\|}{C}}-S-CH_2CH_2CH_2Cl$$
$$I$$

$$I + Cl_2 + H_2O \longrightarrow ClCH_2CH_2CH_2SO_2Cl$$
$$II$$

$$II + NH_3 \longrightarrow Cl(CH_2)_3SO_2NH_2$$

III

$$III + KOH \longrightarrow \underset{NH}{\overset{|}{\boxed{}}} SO_2$$

3-Chloropropyl thiolacetate is prepared from the peroxide-catalyzed addition of thiolacetic acid (22) to allyl chloride (23). A mixture of 76.2 g. thiolacetic acid, 76.5 g. allyl chloride and 0.5 g. benzoyl peroxide are heated in a 500 ml. three-necked flask with stirring and exclusion of air at 60°C. for 6 hr. Subsequent vacuum distillation gives 120 g. chloropropyl thiolacetate (79%); b.p. 83–84°C./10 mm. The product is a colorless oil.

To 596 g. (3.90 moles) 3-chloropropyl thiolacetate in a 5 l. three-necked flask is added 1 l. of water and about 500 g. of crushed ice. The flask is cooled in an ice bath and the contents swirled vigorously while chlorine is passed through the mixture at a rapid rate. The temperature is maintained at 5–10°C. by addition of more ice. The mixture changes from colorless to yellow, to pink, and then to orange which persists for about an hour, finally fading to a colorless turbidity. When a persistent color of chlorine appears in the mixture, the reaction is stopped, the aqueous supernatancy decanted, washed twice with ether and discarded. The residual heavy oil in the flask and the ether extracts are combined, washed with water, and dried over anhydrous sodium sulfate. After filtering and distilling the ether, the resulting yellow oil is distilled to give about 590 g. (87%) of chloropropylsulfonyl chloride, boiling at 107–108°C./6 mm.

A solution of 177.5 g. (1.0 mole) of the sulfonyl chloride in 500 ml. ether is added to a stirred mixture of 138 ml. of concentrated aqueous ammonia and 1 l. of ether in a 3 l. flask cooled in an ice bath. The rate of addition is such as to maintain the temperature at 5°C.; the mixture is stirred 30 min. after addition is complete. The ether solution is dried as above, filtered, and enough low boiling petroleum ether added to give a faint turbidity. On cooling in a freezer, about 56 g. of white needles are obtained, m.p. 64.0–64.5°C. This is sulfonamide III. The organic filtrate is evaporated, as is the aqueous layer of the reaction, and the solids are combined and extracted thrice with 500 ml. portions of hot benzene. Cooling this solution gives about 48 g. of needles with the same 64.0–64.5°C. melting point as the earlier product.

To a solution of 115 g. (0.73 mole) of 3-chloropropanesulfonamide in 1 l. absolute ethanol (freshly distilled from KOH) is added 40.9 g. (0.73 mole) of potassium hydroxide in 200 ml. absolute ethanol. The solution becomes turbid. It is refluxed for 45 min., a white precipitate forms and the solution becomes neutral. A solution of 2.0 g. KOH in ethanol is added and refluxing is continued for 30 min., at which point the basic mixture is cooled and filtered, and the salt washed with two 25 ml. portions of ethanol. The filtrate and washing are neutralized with concentrated HCl and again filtered, and the alcohol removed at reduced pressure to give 89.5 g. of a light-yellow oil, with some KCl still present. Distillation of the oil gives about 3.5 g. of a vile-smelling yellow liquid, 74 g. of an odorless yellow liquid (b.p. 156–157°C./2 mm.), and a black residue. The main product solidified; m.p. 23.0–23.1°C. This product is treated with decolorizing carbon, after redistilling, to give about 65 g. of propanesultam, b.p. as above, n_D^{25} 1.4826. This product can be further purified by low temperature crystallization from ether–alcohol.

N-Benzenesulfonyl propanesultam is prepared by adding 5.0 g. of the sultam and 5.2 ml. benzenesulfonyl chloride to 16 ml. pyridine, allowing to stand 72 hr. and pouring into 250 ml. ice water. The tan precipitate is recrystallized from ethanol, decolorized with carbon in an acetone solution, and recrystallized from ethanol to give 1.5 g. white plates, m.p. 169.5–170.0°C.

291. Preparation of Polypropanesultam (20)

In a small, dry reaction vessel equipped with nitrogen inlet and outlet is placed, after first thoroughly flushing with nitrogen, 0.0103 g. *N*-benzene-sulfonylpropanesultam and 1.10 g. of purified propanesultam. At room temperature, the mixture is a liquid and dry nitrogen can conveniently be bubbled through it to aid in agitation in order to dissolve the cocatalyst sulfonyl sultam. Then about 3 mg. sodium hydride is added under nitrogen, the vessel shaken till all the hydride has reacted, and the mixture placed in an oil bath at 130°C. for 18 hr., under nitrogen. After cooling, the hard, slightly yellow cake is ground in water in a mortar, the solid collected by centrifuging, washed twice with water, acetone, and dried at 60°C. in vacuum. About 0.7 g. of polysulfonamide is obtained, with m.p. 257–260°C. and intrinsic viscosity of 0.7 dl./g. (concentrated sulfuric acid). Cold-drawable fibers can be pulled from a melt of the polymer.

The acidity of sulfonamide hydrogens permits subsequent alkylation of the nitrogen. This reaction sequence has been carried out on polypropanesultam to modify its properties. The effect of *N*-substitution is generally in the expected direction: lower melting point and increased solubility.

292. Preparation of *N*-Methylated Polypropanesultam (24)

To a solution of 11.7 g. sodium hydroxide in 230 ml. water in a home blender is added 3 g. of polypropanesultam. The polymer dissolves on stirring, and then 1.88 g. dimethyl sulfate (Caution! Toxic) is added when the temperature of the stirred solution is 35°C. The mixture is stirred very vigorously, and the temperature rises to about 52°C. When the exotherm subsides, aqueous concentrated ammonia (about 20 ml.) is added to react with residual alkylating agent, and concentrated hydrochloric is added in sufficient amount of precipitate the polymer and cause the slurry to remain acidic after standing. The polymer is separated by centrifugation and washed extensively with water, ethanol, and ether and finally dried in vacuum at

55°C. A clear film can be melt-pressed at about 190°C., and the inherent viscosity is not significantly altered from the original. The polymer is about 60% N-methylated. The melting point of the polymer is between 150 and 185°C., depending on the uniformity of the alkylation reaction throughout the molecular system.

III. N-Carboanhydrides of α-Amino Acids (25–31)

Many naturally occurring fibers (e.g., wool) are polypeptides, i.e., polyamides based on naturally occurring amino acids. The synthesis of high molecular weight polypeptides with a predetermined sequence of amino acids is an extremely laborious procedure and not suited to polymer preparation. However, **amino acids** can be converted to **derivatives,** according to schemes such as the following:

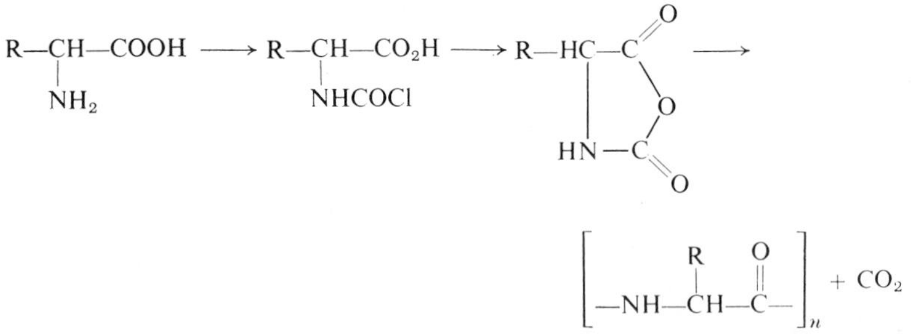

$$R-CH-COOH \longrightarrow R-CH-CO_2H \longrightarrow \ldots$$
$$|\qquad\qquad\qquad\quad |$$
$$NH_2 \qquad\qquad\qquad NHCOCl$$

$$\left[-NH-\underset{\underset{H}{|}}{\overset{\overset{R}{|}}{C}}H-\overset{\overset{O}{\|}}{C}- \right]_n + CO_2$$

These are ring-opening type polymers, since the polymer presumably grows by reaction of an active center on the end of the growing chain with a new cyclic monomer unit by an ionic chain mechanism (31). Homopolymers are usually intractable; copolymers are more readily handled.

N-Carboanhydrides (NCA's) can be polymerized with a variety of catalysts, such as water, primary, secondary, and tertiary amines, and strong bases such as sodium methoxide. The mechanism is complex (31,32) and depends on the structure and type of initiator and whether the NCA is N-substituted. Basically, two mechanistic paths are followed, sometimes either wholly individually, or both in part. The first is often called the **"primary amine mechanism"** and can be pictured as attack of a primary amine at the five-carbon atom with ring opening, proton transfer, and loss of carbon dioxide.

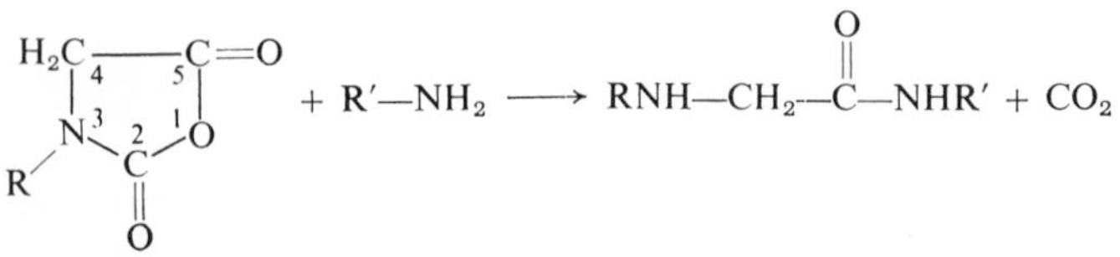

$$H_2C-C=O + R'-NH_2 \longrightarrow RNH-CH_2-\overset{\overset{O}{\|}}{C}-NHR' + CO_2$$

R = H, alkyl or aryl.

Propagation continues by reaction of the product with more NCA. With tertiary amines and certain hindered secondary amines (e.g., diisopropylamine), another mechanism (31) is invoked wherein proton abstraction from nitrogen is the first step, followed by addition of the resulting anion to another molecule of NCA:

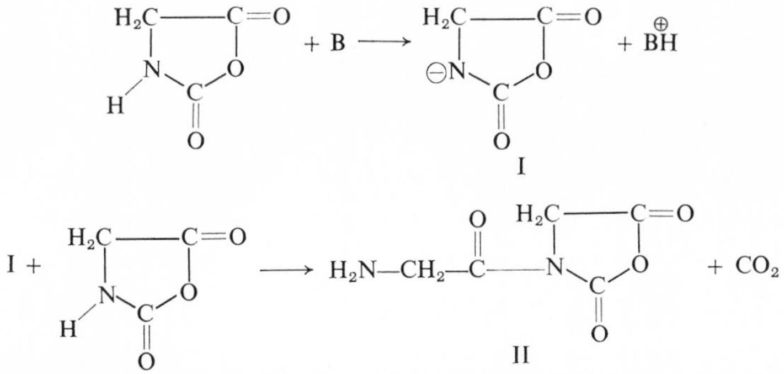

Propagation occurs, as before, via addition of the terminal primary amine to NCA or to terminal NCA of a growing unit such as II.

For N-substituted NCA's, such as that from sarcosine (N-methylglycine), polymerization is evidently possible only by initiation with primary and secondary amines and strong bases such as the methoxide ion. With the protic amines, addition to the 5-carbon, as in the first mechanism described, is believed to occur. It has been shown (32) that with sodium methoxide initiator, N-substituted NCA's undergo hydrogen abstraction at the 4-carbon, the resulting anion attacking another NCA:

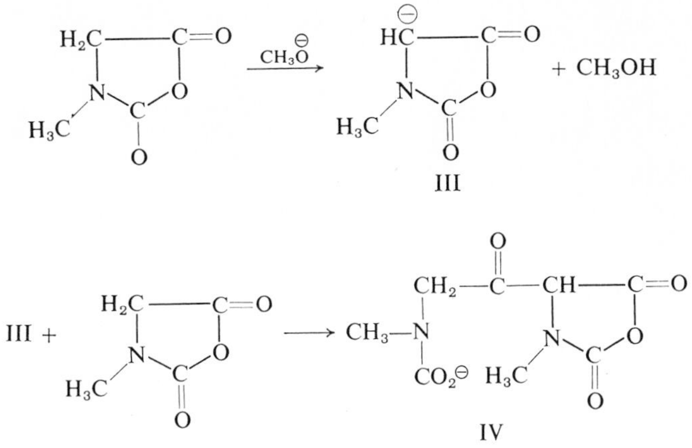

IV is considered to propagate by attack of the carbamate anion at the 5-carbon of an NCA to regenerate a carbamate ion and form a mixed anhydride, the latter decomposing to CO_2 and an amide.

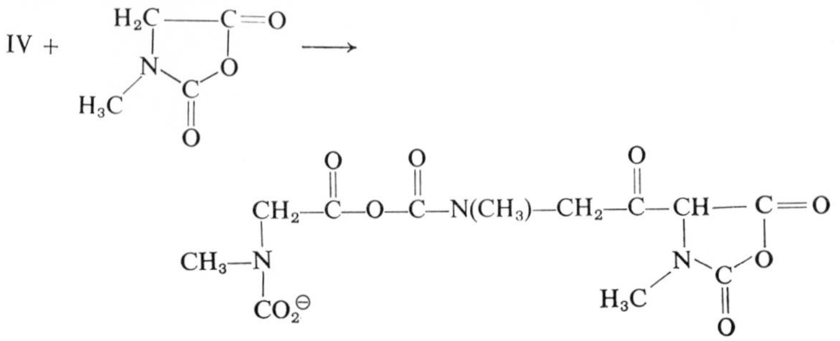

Much of this view (32) is based on the fact that no radioactivity is found in the polymer when radioactive sodium methoxide is used to initiate sarcosine NCA polymerization and only traces are found in polymer from γ-benzyl-L-glutamate NCA; also, sodium benzylcarbamate initiates the polymerization of γ-benzyl-L-glutamate NCA with the same kinetics as does sodium methoxide.

The complex character of NCA polymerization and the diversity of mechanistic views advanced, including alternatives to the foregoing, have been treated at length by Szwarc (33).

293. Preparation of L-4-Isobutyloxazolide-2,5-dione (26,29)

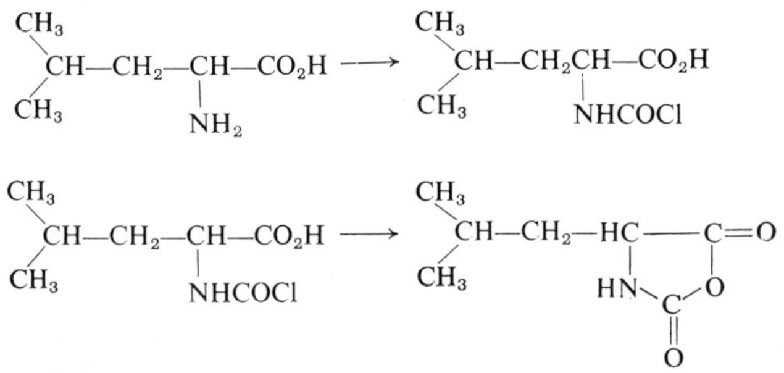

Caution! Phosgene Is Very Dangerous and Must be Used Carefully in a Well Ventilated Hood. All Off-Gases Should be Adequately Scrubbed.

Pure L-leucine is recrystallized from water and dried. A sample of this amino acid weighing 32 g. is agitated with purified dioxane (400 ml.) in a three-necked, 2 l. flask. Phosgene is bubbled in a slow stream from a cylinder into the slurry for 45 min. with the temperature maintained at approximately

40°C. After the addition of phosgene is complete, a rapid stream of dry air is passed through the solution for 16 hr. to remove excess phosgene. The dioxane is then removed *in vacuo* at 40°C. The residue crystallizes almost immediately. It is recrystallized immediately prior to use from a mixture of ether and light petroleum. The product melts at 76–77°C. and is very sensitive to moisture. It should be recrystallized and handled in a dry box.

In this preparation it is essential that pure L-leucine is used and not material which is contaminated with other amino acids such as tyrosine.

294. Preparation of 4-Benzyloxazolid-2,5-dione (26–28)

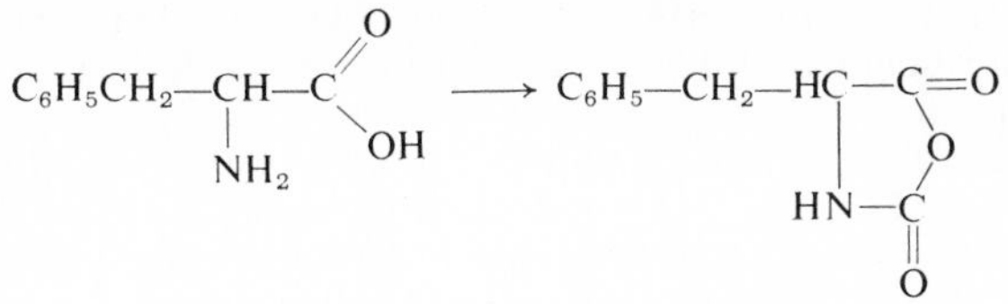

Caution! Phosgene Is Very Dangerous and Must be Used Carefully in a Well Ventilated Hood. All Off-Gases Should be Adequately Scrubbed.

Twenty g. of DL-phenylalanine is dissolved in 400 ml. of pure dioxane and treated with a slow stream of phosgene for 2 hr. at 40°C. Excess phosgene and solvent is removed with a stream of dry air or nitrogen and the residue is heated at about 40°C. in a vaccum. The residual solid is recrystallized from ethyl acetate–petroleum ether. The yield is about 60% of a material melting at 127°C. It is very moisture sensitive (see Preparation 194).

295. Preparation of 4,4-Dimethyloxazolid-2,5-dione (26–28)

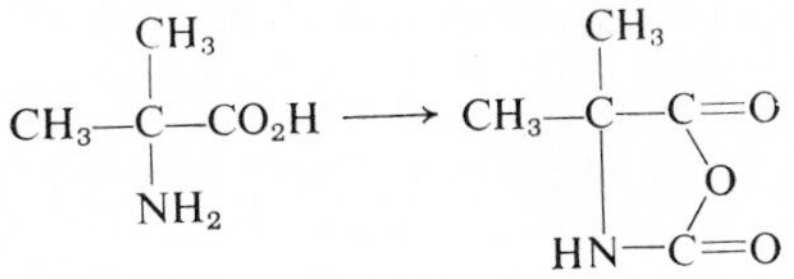

Caution! Phosgene Is Very Dangerous and Must be Used Carefully in a Well Ventilated Hood. All Off-Gases Should be Adequately Scrubbed.

Fifteen g. of α-aminoisobutyric acid in 400 ml. of pure dioxane is treated with a slow stream of phosgene at 50°C. for 9 hr. The dioxane and excess phosgene are removed with a stream of dry air or nitrogen. The oily residue solidifies when warmed at 40°C. in a vacuum. The solid is dissolved in the minimum volume of hot chloroform, which should be purified just prior to use to remove moisture and ethanol stabilizer. The chloroform solution is filtered and treated with 3 volumes of petroleum ether. The crystalline product is obtained in about 80% yield and melts at 95–97°C. It must be recrystallized once more just prior to polymerization and should be kept out of contact with moist air.

296. Copolymerization of 4,4-Dimethyloxazolide-2,5-dione and 4-Benzyl DL-Oxazolide-2,5-dione (26–28)

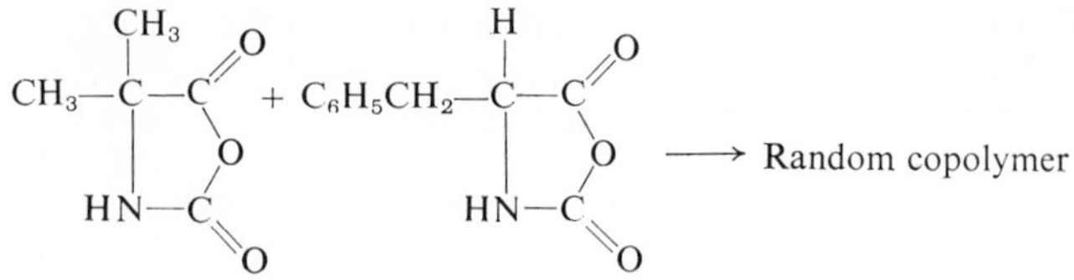

A solution of 2.6 g. (0.02 mole) of 4,4-dimethyloxazolide-2,5-dione and 3.8 g. (0.02 mole) of 4-benzyl-DL-oxazolide-2,5-dione in 70 ml. of benzene is treated with a solution of 0.5 ml. of water in 1 ml. of purified dioxane. The solution viscosity increases perceptibly during 6 days. The solution may be poured onto a glass plate and evaporated to a thin polymeric film.

Similarly, a 1 : 2 copolymer of these reactants may be prepared. Thus, in 70 ml. of benzene is placed 1.3 g. (0.01 mole) of 4,4-dimethyloxazolide-2,5-dione, 3.8 g. (0.02 mole) of 4-benzyl-DL-oxazolide-2,5-dione, and 0.25 ml. of dioxane containing 1% of aniline. Polymerization proceeds over a period of about 10 days. At the end of this period the solution is clear and may be cast to clear, tough film. These films can be stretched and oriented by drawing.

297. Preparation of a Copolymer of L-Leucine and DL-Phenylalanine (26–28)

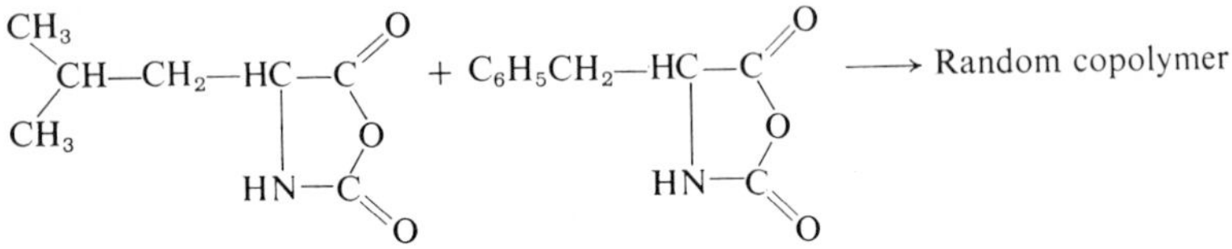

A 1 l., three-necked flask equipped with a stirring shaft, nitrogen inlet tube, and an exit tube is charged with 500 ml. of dry benzene, 3.8 g. (0.02 mole) of 4-benzyl-DL-oxazolide-2,5-dione, and 2.9 g. (0.02 mole) of L-4-isobutyl-oxazolide-2,5-dione. Some of the benzyl derivative will remain undissolved. To this mixture is now added 0.5 g. of water dissolved in 340 ml. of previously dry benzene. After 5 days the solution will be cloudy and quite viscous. All the glass in contact with the reaction mixture will be coated with a film of polymer. In order to bring the undissolved material into solution, some dry chloroform is added. The resulting clear viscous solution is centrifuged to separate a small amount of insoluble matter.

The polymer solution may be poured onto a glass plate and the solvent evaporated to give polypeptide film of good strength. The resulting dry polymer begins to decompose at about 220–230°C. The polymer may also be precipitated from solution by addition of alcohol or light petroleum ether.

When possible, most regular workers in the polypeptide field employ phosgene in the synthesis of NCA's. However, it is **possible to prepare** this ring system **by a route which avoids the use of phosgene** (at the expense of one extra synthetic step) and for workers who do not regularly synthesize polypeptides such a preparation may have practical advantages. The synthesis of poly-γ-L-glutamic acid and its predecessor benzyl ester are described below as an example (34).

298. Preparation of γ-Benzyl-L-Glutamate*

$$HO_2C(CH_2)_2CH(NH_2) \cdot CO_2H + C_6H_5CH_2OH \longrightarrow$$
$$C_6H_5CH_2O_2C(CH_2)_2CH(NH_2) \cdot CO_2H$$

To a mixture of 70 g. L-glutamic acid and 250 ml. of benzyl alcohol 70 ml. concentrated hydrochloric acid is added and the mixture is warmed until the solution just boils and becomes homogeneous. (Overheating is undesirable since excessive amounts of di-ester are formed.) After standing for 2 hr. the crystalline slurry is added to 4.5 l. of acetone. The crystals of ester hydrochloride which separate completely in a further 2 hr. are collected, washed once with acetone, and dissolved in 500 ml. of water. This solution is cooled in ice and neutralized by the careful addition, with vigorous stirring, of solid sodium bicarbonate until pH 8 is attained. After filtration, the crude amino acid γ-ester is washed with ice water and recrystallized from hot water. The pure γ-benzyl-L-glutamate is collected, washed with ice water, then acetone, and dried in a vacuum oven at 60°C. A typical yield of 30 g. (25%) pure ester results.

299. Preparation of N-Benzyloxycarbonyl-γ-Benzyl-L-Glutamate

$$C_6H_5CH_2O_2C(CH_2)_2\underset{\underset{NH_2}{|}}{CH} \cdot CO_2H + C_6H_5CH_2OCOCl \longrightarrow$$
$$C_6H_5CH_2O_2C(CH_2)_2\underset{\underset{NH \cdot CO \cdot OCH_2C_6H_5}{|}}{CH} \cdot CO_2H$$

To 2 l. of water at 65°C. in a 5 l. beaker 20 g. of sodium bicarbonate and 23.7 g. of γ-benzyl-L-glutamate are added and the mixture is stirred until dissolution is complete. To the resulting stirred solution 20 ml. of fresh benzyl chloroformate (**FUME HOOD!**) is quickly added and the stirring is continued for a further 3 hr. By-products are extracted with 500 ml. of ether and the aqueous layer is filtered if necessary and acidified to congo-red paper with concentrated hydrochloric acid. The oil formed is extracted by 500 ml. of ether, the ether dried over anhydrous sodium sulfate and then evaporated *in vacuo*. The solid or viscous oily residue remaining is dissolved in carbon tetrachloride and the solution is concentrated *in vacuo* to about 300 ml. On standing overnight, N-benzyloxycarbonyl-γ-benzyl-L-glutamate crystallizes. The yield is approximately 20 g. (55%).

300. Preparation of L-4-(Butyl-γ-Benzyloxycarbonyl)oxazolid-2,5-dione (γ-Benzyl-L-Glutamate NCA)

A mixture of 20 g. N-benzyloxycarbonyl-γ-benzyl-L-glutamate and 20 ml. freshly distilled thionyl chloride is warmed in a flask (guarded with a calcium chloride tube) on a water bath maintained at 60–70°C. until a distinct yellow-orange color is formed. The color changes from white through yellow to

* We are most grateful to Dr. H. Block and C. H. Bamford, The University of Liverpool, for providing in their entirety preparations 298–302.

$$C_6H_5CH_2O_2C(CH_2)_2CH.CO.OH \quad + SOCl_2 \longrightarrow$$
$$|$$
$$HN.CO.OCH_2C_6H_5$$

$$C_6H_5CH_2O_2C(CH_2)_2HC . CO$$
$$| \qquad \diagdown$$
$$| \qquad O + C_6H_5CH_2Cl$$
$$HN-CO$$

$$+ SO_2 + HCl$$

reddish-brown; too prolonged a reaction results in a product which is impossible to purify while too short a contact time leads to poor yields. After cooling, the reaction mixture is solidified under 60–80°C. petroleum ether, filtered and washed with cyclohexane. It is repeatedly recrystallized from hot ethyl acetate (1 ml./g. of dry product) by cooling in ice until colorless and chloride-free. The chloride impurities, which are ionizable, can be detected by decomposing about 0.1 g. samples of monomer with boiling dilute nitric acid and adding silver nitrate. *It is essential that this test be negative if high molecular weight polymers are to be obtained in the next stage.*

Typical yield from two recrystallizations is approximately 7 g. (50%).

Note that the monomer is moisture-sensitive and that it is advisable to convert monomer to polymer at the earliest opportunity.

301. Preparation of Poly(γ-Benzyl-L-glutamate)

$$C_6H_5CH_2O_2C(CH_2)_2HC-CO \qquad \qquad \left[\begin{array}{c} (CH_2)_2.CO_2CH_2C_6H_5 \\ | \\ NH.CH.CO-\!\!\!\!-\!\!\!\!- \end{array} \right]_n + CO_2$$
$$| \qquad \diagdown \qquad \xrightarrow{n\text{Bu}_3\text{N}}$$
$$| \qquad O$$
$$HN-CO$$

For the polymerization, pure, dry ethyl acetate, methylene chloride, and tri-n-butylamine are required.

Ethyl acetate is dried over potassium carbonate for 24 hr. and distilled.

Methylene chloride of satisfactory purity is obtained as the residue remaining after distilling one third by volume of the general purpose reagent. This removes water, hydrogen chloride, and acid chlorides.

Tri-n-butylamine which has been allowed to stand over barium oxide for 24 hr. is distilled at reduced pressure (86°C./15 mm. Hg), the middle fraction being collected. A standard solution of this amine (0.6 ml.) in methylene chloride (25 ml.) is prepared.

To polymerize the monomer, 5 g. of L-4-(butyl-γ-benzyloxycarbonyl) oxazolid-2,5-dione is dissolved by warming with 5 ml. ethyl acetate and to this solution is rapidly added 10 ml. methylene chloride and 4 ml. of initiator solution, avoiding as far as possible the separation of solid monomer on the walls of the vessel. The reaction mixture is then refluxed on a water bath for 30 min. after which the polymerization is completed at ambient temperature overnight. The resulting polymer is precipitated by running the reaction mixture into 500 ml. of methanol. The polymer is collected, washed with methanol and dried *in vacuo* at 40°C. If this is the desired end-product of the synthesis, a more convenient physical form can be obtained by dissolving the polymer in 25 ml. of chloroform and casting on to a clean glass sheet. After solvent evaporation the polymer film can be floated off with a little water (cutting the film edges with a knife assists this operation) and the film dried *in vacuo*. A typical yield of 4 g. (95%) results.

302. Preparation of Poly-α-L-Glutamic Acid

$$
\underline{}\left[\begin{array}{c} (CH_2)_2CO_2CH_2C_6H_5 \\ | \\ -NH \cdot CH \cdot CO \underline{} \end{array}\right]_n \xrightarrow{\text{HBr}}
$$

$$
\underline{}\left[\begin{array}{c} (CH_2)_2CO_2H \\ | \\ -NH \cdot CH \cdot CO \underline{} \end{array}\right]_n \underline{} + nC_6H_5CH_2Br
$$

A 1–2% solution of poly-γ-benzyl-L-glutamate in distilled, sodium-dried benzene is made-up and through this is passed a stream of pure, dry hydrogen bromide until poly-α-L-glutamic acid starts to precipitate. The solution is then left to stand until a total of 8 hr. has elapsed since the beginning of the hydrogen bromide treatment. Isolation of the polymer is achieved by pouring into excess petroleum ether and washing well with this solvent. It can be further purified by dissolving in 5% sodium bicarbonate, precipitating into cold 2N hydrochloric acid, filtering, washing well with water, and drying *in vacuo*. Yields are nearly quantitative. It is important to realize that hydrolytic cleavage of the peptide has a disproportionally large effect in reducing the degree of polymerization and hence the exclusion of moisture while the polymer is in the presence of hydrogen bromide is vital if high molecular weight material is required.

IV. Cyclic Esters

It is interesting to note that although cyclic carboanhydrides of α-hydroxy acids do not polymerize to a high molecular weight it is possible to prepare a polyester by the thermal **polymerization of an anhydrosulfite.** Thus, α-hydroxyisobutyric acid gives, with thionyl chloride, α-hydroxyisobutyric acid anhydrosulfite

$$
\begin{array}{c} CH_3 \\ | \\ HO-C-CO_2H \\ | \\ CH_3 \end{array} \xrightarrow{SOCl_2} \begin{array}{c} CH_3 \\ | \\ CH_3C\underline{}C=O \\ \diagdown\diagup \\ O O \\ \diagdown S \diagup \\ \| \\ O \end{array} \xrightarrow{-SO_2} \left[\begin{array}{c} CH_3 O \\ | \diagup\diagdown \\ -OC-C \\ | \\ CH_3 \end{array}\right]_n
$$

which polymerizes when heated, with elimination of sulfur dioxide.

303. Preparation of α-Hydroxyisobutyric Acid Anhydrosulfite (35,36)

In a 3 l., three-necked flask, equipped with a stirrer, a reflux condenser, and a dropping funnel is placed 1000 g. of thionyl chloride. The thionyl chloride is

$$\underset{\underset{CH_3}{|}}{\overset{\overset{CH_3}{|}}{HO-C-CO_2H}} \xrightarrow{SOCl_2} \underset{\underset{O_{\diagdown}{}_{\underset{O}{S}}\diagup O}{}}{\overset{\overset{CH_3}{|}}{CH_3-C}} C=O$$

cooled in an ice–salt bath to approximately 0°C. and 312 g. of α-hydroxyiso-butyric acid is added. The reaction system is attached to a water pump and a pressure of 100–200 mm. is maintained in the flask with stirring in order to remove the evolved hydrogen chloride. After 18 hr. at 0°C. and 100–200 mm. pressure, the flask is allowed to warm to room temperature at this pressure. Excess thionyl chloride is then distilled rapidly through a short still head, then the anhydrosulfite is obtained boiling at 41–48°C. at 8 mm. The yield of crude product is approximately 309 g. (69%). This crude anhydrosulfite is then distilled through an efficient fractionating column. The boiling point of the pure product is 53–55°C. at 16 mm., $n_D^{25} = 1.4290–1.4309$.

304. Prepolymerization of the Anhydrosulfite

In order to remove chance initiators from the anhydrosulfite the material is maintained at reflux for 140–146 hr. under reduced pressure such that the temperature of reflux is about 55°C. Under these condititions, approximately 10% of the anhydrosulfite will polymerize to low molecular weight material. This effectively removes any chance impurities which might give erratic results during polymerization. Redistillation of unpolymerized material purified in this manner gives a product with a refractive index of 1.4298.

305. Polymerization of α-Hydroxyisobutyric Acid Anhydrosulfite (35)

$$\underset{\underset{O_{\diagdown}{}_{\underset{O}{S}}\diagup O}{}}{\overset{\overset{CH_3}{|}}{CH_3-C}} C=O \xrightarrow{-SO_2} \left[\underset{\underset{CH_3}{|}}{\overset{\overset{CH_3}{|}}{-O-C-C}} \overset{O}{\diagup} \right]_n$$

A 300 ml., round-bottom flask is dried by baking in an oven at 110–150°C. for about 3 hr. To the flask, which is cooled under nitrogen, is added 150 ml. of benzene. In order to make sure that the flask and contents are completely dry, approximately 50 ml. of benzene is then distilled from the reaction vessel. The flask is cooled under nitrogen in an ice bath until the benzene has frozen and 50 g. of the anhydrosulfite with a refractive index of 1.4298 is added. The reaction mixture is refluxed for 52 hr. under nitrogen to give a cloudy colorless gel. This is filtered to give a solid polymer which has a molecular weight in excess of 100,000. It melts at 240°C. and has an inherent viscosity of about 1.5 in a solvent consisting of 58.8 parts of phenol and 41.2 parts of 2,4,6-trichloro-phenol. The polymer can be pressed into a clear, colorless film which can be stretched and oriented. It may also be melt-spun to fibrous products.

Chlorobenzene may also be used as a reaction medium. In this case, the polymer remains in solution at the boiling point. Thus, 49.2 g. of the anhydro-sulfite is distilled into 275 g. of frozen, dry chlorobenzene. The reaction mixture is maintained at the reflux. The solution becomes more viscous as time progresses. After $7\frac{1}{2}$ hr., the polymer solution may be cast to a film, or poured into alcohol and precipitated as a white solid, which should also have an inherent viscosity of about 1.5.

It is essential in either of these preparations to have absolutely anhydrous equipment and dry reagents, otherwise polymerization will not proceed to high molecular weight.

In general, unsubstituted **aliphatic polyesters** derived **from lactones** are low melting and tend to revert to monomer. For further information the reader may refer to Carothers' original work (37). Certain lactones, however, deserve mention here.

Propiolactone itself is prepared commercially by the condensation of ketene and formaldehyde.

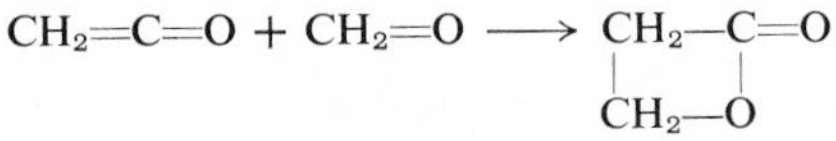

$$CH_2{=}C{=}O + CH_2{=}O \longrightarrow \begin{array}{c} CH_2{-}C{=}O \\ | \qquad | \\ CH_2{-}O \end{array}$$

It polymerizes in the presence of a variety of catalysts, and is, in fact, so liable to spontaneous exothermic polymerization in an uninhibited condition as to constitute a laboratory hazard. The polymer

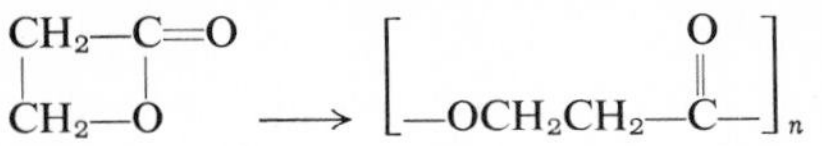

$$\begin{array}{c} CH_2{-}C{=}O \\ | \qquad | \\ CH_2{-}O \end{array} \longrightarrow \left[\begin{array}{c} O \\ \| \\ {-}OCH_2CH_2{-}C{-} \end{array} \right]_n$$

melts below 100°C. and is difficult to obtain in high molecular weight (38).

Although poly(dimethylene carboxylate) is low melting, gem-substitution on the α-carbon raises the melting point of the polymer markedly (see Preparation 305). Thus, **α,α-bis-(chloromethyl)-β-propiolactone,** prepared from silver trichloropivalate, polymerizes in the presence of a trace of alkali to a fiber-forming polymer melting over 300°C. (39).

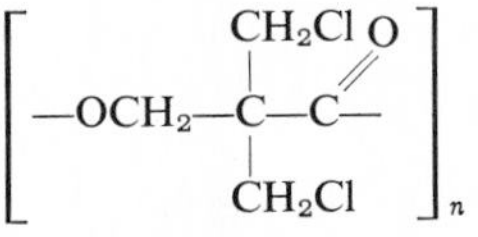

$$\left[\begin{array}{c} CH_2Cl \quad O \\ | \qquad \diagup\!\!\!\!\diagup \\ {-}OCH_2{-}C{-}C{-} \\ | \\ CH_2Cl \end{array} \right]_n$$

306. Preparation of α,α-Bis-(chloromethyl)-β-propiolactone (39)

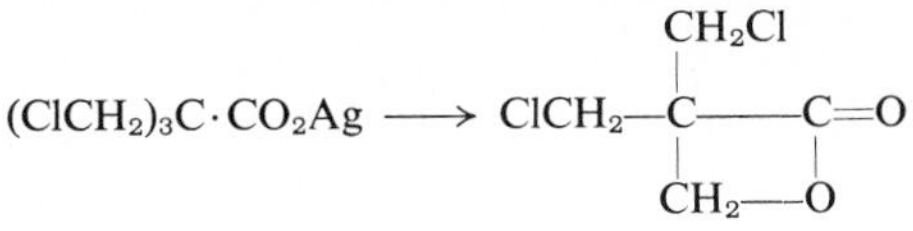

$$(ClCH_2)_3C{\cdot}CO_2Ag \longrightarrow \begin{array}{c} CH_2Cl \\ | \\ ClCH_2{-}C{-\!-\!-}C{=}O \\ | \qquad | \\ CH_2{-\!-}O \end{array}$$

Trichloropentaerythritol (47.9 g., 0.25 mole; see Preparation 212) is placed in a 1 l., round-bottom flask, equipped with an efficient wide bore condenser, and set up in an efficient hood. One hundred ml. of concentrated nitric acid is added, and the mixture is warmed cautiously, preferably with an infrared lamp. The chlorohydrin dissolves, then two layers appear and evidence for initiation of a reaction is noted. The flask is rapidly lowered into a cold water bath to moderate the violent reaction which quickly develops. After the reaction moderates and evolution of nitrogen oxides has nearly ceased, the flask is warmed cautiously until no more brown fumes evolve, then the clear, colorless solution is poured into water to give a quantitative yield of crude β,β',β'' trichloropivalic acid, m.p. 108–110°C. Recrystallization from petroleum ether gives a product melting point 112.8–113°C. (38a).

This is a violent reaction and should not be run on a larger scale. The operator should be protected by shields and gauntlets at all times.

Anhydrous, finely powdered silver salt of β,β',β'' trichloropivalic acid is heated cautiously in an oil-jacketed distillation unit in a slow stream of nitrogen at a pressure of 0.2–0.3 mm. A liquid begins to distill slowly when the jacket temperature reaches 105°C. and somewhat more rapidly when the temperature reaches 110°C. The liquid distillate soon begins to crystallize in the receiver. The jacket temperature is maintained between 110 and 115°C. until distillation slackens and is then raised slowly to 150°C. Very little further distillation occurs above a jacket temperature of 125°C. The solid distillate is collected and consists of pure α,α-bis(chloromethyl)-β-propiolactone melting at 35–36°C. The melting point is unchanged after recrystallization from a mixture of n-hexane and benzene.

307. Polymerization of α,α-Bis-(chloromethyl)-β-Propiolactone (39)

One hundred and fifty g. of α,α-bis-(chloromethyl)-β-propiolactone is heated to 40°C. out of contact with atmospheric moisture until completely molten and 0.1 g. of finely powdered dry potassium hydroxide is added with stirring. Heating and stirring are continued at 40°C. for about 15 min. and then the mixture is heated to 50°C. The mixture soon becomes turbid owing to separation of polymer and within two hours is completely solid. Heating is continued without agitation for a further 4 hr. at 50°C. The product is then heated at 100°C. in a slow stream of nitrogen at a pressure of 0.1 mm. to remove traces of volatile material. The product is a tough, white polymer which has a softening point of about 300°C. and gives a viscous melt from which may be spun filaments which are capable of being cold-drawn.

Recently, polymerization of a series of α,α-disubstituted β-lactones has been reported by Etienne (40). Methods for synthesizing β-lactones have been reviewed in some detail (41a,41b). The method given below, due to Testa (42) is based on an intermediate described earlier (Preparation 288) and is quite suitable for laboratory preparation of the monomer.

308. Preparation of α,α-Diethyl-β-Propiolactone (42)

Eighty g. of ethyl α,α-diethyl-β-aminopropionate is dissolved in 400 ml. of 6N hydrochloric acid and refluxed 22 hr. After cooling, the solution is neutralized with 50% sodium hydroxide to pH = 7 (about 100 ml. alkali). To the solution is added 200 ml. glacial acetic acid, and the mixture cooled to 0°C. A solution of 70 g. sodium nitrite in 250 ml. of water is added over about 30 min., keeping temperature about 0–5°C., then the mixture is stirred an additional 30 min. An oil separates, which is extracted into ether or benzene, dried, and distilled, b.p. 67–69°C. (0.6 mm.). The yield should be 35–40 g. If a test sample does not polymerize it should be redistilled.

309. Polymerization of α,α-Diethyl-β-Propiolactone (40)

$$C_2H_5-\underset{\underset{O}{|}}{\overset{\overset{C_2H_5}{|}}{C}}-O \longrightarrow \left[-OCH_2-\underset{\underset{C_2H_5}{|}}{\overset{\overset{C_2H_5}{|}}{C}}-CO-\right]_n$$

Twenty mg. of triethylene diamine is dissolved in 10 g. of the lactone contained in a dry polymer tube which is sealed. The tube is placed in an oil bath. At 50°C. polymerization is complete in a few minutes; at 100°C., only seconds are required. A white solid is obtained, melting at about 235°C. It is highly crystalline and has an inherent viscosity (trifluoroacetic acid) of 1–2. Clear films which crystallize rapidly may be pressed.

A wide variety of substituted monomers, ranging from dimethyl (pivalo-lactone) to dinonyl, as well as some unsymmetrically substituted monomers has been studied (40). Polymerization may also be carried out in various solvents.

A dimeric lactone, glycolide, can be polymerized to a **polyester of α-hydroxyacetic acid** in the presence of antimony fluoride. The polyester does not tend to revert to glycolide under normal conditions.

310. Preparation of Glycolide (43)

$$HOCH_2CO_2H \longrightarrow O=\underset{O}{\overset{O}{\bigwedge}}=O$$

Four hundred g. of hydroxyacetic acid is heated at atmospheric pressure in a round-bottom flask until the temperature of the liquid is 175–185°C. The temperature is maintained in this range for 2 hr., or slightly longer, until the water ceases to distill. The pressure is then reduced over a period of ½ hr. to about 150 mm. and the temperature maintained at 175–185°C. for an additional 2 hr. The residue so obtained is poured into an enamel pan where it solidifies to a white, brittle solid. This solid is the low molecular weight poly-hydroxyacetic ester which is depolymerized to glycolide. A three-necked reaction vessel is equipped with a stirrer and a neck suitable for introduction of powdered low molecular weight polymer and also equipped with a take-off for distilling the glycolide as it is prepared. The equipment is swept by a steady stream of nitrogen gas and the receiver for the glycolide is cooled in an ice bath. After the ice-cooled receiver, three ice-cooled traps are placed in series in order to catch any glycolide which is carried beyond the receiver by the nitrogen stream. One hundred g. of powdered, low molecular weight polyester (produced as previously described) is thoroughly mixed with 1 g. of antimony trioxide and placed in a supply vessel connected to the inlet neck of the three-necked flask. The polymer is introduced from the supply vessel into the reaction vessel which is maintained at 270–285°C. at a pressure of about 12–15 mm. The solid is added at the rate of about 20 g./hr. to give a 93% yield of glycolide. The glycolide is recrystallized from approximately 2 volumes of ethyl acetate with charcoal.

311. Polymerization of Glycolide to Hydroxyacetic Acid Polymer (43)

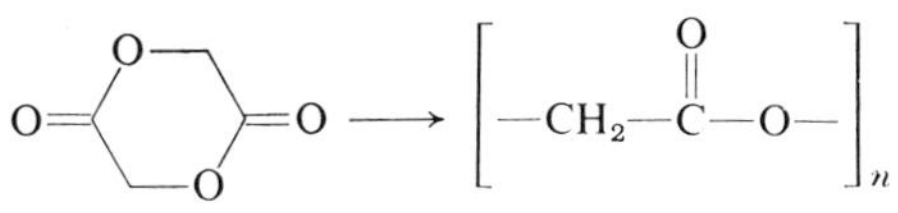

A mixture of 60 g. of pure dry glycolide is placed in a reaction vessel under nitrogen in the presence of 0.03% by weight of antimony trifluoride. The reaction vessel is heated to 195°C. by an oil bath and the contents stirred for 1 hr. at this temperature. The viscosity of the melt increases rapidly during this period and at the end of 1 hr. cannot be stirred further. The mixture is heated for an additional hour at this temperature, then the temperature is raised to 230°C. for an additional $\frac{1}{2}$ hr. The resulting polymer has a high molecular weight and can be fabricated into drawable films and fibers.

It is possible to prepare **optically active lactide,** and polymerize it. As might be expected, the properties of polymers from the antipodes are somewhat different (44).

Recently, ethylene methyl phosphate has been observed to undergo an unusual ring-opening polymerization.

312. Polymerization of Ethylene Methylphosphate (45)

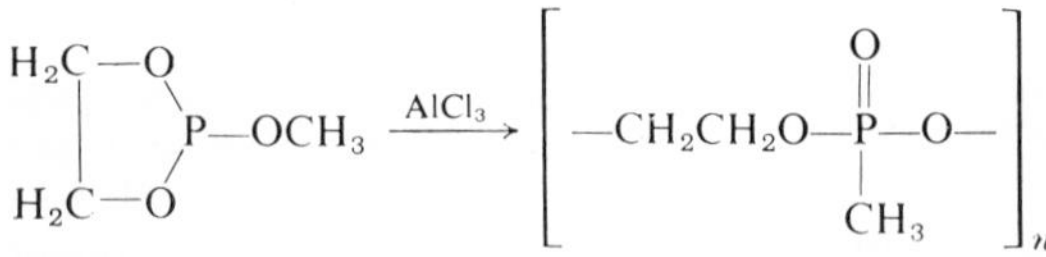

One g. of dry ethylene methylphosphate (46) is sealed in a test tube under nitrogen, together with 0.04 g. anhydrous aluminum chloride. It is maintained at 180°C. for 6 hr. The tube is cooled and evacuated to remove volatile residues. The product is a colorless solid $\eta_{inh} = 1.2$ in DMF (0.5 g./100 ml., 30°C.).

V. Conversion of Cyclic Iminocarbonates to Polyurethanes

Recently, Japanese workers have prepared the **cyclic iminocarbonate**

$$C_6H_5N=C \underset{O-CH_2}{\overset{O-CH_2}{<}}$$

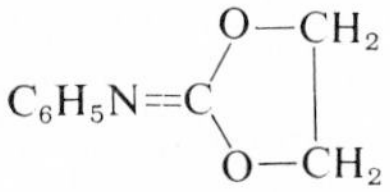

which undergoes a novel ring-opening polymerization to a film and fiber forming polyurethane.

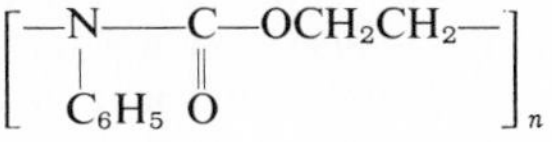

$$\left[\begin{array}{c} -N-C-OCH_2CH_2- \\ | \quad \| \\ C_6H_5 \ O \end{array} \right]_n$$

313. Preparation of Phenyl Imidophosgene(I) (47)

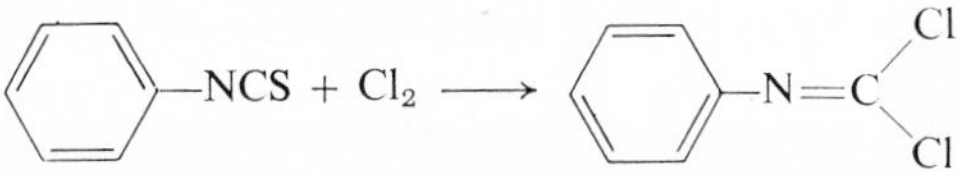

A 1 l. three-necked flask equipped with stopper, condenser, and fritted glass gas inlet tube is charged with 300 g. (2.2 moles) of phenyl isothiocyanate and 275 ml. of carbon tetrachloride. Chlorine is bubbled into the reaction mixture at a slow rate. The solution soon turns a deep cherry-red and a great deal of heat evolves so that it is necessary to cool the reaction vessel in an ice bath. Chlorine addition is continued until 310 g. (4.4 moles) has been absorbed. Any chlorine escaping is trapped with aqueous caustic. The carbon tetrachloride and sulfur chloride are distilled off at atmospheric pressure at 80°C. The product is then fractionated under water aspirator pressure. The fraction boiling at 98–107°C./26 mm. is collected. This material is refractionated through an 18 cm. Vigreux column and the fraction boiling at 104°C./26 mm. collected. The yield of pale yellow I is 316 g. (82%). I is stored under nitrogen in a dry box.

314. Preparation of Disodium Glycoxide(II) (47)

$$HOCH_2CH_2OH + Na \longrightarrow NaOCH_2CH_2ONa$$

$$II$$

A 500 ml. three necked flask is equipped with magnetic stirrer, condenser, nitrogen inlet tube, and solid addition flask (125 ml. Erlenmeyer flask attached by means of large diameter Gooch tubing). The flask is charged with 22.3 g. (0.36 mole) of fractionated ethylene glycol and 300 ml. of dry tetrahydrofuran. From the addition flask is added slowly 34.6 g. of dark gray 50% sodium hydride suspended in mineral oil (0.72 mole pure NaH). The reaction mixture is stirred under N_2 overnight before filtration in a dry box. The light gray product (II) is dried in a vacuum desiccator. The yield of dry II is 36 g. (95%).

315. Preparation of Ethylene N-Phenyliminocarbonate(III) (48)

$$I + II \longrightarrow \text{(structure III)}$$

III

A 2 l. three-necked flask is equipped with a magnetic stirrer, condenser, dropping funnel, and stopper, and is protected from moisture. The flask is charged with 80 g. (0.75 mole) of disodium glycoxide(II) suspended in 600 ml. of benzene. From the dropping funnel is added a solution of 132 g. (0.75 mole) of phenylimidophosgene(I) in 600 ml. of benzene over a 10–15 min. period. The heat of reaction is sufficient to reflux the benzene. After addition is complete, a heating mantle is used in refluxing the reaction mixture for an additional 2 hr. Prolonged addition time or reflux time leads to polymeric side products. After cooling, the sodium chloride is extracted by washing twice with 1 l. portions of water. The benzene solution is dried over anhydrous magnesium sulfate. The benzene is then removed in a rotary evaporator leaving a light-yellow solid (III). The crude yield of III is 83g. (68%), m.p. 72–75°C. Recrystallization from ether gives 78 g. (64%) of colorless III, m.p. 74–76°C. An additional recrystallization gives material melting at 76–77°C. III is stored under nitrogen in a dry box.

316. Bulk Polymerization of III to Give Poly(ethylene-N-phenylurethane) (IV) (49)

$$(-N-CO-OCH_2CH_2-)_n$$

$$III \longrightarrow \text{(structure IV)}$$

IV

Ethylene N-phenyliminocarbonate(III) (76 g.) is dried at 40°C. *in vacuo* (nitrogen bleed) and placed in a previously dried 100 ml. flask protected from moisture by a drying tube. The monomer is melted by heating the flask in a 90°C. oil bath. To the melt is added from a microliter syringe about 10 μl. of gaseous phosphorus pentafluoride (about 0.01% by wt. of monomer). Polymerization proceeds smoothly to give a perfectly white solid mass after 16 hr. An additional 26 hr. at 90°C. is allowed for complete polymerization. The flask is broken and the extremely hard polymer chopped into small pieces. The polymer is dissolved in 1500 ml. of hot chloroform with the aid of a shear-disk stirrer (Chapter 2). The solution is pressure filtered through felt to remove insoluble material and then poured into 3 l. of acetone to precipitate the polymer. The polymer is collected by filtration and then dried in vacuum (nitrogen bleed) at room temperature for 60 hr. and at 100°C. for 2 hr. The yield of white IV is 38 g. (50%). IV has a polymer melt temperature of 190°C. and an inherent viscosity of 2.36 in chloroform or 2.18 in trifluoroacetic acid (0.5% conc. at 25°C.). Clear films can be melt pressed at 180°C. Fibers may be melt spun at ca. 200°C. and drawn up to 200% over a hot plate.

The thermal decomposition temperature of the polymer can be raised from 240°C. (as measured by differential thermal analysis) to 276°C. by end-capping with acetic anhydride. Twelve g. of IV (η_{inh} 0.72) is dissolved in 300 ml. of dry pyridine and 50 ml. of acetic anhydride. The reaction mixture is heated at reflux for 2 hr., cooled, and poured into 2 l. of water precipitating a gummy white solid. This solid is dried in vacuum (nitrogen bleed) at 110°C. for 4 hr., and at room temperature for an additional 9 hr. The polymer is dissolved in 400 ml. of hot chloroform and the resulting solution dried over anhydrous magnesium sulfate. The polymer is reprecipitated by pouring into 2 l. of acetone. The yield of dried polymer was 11.8 g. The end-capped IV had an η_{inh} of 0.72 and a polymer melt temperature of 184°C.

VI. Cyclic Ethers

Practically all **oxiranes** (epoxides) and **oxetanes** (trimethylene oxides) will polymerize.

H_2C———CH_2	H_2C———CH_2	H_2C———CH_2
O	O———CH_2	H_2C O CH_2
Oxirane	Oxetane	Tetrahydrofuran

Polymers ranging from low molecular weight syrups to tough, high molecular weight solids may be obtained, depending upon the condition and type of catalyst. Normally, ionic catalysts, either cationic or anionic, are the only effective types here. Tetrahydrofuran will polymerize readily, however, only in the presence of cationic catalysts. Antimony pentachloride has been the preferred catalyst to polymerize tetrahydrofuran for many years. It is only quite recently that it has been observed that very high molecular weight poly(tetramethylene ether) can be obtained by using phosphorus pentafluoride catalysts (50).

All of the unsubstituted polyethers except the polyacetal derived from formaldehyde melt in the range from 35 to 65°C. As will be seen later, substitution on the chain may tend to raise the melting point. Alkylated derivatives of tetrahydrofuran have resisted polymerization. On the other hand, a **bicyclic epoxide** which may be considered as disubstituted tetrahydrofuran

does polymerize, probably to relieve the strain in the bridge structure (51,52). The melting point of this polymer is very high (>400°C.). Epoxides will polymerize in the presence of either cationic or anionic initiators and may give linear polymers ranging from a very few units up to molecular weights approaching 1,000,000. Bis-epoxides will give network or crosslinked polymers (13). The lower molecular weight products are normally hydroxyl terminated, hence serve as large difunctional molecules which may be built into high polymers by further reaction. See Chapter 3 for examples of polymers based on large difunctional molecules of this type. A wide variety of commercial products is available, and these may be used in the preparations of higher molecular weight block polymers.

The preparation of **polyethylene oxide** with molecular weight of the order of several millions has been accomplished recently by workers at Union Carbide Corp. (53,54,55). Staudinger and Lohmann found in 1933 that the oxides and carbonates of strontium and calcium, etc., are catalysts for the production of polyethylene oxides. However, the rates of polymerization were quite slow and some of their experiments went as long as 2 years. The Carbide research team found that very specially prepared strontium carbonate is capable of polymerizing purified ethylene oxide fairly rapidly to very high molecular weight material. It is necessary that the strontium carbonate prepared be absolutely free of interfering ions. For example, nitrate, chlorate, bisulfate, and other ions in trace quantities completely inhibit the polymerization. Furthermore, it is found desirable to maintain at least $\frac{1}{2}\%$ of water in order to effectively polymerize the ethylene oxide.

317. Preparation of Active Strontium Carbonate Catalyst (54)

$$Sr(OH)_2 + CO_2 \longrightarrow SrCO_3 + H_2O$$

A 22% aqueous solution of pure strontium hydroxide is prepared at 90°C. in distilled water. A stream of carbon dioxide gas is introduced under the surface of the solution and allowed to proceed until precipitation of the carbonate is complete. The solution is filtered and the filtered solid is washed with distilled water. The product is dried to a water content of not less than 0.5–1.0%.

318. Polymerization of Ethylene Oxide (54)

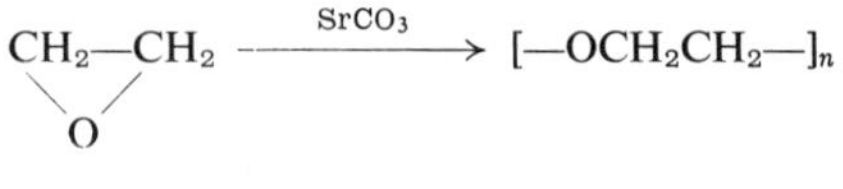

$$CH_2\!-\!CH_2 \xrightarrow{\ \ SrCO_3\ \ } [-OCH_2CH_2-]_n$$
$$\diagdown\!O\!\diagup$$

In a polymer tube is placed 50 ml. of redistilled ethylene oxide containing less than 50 p.p.m. of aldehyde. To the tube is then added about 0.2 g. of strontium carbonate prepared as before. The tube is then sealed and heated to approximately 50°C. and maintained at this temperature. After an induction period of approximately 90 min., polymerization will begin. During the course of the polymerization the tube should be agitated in some manner, either by a rocking or rotating mechanism. After the end of the induction period, polymerization may be extremely rapid. In some cases reaction is so rapid that the tube may explode. Therefore all precautions must be taken to protect the operator against shattering glass. Once polymerization is initiated, it should be complete within approximately 2 hr.

A less active catalyst may be obtained by using J. T. Baker's C.P. grade of strontium carbonate as the polymerization initiator. This again is dried to a water content of not less than 0.5%. The polymerization is carried out using this material in concentrations of about 1.5 g. per 50 ml. of ethylene oxide. The induction period under these conditions may be as long as 20 hr. or more. Polymerization with the commercial strontium carbonate is much less rapid, and there is less danger of the reaction getting out of hand.

The polymer is soluble in chloroform and ethylene dichloride, as well as in acetonitrile and anisole. Viscous solutions may be prepared in these solvents. At elevated temperatures the polymer also is soluble in benzene and toluene. It is miscible with water in all proportions at room temperature and extremely viscous solutions can be prepared. A 20% solution of polymer of high molecular weight in water makes an interesting, elastic, nontacky gel. These gel lumps may contain as much as 80% water and have the feel and appearance of a clear rubber. An impressive demonstration of the properties of these materials is to bounce a ball consisting of 80% water and 20% high molecular weight polyethylene oxide.

Tough films may be obtained either by casting a solution, preferably in an organic medium, onto a glass plate or by melt-pressing solid polymer in a Carver Press. Film obtained in such a manner shows a high degree of crystallinity, sometimes as high as 95%. The polymer chains may be oriented by stretching in the usual manner.

The polymerization of **propylene oxide** again may be brought about by either basic or acidic catalysts. The polymer has regularly spaced asymmetric carbon atoms, hence should be capable of existing in either random or stereoregular configuration,

$$(O-CH_2-\underset{*}{\overset{\overset{\displaystyle CH_3}{|}}{C}H}-O-CH_2-\underset{*}{\overset{\overset{\displaystyle CH_3}{|}}{C}H}-OCH_2-\underset{*}{\overset{\overset{\displaystyle CH_3}{|}}{C}H}-)_n$$

just as in the case of polypropylene and other poly(α-olefins) described in Chapter 4.

C. C. Price and his co-workers have shown (56,57) that l-propylene oxide polymerized over solid potassium hydroxide gives solid polymer, whereas dl-propylene oxide gives a liquid product under the same conditions. Both polymers are of the same molecular weight, albeit quite low.

Using a complex iron catalyst, a research group from Dow Chemical Company has shown that polymerization of dl-propylene oxide will give a solid, crystalline, high molecular weight product (58–61).

319. Preparation of a Ferric Chloride Complex Catalyst (58–61)

A complex catalyst is prepared in a polymer tube by dissolving 1.0 g. of anhydrous ferric chloride in 5 ml. of diethyl ether and adding gradually 1.0 g. of liquid propylene oxide with agitation and cooling at temperatures below 60°C. When condensation of the ferric chloride and propylene oxide is completed, the product is warmed in a vacuum to remove volatile matter leaving a semi-solid brown residue.

320. Polymerization of Propylene Oxide (58–61)

$$\underset{\substack{H \qquad O \qquad H}}{\overset{\substack{CH_3 \qquad\qquad H}}{C\!-\!\!-\!\!C}} \xrightarrow{\quad Fe^{+3} \quad} \left[-OCH\!-\!CH_2\right]_n \longrightarrow$$

To the catalyst residue prepared in the preceding experiment is added 100 g. of propylene oxide. The tube is cooled under nitrogen and sealed. This mixture is heated at 80°C. with agitation for 88 hr., at which time polymerization is complete. There is obtained in this way 94 g. of a brown, rubbery solid polymer. This is dissolved in hot acetone and sufficient concentrated hydrochloric acid is added to convert the iron complex present into soluble ferric chloride. The solution is chilled to -20°C., whereupon solid polymer crystallizes from solution and is separated by filtration. This polymer is reprecipitated twice in acetone in the same manner and about 25 g. of pure white polymer is obtained.

This white solid has a melting point of approximately 70°C. and should have a molecular weight in the range of 100–150,000. It may be dissolved in hot acetone, hot methanol, dioxane, benzene, toluene, tetrahydrofuran, etc. It can be converted by melt-pressing to film which can be cold drawn and oriented.

Epoxides with several symmetrical substituents exhibit a chain stiffening effect noted earlier with poly-α-olefines with branched side groups. The melting points are very high; they are very crystalline and insoluble in all solvents tested.

321. Preparation of 1,1,2,2-Tetramethylethylene Oxide (62)

$$\underset{\substack{CH_3 \qquad\qquad CH_3}}{\overset{\substack{CH_3 \qquad\qquad CH_3}}{C\!=\!\!=\!\!C}} \xrightarrow[\text{Na}_2\text{CO}_3]{\text{CH}_3\text{CO}_3\text{H}} \underset{\substack{CH_3 \qquad O \qquad CH_3}}{\overset{\substack{CH_3 \qquad\qquad CH_3}}{C\!-\!\!-\!\!C}}$$

In a 2 l., three-necked flask, equipped with a stirrer, a condenser, and a dropping funnel and cooled with an ice bath is placed 300 g. of anhydrous sodium carbonate, 300 ml. of methylene chloride and 168 g. of freshly distilled tetramethylethylene. The mixture is stirred and the temperature is held at 5–10°C. To this mixture, is added 372 g. of 40% peracetic acid at such a rate as to keep the temperature below 10°C. Approximately 6 hr. should be required for this addition. The mixture is stirred vigorously during the course of the addition and for 1 hr. after the peracid is all added. Approximately 500 ml. of water is then added and the organic phase is extracted with two 200 ml. portions of methylene chloride. The methylene chloride layer may contain peroxide. It is, therefore, washed with ferrous sulfate solution until it no longer gives a positive peroxide test. The product, tetramethylethylene oxide, boils at 90–91°C. at atmospheric pressure. It has a refractive index at 25°C. of 1.3938. It is obtained in a yield of approximately 70%.

322. Polymerization of 1,1,2,2-Tetramethylethylene Oxide (63)

In a 300 ml., round-bottom flask equipped with a drying tube and a gas inlet and cooled in Dry Ice is placed 5 ml. of tetramethylethylene oxide and 100 ml. of dry methyl chloride. To this solution is added 1 ml. of redistilled boron trifluoride etherate. The entire mixture is allowed to stand at Dry Ice temperature for 24 hr. The solid is filtered, washed with methylene chloride, then with alcohol, and dried. The yield of polymer is essentially quantitative. It is a hard, white solid which does not melt below 300°C. It is completely unaffected by boiling with most solvents such as xylene, tetrahydrofuran, dimethylformamide, or dioxane.

A large number of polyethers derived from **phenyl and naphthyl glycidyl ethers** and their ring-substituted counterparts have been prepared and their properties studied (64,65). Many of these exhibit high melting points and good crystallizability. The polymer from phenyl glycidyl ether itself is illustrative, as well as one of the more interesting members of the series. In the following example, Bu_2Zn–water is the catalyst used, and is possibly the most effective available. Others are also applicable: $Al(OiPr)_3$–$ZnCl_2$ (66), Et_3Al (66), aluminum alkyls–H_2O (67).

A number of cocatalysts are capable of functioning with Bu_2Zn to form a highly active catalyst, including alcohols, phenol, acetone, and water. The latter is the most effective, with acetone nearly equal to it. The zinc alkyl alone is very sluggish; the optimum mole ratio of H_2O/Bu_2Zn, for conversion to polymer is 1.0; for molecular weight, 0.75, although the molecular weight, as indicated by the reduced viscosity, at a ratio of 1.0 is still very high. The active catalyst is thought to be a polymer of –ZnO– with terminal alkyl groups (68,69).

A probable mechanism for polymerization of an epoxide is (64):

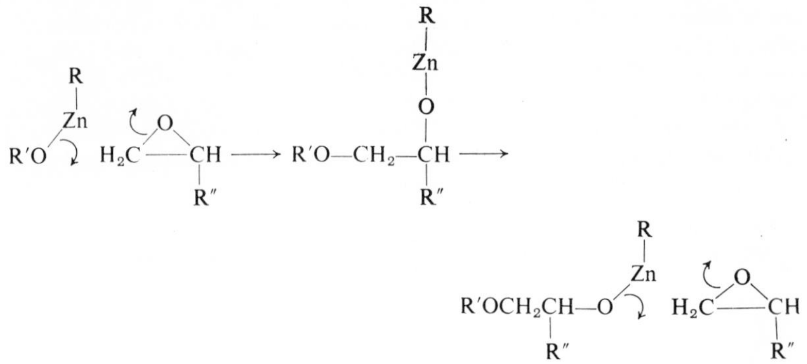

It is interesting to note that epichlorohydrin is not successfully polymerized with this catalyst, though crystalline and amorphous polymers are readily obtained using other catalysts. Both ethylene and propylene oxide are polymerized by zinc alkyl–water.

323. Preparation of Poly(phenyl glycidyl ether) (64,65)

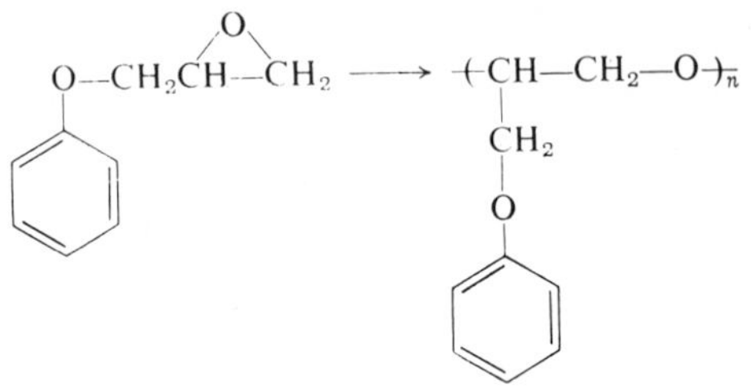

Phenyl glycidyl ether (Shell Chemical) should be carefully fractionally distilled, and a center cut boiling at 141°C./30mm. used. It should show no high or low boiling peaks in gas chromatography on a 2 m. polyester column at 175°C. and an Apiezon L column at 260°C. Toluene is refluxed over sodium for 24 hr., distilled from sodium through a short Vigreux column, and stored under nitrogen.

The polymerization can be carried out by adding the components by means of dry, nitrogen-flushed syringes to a nitrogen-flushed glass ampoule with constricted neck topped with a four-way tube in which the lateral tubing acts as a nitrogen inlet and exit to exclude moisture and air while the components are added through a serum cap in the top vertical tube; the bottom vertical tube is attached to the reaction ampoule, which is shaped much like a wider version of the polymer tubes described for melt polymerization in Chapter 2. To the ampoule is charged 10 g. of phenyl glycidyl ether, 15 g. of toluene, 1.51×10^{-2} ml. water (via microliter syringe), and 1.0 ml. of a toluene solution of dibutyl zinc containing 0.15 g./ml. of the catalyst. The latter two components are both added in the amount of 8.38×10^{-4} moles. The neck of the ampoule is sealed off under nitrogen and the container is rotated in an air oven or oil bath at 90°C. for 24 hr.

The polymer is removed from the tube, chopped in a blender with 200 ml. toluene to give a finely divided, swollen product, and precipitated in 3 l. of ethanol. It is then filtered, washed repeatedly in a blender with ethanol, and finally dried at 60°C. in a vacuum oven for 16 hr. The reduced viscosity in p-chlorophenol containing 2% α-pinene at 47°C. is about 10 (0.2 g./100 ml.). It is necessary to heat the solvent to 140°C. for 30 min. to effect solution. The polymer is crystalline by x-ray diffraction; T_m is 204°C.

Epichlorohydrin has been successfully polymerized to both crystalline (70) and amorphous (71) materials, differing only in their stereoregularity. The amorphous polymer shows good elastomeric properties, especially solvent, ozone and flame resistance (72), and is now produced commercially (73) as a specialty rubber.

324. Preparation of Primarily Amorphous Polyepichlorohydrin (71)

$$CH_2 \overset{O}{\overbrace{\qquad}} CH-CH_2Cl \longrightarrow [-CH_2-CH-O-]_n$$
$$\underset{\underset{Cl}{|}}{\overset{|}{CH_2}}$$

To a nitrogen-flushed 500 ml. resin kettle or three-necked flask equipped with nitrogen inlet and outlet with drying tube, a serum capped inlet, and stirrer, is added a solution of 7.92 g. triisobutylaluminum (0.04 mole) in 32 ml. dry n-heptane. This is diluted with 40 ml. of dry diethyl ether. Then, 0.36 g. of water (0.02 mole) is added to the stirred mixture by microsyringe through the serum cap. A nitrogen blanket is maintained throughout. (Aluminum alkyls react vigorously with oxygen and moisture; proper precautions for safe operation should be taken at all times. There is little danger in the water addition to the alkyl solution because of the dilution involved.) Butane is liberated and a presumably polymeric catalyst having >Al—O—Al< units results. The catalyst solution is stirred at 30°C. for about 4 hr. The system is further diluted with another 200 ml. dry diethyl ether, and 100 g. of distilled epichlorohydrin is added. The solution is stirred at 30°C. for 20 hr., when the polymerization is stopped by the addition of 40 ml. ethanol. The mixture is added to 200 ml. ether in a large beaker and the insoluble polymer is collected on a filter, washed well with ether, slurried with methanol containing 0.4% of an antioxidant e.g., 4,4'-thiobis(6-t-butyl-m-cresol), and dried at 50°C. for 16 hr. in vacuum under nitrogen. The polymer so isolated amounts to about 77 g. and has a reduced viscosity of 0.75 (0.1 g./100 ml. in α-chloronaphthalene at 100°C.). (The remaining monomer is accounted for as ether soluble polymer which can be recovered separately, if desired.) The polymer is mainly amorphous, but extraction with cold acetone followed by precipitation of the acetone-soluble polymer into methanol shows that about 13% of the original ether-insoluble polymer is also acetone-insoluble; this latter fraction is crystalline polymer. The whole of the ether-insoluble polymer may be used in compounding a vulcanized rubber of good properties, using carbon black as a filler and hexamethylene-diamine dicarbamate as a crosslinking agent.

Intrinsic viscosity is related to reduced viscosity by the equation

$$\log \eta_r = \log[\eta] + 0.15[\eta]C$$
$$C = \text{concentration in g./100 ml.}$$

and molecular weight is determined from intrinsic viscosity by

$$[\eta] = 8.9 \times 10^{-5} M_W^{0.73}$$

Although the polymerization of epoxides dates back to the early days of Staudinger, **oxetanes** have been considered only recently. The parent compound is prone to rearrangement in acid media:

$$\text{(oxetane)} \longrightarrow \text{(protonated oxetane)} \longrightarrow HOCH_2CH_2CH_2 + \longrightarrow HOCH_2CH=CH_2$$

However, Rose (74) has reported the successful polymerization of oxetane to linear **polyether.**

$$\text{(oxetane)} \longrightarrow (-OCH_2CH_2CH_2-)_n$$

The preparation of this polymer in high molecular weight is quite tedious and will not be described.

Although the polyethers from oxetane and its symmetrically gem disubstituted derivatives are crystalline, the polymer from 3-methyl-oxetane is not (74).

Table 5.1

Effect of R on Melting Point of Polymer from

R	M.P., °C.	Ref.
$-(CH_2)_5-$	160	75
$-CH_3$	47	74
$-CH_2F$	135	76
$-CH_2Cl$	180	77
$-CH_2Br$	220	78
$-CH_2I$	290	78

Substitution of two groups on the **3-position** of the oxetane **leads to stiffening of the chain.** Bulk is a strong factor in determining the melting point of the polyether. It may be introduced either by heavy atoms, or bulky hydrocarbon residues, e.g., compare the polymer with a lateral, puckered cyclohexylidene group, with a crystalline melting point of 160°C., vs. the dimethyl derivative, melting at about 45°C. (Table 5.1).

325. Preparation of Trichloropentaerythritol

$$(HOCH_2)_4C \longrightarrow (ClCH_2)_3CCH_2OAc \longrightarrow (ClCH_2)_3CCH_2OH$$

Hydrogen chloride gas is bubbled into a mixture of 600 g. of acetic acid and 100 g. of water at 0°C. until a total of 176 g. (4.9 moles) is absorbed. This mixture is charged into a 1 l. Hastelloy B bomb, together with 200 g. (1.5 moles) of pentaerythritol. The bomb is sealed and heated to 160°C. for 8 hr. Due to the corrosive nature of this mixture, it is best to back the stainless steel rupture disk of the Hastelloy bomb with a thin sheet of Teflon fluorocarbon film resin and then with platinum foil to prevent the disk from corroding. After 8 hr., the bomb is cooled to room temperature and the reaction mixture diluted with water. The trichloropentaerythritol acetate is isolated by extraction with methylene chloride. The solvent is removed and the residual oil is refluxed overnight with 500 ml. of methyl alcohol and 50 ml. of concentrated hydrochloric acid. The next day the mixture of methyl acetate and methyl alcohol is distilled slowly. The residue of trichloropentaerythritol crystallizes, is filtered, washed with water, and dried. The crude product weighs about 275 g. and melts in the range of 60–63°C. Recrystallization of a small portion from ethyl acetate raises the melting point to 65.5°C. However, the lower melting product is used directly for the preparation of 3,3-bis(chloromethyl)-oxetane.

326. Preparation of 3,3-bis(Chloromethyl)oxetane

A mixture of 275 g. of trichloropentaerythritol, 500 ml. of methanol, 60 ml. of water, and 80 g. of potassium hydroxide is refluxed 18 hr. An equal volume of water is added and the heavy oil is separated with two 100 ml. portions of ethyl ether. The ether extract is dried over calcium chloride and distilled through an efficient distilling column to give about 125 g. of pure cyclic ether, b.p. 101°C. at 27 mm., or 62°C. at 4 mm. Immediately before polymerization, this product should be fractionated either through an efficient fractionating column, or through a Vigreux column with the first and last 10% being discarded. It is essential that the monomer be of extremely high purity before the polymerization described in Preparation 330 is attempted.

327. Preparation of 3,3-bis(Fluoromethyl)oxetane (76)

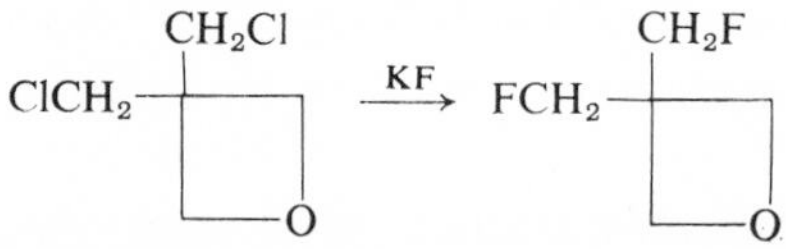

$$ClCH_2 \overset{CH_2Cl}{\underset{O}{\square}} \xrightarrow{KF} FCH_2 \overset{CH_2F}{\underset{O}{\square}}$$

In a three-necked, 1 l. flask equipped with a stirrer and a reflux condenser, is placed a mixture of 156 g. of anhydrous powdered potassium fluoride and 156 g. of bis(chloromethyl)oxetane. To it is added 340 ml. of anhydrous glycol and the mixture is heated with a metal heating bath to a temperature of approximately 160°C. with vigorous and efficient stirring. The mixture is allowed to reflux and is slowly distilled. The distillate separates into two layers, the lower layer consisting of the bis(fluoromethyl)oxetane. The product is obtained in a crude yield of about 70%. The crude distillate is then mixed with twice its volume of water and the mixture is again distilled. The organic product is entrained by the water vapor and it is separated and dried over magnesium sulfate. It then is again distilled in an anhydrous condition to give approximately 40% of pure product, b.p. 56°C. at 29 mm.

328. Preparation of 3,3-bis(Iodomethyl)oxetane (78)

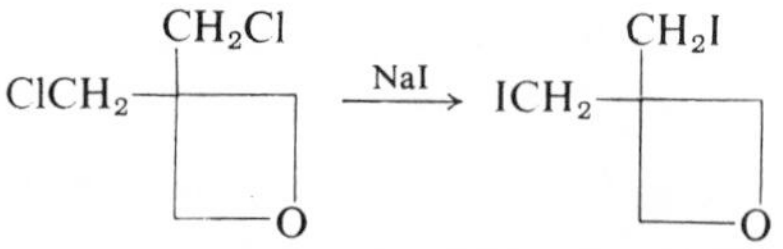

$$ClCH_2 \overset{CH_2Cl}{\underset{O}{\square}} \xrightarrow{NaI} ICH_2 \overset{CH_2I}{\underset{O}{\square}}$$

A mixture of 15.5 g. of 3,3-bis(chloromethyl)oxetane, 150 ml. of methyl ethyl ketone, and 35 g. of dry sodium iodide is refluxed for 24 hr. The solution is then cooled, filtered, and the solvent is partially removed by evaporation. The residue solidifies on standing and is recrystallized from cyclohexane. The yield is 30 g. (89%) of coarse, colorless, very dense crystals with a melting point of 50°C.

329. Preparation of Phosphorus Pentafluoride (79)

$$ClC_6H_5N_2PF_6 \longrightarrow N_2 + PF_5 + ClC_6H_5F$$

Caution! Phosphorus Pentafluoride Is Very Toxic.

The most convenient method for the preparation of phosphorus pentafluoride on a laboratory scale is by the thermal decomposition of an aryldiazonium hexafluorophosphate. The salt in a quantity of 3–12 g. is heated at 150–160°C. in a distillation set-up and the phosphorus pentafluoride is swept into the polymerization vessel with a stream of dry nitrogen. Approximately 1–2 hr. is required to decompose all the diazonium hexafluorophosphate under these conditions.

330. Polymerization of 3,3-bis(Chloromethyl)oxetane (80)

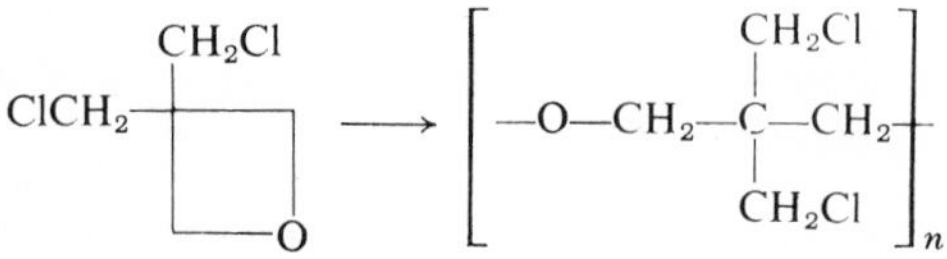

$$ClCH_2 \overset{CH_2Cl}{\underset{O}{\square}} \longrightarrow \left[-O-CH_2-\overset{\overset{\textstyle CH_2Cl}{|}}{\underset{\underset{\textstyle CH_2Cl}{|}}{C}}-CH_2- \right]_n$$

One hundred ml. of anhydrous methyl chloride is condensed into a 500 ml., three-necked flask equipped with a stirrer, a Dry Ice condenser, and a gas inlet tube. Freshly distilled 3,3-bis-(chloromethyl)oxetane (25 g.) is then added all at once. The Dry Ice bath is removed and the mixture is allowed to reflux ($-25°C$.). Into the refluxing reaction mixture is introduced a trace of phosphorus pentafluoride gas. After a short induction period, polymerization takes place very rapidly. Ordinarily, this polymerization is uneventful and the solid polymer precipitates during the course of the first few minutes. Occasionally, however, the polymerization is violent and the content of the reaction flask may be ejected through the top of the condenser. However, no more serious consequences are apt to occur on the scale described.

The methyl chloride is now allowed to evaporate and the solid polymer is isolated and washed several times with methyl alcohol. Poly[3,3-bis-(chloromethyl)trimethylene ether] is obtained as a spongy white solid with an inherent viscosity of about 1.0 in hexamethylphosphoramide. It may be fabricated into clear, tough films by pressing in a Carver press in the range of 175–200°C. These films are highly crystalline and may be stretched and oriented over a hot surface at about 100°C. The polymer has a crystalline melting point of about 177°C. as observed on a polarizing microscope. It may be dissolved to a limited extent in common organic solvents such as hot cyclohexanone or dimethylformamide. It is readily soluble and spinning solutions can be prepared in hexamethylphosphoramide.

3,3-Bis-(fluoromethyl)oxetane, 3,3-bis-(bromomethyl)oxetane, and 3,3-bis-(iodomethyl)oxetane may be polymerized in a like manner.

331. Preparation of the Ditosylate of 1,1-Cyclohexanedimethanol (75)

Tetrahydrobenzaldehyde is made by condensing 1600 g. butadiene and 1064 g. of acrolein at 100°C. for 1 hr. in an autoclave. Yield, 90–100%, b.p. 65°C./20 mm. The product is hydrogenated to cyclohexanealdehyde in ethanol over 5% Pd on charcoal at 1000 p.s.i. The aldehyde need not be isolated, but it is converted to the diol directly. The following is a general procedure for converting aliphatic aldehydes to diols.

In a 5 l. three-necked flask equipped with a stirrer, a condenser, and a dropping funnel is placed 4 moles of the appropriate aldehyde, and 1000 g. of 37% aqueous formaldehyde solution. To this mixture, cooled externally with ice, is now added slowly from a dropping funnel 390 g. of solid potassium hydroxide dissolved in about 2400 ml. of absolute ethanol. The initial two-phase system shortly becomes homogeneous and a mild exothermic reaction is observed. The alcoholic alkali is added at such a rate that the temperature does not exceed 50–60°C. When the alkali is all added, the mixture is allowed to stir for 2–3 hr. and then most of the alcohol is removed by distillation. The residual two-phase system consisting of strong aqueous alkali and the product is poured into an enamel pan and allowed to cool. The desired product crystallizes and is separated from the strong alkaline solution by vacuum filtration. The solid is sucked as dry as possible and is allowed to dry in air. The crude diol, containing a fair amount of sodium carbonate, is now recrystallized from benzene using approximately 200 ml. of benzene for every 100 g. of diol. The hot benzene solution is treated with decolorizing carbon, filtered, and cooled. The pure diol is obtained in essentially quantitative recovery. The yield of 1,1-cyclohexanedimethanol is 85–90% based on tetrahydrobenzaldehyde; m.p. 99.0–99.5°C.

The general procedure for converting diols to ditosylates is as follows.

One mole of glycol in a mixture of 300 ml. of pyridine and 300 ml. of alcohol-free chloroform is treated with stirring and cooling with 400 g. of toluenesulfonyl chloride dissolved in 250 ml. of pyridine and 250 ml. of alcohol-free chloroform. The reaction is exothermic, and hence should be cooled with an external ice bath while the toluenesulfonyl chloride solution is added. The mixture is allowed to warm to room temperature, then stirred overnight, and poured into water. This mixture is warmed on the steam bath with a current of nitrogen passing through to remove the chloroform. The hot aqueous mixture is then allowed to cool and the crystalline solid is filtered, washed with water, and dried. The ditosylate of 1,1-cyclohexane-dimethanol is converted to oxetane without purification; a pure sample melts at 90–91°C.

332. Conversion of Ditosylate to 2-Oxaspirononane (75)

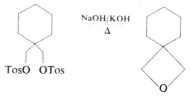

Potassium and sodium hydroxide are powdered and a mixture of equal weights of the two is prepared. For preparation of the oxetane, one part of the ditosylate is intimately mixed with 2–3 parts of the potassium–sodium hydroxide mixture and placed in a round-bottom single-necked flask of adequate capacity. (Some swelling of the mixture occurs on heating.) The mixture of materials is heated in a high vacuum to a temperature of 300–400°C. The gaseous products are trapped in a Dry Ice-cooled flask followed by a Dry Ice-cooled trap. When no more organic material appears to be coming out of the frothing mixture, the distillation is stopped and the traps are allowed to warm to room temperature. A two-layer mixture of liquids is obtained, the bottom layer consisting of water and the top layer consisting of the desired organic material contaminated with by-products. The organic layer is separated, washed with water and dried, then distilled through a spinning-band column. 2-Oxaspirononane is obtained in a yield of about 50%, b.p. 64°C./14 mm.

The polymer, prepared by the technique described in Preparation 330, melts at 160°C.; it is highly crystalline and tough orientable films may be melt pressed.

Thietanes can be polymerized in a similar manner. Foldi and Sweeny have recently described the ring-opening polymerization of 3,3-dimethylthietane, and the conversion of the polythioether to a polysulfone.

333. Synthesis of 5,5-dimethyl-1,3-dioxane-2-one (81)

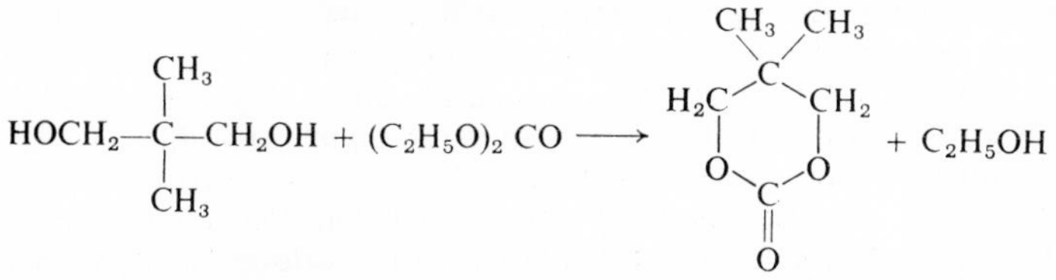

$$\text{HOCH}_2-\overset{\overset{\displaystyle CH_3}{|}}{\underset{\underset{\displaystyle CH_3}{|}}{C}}-\text{CH}_2\text{OH} + (\text{C}_2\text{H}_5\text{O})_2\,\text{CO} \longrightarrow \quad + \text{C}_2\text{H}_5\text{OH}$$

A mixture of 104 g. (1 mole) 2,2-dimethyl-1,3-propanediol, 130 g. (1.1 moles) diethyl carbonate, and 0.5 g. sodium dissolved in 8 ml. absolute alcohol is heated with stirring in a 500 ml. three-necked round-bottom flask provided with a Vigreux column and distilling head. Heating is done at such a rate that the boiling point of the distillate remains below 80°C. (pot temperature 90–150°C.), and is continued for about 3 hr., when nearly the theoretical amount of alcohol is collected (116 ml.). The mixture is then allowed to cool to room temperature, and is taken up in an equal volume of benzene. The benzene solution is washed 3 times with water and dried over calcium chloride. After removing the benzene, the residue is distilled at reduced pressure, b.p. 116–118°C./1 mm.; 95.7 g. of distillate is collected which solidifies in the receiver. The crude compound is dissolved in 95 ml. benzene at 50°C. and precipitated with petroleum ether. The resulting white crystals are dried in air followed by 2 hr. in 60°C. vacuum oven to yield 74 g. of product, m.p. 109.5–110°C.

334. Synthesis of 3,3-Dimethylthietanes (82)

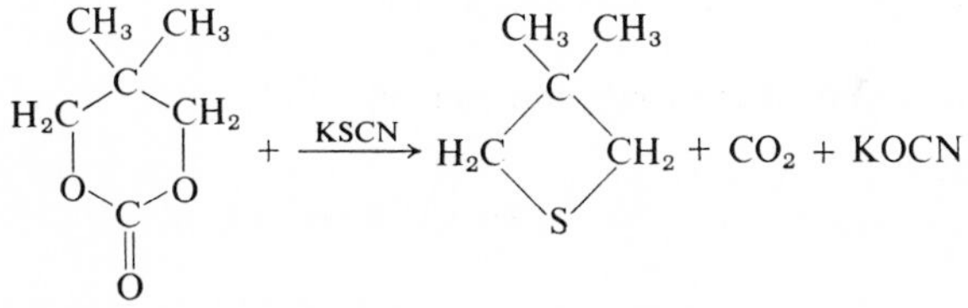

$$\quad + \xrightarrow{\text{KSCN}} \quad + \text{CO}_2 + \text{KOCN}$$

This compound is prepared by heating the cyclic carbonate (see preceding preparation) with an equivalent amount of potassium thiocyanate to 170–185°C. and removing the cyclic sulfides as formed by distillation. Dimethylthietane boils at 116°C. at atmospheric pressure. Yield: 41%.

335. Preparation of Poly(2,2-dimethyltrimethylene sulfide) and Conversion to Poly(2,2-dimethyltrimethylene sulfone) (83)

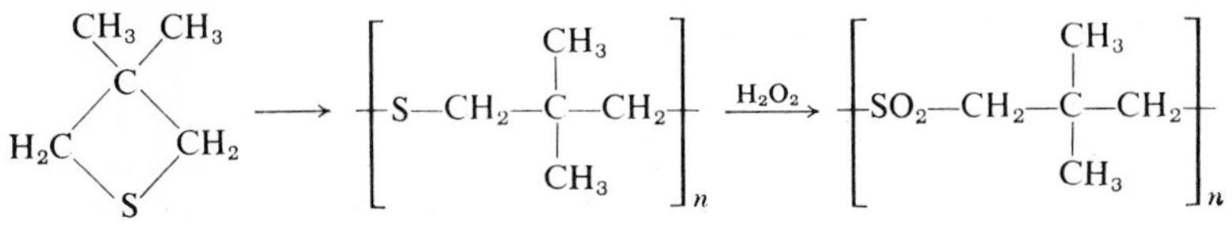

$$\longrightarrow \left[\text{S}-\text{CH}_2-\overset{\overset{\displaystyle CH_3}{|}}{\underset{\underset{\displaystyle CH_3}{|}}{C}}-\text{CH}_2 \right]_n \xrightarrow{\text{H}_2\text{O}_2} \left[\text{SO}_2-\text{CH}_2-\overset{\overset{\displaystyle CH_3}{|}}{\underset{\underset{\displaystyle CH_3}{|}}{C}}-\text{CH}_2 \right]_n$$

About 2.7 ml. of 3,3-dimethylthietane is placed in a test tube stoppered with a serum bottle cap and cooled to 0°C. in an ice bath; 0.15 ml. BF$_3$ etherate is added through the stopper with a small syringe. The solution is warmed to room temperature and set aside. After 16 hr., a viscous clear syrup results, which is left standing for another 2 days to give an immobile gel.

The gel is dissolved with gentle warming in 20 ml. of trifluoroacetic acid. The solution is cooled in ice and 10 ml. 30% hydrogen peroxide is added in three portions with stirring. An exothermic reaction occurs, the color changing to yellow to bright-red and finally back to colorless. The polymer separates as a soft gel. This dissolves on warming, and the resulting clear solution is heated on the steam bath for 2 hr. The polymer is precipitated into water, washed 2 times with water in a home blender, rinsed with alcohol on a funnel and dried in a vacuum oven at 60°C. overnight. The yield of fine white powdery polymer was 1.4 g. The PMT is 260°C. (dec.), η_{inh} (0.5 g./100 ml. in m-cresol) 0.57. A very brittle film can be pressed from the polymer at 152°C. It is highly crystalline.

Compared to the oxetanes and epoxides, the **polymerization of tetrahydrofuran** proceeds rather slowly. Ordinarily, the products are viscous oils; however, Muetterties (50) has found that very high molecular weight polyether can be obtained by using phosphorus pentafluoride as a catalyst, instead of boron fluoride or antimony pentachloride.

336. Preparation of Pure Tetrahydrofuran (50)

Tetrahydrofuran is purified by refluxing over solid sodium hydroxide, distilling under nitrogen, then refluxing over lithium aluminum hydride and distilling therefrom immediately prior to use.

337. Polymerization of Tetrahydrofuran (50)

$$\boxed{}\text{O} \xrightarrow{PF_5} [-OCH_2CH_2CH_2CH_2-]_n$$

To about 350 g. of purified tetrahydrofuran in a suitable sized vessel maintained under nitrogen, is added 1 g. of a solid phosphorus pentafluoride–tetrahydrofuran coordination complex. This material is prepared by saturating tetrahydrofuran with phosphorus pentafluoride (see Preparation 329) at 0°C. and subliming the resulting solid at 70°C. and 0.02 mm. pressure. The mixture of tetrahydrofuran and catalyst is maintained at 30°C. for approximately 6 hr. in order to effect polymerization. The resulting solid, colorless polymer is heated in water to destroy phosphorus pentafluoride residue and is then dissolved in more tetrahydrofuran. The polymer is recovered by pouring the tetrahydrofuran solution into water with violent agitation, preferably in a high speed mixer such as a Waring Blendor. The white shredded polymer is obtained in this manner in a yield of about 59% after air drying. This polymer has an inherent viscosity (0.5% in benzene) of about 3.6, which corresponds to a molecular weight of close to 329,000. The polymer can be molded at temperatures between 100 and 230°C. to a clear, tough film which crystallizes slowly on standing. The crystalline film can be stretched in the usual manner and oriented. The oriented film samples are quite tough. Above the crystalline melting point, which is about 45°C., the polymer films take on a rubbery appearance and feel; however, they maintain their toughness.

Lower molecular weight solid polymer may be prepared by catalysis with antimony pentachloride. Thus, 75 g. of tetrahydrofuran purified as in preceding experiments is cooled in solid carbon dioxide under nitrogen. To this cooled tetrahydrofuran is added 3 g. of freshly distilled antimony pentachloride. The mixture is then stored at 25°C. After 40 min., it has set to a solid; after 24 hr., the polymer is recovered and purified as in the preceding example. Polymer prepared in this manner is a solid, but it is tacky at 40°C. and has an inherent viscosity of only about 0.6.

Poly(tetramethylene oxide) of high molecular weight is crystalline, melting at about 45°C. Again, the tremendous effect of stiffening a polymer chain on the polymer properties is demonstrated by the polymerization of **1,4-epoxycyclohexane.** The polymer is still highly crystalline, but melts above 400°C. (51,52).

338. Preparation of 1,4-Epoxycyclohexane (84)

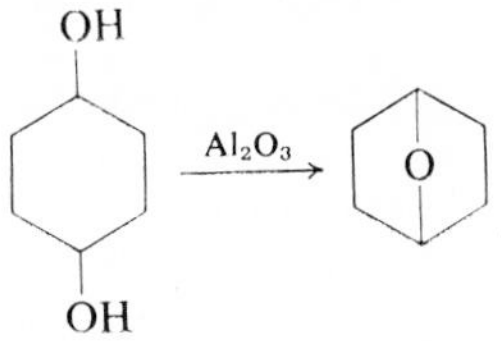

A mixture of *cis* and *trans* cyclohexanediols obtained by the hydrogenation of hydroquinone or purchased from a commercial source should be distilled before use in order to obtain a dry product. The diol mixture boils at about 146°C. at 18–20 mm. To 432 g. of the distilled diol is added an equal weight of activated alumina. The intimately mixed solids are placed in an ordinary distillation apparatus and the solids are heated slowly for 6 hr. at such a temperature that a distillate is obtained very slowly during this period. The resulting product which is obtained in roughly 200 g. yield is isolated, dried over anhydrous potassium carbonate, and distilled, preferably through a precision distilling column. The pure 1,4-epoxycyclohexane boils at 119–119.5°C. The yield of product is approximately 41%.

339. Polymerization of 1,4-Epoxycyclohexane (52)

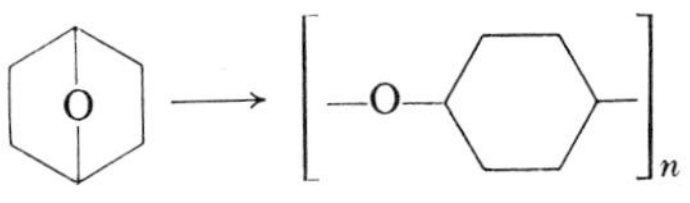

Two catalyst systems have been found effective for the polymerization of 1,4-epoxycyclohexane to high molecular weight, high-melting, crystalline polyether.

In the first technique, a mixture of 1 part of epoxycyclohexane and 2 parts of nitrobenzene is cooled to $-30°C$. To this mixture is added phosphorus pentafluoride (see Preparation 329) gas in a quantity of the order of 1–5 mole %. It is not necessary to accurately measure the amount added. The mixture is maintained at $-30°C$. for approximately 100 hr. when a solid mass has formed. This solid mixture is taken out and broken up with acetone, filtered, washed repeatedly with water and acetone, and dried. The yield is about 50%; the inherent viscosity is of the order of 1, in a solvent consisting of 66 parts of tetrachloroethane plus 100 parts of phenol.

An alternate method for the polymerization of 1,4-epoxycyclohexane involves use of a catalyst combination such as ferric chloride–thionyl chloride which has been shown to be effective for the polymerization of tetrahydrofuran. Thus, to 50 g. of epoxycyclohexane maintained at $0°C$. is added 0.015 g. of anhydrous ferric chloride as a 10% solution in ether, followed by 0.062 g. of thionyl chloride, also added as a 10% solution in anhydrous ether. The mixture is stirred and maintained in a stoppered flask at $0°C$. for 18 hr. At the end of 18 hr., the polymer is mixed with alcohol and the solid material is filtered from residual monomer. The polymer is washed repeatedly with alcohol and water, and dried. The yield of polymer with an inherent viscosity of about 0.6 is about 37%.

An x-ray diffraction pattern of polymer obtained in either of the above two manners indicates that crystallinity does not disappear below $430°C$. The polymer is very insoluble and cannot be dissolved in alcohol, ether, acetone, benzene, dimethylformamide, o-cresol, anisole, or a variety of other organic solvents. It is soluble in a mixture of 66 parts of tetrachloroethane and 100 parts of phenol. It is possible to cast films from this solvent mixture, but the films, even though the inherent viscosity of the polymer is high, are usually brittle and noncoherent.

Trioxane, a heterocyclic acetal, polymerizes by a ring opening mechanism; however, it will be considered in Chapter 6, along with formaldehyde.

VII. Polymerization of Cyclic Hydrocarbons

Certain **carbocycles,** for example, **cyclopentene,** may be bulk polymerized over a molybdenum catalyst to yield all-*cis* polymer according to the following scheme:

340. Ring Opening Polymerization of Cyclopentene (85)*

A 250 ml. three-necked flask is equipped with a stirrer and a nitrogen inlet; the air is replaced by dry nitrogen. The reaction vessel is charged with 20 g. of

* Our thanks to Professor Natta and coworkers for additional details not in the literature.

$$n \quad \begin{matrix} & CH_2 \\ HC & \diagdown \\ \| & \quad CH_2 \\ HC & \diagup \\ & CH_2 \end{matrix} \quad \longrightarrow \quad (\ -\overset{H}{\underset{}{C}}=\overset{H}{\underset{}{C}}-CH_2-CH_2-CH_2-)_n$$

pure dry cyclopentene (the commercial product has to be refluxed under nitrogen, rectified over sodium wire, and stored under nitrogen) and then cooled to $-40°C$. with a Dry Ice–acetone bath. The catalyst is formed in the cooled monomer by adding under stirring 0.160 g. (0.59 mmoles) of pure $MoCl_5$ (powdered and weighed under dry nitrogen) followed by 1.18 mmoles of $Al(C_2H_5)_3$.

Immediately after the addition of $Al(C_2H_5)_3$ the reaction mixture assumes a dark-brown color and the polymerization starts. The polymerization is run at $-40°C$. for 4 hr. under stirring; by this time the reaction mixture has the appearance of a brown lump of soft rubber. The reaction is stopped by adding about 100 ml. of methanol and vigorously stirring for half an hour. The mother liquor is discarded and the polymer is dissolved in 200 ml. of benzene under stirring. The addition of a small quantity of a stabilizer such as phenyl-β-naphthylamine is recommended to prevent crosslinking of the polymer. When the polymer is dissolved (solution is usually free from gel, but it may be necessary to remove suspended catalyst residues by filtration), it is reprecipitated by pouring the solution into an excess of methanol while vigorously stirring.

The polymer is then dried under reduced pressure at room temperature. To obtain a higher purity or to remove very low molecular weights the polymer can be redissolved in benzene and precipitated with acetone. The yield of dried polymer is about 9 g. (45% of the monomer used); the intrinsic viscosity is in the range of 1.8–2.0 dl./g. (in toluene at 30°C.). The polymer is amorphous at room temperature, even under stretching. The IR examination shows that more than 99% of the double bonds present in the polymer are of the *cis* type, the remaining being *trans*-internal and vinyl end groups.

The *cis* polypentene thus obtained is a translucent solid with rubberlike properties. It is soluble at room temperature in aliphatic, cycloaliphatic, aromatic, and chlorinated hydrocarbons. It is insoluble in hot alcohols and ketones. The polymer undergoes crosslinking in the presence of air at room temperature. To store it for a few days it may be better to flush the sample container with nitrogen and to keep it in a freezer; for longer periods it is safer to stabilize it with 1% of phenyl-β-naphthylamine.

Up to this point, we have considered strictly organic monomers. There are a number of organo-inorganic and inorganic compounds which exist as polymerizable cyclic monomers.

VIII. Silicones

A class of polymers of considerable commercial importance is based on a linear, cyclic, or crosslinked arrangement of alternating silicon and oxygen atoms, where the silicon is substituted with organic radicals or hydrogen. They are called organopolysiloxanes, or simply silicone polymers, and can be formulated as

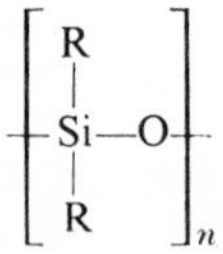

$$\left[\begin{array}{c} R \\ | \\ -Si-O- \\ | \\ R \end{array}\right]_n$$

The usual procedure for preparing silicone polymers is to hydrolyze, either singly or in the appropriate combination, compounds of the type R_3SiCl, R_2SiCl_2, $RSiCl_3$, and $SiCl_4$, depending on the kind of product desired. The intermediates in the reaction are believed to be the corresponding silanols [e.g., $R_2Si(OH)_2$] which condense very rapidly

with the elimination of water and formation of the $-\overset{|}{\underset{|}{Si}}-O-\overset{|}{\underset{|}{Si}}-$ link.

In addition to linear polymer, cyclic forms where n ranges from 3 to 9 are often encountered. These cyclic products can be converted to high molecular weight linear polymer in the presence of alkaline catalysts.

Although many of the silicone "polymers" are of quite low molecular weight, their relationship to the higher molecular weight silicones warrants their inclusion here. The linear silicones, $(CH_3)_3Si[OSi(CH_3)_2]_n—OSi(CH_3)_3$, where n is fairly small, form the basis of the well-known silicone oils. The **cyclic silicones,** formed in hydrolysis reactions of the silane dihalides, especially $[(CH_3)_2SiO]_{3-4}$, **are convertible to** high molecular weight **linear silicone elastomers.** Various curing techniques are available for converting linear and cyclic materials to crosslinked elastomers and resins.

341. Preparation of Cyclic Polysiloxanes (86)

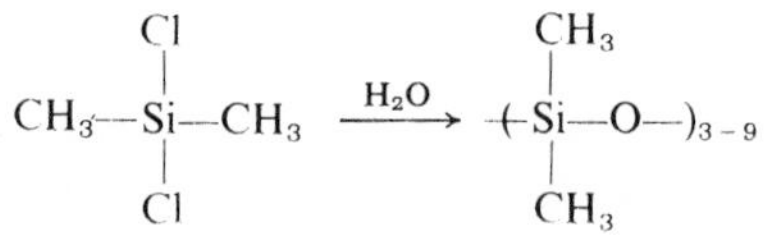

$$CH_3—\underset{\underset{Cl}{|}}{\overset{\overset{Cl}{|}}{Si}}—CH_3 \xrightarrow{H_2O} (\underset{\underset{CH_3}{|}}{\overset{\overset{CH_3}{|}}{Si}}—O—)_{3-9}$$

A. From a dropping funnel protected with a drying tube, 200 ml. of dimethyldichlorosilane is added slowly to 600 ml. of vigorously stirred water maintained at 15–20°C. When the addition is finished, the oily, organic layer is taken up in 150 ml. of ethyl ether, separated from the water phase, and dried over magnesium sulfate. The ether solution is filtered and the ether removed by evaporation. The oily residue contains cyclic products of the type shown in the preceding reaction, plus some high molecular weight materials, probably linear as well as cyclic.

The material obtained from the ether layer, about 100 ml., is fractionated with precision in order to isolate the individual components of the mixture.

The approximate percentages of the components and their boiling points are: $n = 3$, 0.5%, 134°C./760 mm. (m.p. 64°C.); $n = 4$, 42%, 175°C./760 mm., 74°C./20 mm. (m.p. 17.5°C.); $n = 5$, 6.7%, 101°C./20 mm. (m.p. −38°C.); $n = 6$, 1.6%, 128°C./20 mm. (m.p. −3°C.). The trimer and tetramer can be distilled conveniently at atmospheric pressure. Trimer to hexamer constitute about half the total products.

B. The higher molecular weight residue in the still pot is a viscous oil which is pyrolyzed to trimer and tetramer by heating in a slow stream of nitrogen by means of a metal bath to 350°C. with a Claisen head and condenser set for distillation. Up to 350°C. only trace quantities of distillate appear. From 350 to 400°C. the liquid in the flask begins to boil, with the distillate temperature being 135–210°C. Continued heating at 400°C. causes almost the entire contents of the flask to distill. The distillate, totaling about 40 ml., forms a mixture of crystals and liquid and consists of about 44% of the cyclic trimer and 24% of the cyclic tetramer, with the remainder being pentamer and above. This mixture can be fractionated to its components, as described in A.

These reactions demonstrate the tendency of the (R_2Si—O) unit to form cyclic structures under the conditions given. The reverse of this latter process, namely the **formation of low molecular weight linear polymer from low molecular weight cyclic siloxanes** can be accomplished by an equilibration reaction in the presence of sulfuric acid, and is demonstrated in the following way.

342. Preparation of Linear Polysiloxanes (86)

$$[(CH_3)_2SiO]_4 \xrightarrow{\text{H}_2\text{SO}_4} [(CH_3)_2SiO]_n$$

Twenty ml. of octamethylcyclotetrasiloxane is placed in a stoppered flask or bottle with 3.7 ml. of concentrated sulfuric acid and 10 ml. ethyl ether and shaken at room temperature for 1 day. The mixture becomes very viscous. Then 20 ml. ether and 10 ml. water are added and the mixture is shaken for 1 hr. The lower aqueous layer is drawn off and the ether solution is washed three times with 10 ml. portions of water and is then dried over anhydrous potassium carbonate. The ether is distilled from the solution through a Claisen head and the temperature of the distilling flask is raised by means of a metal bath to 310°C., during which time a small quantity of distillate forms. The residue in the distilling flask is a clear, viscous oil, soluble in various hydrocarbon or ether solvents. If purified tetramer, $[(CH_3)_2SiO]_4$ is used as the starting material, a cryoscopic molecular weight determination in cyclohexane indicates a value of about 2740, or 37 $(CH_3)_2SiO$ units.

By carrying out the above reaction on the cyclic tetramer in the presence of a definite amount of hexamethyldisiloxane, one can prepare linear polymers of the structure $(CH_3)_3SiO[(CH_3)_2SiO]_nSi(CH_3)_3$, where n is determined by the amount of chain terminating $(CH_3)_3SiOSi(CH_3)_3$ used. It is these linear polysiloxanes that form the basis of methyl silicone oils. A variety of products is possible having a wide range of viscosities, depending on the value of n in the above formula. They are distinguished by their small change in viscosity over a wide range of temperatures, quite unlike petroleum oils.

The other linear polysiloxanes mentioned are terminated with hydroxyl groups which may condense further on heating and alter the molecular weight and viscosity as a result. The advantage of the **$(CH_3)_3$—SiO terminated polysiloxanes** over these is the stability to heat conferred by the trimethylsiloxy group.

343. Preparation of a Linear Polysiloxane Terminated with Trimethylsiloxy Groups (86)

$$[(CH_3)_2SiO]_4 + [(CH_3)_3Si]_2O \xrightarrow{H_2SO_4} (CH_3)_3SiO[(CH_3)_2SiO]_nSi(CH_3)_3$$

Twenty ml. of the cyclic tetramer from Preparation 341 is mixed with 0.4 ml. of hexamethyldisiloxane and shaken for 24 hr. with 0.8 ml. of concentrated sulfuric acid. After this time, 5 ml. of water is added and shaking continued another hour. The mixture is centrifuged, and the two layers separated. The viscous upper layer of silicone oil has a viscosity of about 130 cs. at 40°C.

Linear silicone polymers, which may have molecular weights of 1,000,000 or more, are conveniently prepared from a **base-catalyzed ring opening polymerization of the cyclic trimer or tetramer,** $[(CH_3)_2SiO]_3$ or $_4$. The gummy products are soluble in aromatic hydrocarbons, and may be compounded, molded and cured, much as a natural rubber might be.

344. The Preparation of Polydimethylsiloxane (87)

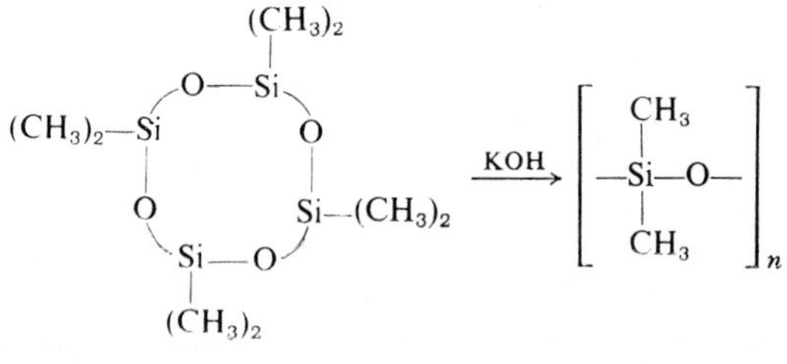

A catalyst solution is prepared by dissolving 1.0 g. of potassium hydroxide (dried at 70°C. in vacuum overnight) in 400 ml. of dry isopropanol in a flask protected with a drying tube and equipped for distillation. Isopropanol is distilled until the volume of the solution is reduced to 250 ml. One-tenth ml. of this solution is then transferred by a pipet to a 100 ml. three-necked flask purged with nitrogen and fitted with a good mechanical stirrer and a nitrogen inlet. The isopropanol is removed in a stream of nitrogen with moderate heating. Then 29.6 g. of octamethylcyclotetrasiloxane is added, the flask is equipped with a drying tube, and heated by means of an oil bath to 165°C.

with stirring for 1–5 hr., without the nitrogen, during which time the reaction mass will become a highly viscous gum. The polymer is transferred to an evaporating dish and heated in an oven at 150°C. for 3 hr. The polymer is soluble in benzene and toluene and has an inherent viscosity in the latter of about 0.7 (0.5% concentration at 25°C.). Catalyst residues may be removed by washing a solution of the polymer with very dilute hydrochloric acid, then with water.

An estimation of number average molecular weight can be made from a determination of the intrinsic viscosity in toluene (6):

$$[\eta] = 2 \times 10^{-4} \overline{M}_n^{0.66}$$

Silicone rubbers are noted for their flexibility over a wider range of temperatures (-90 to 300°C.) and their resistance to moisture, air, and weathering. The polymer so obtained must be properly compounded with fillers and curing agents in order to form a crosslinked, or vulcanized product. If a rubber mill or some similar set of differential rolls is available, the polysiloxane prepared may be compounded as follows to obtain a rubber which resists deformation under compression at elevated temperatures (88). The following ingredients are blended: 20 g. polydimethylsiloxane, 12 g. diatomaceous earth, 17.5 g. titanium dioxide, 0.3 g. benzoylperoxide, and 2.0 g. 2,5-di-t-butylquinone. The mix may then be molded or shaped, and cured by heating at 250°C. in an oven for 24 hr.

Crosslinked silicone resins are the result of replacing the hydrocarbon R groups in $(R_2SiO)n$ units (either in cyclic or linear materials) with oxygen bridges. This can be accomplished by cohydrolysis of tri- or tetrahalosilanes with the dihalosilanes, or by oxidation of linear silicones. In the methylsilicone resins, for instance, the C/Si ratio is less than 2.0; the smaller the ratio, the greater the degree of crosslinking.

345. Preparation of a Methylsilicone Resin by Oxidation (89)

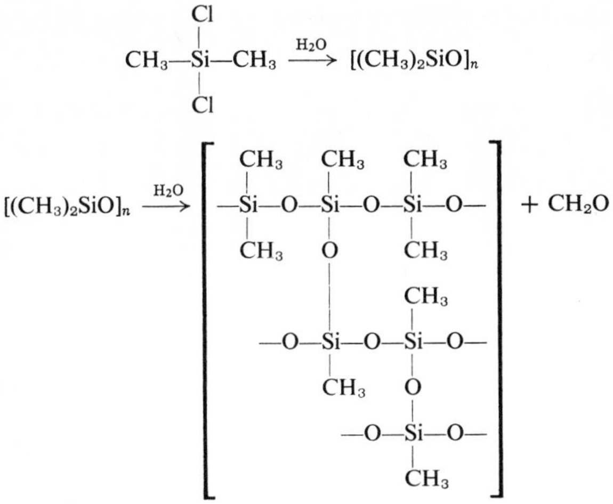

Twenty ml. of dimethyldichlorosilane is hydrolyzed as described in Preparation 341. The resulting oil is heated at 225°C. for 10 hr. in a small distilling flask while a slow stream of air is passed through the liquid. The resulting glassy solid is infusible and insoluble, but is somewhat flexible.

346. Preparation of a Methylsilicone Resin by Cohydrolysis (90)

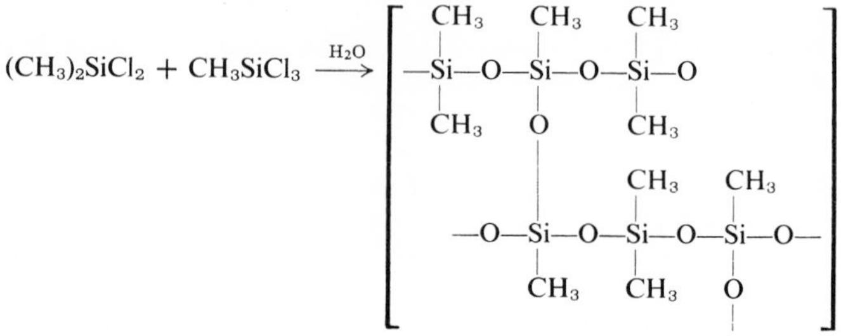

$$(CH_3)_2SiCl_2 + CH_3SiCl_3 \xrightarrow{H_2O}
\begin{bmatrix}
\begin{array}{ccc}
CH_3 & CH_3 & CH_3 \\
| & | & | \\
-Si-O-Si-O-Si-O \\
| & | & | \\
CH_3 & O & CH_3 \\
\end{array} \\
\begin{array}{ccc}
& CH_3 & CH_3 \\
& | & | \\
-O-Si-O-Si-O-Si-O- \\
& | & | \\
& CH_3 & CH_3 & O \\
\end{array}
\end{bmatrix}$$

A mixture of 4.5 g. dimethyldichlorosilane and 1.95 g. methyltrichlorosilane in 50 ml. ether is hydrolyzed by pouring onto 100 g. of cracked ice. The ether solution is evaporated and the oil is heated at 75°C. in air until it becomes a hard, glassy solid. The C/Si ratio of the resin is 1.3 as calculated from the mixture of chlorosilanes. The resin is infusible and insoluble. It is stable in air at 200°C. showing no apparent change over a long period. Heating at 300–400°C. causes rapid oxidation leaving only silica.

A silico-analog of polyisobutylene can be prepared by the polymerization of 1,1,3,3-tetramethyl-1,3-disilacyclobutane catalyzed by noble metal compounds such as platinum(II) chloride, chloroplatinic acid, and potassium hexachloroiridinate (91). This unusual polymerization is believed to occur by action of an electrophilic catalyst species on the ring with formation of a siliconium ion, followed by attack of the latter on a second monomer.

347. Preparation of 1,1,3,3-Tetramethyl-1,3-Silacyclobutane (92)

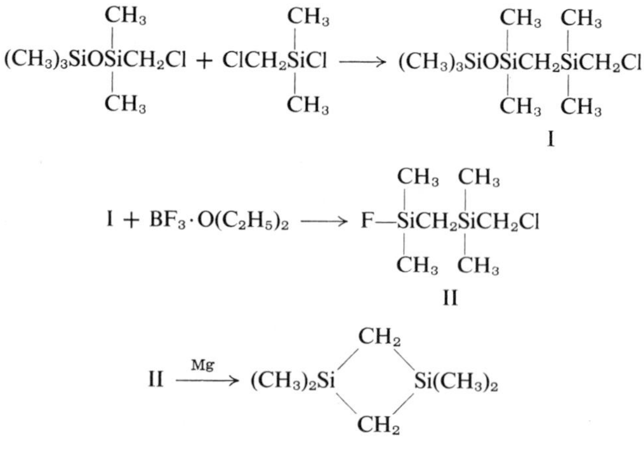

$$(CH_3)_3SiOSiCH_2Cl + ClCH_2SiCl \longrightarrow (CH_3)_3SiOSiCH_2SiCH_2Cl$$

with methyl groups on the silicon atoms, labeled I

$$I + BF_3 \cdot O(C_2H_5)_2 \longrightarrow F-SiCH_2SiCH_2Cl$$

labeled II

$$II \xrightarrow{Mg} (CH_3)_2Si \begin{array}{c} CH_2 \\ \diagup \quad \diagdown \\ \quad \quad Si(CH_3)_2 \\ \diagdown \quad \diagup \\ CH_2 \end{array}$$

A Grignard reagent is prepared from chloromethylpentamethyldisiloxane (93) (103 g., 0.52 mole) and magnesium (12.8 g., 0.52 mole) in 250 ml. of ether. To this is added chloromethyldimethylchlorosilane (75 g., 0.52 mole). After the addition, the mixture is heated to reflux and stirred 15 hr. Saturated ammonium chloride solution is added slowly with stirring until the salts separate to leave a clear, supernatant liquid. The mixture is filtered, the salts washed with ether, and the ether washings combined with the filtrate. Distillation gives 103.2 g. (0.38 mole, 73%) of 1-chloro-2,2,4,4,6,6-hexamethyl-5-oxa-2,4,6-trisilaheptane, b.p. 88–89°C. (8 mm.).

The trisilaheptane (125 g., 0.47 mole) and boron trifluoride ethyl etherate (125 g., 1.06 moles) are mixed and immediately distilled until a head temperature of 125°C. is reached. The distillation residue is extracted with ether and the extracts combined with the distillate. This solution is distilled to give 52.5 g. (0.26 mole, 57%) of 1-chloro-4-fluoro-2,2,4-trimethyl-2,4-disilapentane, b.p. 175–178°C.

Magnesium (7.2 g., 0.30 mole) and 50 ml. of sodium-dried ether are placed in a 500 ml. flask under an atmosphere of nitrogen. A small amount of the chlorofluorodisilapentane is added and the reaction started by the addition of 3 drops of methylmagnesium iodide solution. The reaction mixture is heated to reflux temperature. An additional 225 ml. of ether is added and the remainder of a 58 g. (0.29 mole) sample of the chlorofluorodisilapentane is dissolved in 80 ml. of ether and added over a 95 min. period with rapid stirring. After completion of the addition, stirring and refluxing are continued 15 hr. Decane (200 ml.) is added and the mixture is distilled rapidly until the head temperature is 170°C. Redistillation gives 25 g. (60%) of 1,1,3,3-tetramethyl-1,3-disilacyclobutane, b.p. 117–119°C. n_D^{27} 1.4380.

348. Preparation of Polydimethylsilmethylene (94)

$$(CH_3)_2Si\diamond Si(CH_3)_2 \longrightarrow +Si(CH_3)_2-CH_2+$$

To a small, stirred polymerization vessel having a serum cap, 10 g. of the disilacyclobutane monomer (96) is charged after first flushing with nitrogen. To the monomer is added enough of a concentrated solution of chloroplatinic acid hexahydrate ($H_2PtCl_6 \cdot 6H_2O$) to give 7×10^{-6} moles (3.62 mg.), which amounts to 10^{-2} mole percent of the monomer. The mixture is stirred at 25°C. until it becomes too viscous for further stirring. The contents of the flask are dissolved in benzene and precipitated into methanol, in which the gum is triturated thoroughly with fresh methanol several times. After drying at 60°C. in vacuum under nitrogen, about 8 g. of rubbery, clear product results. It should have a number average molecular weight of about 190,000 by osmometry.

Probably one of the most unequivocal examples of the much sought-after ladder structure in polymers is the high molecular weight, double-chained, cis-syndiotactic polyphenylsilsesquioxane, where cyclotetrasiloxane chains are fused cis-anti-cis (95–97). This linear, soluble polymer is the thermodynamically favored product from the base-catalyzed equilibration of products from the hydrolysis of phenyl-trichlorosilane. Linear, double-stranded polymer is unexpected from a trifunctional monomer according to the classic view of polycondensation as the random reaction of equally reactive functional groups. The validity of the assumption of equal reactivity is doubtful in the sesquisiloxane case; the intramolecular cyclization tendency is also evidently very great and contributes to linearity of the product here, just as in the examples of polyimides considered in Chapter 3.

349. Preparation of "Ladder" Polyphenylsilsesquioxane (95,97)*

Phenyltrichlorosilane (300 g.), diluted with an equal volume of toluene, is run into water with stirring. After removal of the acid layer, the toluene solution of the hydrolysate is distilled to remove residual water and acid, along with 130 g. of toluene. Next, powdered potassium hydroxide (0.14 g.) is added, and refluxing and trapping of the evolved water continued for 9 hr. The solution is cooled, filtered to remove the crystalline octamer, and the filtrate added to 1500 ml. methanol to precipitate our 155 g. phenylsilsesqui-oxane "prepolymer." This is a low molecular weight cage-terminated "ladder" polymer, intrinsic viscosity 0.12 dl./g. in benzene, $\overline{M}_n$ 14,000.

Preparation of high polymer requires equilibration at higher concentrations. Thus, a mixture of 0.5 g. of the above "prepolymer" (which still contains unneutralized base), 0.5 ml. of benzene, and 0.13 g. Dowtherm A is heated for 1 hr. at 250°C. in a loosely-stoppered 16 × 150 mm. test tube. The resulting tough, frothy mass is dissolved in benzene containing a drop of acetic acid and precipitated into excess methanol to give 0.33 g. of polymer having an intrinsic viscosity in benzene of 4 dl./g., $\overline{M}_w$ 4 × 10⁶. Achievement of viscosities in the range 3–6 dl./g. in larger scale operation requires adjustment of reaction vessel geometry so as to maintain comparable rates of solvent diffusion out of the reaction mass. The polymer is soluble in benzene, tetrahydrofuran, and methylene chloride, and orientable films can be solvent-cast. The polymer is of poor crystallinity and is not meltable. The cis-syndio-tactic double-chain structure in polyphenylsilsesquioxanes is best characterized in solution by the strong, well-defined SiOSi IR bands near 1044 and 1156 cm.⁻¹ (95,97); these are not seen in the cage-like forms, nor in the conventional phenyl silicone hydrolysate resins, which have a very different form of molecular structure (98).

* Our thanks are due Dr. J. F. Brown, General Electric Co., for making this preparation available to us.

IX. Preparation and Polymerization of Phosphonitrilic Chloride

Phosphonitrilic chloride is obtained by the reaction of phosphorus pentachloride and ammonium chloride. It does not exist in the monomeric state but is isolated in the form of ring compounds, predominately the trimer and tetramer.

The purified cyclic materials can be polymerized quite readily to linear polymer with the structure

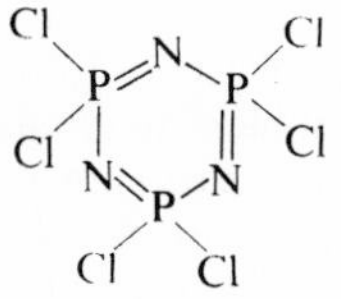

which is very similar in properties to ordinary rubber (100,101). It has been called inorganic rubber. Pieces of film can be stretched and will give a typical fiber diagram (99).

The polymer is extremely hydrolytically unstable and unless particular care is taken, polymerization of the cyclic monomer leads to an insoluble crosslinked product. The following procedure provides a polymer which is readily soluble in benzene under anhydrous conditions. This soluble product can be converted to hydrolytically stable products by treating it under anhydrous conditions with a variety of anions. A typical example is the reaction with trifluoroethoxyl anion.

350. Preparation of Phosphonitrilic Chloride (100)

$$NH_4Cl + PCl_5 \longrightarrow (PNCl_2)_3 + (PNCl_2)_4$$

To a solution of 450 g. of phosphorus pentachloride in 1200 ml. of dried *sym*-tetrachloroethane is added 140 g. of dry ammonium chloride. This mixture is refluxed for about 12 hr. or until evolution of hydrogen chloride has ceased. A calcium chloride tube is now attached to the open end of the condenser and the mixture is cooled. The residual ammonium chloride is filtered and the solvent is distilled under water pump vacuum, the temperature not exceeding 50–60°C. The residual mass is now transferred to an open dish and allowed to cool. The oily material and traces of excess solvent are removed by suction on a funnel, and the product is now washed with a little 50% aqueous ethyl alcohol. The residual powder, which consists almost entirely of phosphonitrilic chloride trimer, is recrystallized from benzene for purification. Before polymerization, the monomer should be recrystallized an additional two times. The product melts at 114°C.

351. Polymerization of Phosphonitrilic Chloride (101)

$$(PNCl_2)_3 \longrightarrow [-PNCl_2-]_n$$

Phosphonitrilic chloride (250 g.) is purified by recrystallization from approximately 400 ml. of warm n-heptane (below 75°C.) after decoloration with activated charcoal. Recrystallized phosphonitrilic chloride (116 g., 0.33 mole) is evacuated in a constricted Pyrex tube, with intermittent melting (at 114°C.) to remove occluded air, and the tube is then vacuum-sealed and immersed in a constant temperature bath at 250°C. for 48 hr. After this time the product is a transparent, immobile rubbery material in which crystallization of residual trimer and other oligomers occurs slowly at 25°C. The tube is then wrapped in a towel and broken. The polymer is cut into small pieces ($\frac{1}{4}$ in. cube), preferably in a stream of dry nitrogen, and is added to 500 ml. of dry benzene. It dissolves to a viscous, colorless solution after 24–48 hr. of continuous agitation.

352. Preparation of Modified Phosphonitrilic Chloride Polymer (101)*

$$\left[\begin{array}{c} Cl \\ | \\ -N{=}P- \\ | \\ Cl \end{array} \right]_n \xrightarrow{\ CF_3CH_2ONa\ } \left[\begin{array}{c} OCH_2CF_3 \\ | \\ -N{=}P- \\ | \\ OCH_2CF_3 \end{array} \right]_n$$

The phosphonitrilic chloride polymer (1.725 moles of $NPCl_2$) is dissolved in dry benzene (1000 ml.) and treated with a solution of sodium trifluoroethoxide (3.45 moles) in diethyl ether (1500 ml.) for 28 hr. at 57°C. The mixture is then neutralized to litmus with concentrated hydrochloric acid, and the precipitate filtered, washed with methanol and with water, and dried. This product is a mixture of fully substituted oligomers and polymers. The high polymers are obtained by fractional precipitation of an acetone solution of the products into benzene to give poly[bis(trifluoroethoxy)phosphonitrile] (55 g.).

The number average molecular weight is 90,000; the weight average molecular weight by light-scattering in ethyl trifluoroacetate is 1,700,000 ($\pm$ 500,000); and the intrinsic viscosity of the polymer in acetone at 30°C. is 1.92.

X. Some Fluorinated Cyclic Polysulfides

Sulfur and tetrafluoroethylene react in the vapor phase as follows:

$$CF_2{=}CF_2 + S_x \longrightarrow \begin{array}{c} CF_2{\diagup}S{\diagdown} \\ | \quad\quad S \\ CF_2{\diagdown}S{\diagup} \end{array} + \begin{array}{c} CF_2{\diagup}S{\diagdown}S \\ | \quad\quad\quad | \\ CF_2{\diagdown}S{\diagup}S \end{array}$$

These monomers are easily ring-opened to give copolymers of sulfur and TFE of high molecular weight.

* We wish to thank Drs. H. R. Allcock, R. L. Kugel, and K. J. Vallan, American Cyanamid, for their assistance in this preparation.

353. Preparation of Tetrafluoro-1,2,3,4-Tetrathiane and Tetrafluoro-1,2,3-Trithiolane (102)

$$S_x + CF_2=CF_2 \longrightarrow$$

$$\text{F}_2\underset{\text{F}_2}{\overset{\text{S}}{\bigsqcup}}\overset{\text{S}}{\underset{\text{S}}{\big)} + \text{F}_2\underset{\text{F}_2}{\overset{\overset{\text{S}}{\diagdown}\text{S}}{\bigcirc}}\overset{\text{S}}{\underset{\text{S}}{\diagup}} \longrightarrow$$

The preparation of cyclic polysulfides by reaction of tetrafluoroethylene with the vapors of boiling sulfur at atmospheric pressure is carried out as follows. The preferred apparatus is a 1 l. round-bottom glass reactor provided with an inlet tube to deliver the tetrafluoroethylene into the sulfur vapors, and an upright outlet neck 35 cm. in length and 25 mm. i.d., the latter serving also as condenser for the sulfur vapors. Nine hundred g. (28 g-atoms) of sulfur is placed in the reactor, blanketed with nitrogen, and heated to the refluxing point, about 445°C. at atmospheric pressure. Then 480 g. (4.8 moles) of tetrafluoroethylene is passed through the sulfur vapors over a period of 4 hr. Heating is regulated so that the temperature of the escaping reaction products at the head of the outlet tube is 280–300°C. The products are passed through an air-cooled downward condenser and collected in an acid-washer receiver. Volatile products not condensed in the receiver are collected in a trap cooled at −80°C.

The volatile fraction consists of 60 g. of low-boiling liquid, mainly thiocarbonyl fluoride, b.p. ca. −60°C. trifluorothioacetyl fluoride, b.p. ca. −25°C.; bis(trifluoromethyl) disulfide and carbon disulfide, b.p. 29–31°C. for the azeotrope; and bis(trifluoromethyl) trisulfide, b.p. 84–85°C. The main product is 1098 g. of liquid containing some solid material. Rapid distillation of this condensate at <5 mm. gives 813 g. of yellow oil. Fractionation of this oil through an acid-washed packed column into acid-washed receivers gives two products. The first is 97 g. (10% yield) of tetrafluoro-1,2,3-trithiolane, b.p. 26–32°C. (15 mm.), a yellow oil with a pronounced tendency to polymerize.

The major product is 480 g. (44% yield) of pale yellow tetrafluoro-1,2,3,4-tetrathiane, b.p. 59–61°C. (15 mm.), m.p. 12.5°C., n25 1.5447.
D

354. Preparation of Poly(tetrafluoro-1,2,3-trithiolane) (102)

$$\text{F}_2\text{C}\underset{\text{F}_2\text{C}}{\overset{\text{S}}{\bigsqcup}}\overset{\text{S}}{\underset{\text{S}}{\diagup} \longrightarrow [-CF_2CF_2SSS-]_n$$

A solution of 164 g. (0.84 mole) of tetrafluoro-1,2,3-trithiolane in 210 ml. of pentane is cooled to −80°C. To this solution is added a solution of 0.1 g. of trimethyl phosphite in 0.7 g. of pentane, and the mixture is allowed to stand for 1 hr. at −80°C. The solvent is decanted and the solid poly(tetrafluoro-1,2,-3-trithiolane) which forms is dissolved in toluene and reprecipitated with pentane. A second reprecipitation, followed by washing with pentane yields 30 g. (18%) of polymer having an inherent viscosity of 1.21 in 0.1% solution in toluene at 25°C. The polymer can be pressed to an opaque white film, which clarifies at 95–100°C.

355. Preparation of Poly(tetrafluoro-1,2,3,4-tetrathiane) (102)

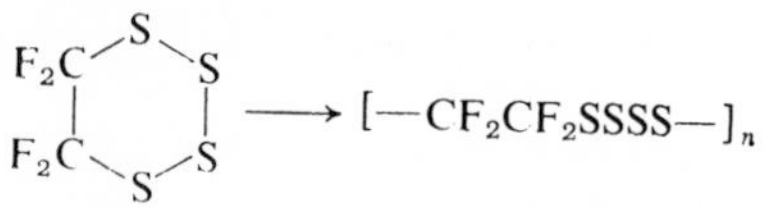

$$\text{tetrafluoro-1,2,3,4-tetrathiane ring} \longrightarrow [-CF_2CF_2SSSS-]_n$$

Tetrafluoro-1,2,3,4-tetrathiane is polymerized by adding 200 g. (0.88 mole) of the monomer over a 30 min. period to 1200 ml. of rapidly stirred aceto-nitrile maintained at −40°C. The precipitated polymer is isolated by filtration and washed successively with 300 ml. portions of ethanol, ether, ether, pentane, and pentane. The dried product weighs 170 g. (85% yield).

A 100 g. portion of the polymer is dissolved in 400 ml. of chloroform and reprecipitated by pouring the solution into 500 ml. of vigorously stirred, cold (0°C.) pentane. After having been washed with two 500 ml. portions of pentane and dried, the recovered polymer weighs 94 g. (80% yield overall).

The inherent viscosity $[\eta]$ of this product is about 1.0 in 0.1% solution in toluene at 25°C. if the solution is made up in the dark. A solution prepared under conditions of normal laboratory illumination gives about 0.8, indicating that some cleavage of the polymer chain has occurred. A similar polymer is prepared in 80% yield by addition of the monomer to stirred acetone at room temperature followed by reprecipitation from toluene. The crystalline melting point of various samples as judged by clarification on a melting point block is 55–60°C. Tough, cold-drawable films can be obtained by pressing freshly prepared samples at 90–100°C.

XI. Polymerization of Sulfur (S_8)

Another inorganic cyclic monomer which will open to give linear polymer which is not usually considered as such is **ordinary sulfur** (S_8). This may be converted to a linear high polymer with molecular weights of the order of 1,500,000 or more. The melted sulfur can be drawn out into fiber with surprisingly good tensile properties, provided the melt is quenched rapidly in water. It will crystallize to give a typical fiber diagram. Unfortunately, this extremely inexpensive high polymer does not remain in the polymeric condition at room temperature, but reverts rapidly to the cyclic S_8 monomer and loses all its polymer characteristics (99,103).

356. Polymerization of Sulfur

$$S_8 \text{ ring} \longrightarrow (S-S-S-S-S-S-S-S)_n$$

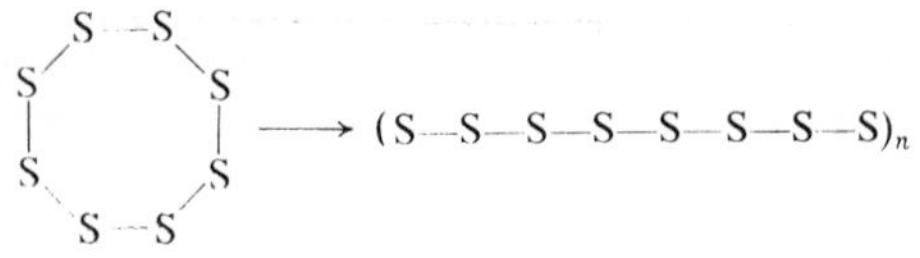

Ordinary rhombic sulfur is heated in a test tube gradually to 180°C. Melting of the rhombic material occurs at about 113°C., and at 180°C. the previously fluid material turns brown and becomes extremely viscous. The viscosity reaches its maximum at about 187°C. Fibers may be drawn from the viscous mass at that temperature and after quenching have surprisingly good tensile strength. As a variation on this experiment, a Carver press is heated to 180–187°C., and a lump of the polymeric sulfur prepared above and quenched in ice water is immediately pressed out into a film. The film is removed from between the two sheets of aluminum used for pressing and quenched rapidly in an ice water mixture. A rubbery tough, dark-brown film is obtained.

REFERENCES

1. H. K. Hall, Jr., *J. Am. Chem. Soc.*, **80**, 6404 (1958).
2. H. K. Hall, Jr., *J. Am. Chem. Soc.*, **80**, 6412 (1958).
3. H. K. Hall, Jr., M. K. Brandt, and R. M. Mason, *J. Am. Chem. Soc.*, **80**, 6420 (1958).
4. H. K. Hall, Jr. and A. K. Schneider, *J. Am. Chem. Soc.*, **80**, 6409 (1958).
5. H. K. Hall, Jr. and R. Zbinden, *J. Am. Chem. Soc.*, **80**, 6428 (1958).
6. A. Hamann, *Faserforsch u. Textiltech.*, **9**, 351 (1958).
7. D. D. Coffman, W. L. Cox, E. L. Martin, W. E. Mochel, and F. J. Van Natta, *J. Polymer Sci.*, **3**, 85 (1948).
8. H. R. Mighton, U.S. Pat. 2,647,105 (July 28, 1953).
9. W. E. Hanford and R. M. Joyce, *J. Polymer Sci.*, **3**, 167 (1948).
10. P. H. Hermanns, D. Heikens, and P. F. van Velden, *J. Polymer Sci.*, **30**, 81 (1958).
11. C. E. Barnes, W. O. Ney, and W. R. Nummy, U.S. Pat. 2,809,958 (October 15, 1957).
12. Private communication from Professor Hisaya Tani, University of Tokyo.
13. W. O. Ney, W. R. Nummy, and C. E. Barnes, U.S. Pat. 2,638,463 (May 12, 1953).
14. R. W. Holley and A. D. Holley, *J. Am. Chem. Soc.*, **71**, 2129 (1949).
15. R. Graf, G. Lohaus, K. Börner, E. Schmidt, and H. Bestian, *Angew. Chem. Intern. Ed.*, **1**, 481 (1962).
16. E. Testa and L. Fontanella, *Ann.*, **625**, 95 (1959).
17. R. Graf, G. Lohaus, K. Börner, E. Schmidt, and H. Bestian, *Angew. Chem. Intern. Ed.*, **1**, 481 (1962).
18. H. Rinke and E. Istel, in *Houben-Weyl*, Vol. 14, (Pt 2), p. 118.
19. L. Fontanella and E. Testa, *Ann.*, **616**, 148 (1958).
20. A. D. Bliss, W. K. Cline, C. E. Hamilton, and O. J. Sweeting, *J. Org. Chem.*, **28**, 3537 (1963).
21. W. H. Libby, U.S. Pat. 2,983,713 (1961)
22. E. K. Ellingboe, *Org. Syn.*, **31**, 105 (1951).
23. B. Djoberg, *Ber.*, **74B**, 64 (1941).
24. C. J. Berg, U.S. Pat. 3,216,980 (to 3M Co.) (November 9, 1965).
25. W. T. Astbury, *Nature*, **162**, 596 (1948).
26. D. Coleman, *J. Chem. Soc.*, **1950**, 3222.
27. D. Coleman and A. C. Farthing, *J. Chem. Soc.*, **1950**, 3218.
28. A. C. Farthing, *J. Chem. Soc.*, **1950**, 3213.

29. H. Leuchs and E. Geiger, *Ber.*, **41**, 1721 (1908).

30. S. G. Wiley, J. Watson, and W. E. Hanby, *Nature*, **161**, 132 (1948).

31. C. H. Bamford and H. Block, in *Polyamino Acids, Polypeptides Proteins*, M. A. Stahmann, Ed., University of Wisconsin Press, Madison, 1962, p. 65.

32. M. Goodman and U. Arnon, *J. Am. Chem. Soc.*, **86**, 3384 (1964).

33. M. Szwarc, *Advan. Polymer Sci.*, **4**, 1 (1965).

34. C. H. Bamford, A. Elliott, and W. E. Hanby, *Synthetic Polypeptides*, Academic Press, New York, 1956, p. 28. E. Katchalski and M. Sela, *Advances in Protein Chemistry*, **13**, 243, 1958. S. Sugai, K. Kamashima, S. Makino, and J. Noguchi, *J. Polymer Sci. A-2*, **4**, 183 (1966).

35. T. Alderson, U.S. Pat. 2,811,511 (October 29, 1957).

36. E. E. Blaise and M. Montagne, *Compt. Rend.*, **174**, 1173, 1553 (1922).

37. H. F. Mark and G. S. Whitby, Eds., High Polymers, vol. I, *The Collected Papers of Wallace H. Carothers*, Interscience, New York, 1940.

38. H. E. Zaugg, *Org. React.*, **8**, 305 (1954).

38a. A. Mooradian and J. B. Cloke, *J. Am. Chem. Soc.*, **67**, 942 (1945).

39. R. J. W. Reynolds, Can. Pat. 549,347 (November 26, 1957).

40. R. Thiebaut, N. Fischer, Y. Etienne, and J. Coste, *Ind. Plastiques Mod. (Paris)*, **14**, 2, 13 (1962).

41a. A. Weissberger, Ed., *The Chemistry of Heterocyclic Compounds*, **19** (Pt. 1), Interscience, New York, 1964, 729–884.

41b. H. Zaugg, *Org. React.*, **8**, 305 (1954).

42. E. Testa, L. Fontanella, G. F. Cristiani, and L. Mariani, *Ann.*, **639**, 166 (1961).

43. C. E. Lowe, U.S. Pat. 2,668,162 (February 2, 1954).

44. J. Kleine and H. Kleine, *Makromol., Chem.*, **30**, 23 (1959).

45. T. Shimidzu, T. Hakozaki, T. Kagiya, and K. Fukui, *J. Polymer Sci. B.*, **3**, 871 (1965).

46. A. Y. Arbuzov and V. M. Zoroastrova, *Izv. Akad. Nauk SSSR, Otd. Khim. Nauk* **1950**, 770.

47. R. S. Bly, G. A. Perkins, and W. L. Lewis, *J. Am. Chem. Soc.*, **44**, 2899 (1922).

48. T. Mukaiyama, T. Fujisawa, and T. Hyugaji, *Bull. Soc. Chem. Japan*, **35**, 687 (1962).

49. T. Mukaiyama, T. Fujisawa, H. Nohira, and T. Hyugaji, *J. Org. Chem.*, **27**, 3337 (1962).

50. E. L. Muetterties, U.S. Pat. 2,856,370 (October 14, 1958).

51. E. L. Wittbecker, Paper presented at 129th Meeting of the American Chemical Society, Dallas, Texas, April 1956.

52. E. L. Wittbecker, H. K. Hall, Jr., and T. W. Campbell, *J. Am. Chem. Soc.*, **82**, 1218 (1960).

53. F. E. Bailey, Jr., G. M. Powell, and K. L. Smith, *Ind. Eng. Chem.*, **50**, 8 (1958).

54. F. N. Hill, F. E. Bailey, Jr., and J. T. Fitzpatrick, *Ind. Eng. Chem.*, **50**, 5 (1958).

55. K. L. Smith and R. Van Cleve, *Ind. Eng. Chem.*, **50**, 12 (1958).

56. C. C. Price and M. Osgan, *J. Am. Chem. Soc.*, **78**, 4787 (1956).

57. C. C. Price, M. Osgan, R. E. Hughes, and C. Shambelan, *J. Am. Chem. Soc.*, **78**, 690 (1956).

58. M. E. Pruitt and J. M. Baggett, U.S. Pat. 2,706,181 (April 12, 1955).

59. M. E. Pruitt and J. M. Baggett, U.S. Pat. 2,706,189 (April 12, 1955).
60. M. E. Pruitt and J. M. Baggett, U.S. Pat. 2,811,491 (Oct. 29, 1957).
61. M. E. Pruitt, J. M. Baggett, R. J. Bloomfield, and J. H. Templeton, U.S. Pat. 2,706,182 (April 12, 1955).
62. W. J. Hickinbottom and D. R. Hogg, *J. Chem. Soc.*, **1954**, 4200.
63. T. L. Cairns and R. M. Joyce, U.S. Pat. 2,455,912 (December 14, 1948).
64. K. T. Garty, T. B. Gibb, Jr., and R. A. Clendinning, *J. Polymer Sci. A*, **1**, 85 (1963).
65. T. B. Gibb, Jr., R. A. Clendinning, and W. D. Niegisch, *J. Polymer Sci. A*, **4**, 917 (1966).
66. A. Noshay and C. C. Price, *J. Polymer Sci.*, **34**, 165 (1959).
67. E. J. Vandenberg, *J. Polymer Sci.*, **47**, 486 (1960).
68. J. Furukawa, T. Tsuruta, R. Sakata, T. Saegusa, and A. Kawasaki, *Makromol. Chem.* **32**, 90 (1959).
69. R. Sakata, T. Tsuruta, T. Saegusa, and J. Furukawa, *Makromol. Chem.*, **40**, 64 (1960).
70. E. J. Vandenberg, U.S. Pat. 3,158,580 (to Hercules) (November 24, 1964).
71. E. J. Vandenberg, *J. Polymer Sci.*, **47**, 486 (1960); S. Ishida and S. Murihashi, *ibid.*, **40**, 571 (1959).
72. W. D. Willis, J. O. Amberg, A. E. Robinson, and E. J. Vandenberg, *Rubber World*, **October**, p. 88 (1965).
73. W. R. Leach, *Rubber World*, **November**, p. 71 (1965).
74. J. B. Rose, *J. Chem. Soc.*, **1956**, 542, 546.
75. T. W. Campbell and V. S. Foldi, *J. Org. Chem.*, **26**, 4654 (1961).
76. Y. Etienne, *Ind. Plastique Mod.*, **9**, 37 (1957).
77. A. C. Farthing, *J. Chem. Soc.*, **1955**, 3648.
78. T. W. Campbell, *J. Org. Chem.*, **22**, 1029 (1957).
79. May be obtained from Ozark-Mahoning Company.
80. T. W. Campbell, U.S. Pat. 2,831,825 (April 22, 1958).
81. D. G. Hummel et al., *J. Am. Chem. Soc.*, **82**, 2928 (1960).
82. S. Searles, Jr. and E. F. Lutz, *J. Am. Chem. Soc.*, **80**, 3168 (1958).
83. V. S. Foldi and W. Sweeny, *Makromol. Chem.*, **72**, 208 (1964).
84. E. A. Fehnel, S. Goodyear, and J. Berkowitz, *J. Am. Chem. Soc.*, **73**, 4978 (1951).
85. G. Natta, G. Dall'Asta, and G. Mazzanti, *Angew. Chem. Intern. Ed.*, **3**, 723 (1964); French Pat. 1,394,380.
86. W. Patnode and D. F. Wilcock, *J. Am. Chem. Soc.*, **68**, 358 (1946).
87. E. L. Warrick, U.S. Pat. 2,634,252 (April 7, 1953).
88. C. W. Pfeifer, U.S. Pat. 2,666,041 (January 12, 1954).
89. J. F. Hyde and R. C. Delong, *J. Am. Chem. Soc.*, **63**, 1194 (1941).
90. E. G. Rochow and W. F. Gillian, *J. Am. Chem. Soc.*, **63**, 798 (1941).
91. W. A. Kriner, *J. Polymer Sci. A-1*, **4**, 444 (1966).
92. W. H. Knoth, Jr. and R. V. Lindsey, Jr., *J. Org. Chem.*, **23**, 1392 (1958).
93. R. H. Krieble and J. R. Elliott, *J. Am. Chem.*, **67**, 1810 (1945).
94. W. A. Kriner, *J. Polymer Sci. A-1*, **4**, 444 (1966).
95. J. F. Brown, Jr., L. H. Vogt, Jr., A. Katchman, J. W. Eustance, K. M. Kiser, and K. W. Krantz, *J. Am. Chem. Soc.*, **82**, 6194 (1960).
96. J. F. Brown, Jr., *J. Polymer Sci. C*, **1**, 83 (1963).
97. J. F. Brown, Jr., L. H. Vogt, Jr., and P. I. Prescott, *J. Am. Chem. Soc.*, **86**, 1120 (1964).

98. J. F. Brown, Jr., *J. Am. Chem. Soc.*, **87**, 4317 (1965).
99. K. H. Meyer, *Natural and Synthetic High Polymers*, Interscience, New York, 1950.
100. C. J. Brown, *J. Polymer Sci.*, **5**, 465 (1950).
101. H. R. Allcock and R. L. Kugel, *J. Am. Chem. Soc.*, **87**, 4216 (1965).
102. C. G. Krespan and W. R. Brasen, *J. Org. Chem.*, **27**, 3995 (1962).
103. A. V. Tobolsky and A. Eisenberg, *J. Am. Chem. Soc.*, **81**, 780 (1959).
104. K. H. Meyer, *Natural and Synthetic High Polymers*, Interscience, New York, 1950.

CHAPTER 6

Nonclassical Routes to Polymers

There are a number of polymer-forming reactions which cannot be properly classified as members of any of the previously described general categories. These are grouped in this chapter.

I. Cyclopolymerization

It is possible for certain structurally favorable **unconjugated dienes** to **copolymerize** according to the equation:

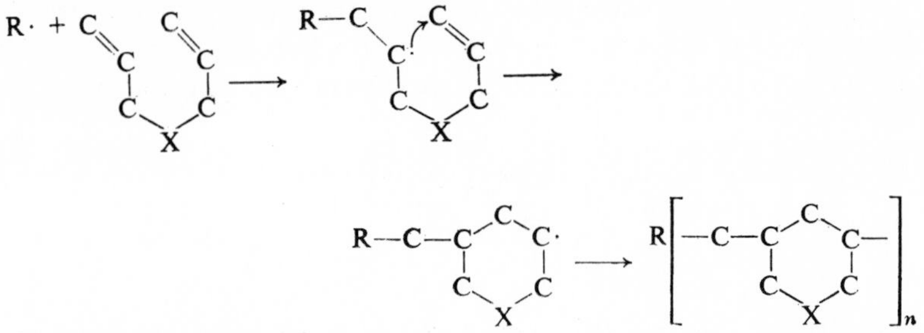

Polymerization of this type were first reported by Butler (1). Others who published at about the same time are Marvel (2) and Jones (3). The following example is due to the latter author.

357. Preparation of Linear Poly(acrylic anhydride) by Cyclopolymerization

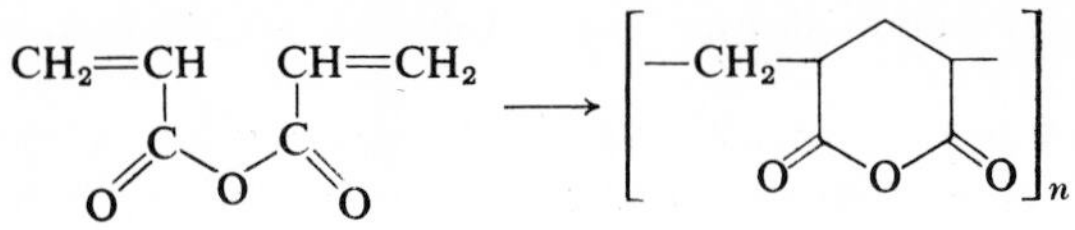

A solution of 20 g. of acrylic anhydride of at least 98% purity in 200 ml. of anhydrous benzene is mixed with 0.4 g. of benzoyl peroxide in a polymer tube, and sealed under an atmosphere of nitrogen (see Chapter 2). The tube is agitated at 50°C. for 25 hr., then the resulting thick polymer slurry is cooled to room temperature and the polymer is isolated by suction filtration under

399

nitrogen. It is dried at 50°C. in a high vacuum for 24 hr. The yield is 20 g. with an inherent viscosity of about 2 measured in dry dimethylformamide. This viscosity number corresponds to a molecular weight in the range of 200,000.

Although the monomer from which the polymer is made is a divinyl compound, the polymer obtained is linear, as evidenced by the fact that it is completely soluble at room temperature in such solvents as dimethylformamide, γ-butyrolactone, and N-methyl pyrrolidone. It is insoluble in most nonpolar solvents such as benzene and hexane. The polymer can be pressed to bars or to thin films at 180°C. Thin films of polyacrylic anhydride hydrolyze quite readily and the product is identical in every respect with polyacrylic acid.

For another unusual example of cyclopolymerization, see Chapter 6, Section IV.

II. Polymerization of the Carbonyl Group

With few exceptions, the only unsaturated compounds polymerizable to high molecular weight are those containing $C-C$ linkages. One notable exception is the carbonyl group.

The polymerization of monomeric formaldehyde has been known and described for many years (4). The earlier researches of Staudinger (5,6) produced films and fibrous material. However, it is only recently that tough, high molecular weight material has been obtained. Schneider (7) has shown that the cyclic monomer **trioxane** can be polymerized by

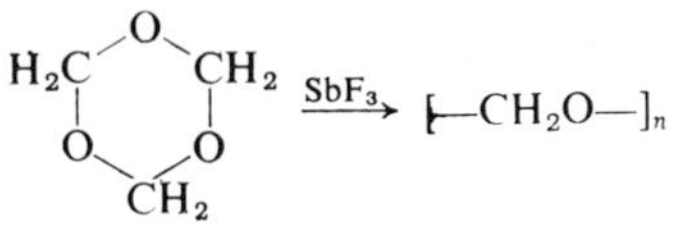

$$\underset{\underset{\displaystyle CH_2}{\underset{\displaystyle O\diagup \diagdown O}{H_2C\diagup \overset{\displaystyle O}{\diagdown} CH_2}}}{} \xrightarrow{\ SbF_3\ } [-CH_2O-]_n$$

a variety of Friedel-Craft type catalysts, particularly antimony trifluoride, to a high molecular weight film-forming material which can be cold-drawn and oriented. Furthermore, MacDonald (8) has shown that high molecular weight linear polymer with a high degree of thermal stability and toughness can be obtained. First, **paraformaldehyde,** is pyrolyzed to gaseous monomeric formaldehyde.

$$\text{Paraformaldehyde} \longrightarrow CH_2O \longrightarrow [-CH_2O-]_n$$

The monomeric formaldehyde is then passed into a solution containing one of a variety of different catalysts. The monomeric formaldehyde under these conditions polymerizes to high molecular weight linear materials.

Subsequently, a great deal of research has been carried out in industrial laboratories to develop useful resins based on polyacetal polymers and copolymers, both from monomeric formaldehyde and trioxane.

Two resins are commercially available: Delrin (du Pont) and Celcon (Celanese). The next two experiments describe the polymerization of monomeric formaldehyde. Following are some examples of the polymerization and copolymerization of trioxane.

358. Polymerization of Anhydrous Formaldehyde to Polyoxymethylene

$$CH_2O \longrightarrow [-OCH_2-]_n$$

Anhydrous monomeric formaldehyde is prepared by pyrolyzing 100 g. of anhydrous paraformaldehyde according to techniques described by Walker (4). The vapors are passed through 2 traps, maintained at $-15°C$. The formaldehyde monomer is then passed through a vigorously stirred reaction medium consisting of 600 ml. of anhydrous pentane and 0.2 g. of triphenyl phosphine at 25°C. Polymerization occurs as rapidly as the formaldehyde is introduced, yielding a total of about 90 g. of a snow-white powdery product. The inherent viscosity is about 2 in p-chlorophenol. This product gives translucent films when compression molded at 180–220°C. The films are quite tough and are oriented by stretching.

359. Polymerization of Monomeric Formaldehyde Vapor to High Molecular Weight Polyoxymethylene (8)

$$CH_2O \longrightarrow [-OCH,-]_n$$

Seventy-five g. of anhydrous paraformaldehyde is pyrolyzed (4) over a 2 hr. period to produce monomeric gaseous formaldehyde, which is passed through two traps at $-15°C$. and then into a reaction vessel containing 800 ml. of carbon tetrachloride, 0.05 g. of diphenylamine, and 0.078 g. of tributyl-amine. The reaction mixture is stirred vigorously and maintained at approximately 25°C. Polymerization proceeds throughout the addition of the monomeric formaldehyde to give a slurry of polymer. This is filtered, washed with ether, and air dried to give about a 35% yield of snow-white, high molecular weight polyformaldehyde. This polymer should have an inherent viscosity of about 1.8 as measured in p-chlorophenol. Again, tough, translucent films can be compression-molded at about 190°C. and then stretched and oriented.

Trioxane is easily polymerized at slightly elevated temperatures by boron trifluoride etherate in cyclohexane as the reaction medium; high conversions can be reached in a few hours (9). **An unusual catalyst, dioxymolybdenum diacetylacetonate,** will polymerize trioxane with extreme rapidity under very similar conditions (10). These two methods are given in the next two examples. The molybdenum dioxide complex is unusual in that it does not appear to operate via a cationic mechanism. Rather, it may operate more by a cyclic monomer insertion between the chain and the metal, reminiscent of the usual picture of coordination catalyst action in olefin polymerization.

360. Polymerization of Trioxane with Boron Trifluoride Dibutyl Etherate (9)

$$\text{(trioxane)} \longrightarrow HO\text{+}CH_2O\text{+}_nH$$

Trioxane can be purified by distillation from sodium hydroxide pellets through a column packed with glass helixes; b.p. 114.5°C./760 mm. Satisfactory results can usually be obtained also by recrystallization of commercial trioxane from methylene chloride. In both cases, precautions should be taken to minimize contact with air and moisture.

A 1 l. resin kettle is equipped with stirrer, condenser, nitrogen inlet, thermometer, and one serum cap closure. The vessel is thoroughly swept with nitrogen after baking dry. Then 420 g. trioxane is dissolved in 180 ml. dry cyclohexane at 55°C. When solution is complete, 0.09 ml. boron trifluoride dibutyl etherate (Allied Chemical) is added as the requisite amount of a standard solution of the catalyst in cyclohexane.

The heating bath required for the initial 55°C. temperature is removed and a cooling bath is raised into place intermittently in order to maintain the maximum reaction temperature at 60°C. The polymer begins to separate as a white powder. After little more than an hour, the yield is about 60%. The reaction mixture is poured into 1 l. of acetone containing 3 ml. tributyl-amine, the mixture stirred in a blender and the polymer filtered. After washing with acetone to remove amine, it is air-dried at 60°C. The inherent viscosity is 1.7–2.0 (0.1 g./100 ml. in p-chlorophenol/α-pinene (98/2) at 60°C.). The product can be stabilized as described in a subsequent example of stabilization.

361. Polymerization of Trioxane with Molybdenum Dioxydiacetylacetonate (10)

The catalyst, $MoO_2(CH_3COCH=C(O—)CH_3)_2$, is easily prepared from molybdenum trioxide and acetylacetone by the method of Fernelius, Tarada, and Bryant (11). For the following polymerization, it should be washed with additional dry n-heptane and dried in vacuum at 50°C. overnight.

To a dry, nitrogen-flushed, 8 oz. beverage bottle is charged 60 g. trioxane recrystallized from methylene chloride (4 g./ml.) and 30 ml. of dry cyclohexane. The mixture is heated in a hot water bath and swirled by hand to bring the trioxane into solution. The bottle is again well-flushed with nitrogen and 0.01 g. of the molybdenum dioxydiacetylacetonate added. The bottle is closed with septum and crown cap, shaken to disperse the catalyst, and immersed in a 100°C. oil bath. (A proper lab shield should be used at all times. The speed of the reaction, once it begins, is interesting to observe, however.) Within a few minutes after the contents reach about 85°C., polymer will begin to separate with the appearance of falling snow. The mixture acquires a bluish cast and a mass of polymer quickly forms, giving a nearly solid clump. (If no polymer forms in half an hour, the bottle can be opened—see below—and another 0.01 g. catalyst added. Rather impure trioxane can be responsible for deactivation of the initial catalyst quantity.) The mixture is heated another 10 min. and removed with caution from the bath. (Face shield, heavy gloves, and tongs should be used in removing the hot bottle. However, no untoward episodes have been known to occur with this system.)

After the bottle is allowed to cool, it is opened and the contents scraped into a blender containing 400 ml. concentrated ammonium hydroxide and washed thoroughly. The mixture is filtered and the polymer allowed to stand one hour in 300 ml. ammonium hydroxide solution. This treatment serves to remove most of the catalyst and blue color. The polymer is filtered, washed with water in a blender three times, filtered, and dried in vacuum at 50°C.

The inherent viscosity is about 1.4 [0.5 g./100 ml., p-chlorophenol/α-pinene (98/2) at 60°C.], and the overall yield is about 30 g. (65%). There is some evidence that at least a portion of the molecules are capped on one end by an acetylacetonate fragment from the catalyst. The polymer can be acetylated as described in Preparation 363 to increase its stability. The polymerization procedure given above can be used to copolymerize trioxane with ethylene glycol formal.

Polyacetals, whether from monomeric formaldehyde or trioxane, **are thermally unstable.** Unzipping by loss of aldehyde from —O—CH-(R—)OH chain ends occurs readily on heating, and, with some poly-aldehydes, at a noticeable rate at room temperature. One approach to stabilizing the polymer is to **cap the chain ends by acylation or etherification** in a post-polymerization treatment or by chain-transfer with a suitable reactant during polymerization. Another is to **copolymerize a small amount of an epoxide or other cyclic ether** (e.g., ethylene glycol formal). This introduces a few randomly placed carbon–carbon bonds in each chain, and when unzipping from a chain end occurs, it is effectively stopped when it reaches one of these units.

$$-CH_2-CH_2-O-(CH_2-O)_mH \longrightarrow -CH_2-CH_2-OH + m\text{-}CH_2O$$

Unstable   Stable

Thus, a copolymer of trioxane–ethylene oxide will lose formaldehyde only to a certain extent when heated, then will become stable, while uncapped homo-polyformaldehyde will essentially disappear. The copolymer can be pretreated with aqueous ammonia in dimethylformamide at 158°C. for a short time to give a polymer of very high thermal stability; terminal hemiacetal groups are degraded to the point where terminal hydroxy–ethyl groups replace them.

Polyformaldehydes of any kind are susceptible to oxidative and acidolytic degradation by attack at in-chain methylenes and oxygen, respectively. Besides antioxidants, small amounts of polyamides are often added as stabilizers, the latter possibly acting to remove any formaldehyde formed before it is oxidized to formic acid which could attack the in-chain oxygens.

The following example illustrates the preparation of a trioxane–ethylene oxide copolymer. Following that is a procedure for stabilizing a polyformaldehyde by acetylation.

362. Copolymerization of Trioxane with Ethylene Oxide (9)

An 8 oz. beverage bottle is thoroughly baked dry and cooled in a nitrogen stream. It is charged with 50 g. of purified trioxane, flushed with nitrogen, and capped by means of a septum and crown cap with hole. The trioxane is melted at 65°C. and 1.5 g. of liquid ethylene oxide is injected below the surface of the trioxane using a cold syringe with a long needle. Then, 0.007 ml. of boron trifluoride dibutyl etherate in 5 ml. cyclohexane is added. The bottle is then tumbled in a bath at 60°C. (The customary precautions should be taken, when handling the closed bottle.) After 40 min., the contents of the bottle, after cooling and venting cautiously, are washed into 1 l. acetone containing 3 ml. tributylamine, filtered, washed well with acetone, and air dried at 60°C. The yield is about 45 g. (90%) and the inherent viscosity is about 1.0 (0.1 g./100 ml., p-chlorophenol-α-pinene (98/2) at 60°C.). The crystallinity is somewhat less than homopolymeric formaldehyde, and T_m is about 173°C. compared to about 180°C. for homopolymer.

363. Stabilization of a Polyformaldehyde (9)

$$\sim\!OCH_2OH + (CH_3CO)_2O \longrightarrow \sim\!OCH_2O\overset{\displaystyle O}{\overset{\|}{C}}\!\!-\!CH_3$$

To a nitrogen-flushed 1 l. three-necked flask equipped with stirrer, condenser, and drying tube is charged 50 g. of polyformaldehyde (from either monomer or trioxane, as in Preparations 358–361), 400 ml. acetic anhydride and 0.2 g. anhydrous sodium acetate. The mixture is refluxed for 45 min., cooled, the precipitated polymer freed of acetic anhydride by repeated washings with acetone in a blender, and air dried at 60°C. The recovery should be about 80°C., with some decrease in inherent viscosity from the original. The thermal stability is far better than the original polymer.

An interesting property of **trioxane** is its **ability to polymerize in the solid state.** The polymerization may be affected with cationic catalysts (12,13) or ionizing radiation (14). This polymerization is an example of a *topochemical reaction* in that the crystal structure of the product (polymer) is directly related to the crystal structure of the reactant (monomer). The topochemical polymerizations of 3,3-bis(chloromethyl)oxetane, β-propiolactone, and diketene have also been described (14). Topochemical polymerizations give polymers which are nearly 100% crystalline. Solid state phenomena are often greatly influenced by trace impurities, mechanical stress, etc. That topochemical polymerizations are difficult to reproduce quantitatively is thus hardly surprising (15).

364. Solid State Polymerization of Trioxane*

An argon (or nitrogen) flushed pop bottle containing 20 g. granular trioxane (50–100 g. could equally well be used) is capped with a Buna N septum and partially evacuated. (Commercial trioxane usually is satisfactory, but recrystallization from dichloromethane may sometimes be desirable.) Silicon tetrafluoride gas (100 ml.) is introduced into the bottle with a syringe. After 30 hr. at 50°C., 50 ml. 5% sodium hydroxide is added and the polymer is washed successively in a blender with 5% sodium hydroxide, water, and methanol. Conversion is 50–90%. Polyoxymethylene from solid state polymerizations consists of characteristic microscopic fibers which give pulp-like slurries and felt-like mats after filtration. The polymer melts about 185°C.; pressing at 200°C. gives tough flexible films which melt about 175°C. Inherent viscosities (0.5% solution in p-chlorophenol containing 2% α-pinene at 60°C.) usually are greater than 1.0.

Trithiane, the sulfur analog of trioxane, has also been polymerized by BF_3 gas in the melt at 225°C. (16) and by gamma radiation in the solid state (17). The polycondensation of $(ClCH_2)_2S$ and Na_2S has also been carried out (18). The T_m, reported on polymer from ring-opening of trithiane, is over the range 245–260°C.

Other interesting polyacetals have been prepared by polymerization of the carbonyl group of acrolein, acetaldehyde, dichloroacetaldehyde, n-butyraldehyde, and of the thiocarbonyl group of thiocarbonyl fluoride. The following are representative examples.

365. Preparation of Polyacrolein by Anionic Polymerization (19)†

A 250 ml. round-bottom flask with stirrer, dropping funnel, thermometer, nitrogen inlet, and an opening plugged with a serum cap, is flushed with nitrogen and heated with a bare flame to remove traces of water. After cooling under dry nitrogen, a mixture of 20 ml. of acrolein and 80 ml. of tetrahydrofuran is added to the flask through the dropping funnel under nitrogen. The acrolein should be at least 99% pure and should be dried by refluxing with calcium hydride. The tetrahydrofuran also must be specially dried. Any standard technique may be used.

* We wish to express our gratitude to Prof. Rolf Schulz of Mainz for this preparation.

† The details of this experiment were kindly provided by Dr. D. B. Miller, Stanford Research Institute.

The reaction mixture is cooled to $-50°C$. with vigorous stirring. 2 ml. of a solution $0.07N$ in anhydrous sodium cyanide dissolved in dry dimethylformamide is now added from a hypodermic through the serum cap. The temperature during the course of the polymerization must not rise above $-50°C$. After 100 min., 2 ml. methanol is added to stop the polymerization. The viscous solution is poured with stirring into 1 l. of petroleum ether to precipitate the polymer. It may be further purified by dissolving in tetrahydrofuran and precipitating with petroleum ether a second time. The yield of polymer is about 9 g. (54%).

366. Preparation of Polyacetaldehyde (20)

$$\begin{array}{c} CH_3 \\ | \\ C{=}O \\ | \\ H \end{array} \quad \xrightarrow[\text{ethylene}]{BF_3} \quad \left[\begin{array}{cc} CH_3 & CH_3 \\ | & | \\ {-}O{-}C{-}O{-}C{-} \\ | & | \\ H & H \end{array} \right]_n$$

Using a liquid nitrogen bath, polymerization grade ethylene (250 ml.) b.p. $-104°C$. is condensed in a 1 l., four-necked flask equipped with a stirrer, thermometer (reading to $-200°C$.), gas inlet tube, and a short condenser. The condenser terminates in a gooseneck adapter which is connected with a glass T to a dry nitrogen line and a double bubbler filled with mineral oil.

After the ethylene has condensed, the gas inlet tube is replaced by an adapter with a serum stopper cap. Moisture must be rigorously excluded throughout the operation.

Stirring is started, and 39 g. (50 ml., 0.88 mole) of pure acetaldehyde is injected slowly from a hypodermic in order to avoid excessive boiling of the ethylene (the syringe may be precooled in a polyethylene dry bag in a refrigerator at $0°C$.). The internal temperature of the reaction mixture is kept between -100 to $-120°C$. by lowering and raising the liquid nitrogen bath. Care should be taken that no freezing of the reaction mixture occurs.

Gaseous BF_3 (3 ml., 0.13 mmole) is now injected into the mixture with a hypodermic syringe. In 10–20 min. the stirrer stops due to the formation of polymer. The reaction is allowed to stand for an additional 30 min. while the ethylene is allowed to evaporate slowly; excess ethylene may be decanted with nitrogen blanketing. One hundred ml. of anhydrous pyridine is added; on stirring at room temperature, the polymer dissolves completely in the pyridine. The polymer may be isolated at this stage by pouring the pyridine solution into cold water, but it is relatively unstable. To increase stability, the polymer is end-capped by adding 300 ml. of acetic anhydride to the pyridine solution of polymer, and stirring the mixture under nitrogen for 1–2 hr. The brownish-green viscous solution is poured into 1 kg. of ice and 1 l. of water, thereby precipitating the polymer. The polymer is then kneaded by hand (rubber gloves!) in several changes of water and ice in order to completely destroy the acetic anhydride. The washing is complete when the wash water is colorless. Dry weight of the polymer: 34–37 g. (87–94%) $\eta = 1$–2 (0.5% in butanone). An even more stable product is obtained if the polymer is dissolved in ether, rinsed with 1% acetic acid to remove pyridine, 1% sodium carbonate, then several times with distilled water.

367. Preparation of Crystalline Isotactic Poly-*n*-butyraldehyde (21)*

$$
\begin{array}{c}
C_3H_7 \\
| \\
C=O \\
| \\
H
\end{array}
\quad
\xrightarrow[\text{pentane}]{\text{LiOt,Bu}}
\quad
\left[
\begin{array}{c}
C_3H_7 \quad C_3H_7 \\
| \qquad\ | \\
-O-C-O-C- \\
| \qquad\ | \\
H \qquad\ H
\end{array}
\right]_n
$$

Twenty ml. of a 1% solution of sublimed lithium-*tert*-butoxide in toluene is added to 240 ml. of anhydrous pentane (anhydrous conditions throughout are essential) in a four-necked, 500 ml. round-bottom flask equipped with a stirrer, thermometer, reflux condenser, and an outlet closed with a serum stopper. The reflux condenser is terminated with a gooseneck adapter which is connected through a glass T with a nitrogen line and a bubbler filled with mineral oil.

The reaction flask is then immersed in a Dry Ice/acetone bath and the stirrer started. When the temperature reaches $-75°C.$, 60 ml. (49 g., 0.67 mole) of freshly distilled *n*-butyraldehyde is injected. Polymerization starts almost immediately as indicated by the precipitation of white polymer. The temperature rises to $-58°C.$ After 30 min. the temperature of the reaction mixture again reaches $-78°C.$ The polymerization is allowed to proceed for an additional hour and is then quenched by adding 100 ml. of acetone containing 5 ml. of glacial acetic acid. The mixture is now allowed to come to room temperature. The polymer is filtered under a nitrogen blanket through a coarse filter funnel and washed with 200 ml. of acetone.

The polymer must be capped in the following manner to prevent rapid thermal degradation. The acetone-wet polymer is placed with 400 ml. of acetic anhydride and 50 ml. of pyridine in a three-necked flask equipped with a stirrer, thermometer, and a short (12 in.) distillation column. The stirrer is started, and the reaction mixture is heated to boiling. The lower boiling material is taken off during a period of 30 min. When the boiling point of the mixture has risen to 135°C., the still head is replaced by a reflux condenser, and the mixture is allowed to reflux for 15 min. Poly-*n*-butyraldehyde never goes in solution but swells under these conditions.

The cooled suspension is filtered, washed with acetone (500 ml.) until free of acetic anhydride, and dried in a desiccator over KOH. Yield: 24–27 g. (50–55%) $\eta = 0.3.$ The polymer is crystalline and highly isotactic.

Di- and trichloroacetaldehyde (chloral) have been polymerized to a high molecular weight (22,23). Both are rather unstable, with decomposition starting at fairly low temperatures; however, both can be **end-capped** by esterification to give a reasonably stable material. Poly-(chloral) is very intractable but the polydichloroacetaldehyde is soluble in convenient solvents, from which films can be cast. It cannot be melted without decomposition. An example of dichloroacetaldehyde polymerization follows.

* We wish to thank Dr. Otto Vogl of du Pont for details.

368. Preparation of Polydichloroacetaldehyde (22)

$$Cl_2CHCHO \longrightarrow \underset{\underset{CHCl_2}{|}}{+CH-O+_n}$$

Commercial dichloroacetaldehyde (FMC Corp.) can be satisfactorily purified by drying over P_2O_5 and fractionally distilling with retention of a heart-cut for polymerization (b.p. about 88–90°C./760 mm.). The aldehyde thus obtained is about 95% pure, with chloral as the major contaminant. Little or no chloral is incorporated in the polymer derived from this material.

In a 250 ml. resin kettle, dried at 120°C. and cooled under dry nitrogen, and equipped with a nitrogen inlet and exit, drying tube, and serum cap, is placed 150 g. dichloroacetaldehyde, purified as above. The aldehyde is cooled to 0°C., and 0.20 mmole of boron trifluoride diethyl etherate is injected with a dry syringe. The mixture is stirred at 0°C. for 5 hr. The polymer is transferred to a blender and washed 3 times with methanol, then air dried 3–4 hr. at room temperature in circulating air by spreading the polymer out in a thin layer in a flat dish or pan. The conversion is about 105 g. (70%).

The polymer should be stabilized without undue delay by refluxing 100 g. polymer in 600 ml. acetic anhydride containing 0.5 ml. pyridine for 15 min. After cooling the mixture and filtering the polymer, the latter is washed repeatedly with methanol in a blender and again air dried as above. Uncapped polymer is destroyed by heating the polymer in dimethylformamide (1 g./10 ml). at 130°C. for 30 min. The polymer is precipitated in a large excess of methanol, washed repeatedly in methanol, then dried in vacuum at 50°C. for 12 hr. The reduced viscosity is about 3.5 (0.1 g./100 ml. in tetrahydrofuran at 25°C.). The yield including the capping step is about 80%.

The polymer cannot be melted without decomposition. However, films can be cast from tetrahydrofuran. Capped polymer is relatively stable at 190°C. (weight loss of 0.26%/min.), but at 220°C. degradation becomes fairly rapid (weight loss of 3.47%/min.).

Thiocarbonyl fluoride is an unusual monomer, made by pyrolysis of the dimer. It polymerizes at low temperature, catalyzed by a weak base such as dimethylformamide. The polymer is tough and crystalline, melting at about 35°C., above which temperature it is an elastomer. It can be copolymerized with olefins, using as catalyst a mixture of triethylboron and oxygen.

369. Preparation of Thiocarbonyl Fluoride, $CF_2{=}S$ (24)

$$\underset{\underset{S}{\diagdown \diagup}}{\overset{\overset{S}{\diagup \diagdown}}{CF_2 \qquad CF_2}} \longrightarrow CF_2S$$

One hundred and eight g. of thiophosgene dimer (25), 179 g. of antimony trifluoride, and 250 ml. of tetramethylene sulfone are heated with stirring at 90–100°C. for 2 hr. During this time, volatile products are formed that are collected in an ice-cooled trap. By distillation of the condensate, there is obtained about 45 g. of 2,2,4,4-tetrafluoro-1,3-dithietane, b.p. 47–48°C. This compound is purified by shaking first with 25 ml. of 10% sodium hydroxide and then with 5 ml. of 30% hydrogen peroxide. After drying over silica gel, the colorless dithietane is distilled to obtain pure material, b.p. 48°C., m.p. −6°C., n_D^{25} 1.3908, d_4^{20} 1.6036.

The above dithietane is pyrolyzed by dropwise addition over a 2 hr. period to a platinum tube 0.5 in. in diam. and 25 in. long that is heated to 475–500°C. over a length of 12 in. During the pyrolysis, about 20 ml./min. of helium is passed through the tube. Gases emerging from the tube are condensed by passage through a trap cooled with solid carbon dioxide and acetone and then through a trap cooled with liquid nitrogen. Contents of both traps are combined and distilled through a column packed with Hastelloy helixes to obtain thiocarbonyl fluoride as a colorless liquid boiling at −54°C.

370. Anionic Polymerization of Thiocarbonyl Fluoride (26)

$$CF_2S \longrightarrow (-CF_2S-)_n$$

A glass flask containing 75 ml. of thiocarbonyl fluoride, which is about 100 g., is connected by means of glass tubing to a dry polymerization flask that has a small neck covered with a rubber serum cap and is fitted with a stirrer. One hundred ml. of dry diethyl ether is added to the polymerization flask. Both flasks are frozen by cooling with liquid nitrogen, the system is evacuated, and thiocarbonyl fluoride is distilled into the polymerization flask. The liquid nitrogen bath surrounding the polymerization flask is replaced with a solid carbon dioxide–acetone bath and dry nitrogen added until the pressure inside the flask is at atmospheric pressure. When the contents of the polymerization flask are completely melted, the stirrer is started and 5 drops of dimethylformamide is added from a No. 22 hypodermic needle. Polymerization begins almost immediately and is essentially complete after 2 hr. during which time the polymer separates as a white, spongy mass. It is removed from the flask and boiled in water containing 5 ml. of 50% nitric acid to destroy dimethylformamide and dispel ether. Inherent viscosities of 0.5% solutions of the polymer in chloroform vary from 4 to 6. Polymer films obtained by hot-pressing at 150°C. and 10,000 lb. ram pressure are elastomeric as removed from the press. At room temperature, they slowly become opaque because of crystallization of the polymer, which melts at 35°C.

371. Copolymerization of Thiocarbonyl Fluoride and Propylene (26)

$$CF_2S + \overset{\overset{\displaystyle CH_3}{\displaystyle |}}{CH}=CH_2 \longrightarrow \text{Copolymer}$$

A polymerization flask as in the previous experiment having a small neck covered with a serum cap and fitted with a stirrer is cooled with a solid carbon dioxide–acetone bath and charged with 300 ml. of dichlorodifluoromethane and 70 ml. (about 43 g.) of propylene. A glass flask containing 35 ml. of thiocarbonyl fluoride (about 47 g.) as measured at −78°C. is connected to the polymerization flask and then frozen by cooling with liquid nitrogen. The system is evacuated and thiocarbonyl fluoride is distilled into the polymerization flask. Then the liquid nitrogen bath is replaced with a solid carbon dioxide–acetone bath and the solid contents of the polymerization flask are allowed to melt under vacuum to remove dissolved oxygen. As soon as melting is complete, nitrogen is added until atmospheric pressure is re-established. The solution is stirred and 0.75 ml. of 10% triethylborane in heptane is injected through the serum cap followed by injection of 9 ml. of gaseous oxygen. After 2.5 hr., methanol is added to the polymerization mixture, which is then allowed to warm to room temperature. Dichlorodifluoromethane and excess propylene evaporate, and the polymer remaining is dissolved in 300 ml. of chloroform and precipitated by pouring this solution into methanol. About 51 g. of polymer is obtained, which has a sulfur content of 32.02%, corresponding to a mole ratio of CF_2S/propylene of 2.34:1.

III. Polymerization by the Tischenko Reaction

The Tischenko Reaction is normally not a reaction which goes in high enough yield to be a polymer forming reaction. W. Sweeny has found that with the proper selection of catalyst, aromatic dialdehydes such as terephthaldehyde can be converted to polyesters with sufficiently high molecular weight to permit formation of tough films. The melting point is low however, since the polyester is really a copolymer of the following units:

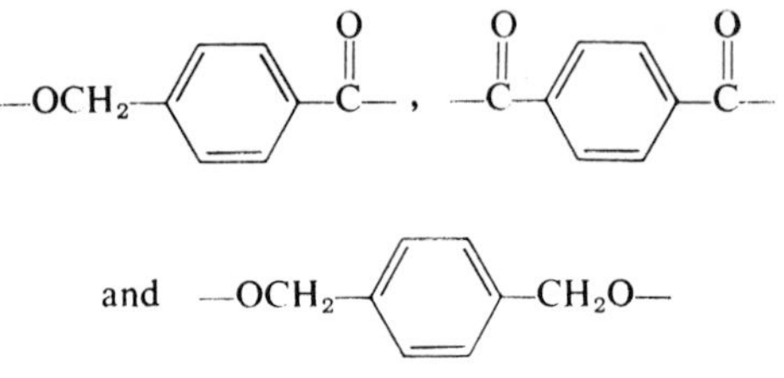

372. Tischenko Polymerization of Terephthalaldehyde (27)

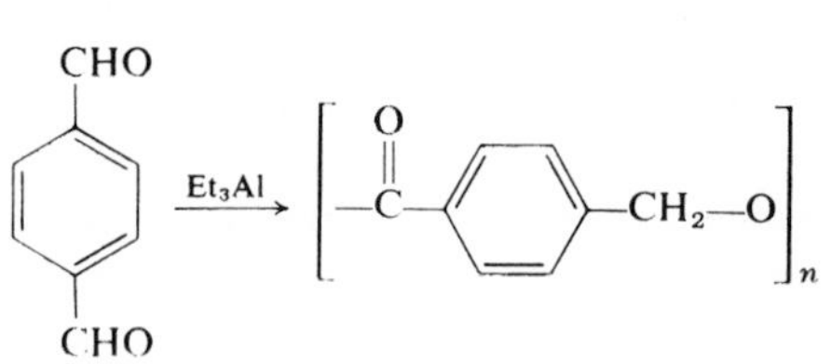

Terephthalaldehyde (2.5 g.) is suspended in 50 ml. of dry cyclohexane under nitrogen. The suspension is warmed to 80°C. and 0.5 ml. of a solution (0.8M) of triethylaluminum in cyclohexane is added. After stirring overnight at 80°C. under nitrogen, a light-yellow suspension remains in the flask. Methanol (100 ml.) is added to the reaction mixture and the polymer is then filtered, washed with an additional 200 ml. of methanol, and air dried. The polymer is purified by dissolving in 20 ml. of trifluoroacetic acid containing

1 ml. of tetrachloroethane. The solution is filtered, and reprecipitated by pouring into a large excess of methanol. The polymer is then washed with excess methanol and dried at 60°C. under vacuum to give 1.9 g. of white polymer of 0.31 inherent viscosity (0.5 g./100 ml.) measured in a 40–60 wt. % mixture of tetrachloroethane and phenol at 30°C. This polyester can be melt pressed at 120°C. to give a flexible tough film.

IV. Polymerization of Monoisocyanates

For many years, isocyanates have been known to trimerize in the presence of certain basic catalysts according to the equation:

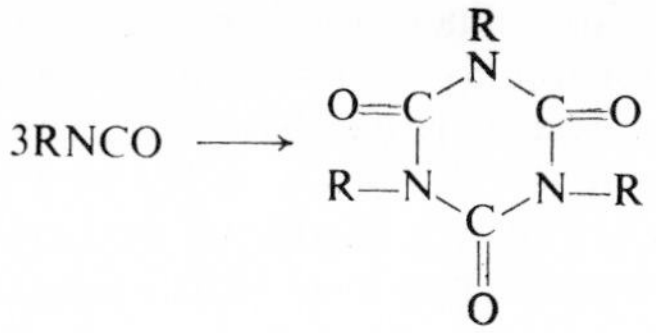

$$3RNCO \longrightarrow \begin{array}{c} R \\ N \\ O=C \quad C=O \\ R-N \quad N-R \\ C \\ \| \\ O \end{array}$$

However, polymerization to a linear product without cyclization was not observed until 1959, when Shashoua, Sweeny, and Tietz (28) showed that **basic catalysts** such as sodium cyanide in dimethylformamide **will polymerize the C=N group to a linear high polymer,** provided the reaction is carried out at **low temperatures:**

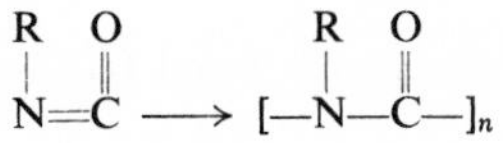

$$\begin{array}{cc} R & O \\ | & \| \\ N=C \end{array} \longrightarrow [-N-C-]_n$$

Structurally, the products are **1-nylons,** i.e., polyamides of the hypothetical *N*-substituted carbamic acids.

The polymers can be obtained with molecular weights approaching 1,000,000. If **R** is sufficiently large, e.g., *n*-butyl, the polymers are soluble in benzene, and tough films can be cast. The polymer where R is *n*-butyl melts over 200°C. and is crystalline.

1-Nylons tend to depolymerize in the melt, or in solution at room temperature in the presence of catalyst. High molecular weight products may have inherent viscosities as high as 15. Very dilute solutions (2–3%) are viscous enough to cast to very thin films.

373. Polymerization of *n*-Butyl Isocyanate (28)

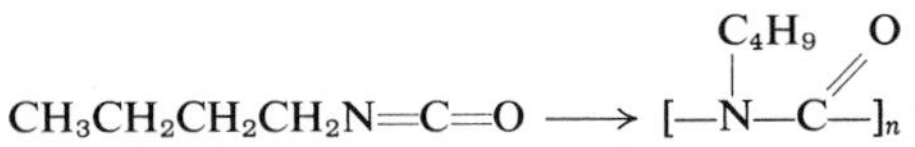

$$CH_3CH_2CH_2CH_2N=C=O \longrightarrow \begin{array}{c} C_4H_9 \quad O \\ | \quad \mathbin{/\!/} \\ [-N-C-]_n \end{array}$$

The monomer is prepared by the Curtius reaction from the corresponding acid chloride. It should be distilled immediately before use, b.p. 113–115°C., and should be stored under nitrogen. The catalyst for the polymerization is prepared by saturating dry dimethylformamide with anhydrous sodium cyanide under nitrogen for about 1 hr. The resulting solution is a powerful anionic catalyst, see Chapter 4, Preparation 226.

A 250 ml., three-necked flask is now equipped with a stirrer and two side-arm adapters. To one of these is attached a calcium chloride tube and a low temperature immersion thermometer to determine the temperature of the reaction medium. The other is fitted with a nitrogen "T" inlet tube, the vertical arm of which is sealed with a rubber bulb. The empty flask is flamed out under nitrogen and allowed to cool in an inert atmosphere. Dimethylformamide (30 ml.) is now added and the flask and contents cooled to about $-58°C$. which is close to the melting point of pure DMF. Ten ml. of freshly distilled n-butyl isocyanate is added and the mixture is stirred and allowed to cool again to $-58°C$. The rubber bulb is pierced with a hypodermic needle and 1 ml. of the catalyst solution is added dropwise over a period of 3 min. with vigorous stirring. After stirring for approximately 15 min. at $-58°C$., 50 ml. of methanol is added to inactivate the catalyst and precipitate the polymer. The polymer is filtered and washed repeatedly with methanol, then dried at $40°C$. in a vacuum. The molecular weight is extremely high, and inherent viscosities of the order of 15 in benzene should be obtained routinely. The yield is about 75%. The polymer is soluble in benzene, however, only to the extent of 2–3%. The viscosity is so high that solutions of this concentration can be successfully cast to film. These films are clear and tough. In appearance, they are very similar to polyethylene.

Poly(n-butyl-1-nylon) has a softening temperature of about $180°C$. and a melting point of about $209°C$. It gradually reverts to monomeric products when maintained at this melting point for any period of time.

374. Polymerization of p-Methoxyphenyl Isocyanate (28)

Polymerization of this monomer is carried out essentially in the same manner as in the previous example. Thirty five g. of p-methoxyphenyl isocyanate, b.p. $82°C./2$ mm., is mixed with 100 ml. of dry dimethylformamide at $-58°C$. and treated with 12 ml. of a saturated solution of sodium cyanide in anhydrous dimethylformamide. After polymerization is completed at $-58°C$., the polymer is isolated as described in the previous example in a yield of about 35%. The molecular weight is somewhat lower, the viscosity being in the range of 0.7 in dimethylformamide. In the case of p-methoxyphenyl isocyanate, the polymer tends to revert to dimer in the presence of the polymerization catalyst, so the polymerization should be quenched as soon as high molecular weight has been reached. Poly(N-p-methoxyphenyl-1-nylon) is soluble in dimethylformamide at fairly high concentrations and films can be cast from this solvent and viscosity determinations carried out. The polymer melt temperature is approximately $212°C$.

This type of polymerization can also be applied to 1,2-diisocyanates. In these cases, polymerization occurs by a cyclopolymerization reaction.

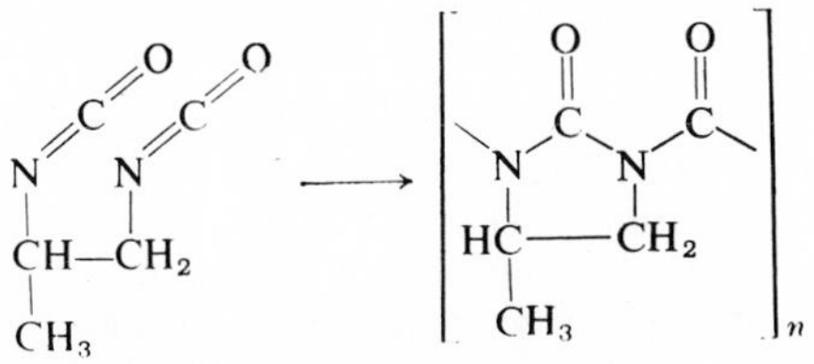

375. Preparation of 1,2-Propylene Diisocyanate (29)

(1) $N_2H_4 + CH_3O_2CCH(CH_3)CH_2CO_2CH_3 \longrightarrow$

$$NH_2NHCOCH(CH_3)CH_2CONHNH_2$$

(2) $NH_2NHCOCH(CH_3)CH_2CONHNH_2 \longrightarrow OCN—CH(CH_3)CH_2NCO$

A. 2-Methylsuccinic Dihydrazide. Hydrazine hydrate (545 g., 10.9 moles), dissolved in 7 l. of 95% ethanol and 1 l. of water, is mixed with 429 g. (2.7 moles) of dimethyl-2-methyl succinate. This ester, b.p. 85–86°C. at 16 mm., is obtained by catalytic hydrogenation of dimethyl itaconate. The mixture is refluxed overnight and then concentrated; 367 g. (84%) of 2-methylsuccinic dihydrazide, m.p. 160–162°C. crystallizes.

B. 1,2-Propylene Diisocyanate. A 2 l. beaker equipped with a thermometer and a mechanical stirrer and externally cooled in an ice bath is charged with 600 g. of ice, 100 ml. of carbon tetrachloride, 70 ml. of concentrated hydrochloric acid, and 57 g. (0.36 mole) of 2-methylsuccinic dihydrazide. A solution of 50 g. (0.73 mole) of sodium nitrite in 100 ml. of water precooled to 0°C. is added dropwise to the stirred mixture over a period of 20 min. The temperature of the reaction mixture is maintained below 8°C. by addition of pieces of ice, and stirring is continued for 0.5 hr. after all the nitrite is added. The layers are separated, and the benzene solution of the azide is combined with two benzene extracts of the aqueous layer. The final volume should be about 400 ml. The solution is dried overnight over anhydrous calcium chloride and then refluxed for 4 hr. to complete decomposition of the azide. The refluxing solution develops a blue color which disappears when the decomposition is essentially complete. The solvent is removed and the diisocyanate is then distilled at reduced pressure. After a short forerun, 19.6 g. (42%) of pure 1,2-propylene diisocyanate is collected as a lachrymatory liquid, b.p. 83.5°C. (25 mm.); n_D^{26} 1.4398.

376. Polymerization of 1,2-Propylene Diisocyanate (29)

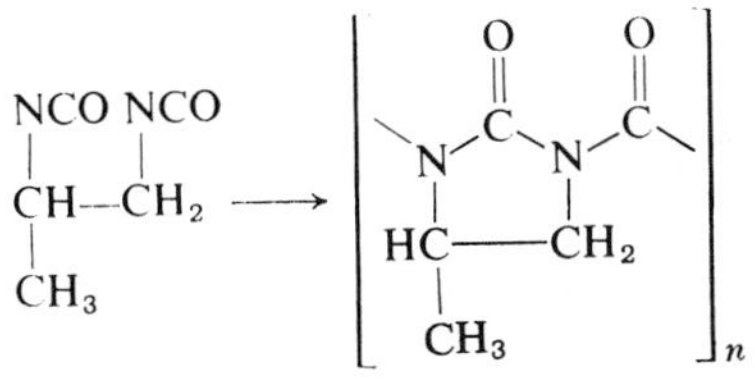

A 100 ml., three-necked flask equipped with a mechanical stirrer, calcium chloride tube, and low temperature thermometer is charged with 50 ml. of dry DMF and then cooled to $-40°C$. in a Dry Ice–acetone bath. 1,2-Propylene diisocyanate, 5.2 g., precooled to $-38°C$., is stirred into the flask; 1 ml. of a saturated solution of sodium cyanide in DMF is now added to the stirred mixture by means of a hypodermic syringe over a period of 3 min. The temperature will rise to $-14°C$. within 6 min. after addition of the initiator, and the polymerization mixture thickens to a smooth, viscous dope. The cold bath is removed and the mixture stirred for 0.5 hr. Polymer is isolated by precipitation in methanol stirred vigorously in a Waring Blendor. The dried polymer should weigh 4.6 g. (89%) and melt at 287°C. The inherent viscosity of the polymer should be in the range of 1.3–1.4 (0.5 g./100 ml., DMF, 30°C.).

Clear, flexible films are obtained when a 10% solution in formic acid or nitromethane are spread on a glass plate and the solvent evaporated.

V. Polycarbodiimides

It has recently been found that certain **phospholene oxides,** notably

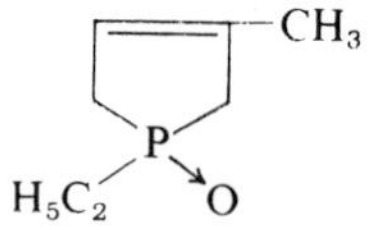

$$
\begin{array}{c}
\text{[phospholene oxide ring with } CH_3 \text{ substituent, } P \text{ in ring, } =O \text{ and } H_5C_2 \text{ substituents on } P\text{]}
\end{array}
$$

serve as unique catalysts for the following reaction.

$$RNCO \longrightarrow R-N=C=N-R$$

This reaction has been studied in detail (30–33); the yields are so high that additions of traces of the catalyst will convert diisocyanates to high molecular weight polymers (31,32) capable of being melt pressed into tough films. Melt viscosities are high, and solubility in general low. This is probably due to reversible crosslinking of the type

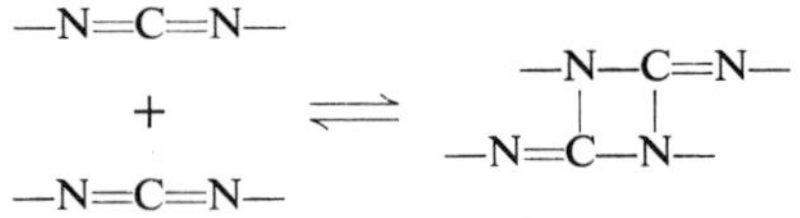

$$
\begin{array}{ccc}
-N=C=N- & & -N-C=N- \\
+ & \rightleftharpoons & \quad | \quad | \\
-N=C=N- & & -N=C-N-
\end{array}
$$

This is suggested by the fact that a low melting, easily soluble polymer is obtained from the hindered mesitylene diisocyanate.

Metastable solutions of polycarbodiimides can be produced by adding small amounts of highly polar substances such as dimethyl sulfoxide to the reaction medium.

In the solid state, polycarbodiimides are quite inert to water, amines, etc., but are quite reactive in solution, for example, polyguanidines are easily made by reaction of amines with solutions of polycarbodiimides (33).

377. Preparation of 1-Ethyl-3-methyl-3-phospholene-1-Oxide (30,34)

A 2 l. four-necked flask is fitted with a spiral condenser topped with a Dry Ice condenser, thermometer, 1 l. dropping funnel with pressure equalizing side arm and a magnetic stirrer. To this flask is added 1 g. of copper stearate, 780 g. (5.96 moles) of dichloroethylphosphine and from the dropping funnel 447 g. (6.56 moles) of freshly distilled isoprene. The reaction mixture is stirred and refluxed under nitrogen for 42 hr., cooled, allowed to stand for 2 days, and then refluxed without stirring for 5 days. Excess isoprene is then distilled from the mixture and 850 ml. of water is added dropwise with stirring to the reaction flask, which is cooled in an ice bath. The dark-brown aqueous solution is transferred to a 5 l. flask and 1250 ml. of 30% sodium hydroxide solution is added gradually to make the solution slightly alkaline (pH 8). The mixture is filtered and the aqueous solution is extracted continuously with chloroform for 12 days. The chloroform is removed, and the residue vacuum distilled through a 25 cm. Vigreux column to give 435 g. (51%) of water-white liquid with a slight odor of phosphine. The product is further purified by oxidation at 50°C. with excess 3% hydrogen peroxide for 6 hr. The aqueous mixture is extracted continuously with benzene and the oxide is recovered by distillation, b.p. 115–119°C. (1.2–1.3 mm.), n_D^{25} 1.5050. This is the preferred catalyst for formation of polycarbodiimides. A somewhat less effective catalyst (in terms of rate) is described elsewhere (35).

378. Polymerization of Methylenebis-(4-phenyl isocyanate) (32)

In a three-necked, 500 ml. flask equipped with stirrer, condenser, and nitrogen inlet is placed 150 ml. of xylene, 20 g. of methylenebis(4-phenyl isocyanate), and 0.03 g. of 1-ethyl-3-methyl-3-phospholene-1-oxide. The mixture is heated to reflux; first the solution becomes milky, then a second liquid phase begins to separate. This liquid phase becomes more and more viscous and eventually yields high molecular weight fibrous material. The fibrous nature of the product results from the shearing action of the stirrer blade on the rapidly thickening prepolymer which separates initially.

After the polymer is separated and air dried, these short filaments can be separated manually from the bulk of the polymer and can be cold drawn. The drawn filaments are slightly cream-colored and quite tough. X-ray examination of the fibers showed approximately 30% lateral crystallinity, and 5% longitudinal crystallinity, coupled with a high degree of orientation.

379. Preparation of Poly(3,3'-dimethoxy-4-4'-biphenylene carbodiimide) (32)

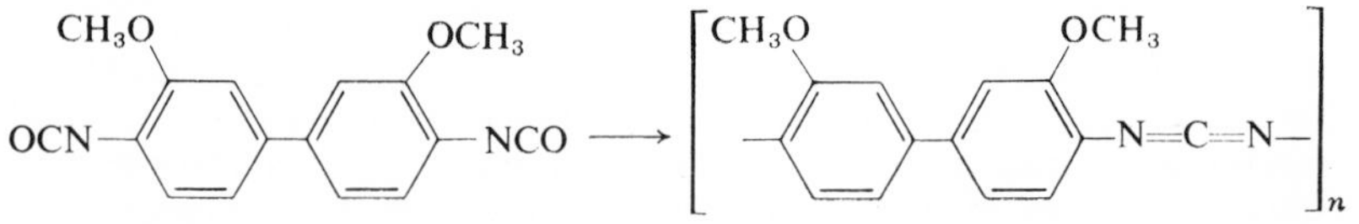

Ten g. of 3,3'-dimethoxy-4,4'-biphenylene diisocyanate is dissolved in 100 ml. of hot (~100°C.) xylene. The solution is filtered free of a small amount of undissolved foreign matter and polymerized with 0.04 g. of 1-ethyl-3-methyl-3-phospholene oxide in a three-necked flask with refluxing and stirring. Polymerization is very rapid; however, for high molecular weight, the mixture should reflux 4–6 hr. The white, finely divided polymer is filtered, washed with benzene, and dried. The yield is 8–9 g. The polymer has a high x-ray crystallinity. It can be melt-pressed at 250°C. to a clear film with a slight yellow color. The film, cut in strips, can be stretched 3–4 times at 160°C. The film exhibits typical necking phenomena on stretching, and shows strong birefringence which disappears at about 190°C. X-ray examination of the drawn polymeric material shows that the product is crystalline with good longitudinal order and a fairly high degree of orientation.

380. Polymerization of Mesitylene Diisocyanate (32)

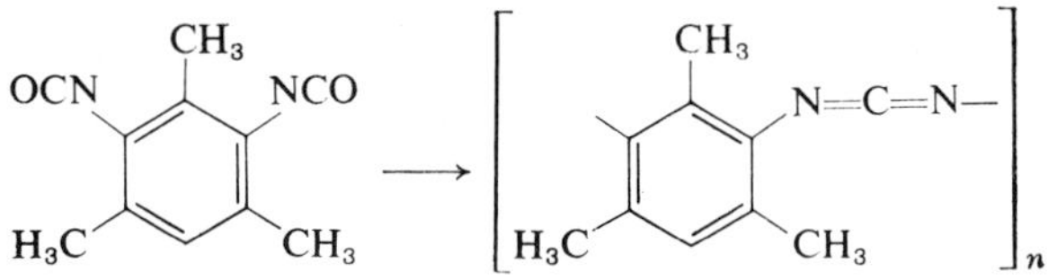

Fifteen g. of mesitylene diisocyanate is dissolved in 150 ml. of xylene, and 0.15 g. of the preferred phospholene oxide catalyst is added to the refluxing solution. Polymerization is slow because of steric hindrance. After 24 hr., a moderately viscous solution results from which a tough film may be obtained by evaporation of the solvent. The polymer may also be precipitated by the addition of isopropyl alcohol, washed, and dried. The polymer has a melting point (hot bar) of 130°C. A clear, tough film can easily be melt pressed at 100°C. This film may be stretched at 100°C.; x-ray examination of the stretched polymer shows a low degree of crystallinity and orientation.

381. Preparation of Polycarbodiimide from 2,4-Tolylene Diisocyanate (32)

2,4-Tolylene diisocyanate is distilled through a spinning-band column. After a small forecut, distillation proceeds smoothly at 81°C. (1.3 mm.). Polymerization of a 10% solution in boiling decahydronaphthalene is carried out with catalytic quantities of 1-ethyl-3-methyl-3-phospholene oxide. The reaction is complete in less than an hour, and the polymer is obtained in small fluffy particles very reminiscent of puffed cereal in appearance and texture. These little particles are white and give very tough, clear, nearly colorless film when pressed at 275°C. Strips of this film can be cold drawn; however, the film strips relax in boiling water and exhibit no crystallinity and extremely low x-ray orientation.

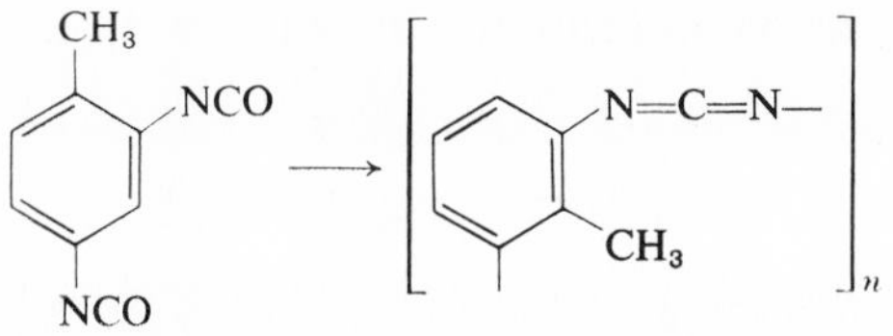

382. Preparation of Polycarbodiimide from 2,4-Tolylene Diisocyanate (33)

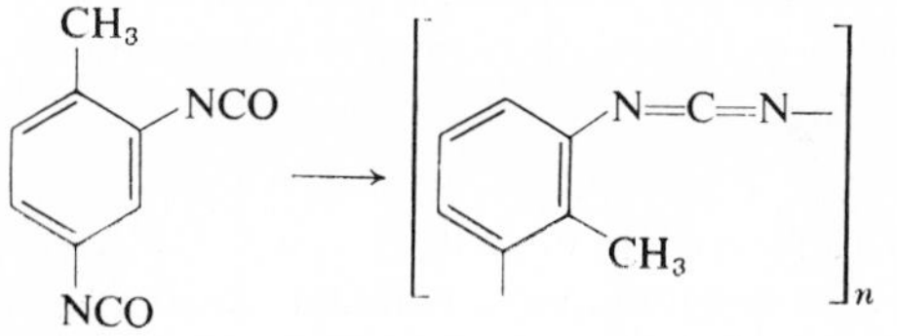

A mixture of 11.0 g. of 2,4-tolylene diisocyanate, 50 ml. of toluene, 4.0 ml. of dimethyl sulfoxide and 0.03 g. of 3-methyl-1-ethyl-3-phospholine-1-oxide is refluxed for about 1 hr. The extremely viscous solution can be cast to a film which is very tough. Strips of film can be hot-drawn, but develop no crystallinity.

383. Preparation of a Polyguanidine (33)

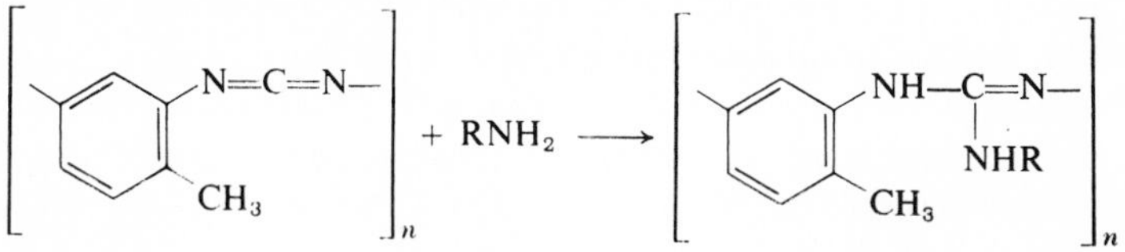

If the solution prepared in the previous experiment is poured into a rapidly agitated solution of 15 g. of aniline and 100 ml. toluene, a polyguanidine precipitates, which on filtering and drying can be pressed into a stiff, clear film at 275°C. Other amines may be used; tertiary butylamine gives a soluble product. Polyguanidines are soluble in dilute acids, and have detergentlike properties.

VI. Polymerization of Diazo Compounds

An interesting type of polymerization is the **conversion of a diazo-alkane to a polyhydrocarbon** in the presence of a catalyst such as boron fluoride. The reaction proceeds according to the equation:

$$RCHN_2 \longrightarrow N_2 + [-\overset{\overset{\displaystyle R}{|}}{C}H-]_n$$

A wide variety of catalysts will bring about this polymerization. Several different mechanisms may be involved, depending on the catalyst. For example with boron fluoride or borate esters, an intermediate such as $BF_3 \cdot CH_2^+$ may be involved, while with copper powder, or colloidal gold, a carbene structure may be important (36–38).

It has been found possible to prepare high molecular weight **polymethylene** by polymerization of **diazomethane**. Laterally substituted polyhydrocarbons have not been prepared in as high molecular weights as has polymethylene. There are, apparently, steric factors working against the growth of high molecular weight polymer chains. Because of the unusual nature of this polymerization, several examples will be given even though the molecular weights obtained in some of them are not particularly high.

Diazo polymers are living polymers, and block polymers can be produced, according to Bawn, Ledwith, and Matties (39,40).

The synthesis of **isotactic polyethylidene** has been carried out, using finely divided gold as catalyst. This polymer has the structure:

$$CH_3CHN_2 \longrightarrow [-\overset{\overset{\displaystyle CH_3}{|}}{C}H-\overset{\overset{\displaystyle CH_3}{|}}{C}H-\overset{\overset{\displaystyle CH_3}{|}}{C}H-\overset{\overset{\displaystyle CH_3}{|}}{C}H-]_n$$

and is reported to have a crystalline melting point of 195°C. (38,41).

Although the structure of polymers from diazo decomposition are represented as polymethylenes, the polymers contain small amounts of nitrogen, making the absolute structure uncertain.

The diazoalkanes are toxic and potentially explosive and the following experimental examples should be carried out using due safety precautions (42).

384. Polymerization of Diazomethane (37)

$$CH_2N_2 \longrightarrow (-CH_2-)_n$$

A solution of 13.7 g. of diazomethane in about 700 ml. of ether is treated with 0.3 g. of freshly distilled trimethyl borate at approximately 0°C. Nitrogen evolves slowly and a precipitate begins to form in the solution. After 24 hr., the diazomethane is entirely decomposed as shown by the lack of color in the solution. The rubbery solid is obtained by filtration and weighs about 3–5 g. It may be pressed to a thin film in a Carver Press at 180–200°C.

Polymerization may also be carried out as above, but with 0.1 ml. of boron fluoride etherate as catalyst (43).

385. Preparation of Diazododecane (37)

$$C_{11}H_{23}CH_2NHCONH_2 \longrightarrow C_{11}H_{23}CHN_2$$

A mixture of 160 g. of dodecyl urea and 640 ml. of glacial acetic acid is heated on a steam bath until a clear solution is obtained. This solution is cooled to 0°C. with vigorous stirring, and a solution of 200 g. of sodium nitrite in 350 ml. of water with stirring is added over a period of 15 min. After 15 min. at 0°C. an equal volume of ice water is added and the precipitated nitrosododecylurea is collected on a filter at 0°C. Aqueous potassium hydroxide (250 ml., 40%), ethanol (500 ml.), and ligroin (500 ml.) are mixed and cooled to 0°C. The crude nitrosododecylurea is then added during 30 min. with vigorous agitation. After a further 15 min. stirring at 0°C., the upper layer is removed and filtered. This solution of 1-diazododecane is used without purification in Preparation 386. For estimation of the concentration of diazododecane, an aliquot of about 30 ml. is added to 0.5 g. of benzoic acid in benzene. Nitrogen is evolved and the color of the diazo compound is discharged. The excess benzoic acid is then titrated with standard sodium hydroxide solution and the quantity of diazododecane present in the original aliquot is calculated. One molecule of benzoic acid is equivalent to one of diazo compound. The yield of diazo compound is low, about 5.2 g./l.

386. Preparation of a Copolymer of Diazomethane and Diazododecane (37)

$$CH_2N_2 + C_{11}H_{23}CHN_n \longrightarrow Copolymer$$

To a solution of 2.2 g. of diazododecane and 6 g. of diazomethane in a total of about 700 ml. of ether–ligroin is added 0.5 g. of freshly distilled trimethyl borate. The mixture is allowed to stand for 24 hr. and the precipitated polymer is collected, washed, and dried. The yield is about 2 g. of a translucent rubbery solid soluble in chloroform, benzene, and other similar solvents. It becomes soft at about 250°C. but does not decompose completely until 370°C. It is very high molecular weight with an intrinsic viscosity in the range of 6–7 in chloroform.

387. Preparation of Phenyldiazomethane (5)

$$C_6H_5CH{=}NNH_2 \longrightarrow C_6H_5CHN_2$$

Nine g. of benzalhydrazine is suspended in 50 ml. of low boiling petroleum ether and shaken with 15 g. of yellow mercuric oxide with external cooling. When all of the mercuric oxide appears to have reacted, the reddish brown petroleum ether solution is decanted from the residue and most of the petroleum ether is removed in a vacuum at 0°C. For purification, the phenyldiazomethane is distilled in a vacuum of at least 1 mm. The product is explosive and high temperatures must be avoided. Phenyldiazomethane is a brown-red liquid which boils at about 35° at 1 mm. pressure. For polymerization, the product should be repeatedly distilled. The yield from 9 g. of benzalhydrazine should be approximately 4–5 g.

388. Polymerization of Phenyldiazomethane (44)

$$C_6H_5CHN_2 \longrightarrow \left[\begin{matrix} C_6H_5 \\ | \\ -CH- \end{matrix} \right]_n$$

A solution of 4 g. of phenyldiazomethane (Preparation 387) in 100 ml. of toluene is cooled to $-80°C$. To this solution is added 2 ml. of a 0.4 molar solution of boron trifluoride dissolved in toluene. The temperature is maintained at $-80°C$. for 2–3 days. The polymer is isolated by pouring the toluene solution into methyl alcohol and is purified by dissolving in benzene and reprecipitating into methanol. The yield of polymer should be about 80–85%. This polymer melts in the range of 220–240°C. It is brittle and of relatively low molecular weight.

VII. Preparation of Poly-p-xylylene

Up to 1960, two methods had been discovered for the synthesis of **poly(p-xylylene)**: the first, by Szwarc (45,46), was the pyrolysis of p-xylene to form quinodimethane which polymerizes on quenching; the second involved the decomposition of a p-xylene trimethyl ammonium halide in strong alkali (47,48,49), a method claimed to give a less branched and crosslinked product. In both cases, the cyclic dimer, di-p-xylylene (paracyclophane), is an interesting by-product, and, as it turns out, a useful one in its own right for the synthesis of poly(p-xylylene).

Now, **a number of new synthetic methods have been developed** so that a great variety of aromatic- and aliphatic-substituted poly(p-xylylenes) can be prepared with acceptable molecular weight. These include: (i) pyrolysis of the cyclic dimer (di-p-xylylene) and its ring-substituted derivatives (50); (ii) treatment of α-halogenated p-xylenes, from α-monohalo- to $\alpha,\alpha,\alpha,\alpha',\alpha'$-pentahalo-, with base (51); (iii) pyrolysis of bis(tri-chloromethyl)benzene over copper above 300°C. (52); and (iv) electrolysis of α,α'-dihalobenzenes (53). These methods are considered in the discussion and preparative examples that follow.

Poly(p-xylylene) itself is stable at elevated temperatures (300°C.), and is crystalline. It is hard to fabricate from a melt or solution, and only weak, brittle fibers have been obtained. Tough, clear, drawable films may be obtained directly, however, from several of the following procedures when the monomer is quenched on the interior surface of the collection flask.

389. Preparation of Poly-p-xylylene by the Pyrolysis of Xylene (54,56)

The successful dehydrogenation of p-xylene requires high temperatures (700–1100°C.) and reduced pressures (1–5 mm.). The most suitable technique

$$CH_3-\langle\!\!\!\!\bigcirc\!\!\!\!\rangle-CH_3 \xrightarrow{H_2} CH_2=\langle\!\!\!\!\bigcirc\!\!\!\!\rangle=CH_2 \longrightarrow$$

$$\left[-CH_2-\langle\!\!\!\!\bigcirc\!\!\!\!\rangle-CH_2-\right]_n$$

for converting p-xylene to transient quinonedimethide, which then polymerizes on cooling, is to pass vapors of p-xylene through a quartz tube heated by an external electric heater to temperatures in the range of about 900–1000°C. The monomer is vaporized by boiling at reduced pressure and the vapors are passed first through a capillary tube in order to give a constant flow of gas and then into the quartz pyrolysis tube, 19 in. long and 2 in. in diameter, held at the required polymerization temperature (900–1000°C.), preferably by the use of a multiple unit furnace. A furnace such as is used in combustion analyses is satisfactory. The exit gases are passed from the hot tube directly into a series of four traps. The first consists of a 1 l., round bottom standard taper flask held at room temperature, followed by three cold traps maintained at dry ice temperature. The entire system is kept at a pressure of 1–5 mm. by the use of an oil pump.

The p-xylene vapors are passed through the quartz tube where they are dehydrogenated. On exiting into the flask maintained at room temperature, the monomer will polymerize on the surface of the flask wall as a continuous tough, clear film. In addition, smaller amounts of polymer will be collected as a solid fluff in the succeeding traps maintained at −80°C. Residual xylene also collects in the traps as well as gaseous by-products, exclusive of hydrogen. The polymerization is surprisingly efficient under the conditions described. Xylene will be converted to poly-p-xylylene in conversions varying from 12 to 20%, the remaining xylene being recovered as such.

Ordinarily, the film of polymer laid down on the inside walls of the collecting flask may be removed in one piece. This film can be stretched at very high temperatures to give oriented product. Inherent viscosities may be determined at very high temperatures (305°C.) in benzyl benzoate. The viscosities obtained are often anomalously low because polymers prepared in this manner are not strictly linear, but are at least partially crosslinked.

390. Purification of Trimethyl(p-methylbenzyl)ammonium Bromide (57)

$$CH_3-\langle\!\!\!\!\bigcirc\!\!\!\!\rangle-CH_2Br + N(CH_3)_3 \longrightarrow CH_3-\langle\!\!\!\!\bigcirc\!\!\!\!\rangle-CH_2\overset{+}{N}(CH_3)_3Br$$

This salt is prepared in approximately 90% yield by quaternization of p-methylbenzyl bromide with trimethylamine. Purification of the salt is carried out as follows. Three hundred g. of the salt is dissolved in 200 ml. of boiling absolute alcohol. This hot solution is filtered and cooled to about 1°C. in an ice bath. The product is then filtered, air dried, and oven dried at 110°C. in a vacuum. Approximately 65% of the crude salt is recovered as a white, pure product, m.p. 201–203.5°C.

391. The Preparation of Poly-*p*-xylene from Trimethyl(*p*-methylbenzyl)-ammonium Bromide (49)

$$CH_3-\langle\!\!\langle\;\;\rangle\!\!\rangle-CH_2-\overset{+}{N}(CH_3)_3 \quad \underset{\bar{Br}}{\xrightarrow{\;NaOH\;}} \quad \left[-CH_2-\langle\!\!\langle\;\;\rangle\!\!\rangle-CH_2-\right]_n$$

A 3 l., three-necked flask is equipped with a paddle type stirrer, a reflux condenser, a nitrogen inlet with a stoppered opening for rapidly adding chemicals to the flask. In the flask is placed a solution of 800 g. of sodium hydroxide in 1200 g. of distilled water. This alkali solution is heated to the boiling point with stirring. To the boiling alkali, blanketed with nitrogen, is added all at once a solution of 234 g. of trimethyl(*p*-methylbenzyl)ammonium bromide dissolved in 250 ml. of water. The resulting mixture is allowed to reflux for $3\frac{1}{2}$–4 hr. during which time the solid poly-*p*-xylylene is formed as a suspended white solid. The reaction mixture is poured into 10 l. of water and the resulting polymer suspension is filtered. The solid polymer is washed on the filter with several portions of hot water, then is extracted with 250 ml. portions of boiling ethyl alcohol. The extracted polymer is then washed with ether and dried in a vacuum. The yield of poly-*p*-xylylene should be about 60 g. Poly-*p*-xylylene is soluble in benzyl benzoate at 305°C. The inherent viscosity may be measured on a solution of the polymer at the specified temperature. A technique for determining the viscosity of solutions at elevated temperatures will be found in Chapter 2.

Poly-*p*-xylylene prepared in this manner is also a very high melting crystalline polymer which is rather difficult to fabricate. However, it can be pressed to films in a laboratory press at temperatures in excess of 350°C. Films are ordinarily highly crystalline and rather brittle.

Di-*p*-xylylene and a variety of its substituted derivatives undergo pyrolytic polymerization (58) as does *p*-xylene, but several advantages result when the cyclic dimer is used: yields are higher, a linear polymer is formed (in contrast to branched and slightly crosslinked products), pyrolysis temperatures are lower, low molecular weight by-products are absent, and a much greater variety of substituted polymers can be made because of the lower temperatures required. The pyrolysis vapors are condensed on a cool surface, as with pyrolysis of *p*-xylene; a threshold surface temperature is observed for each di-*p*-xylylene, above which condensation and polymerization will not occur at the reduced pressure in question. Thus, if monoacetyl-di-*p*-xylylene is pyrolyzed and the vapors passed first over a surface at 90°C. and then a second surface at 25°C., the polymer recovered from the first surface is poly(acetyl-*p*-xylylene) and from the second, poly(*p*-xylylene). This indicates that the active species of both halves of the starting di-*p*-xylylene are present in the pyrolisate and polymerize only below their respective threshold temperatures. Whether the active units are present in the quinoid or diradical (shown) form is not known with certainty.

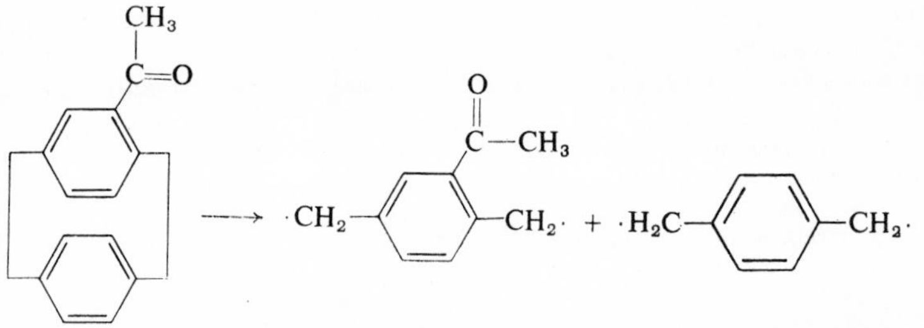

392. Preparation of Poly(p-xylylene) from Di-p-Xylylene by Pyrolytic Polymerization (58)

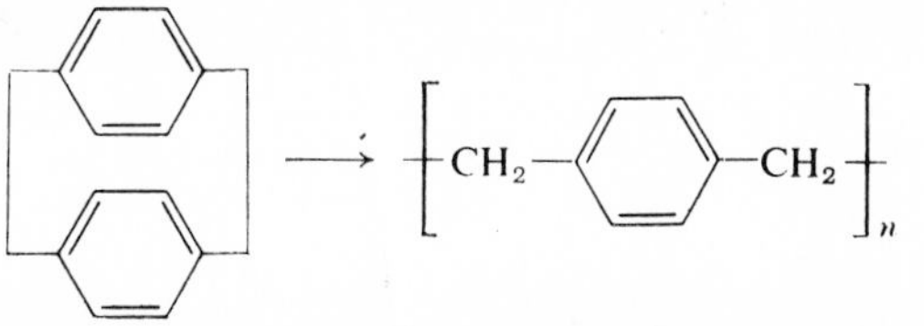

The isolation of di-p-xylylene (paracyclophane) is described in Organic Synthesis from a Hoffman elimination reaction on p-methylbenzyl trimethyl ammonium hydroxide. Poly(p-xylylene) is formed as the main product, since the reaction is very similar to that described in Preparation 391, this chapter. The cyclic dimer is obtained in 10–12% yield (59). Its preparation from xylene pyrolysis is also possible (60).

The apparatus consists of a 1 in. i.d. Vycor tube about 24 in. in length. It is mounted horizontally in a suitable furnace with the first 6 in. of the tube extending from the furnace. This is the zone from which distillation or sublimation of the sample is effected, and is brought to the necessary temperature by heating tapes; a thermocouple is fixed against the glass to estimate the temperature. As an alternative, the distillation zone can be a separate piece of glass consisting of a sample chamber fixed for heating by means of refluxing solvent vapor in the manner of an Abderhalden drying apparatus, and connected to the pyrolysis tube by a standard Vycor joint. The temperature of the pyrolysis section is measured by a thermocouple in the middle of the furnace between the tube and furnace wall. Glass wool is packed around the tube at the ends of the furnace to reduce air currents and temperature fluctuation in the furnace chamber. The pyrolysis tube leads into another 24 in. in length by 1 in. i.d. piece of glass tubing, serving as the deposition area, the first 15 in. of which are heated (by IR lamps, conveniently) to 90°C., and the remaining 9 in. are kept at room temperature. The threshold temperature of p-xylylene is 30°C. The end of the deposition tube is connected by vacuum tubing to a Dry Ice trap and then a vacuum pump.

Di-p-xylylene (1.5 g.) is placed in the distillation zone in a porcelain boat, the pressure is reduced to about 100 microns and the distillation zone is brought to 175°C. after the pyrolysis section has first been heated to 500–600°C. Distillation occurs over a period of about 20 min. to give essentially complete conversion to a film of polymer which can be stripped from the wall of the deposition tube, extracted with boiling carbon tetrachloride and dried. It is soluble only, but completely, in benzyl benzoate or the chlorinated biphenyls above 200°C. The film shows good mechanical strength: 6800 p.s.i. tensile strength, 10–15% elongation and 350,000 p.s.i. tensile modulus. The crystalline melting point (by x-ray) is 400°C. and the glass temperature is 80°C.

393. Preparation of Dichloro-Di-*p*-Xylylene (61)

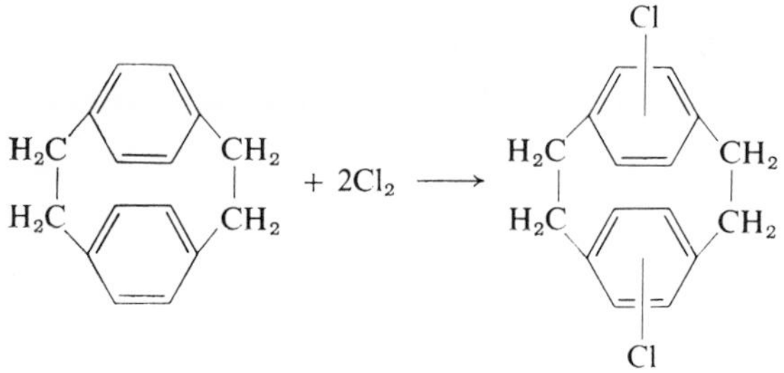

A mixture of 12 g. of di-*p*-xylylene, 350 ml. of carbon tetrachloride, and 0.1 g. of iron powder is placed in a 1 l., three-necked flask equipped with stirrer, drying tube, and addition funnel. The flask is cooled in a water bath. A solution of 8.4 g. of chlorine and 150 ml. of carbon tetrachloride is added from the funnel to the stirred suspension over a 60 min. period. The reaction is complete at the end of 1 hr., as evidenced by the disappearance of the characteristic chlorine color in the solution. The iron is removed by filtration, and carbon tetrachloride by distillation. The product is purified by distillation in a high vacuum, to yield about 13 g. of product melting at 160–170°C., indicating presence of isomers.

394. Polymerization of Dichloro-Di-*p*-Xylylene (61)

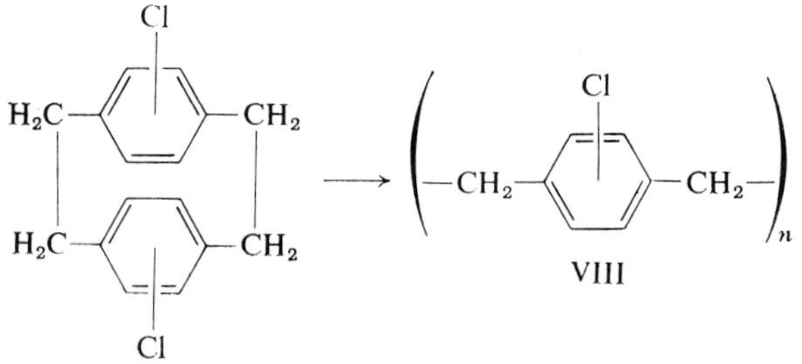

Pyrolysis is carried out in a 3 ft. length of 25 mm. diam. Pyrex tubing, sealed at one end, and capable of being evacuated. Monomer is placed in the bottom of the tube, which is then placed in a furnace at 550–600°C. to a depth of 12 in. Polymerization occurs on the air-cooled section of the tubing immediately following the pyrolysis zone. 1.4 g. of monomer is pyrolytically polymerized over a 10 min. period at 580°C. and 1 mm. pressure to give 1.3 g. (93% yield) of polychloro-*p*-xylylene. The polymer which collects on the air-cooled section of the tubing immediately following the pyrolysis zone as a film has a melting point of 275–280°C.

This thermoplastic polymer is opaque to translucent in appearance. It is substantially insoluble in all common organic solvents. However, it is readily and completely soluble in α-chloronaphthalene at 170°C. and exhibits a reduced viscosity of 1.4 in this solvent at 150°C.

It is of interest to note that p-bis(trichloromethyl)benzene can be pyrolyzed at 300–600°C. over a copper gauze to give the isolable (at −78°C.) monomer, α, α, α', α' -tetrachloro-p-xylylene. The latter can be polymerized directly by allowing the pyrolysis vapors to condense on a surface below the threshold of 140°C. The resulting polymer softens at 280–290°C. but does not melt up to 350°C. (52).

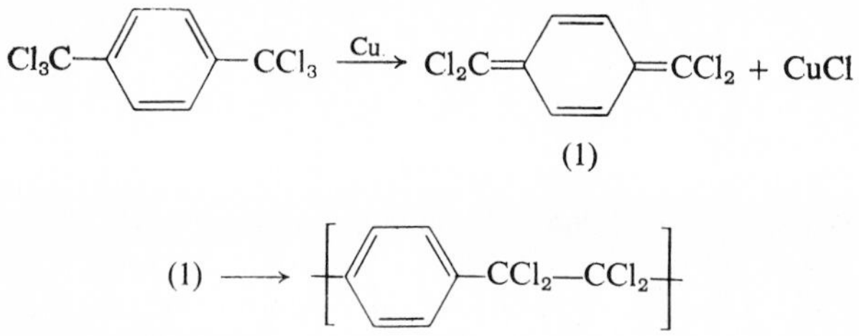

$$Cl_3C-\!\!\left\langle\bigcirc\right\rangle\!\!-CCl_3 \xrightarrow{Cu} Cl_2C=\!\!\left\langle\bigcirc\right\rangle\!\!=CCl_2 + CuCl$$

(1)

$$(1) \longrightarrow \left[\!\left\langle\bigcirc\right\rangle\!\!-CCl_2-CCl_2\!\right]$$

The action of strong bases on α-halo-p-xylenes affords an approach to a variety of poly(p-xylylenes), and at the same time gives some insight into the mechanism of how these compounds interact with bases (51). The reaction evidently proceeds through a 1,6-elimination of hydrogen halide to give a quinodimethane which undergoes self-addition to high molecular weight polymer. When a dilute solution of potassium t-butoxide is added to an excess of α,α'-dichloro-p-xylene, polymer 3, below, is formed.

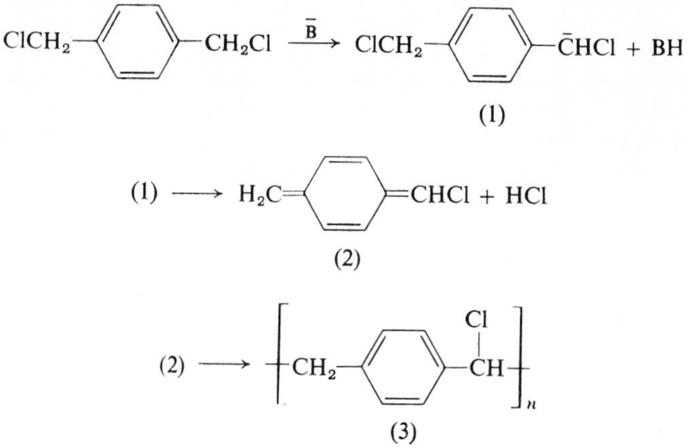

$$ClCH_2-\!\!\left\langle\bigcirc\right\rangle\!\!-CH_2Cl \xrightarrow{\bar{B}} ClCH_2-\!\!\left\langle\bigcirc\right\rangle\!\!-\bar{C}HCl + BH$$

(1)

$$(1) \longrightarrow H_2C=\!\!\left\langle\bigcirc\right\rangle\!\!=CHCl + HCl$$

(2)

$$(2) \longrightarrow \left[CH_2-\!\!\left\langle\bigcirc\right\rangle\!\!-\overset{\overset{\displaystyle Cl}{|}}{C}H\right]_n$$

(3)

Polymer 3 loses HCl when treated with excess base to give

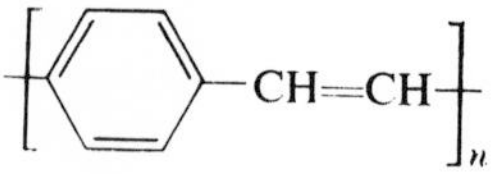

$$\left[\!\!\left\langle\bigcirc\right\rangle\!\!-CH\!=\!CH\right]_n$$

The more α-halogens present in a p-xylene, the weaker the base necessary to effect polymerization. In the tetrachloro compound, sodium hydroxide is sufficient, as in the next preparation. Higher molecular weights result when the reaction is carried out in t-butanol–methanol mixture, but some HCl elimination and methoxyl substitution also occur, though to a minor degree. Thus, these structural units are evidently present besides the predominant one:

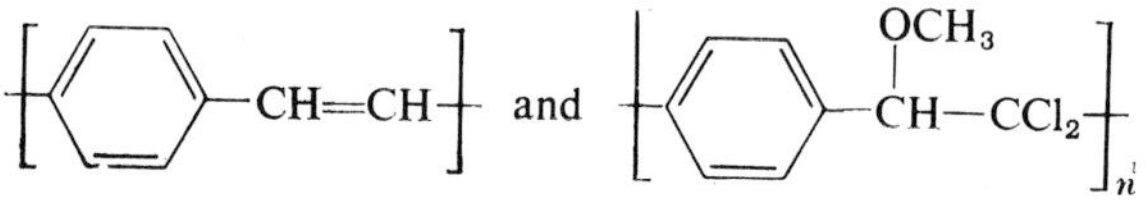

$$\left[\!\!\left\langle\bigcirc\right\rangle\!\!-CH\!=\!CH\right] \;\text{and}\; \left[\!\!\left\langle\bigcirc\right\rangle\!\!-\overset{\displaystyle OCH_3}{\underset{\displaystyle}{CH}}\!-CCl_2\right]_n$$

395. Preparation of Poly(α,α,α'-trichloro-p-Xylylene) (51)

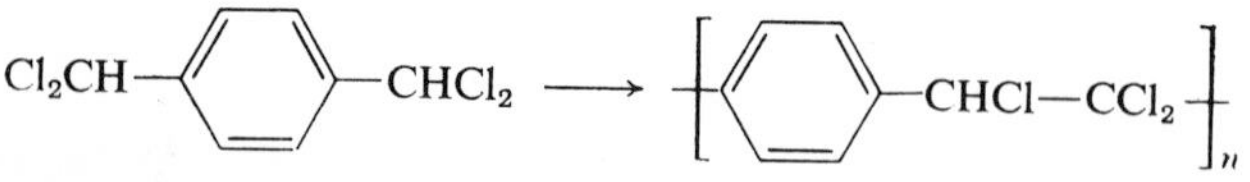

$$Cl_2CH\!-\!\left\langle\bigcirc\right\rangle\!-CHCl_2 \longrightarrow \left[\!\!\left\langle\bigcirc\right\rangle\!\!-CHCl\!-\!CCl_2\right]_n$$

Terephthaldehyde (200 g.) is refluxed and stirred for 1 hr. with a mixture of 600 g. phosphorous pentachloride in 1500 ml. carbon tetrachloride, using a condenser with drying tube to exclude moisture. The major part of the excess phosphorous pentachloride and solvent are distilled and the residue poured onto about 500 g. cracked ice. The resulting solid is filtered and recrystallized several times from heptane to give about 260 g. (about 70%) $\alpha,\alpha,\alpha',\alpha'$-tetrachloro-$p$-xylene, m.p. 92-93°C.

To a solution of 0.80 g. sodium hydroxide (0.02 mole) in 30 ml. of 95/5 (by volume) t-butanol–methanol is added 4.88 g. $\alpha,\alpha,\alpha',\alpha'$-tetrachloro-$p$-xylene (0.02 mole). The mixture is stirred and refluxed for 1 hr., then poured into 300 ml. methanol, filtered, washed in a blender with methanol and water, successively, and finally dried in vacuum at 40°C. About 2.1 g. (50%) of white polymer is obtained which is soluble in tetrahydrofuran; the reduced viscosity in that solvent is around 3.0 (0.2 g./100 ml., 20°C.). Strong films can be obtained by casting from THF solution or by compression molding at 190°C. The T_g is around 160°C.

In the electrolytic methods for synthesizing poly(p-xylenes), a mercury or lead cathode is used in conjunction with a carbon rod anode and the Anatrol* constant potential power supply, with the monomer dissolved in acidified dioxane–water solution. The reaction very probably goes through the intermediate quinodimethane, common to

* Anatrol is a trademark of the Continental Oil Company.

all poly(p-xylylene) syntheses it would appear. A host of substituted polymers can be prepared by this method; the following is illustrative:

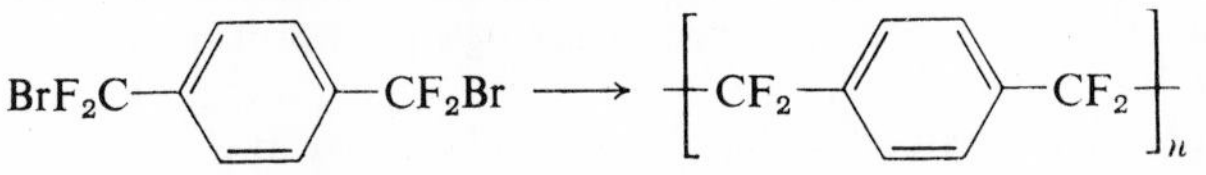

VIII. Polymerization of Norbornylene

The polymerization of olefins by organometallic titanium catalysts (cf. Chapter 4), proceeds uneventfully in virtually all reported cases, without rearrangement of the carbon skeleton. However, in the case of **norbornylene** it is possible to get two types of polymer, the structures of which depend on the ratio of catalyst components. With a molar ratio of titanium tetrachloride to lithium aluminum tetraheptyl greater than one, a low yield of a stiff brittle polymer (A) is produced. However, with an excess of lithium aluminum tetraheptyl, a polymer (B) is formed by an unique ring-opening polymerization (62–64):

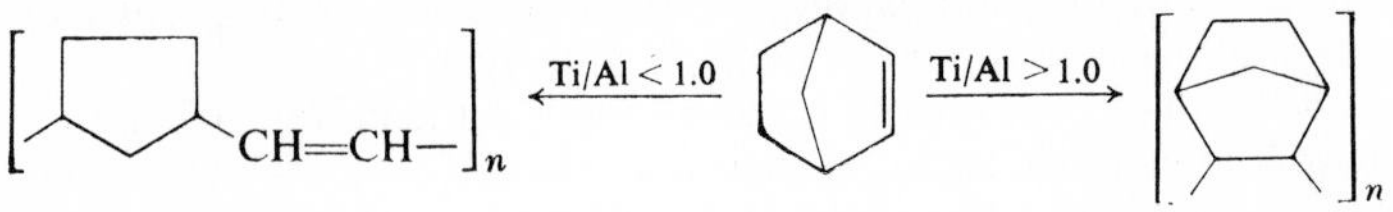

B   A

The mechanism of formation of B is believed to be the following:

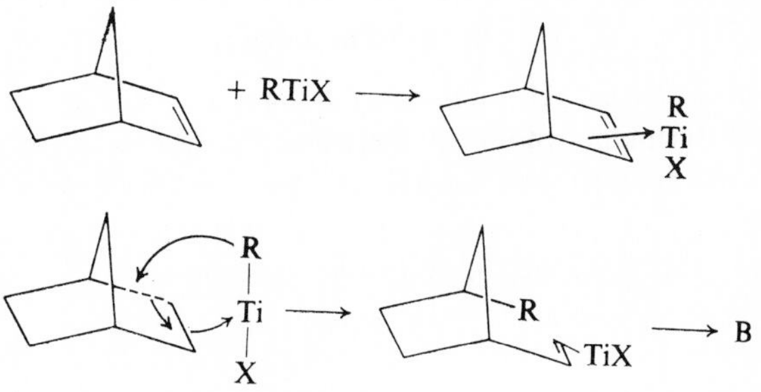

396. Lithium Aluminum Tetraoctyl (64)

$$LiAlH_4 + CH_3(CH_2)_5CH{=}CH_2 \longrightarrow LiAl(C_8H_{16})_4$$

A mixture of 13 g. (0.34 mole) of lithium aluminum hydride, 285 ml. (2.0 moles) of 1-octene, and 300 ml. of decahydronaphthalene is heated to reflux under nitrogen in a 1 l., three-necked flask, fitted with a stirrer, reflux condenser, and Glascol heater. The temperature gradually rises from 115 to 135°C. over a period of 5 hr., at which time the reaction is complete. The reaction mixture is filtered with suction through paper while hot under a nitrogen atmosphere to remove residual solid. The insoluble residue is pyrophoric and should be quickly quenched in isopropanol. Upon cooling, the filtered solution deposits crystals which are conveniently freed of solvent by forcing nitrogen in the flask and removing the solvent by means of a filter stick. The last trace of solvent is removed by drying under vacuum at room temperature. The white crystalline solid is dissolved in about 1 l. of xylene and standardized by titration of an aliquot with standard acid using a pH meter. The concentration of the solution usually ranges from 0.35 to 0.40 molar in lithium aluminum tetraoctyl. Exposure of the solution or solid to air or moisture leads to a loss of activity.

397. Polymerization of Norbornylene (64)

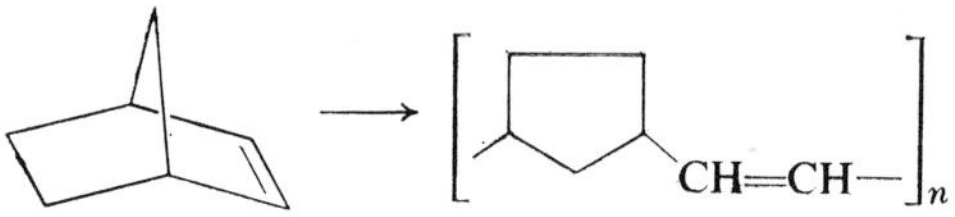

The following polymerization is carried out in an inert atmosphere in any convenient equipment. A solution of 0.02 mole of lithium aluminum tetraheptyl in xylene (prepared above and standardized) is added to 1.1 ml. (0.01 mole) of titanium tetrachloride in 50 ml. of decahydronaphthalene. The mixture is allowed to stand for 10 min. and then 47 g. (0.5 mole) of norbornylene in 94 ml. of benzene is added. After standing for 24 hr., the polymer is worked up (see Chapter 4) to give 14.5 g. (31%) of a white powder. The powder can be pressed to a clear, stiff, tough film at 225°C. Low molecular weight benzene-soluble polynorbornylene can be separated by extraction of 34 g. of the polymer using 300 ml. of benzene in a Soxhlet extractor. The extraction is performed under a nitrogen atmosphere.

IX. 1-n-Polyamides

Polyamides based on methylenediamine may be prepared **by the reaction of formaldehyde with dinitriles** (65–68) in a strongly acidic medium. The products are **1-n-nylons**, where n is the number of carbons in the nitrile. The polymerization is catalyzed by strong acids and is thought to take place by the following mechanism:

$$CH_2O + H^+ \rightleftharpoons {}^+CH_2OH$$

$$^+CH_2OH + {-}R{-}CN \rightleftharpoons {-}R{-}\overset{+}{C}{=}N{-}CH_2OH$$
$$\text{I}$$

$$I + H_2O \rightleftharpoons {-}R{-}\overset{\displaystyle OH}{\overset{|}{C}}{=}N{-}CH_2{-}OH + H^+$$
$$\text{II}$$

$$II + H^+ \rightleftharpoons {-}R{-}\overset{\displaystyle OH}{\overset{|}{C}}{=}N{-}CH_2{}^+ + H_2O$$
$$\text{III}$$

$$\text{III} + \text{—R—CN} \rightleftharpoons \text{—R—}\overset{\overset{\displaystyle OH}{|}}{C}\text{=N—CH}_2\text{—N=}\overset{+}{C}\text{—R—}$$

IV

$$\text{IV} + H_2O \rightleftharpoons \text{—R—}\overset{\overset{\displaystyle OH}{|}}{C}\text{=N—CH}_2\text{—N=}\overset{\overset{\displaystyle OH}{|}}{C}\text{—R—} + H^+$$

V

$$\text{V} \rightleftharpoons \text{—R—}\overset{\overset{\displaystyle O}{\|}}{C}\text{—NHCH}_2\text{—NH—}\overset{\overset{\displaystyle O}{\|}}{C}\text{—R}$$

All the reactions involved are reversible, and the reaction product must be washed free of acid, or fairly rapid degradation will result from prolonged contact with the aqueous acids used.

Although the polymer structure is mostly that of a linear polymethyleneamide, there is evidence for some chain branching and the presence of an unaccountably large number of —CN groups. The polymer melt temperature is around 300°C. for 1-6 nylon, some 35°C. higher than 6-6 nylon. The difference is due at least in part to the closer arrangement of the amide groups in 1-6 nylon.

398. Preparation of Polymethyleneadipamide (1-6 Nylon)

$$NC\text{—}(CH_2)_4\text{—CN} + CH_2O + H_2O \longrightarrow$$

$$\left[\text{—}\overset{\overset{\displaystyle O}{\|}}{C}\text{—}(CH_2)_4\text{—}\overset{\overset{\displaystyle O}{\|}}{C}\text{—NH—CH}_2\text{—NH—} \right]_n$$

In a 5 l., three-necked flask equipped with a stirrer and dropping funnel are placed 78.0 g. (0.50 mole) of adiponitrile, 15.4 g. (0.171 mole) of trioxane, and 600 ml. 98% formic acid. The solution is cooled to 10°C. and 200 g. (2.0 moles) of concentrated sulfuric acid is added with stirring and cooling during 10 min. The solution is then stirred for about 1 hr. at 26–28°C. At this point a gel forms, to which is then rapidly added, with vigorous stirring, 4 l. of water. The white powder is filtered, washed successively with dilute sodium carbonate solution, water, and ethanol. After drying in vacuum at 70°C., the yield of polymer having an inherent viscosity in m-cresol (0.5% conc. at 25°C.) of 0.6–1.2 is obtained in a yield 31–47 g. (40–60%). The polymer melt temperature is about 290–300°C. with decomposition. Other solvents are formic acid and phenol.

X. Polyphenylene Ethers

The preparation of high molecular weight **polyphenylene ethers**

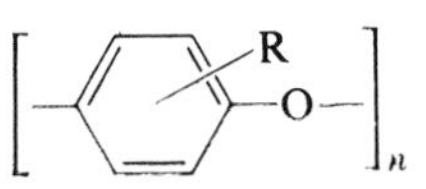

$$\left[\text{—}\underset{}{\boxed{}}\overset{R}{\diagup}\text{—O—} \right]_n$$

has been of interest to polymer chemists for some time. Hunter and his students (69), and later Staffin and Price (70) studied the ferricyanide oxidation of 2,6-dialkyl-4-halophenols to polymers of moderate molecular weight. This was presumed to involve displacement of halogen by an aryloxy radical:

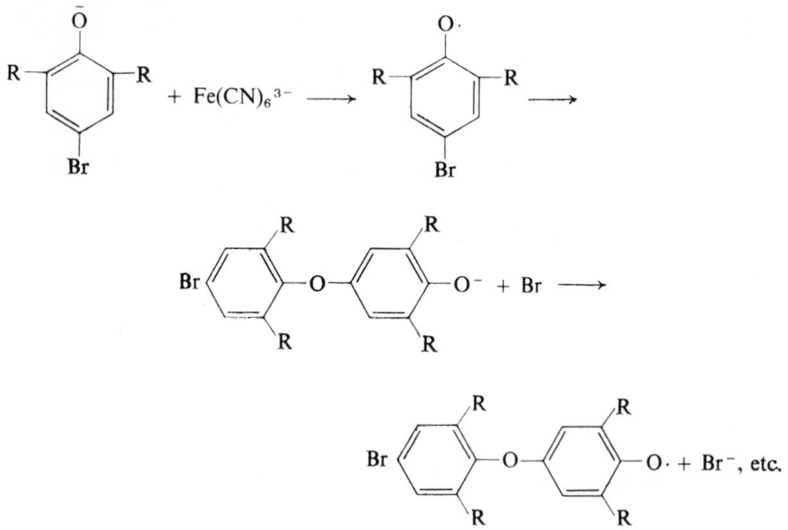

A more sophisticated **oxidation of a 2,6-disubstituted phenol** was reported later by Hay, Blanchard, Endres, and Eustance (71). These workers found that passing air through a vigorously agitated solution of a 2,6-dialkyl phenol in an organic solvent containing an amine and a copper(I) catalyst gave polymer. The reaction is rapid and high molecular weight polyphenylene ethers are obtained when R is not too large.

399. Preparation of Poly(2,6-dimethyl-p-phenylene ether)

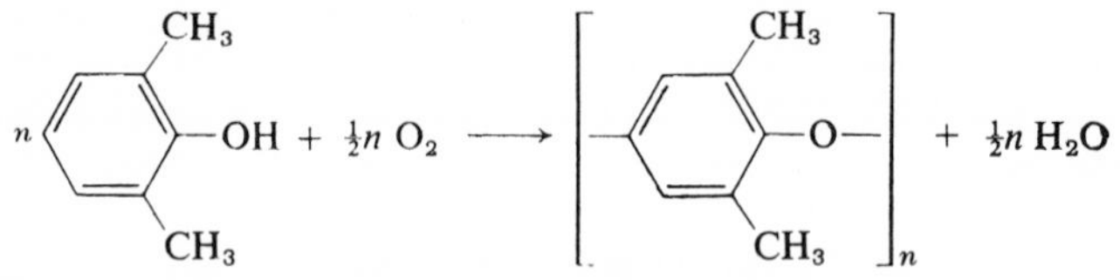

A mixture of 9 ml. of pure pyridine and 30 ml. of pure nitrobenzene and 0.04 g. of cuprous chloride is shaken in an atmosphere of oxygen until the Cu(I) is converted to Cu(II). This occurs fairly rapidly; if desired, this reaction and the subsequent polymerization may be followed quantitatively by using a closed system and a gas burette. After the catalyst is prepared, 0.977 g.

(0.008 mole) of pure 2,6-dimethylphenol is added, and vigorous agitation is continued. The absorption of oxygen is complete in about $\frac{1}{2}$ hr. The polymer is precipitated by pouring into 1% concentrated aqueous hydrochloric acid in methanol (150 mol). The solid is filtered, slurried with 5% concentrated hydrochloric acid in methanol, filtered, dissolved in chloroform, filtered, and reprecipitated into methanol. The yield is about 0.8 g. of a polymer with an inherent viscosity of about 1.0, as measured in chloroform, and an osmotic molecular weight of 28,000.

XI. Polyacetylenes

The oxidative coupling of diacetylenes has also led to the formation of reasonably high polymer, capable, in the case of m-diethynylbenzene, of giving clear, flexible, yellow films. The films are interesting in that when ignited in air at room temperature, they explosively pyrolyze, but with only a weight loss of 5–6%, accounting for all of the hydrogen content (2.7%) and some of the carbon (72).

400. Preparation of m-Diethynylbenzene (73)

Bromine (1300 g., 8.13 moles) is added over 2 hr. with stirring to a cooled solution of 750 g. mixed divinylbenzene (40% = 2.3 moles m- and p-divinyl-benzene) in 1200 ml. of chloroform. The reaction mixture is then cooled to 5°C.; a voluminous precipitate settles out which is separated by filtration. Recrystallization from chloroform yields 264 g. (0.59 mole) of 1,4-bis(1,2-dibromoethyl)benzene; m.p. 155–157°C. The two filtrates are combined and the chloroform removed on a rotating evaporator at 100°C. (3 mm.). The residue is then fractionated in a molecular still. Distillation at 50°C. (40–70 μ) and then at 80°C. (20–50 μ) separates most of the dibromodiethylbenzenes. The residue, a viscous sirup, is distilled at 150°C. (12–30 μ). The distillate crystallizes when triturated with cold alcohol and after recrystallization from alcohol yields about 420 g. 1,3-bis(1,2-dibromoethyl)benzene; m.p. 65–66.5°C.

To a solution of 18 g. (0.46 mole) of potassium in 1 l. of t-butanol at the temperature of reflux is added 50 g. (0.11 mole) of 1,3-bis(1,2-dibromoethyl)-benzene. After 1 hr. the reaction mixture is made up to 4 l. with ice water and the product isolated by ether extraction and distillation to yield m-diethnyl-benzene, b.p. 78°C. (14 mm.), n_D^{20} 1.5825, in about 70% yield (9 g.).

401. Preparation of Polydiethynylbenzene (72)

To a 125 ml. flask is added 65 ml. dry pyridine, 0.5 g. copper (I) chloride, and 12.5 g. diethynylbenzene. The solution is kept in a 30°C. bath, is vigorously stirred, and oxygen is bubbled through it. The temperature rises as reaction takes place. At the end of the reaction a pale-yellow polymer separates essentially in quantitative amount. It is soluble in chlorobenzene and nitrobenzene above 100°C. Clear, flexible, yellow films can be cast at 170°C. under nitrogen from a nitrobenzene solution (about 30% concentration). The intrinsic viscosity may be no higher than 0.25 dl./g. (nitrobenzene, 150°C.). Molecular weight estimates based on infrared determination of acetylene end groups are 7000 or more.

XII. Dimethylketene Polymers

Ketenes show the structural possibilities of polymerization through the opening of a carbon–carbon double bond and through the carbonyl in the fashion of an aldehyde; actually, both polymers are known (74,75). Polymerization of the double bond using a strong Friedel-Crafts catalyst at low temperature gives a polyketone, and

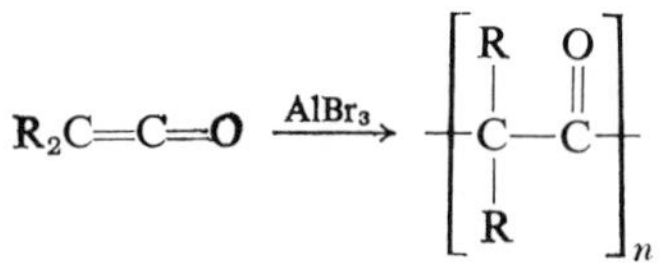

$$R_2C{=}C{=}O \xrightarrow{AlBr_3} \left[\begin{array}{c} R \quad O \\ | \quad\quad || \\ C{-}C \\ | \\ R \end{array} \right]_n$$

polymerization of the carbonyl to a polyacetal occurs with an anionic initiator, also at low temperature.

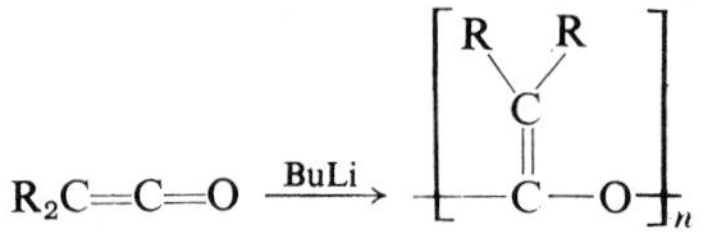

$$R_2C{=}C{=}O \xrightarrow{BuLi} \left[\begin{array}{c} R \quad R \\ \diagdown / \\ C \\ || \\ C{-}O \end{array} \right]_n$$

A third dialkylketene polymer has also been made **which has the polyester structure** resulting from an alternation of the first two modes of polymerization (76). In this case, a trialkylaluminum catalyst at -25°C. is needed.

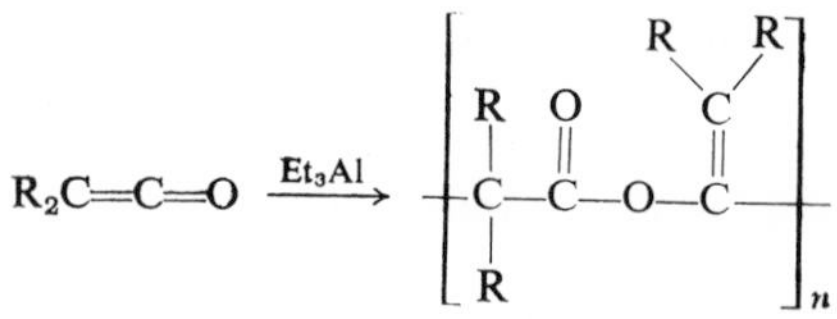

$$R_2C{=}C{=}O \xrightarrow{Et_3Al} \left[\begin{array}{c} \quad\quad\quad R \quad R \\ \quad\quad\quad \diagdown / \\ R \quad O \quad C \\ | \quad\quad || \quad\quad || \\ C{-}C{-}O{-}C \\ | \\ R \end{array} \right]_n$$

Dimethylketene and acetone have also been **copolymerized** to a polyester by means of lithium alkoxide catalyst (77).

$$(CH_3)_2C=C=O + CH_3\overset{\overset{\displaystyle O}{\|}}{C}CH_3 \longrightarrow \left[\begin{array}{c} CH_3 \ \ O \ \ \ \ \ \ \ \ CH_3 \\ \ \ | \ \ \ \ \| \ \ \ \ \ \ \ \ \ \ | \\ C-C-O-C- \\ \ \ | \ \ \ \ \ \ \ \ \ \ \ \ \ \ | \\ CH_3 \ \ \ \ \ \ \ \ \ \ CH_3 \end{array} \right]_n$$

Dimethylketene boils at 34°C. at atmospheric pressure, and may be prepared by pyrolysis of dimethylmalonic anhydride (no doubt polymeric) or by decomposition of the commercially available dimer, 1,1,3,3-tetramethylcyclobutanedione (Eastman Organic Chemicals Dept.) using a modification of a conventional ketene lamp. Both methods are described in detail in Volume III of *Organic Reactions* (78). Dimethylketene forms an explosive peroxide when exposed to air at low temperatures, so it must be thoroughly protected by an inert atmosphere in all phases of its preparation and use (79).

402. Preparation of a Polyketone from Dimethylketene (74,76)

$$(CH_3)_2C=C=O \longrightarrow \left[\begin{array}{c} CH_3 \ \ O \\ \ \ | \ \ \ \ \| \\ C-C- \\ \ \ | \\ CH_3 \end{array} \right]_n$$

Dimethylketene is purified by cooling a sample to −80°C. in an inert atmosphere and adding about 1% wt./vol. of aluminum triethyl. At this temperature, polymerization is too slow to be a problem. After about 3 hr., the pressure is reduced and dimethylketene (15 ml.) is allowed to distill into a small reaction vessel (e.g., a 100 ml. test tube) kept at −78°C., with a sidearm to receive the distillate. An atmosphere of dry, oxygen-free nitrogen is maintained throughout the operation. When distillation is completed, the reaction vessel is brought to atmospheric pressure with nitrogen and 15 ml. of dry toluene, previously cooled to −78°C., is added, followed by 1 ml. of dry heptane containing 0.1 g. distilled aluminum bromide. The bath temperature is raised to and held at −50°C. for 20 hr., during which time the viscosity becomes very great. Methanol is then added slowly to destroy the residual dimethylketene and finally the polymer is coagulated completely with excess methanol. (Alternatively, some of the residual monomer can be removed by low pressure distillation, in company with some toluene.) The polymer is washed in a blender with cold water repeatedly and then with warm 1% HCl, and again with methanol. About 3 g. of polymer is obtained after drying at 60°C. in vacuum. If the polymer is successively extracted with boiling solvents, about 6% is removed by acetone; about 1% with ether; about 8% with benzene; and, about 4% with toluene. The remainder is crystalline, has an intrinsic viscosity (nitrobenzene, 135°C.) of about 0.7 dl./g., and has a T_m of about 250°C. (polarizing microscope).

By using aluminum bromide diethyl etherate, a higher conversion is possible. A lower temperature and higher monomer concentration increase the intrinsic viscosity.

403. Preparation of a Polyester from Dimethylketene by Alternating Double Bond–Carbonyl Polymerization (77)

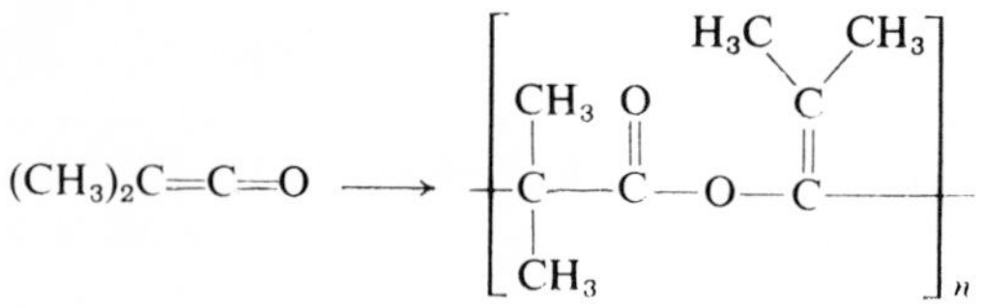

$$(CH_3)_2C{=}C{=}O \longrightarrow \left[\begin{array}{c} \underset{\overset{|}{CH_3}}{\overset{CH_3}{\overset{|}{C}}} - \overset{O}{\overset{||}{C}} - O - \overset{\overset{H_3C \quad CH_3}{\diagdown\diagup}}{\underset{}{C}} \end{array} \right]_n$$

This polymerization is run as in the preceding example, using 0.1 g. aluminum triethyl to 20 ml. dimethylketene, without solvent. The temperature is maintained at $-25°C$. for 12 hr., when the mixture has solidified. Again, unreacted monomer can be distilled at reduced pressure. Excess methanol is added, the polymer is washed thoroughly in 1% HCl and again in methanol, then dried in vacuum at 60°C. to give about 8 g. of white powder. About 22% of the polymer is removed by boiling ether extraction. Most of the remainder (70%) is soluble in boiling benzene, but insoluble in boiling acetone. It is this benzene-extractable fraction that is assigned the regular polyester structure shown above. It is crystalline, with T_m of 160–170°C.; the intrinsic viscosity (tetralin, 135°C.) is about 0.4.

404. Preparation of a Polyacetal from Dimethylketene (75)

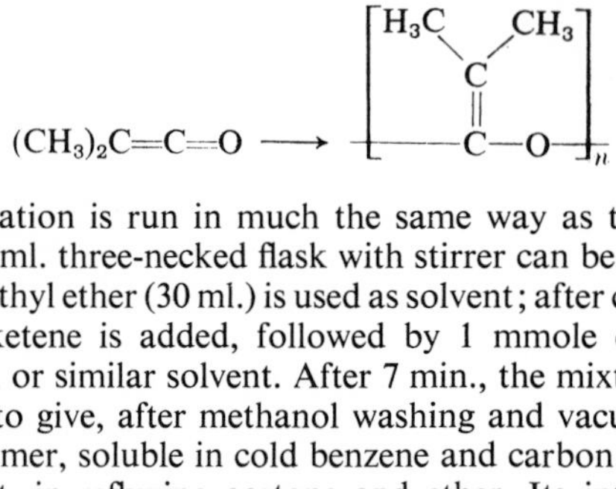

$$(CH_3)_2C{=}C{=}O \longrightarrow \left[\begin{array}{c} \overset{\overset{H_3C \quad CH_3}{\diagdown\diagup}}{\underset{}{C}} \\ \overset{||}{C} \\ \overset{|}{C} - O \end{array} \right]_n$$

This polymerization is run in much the same way as the preceding two, except that a 250 ml. three-necked flask with stirrer can be conveniently used if desired. Dry diethyl ether (30 ml.) is used as solvent; after cooling to $-78°C.$, 9 g. of dimethylketene is added, followed by 1 mmole of butyllithium in pentane, heptane, or similar solvent. After 7 min., the mixture is poured into excess methanol to give, after methanol washing and vacuum drying, about 7 g. of white polymer, soluble in cold benzene and carbon tetrachloride and, for the most part, in refluxing acetone and ether. Its intrinsic viscosity in chloroform is 0.21 dl./g. It is thermally stable up to 170°C., softens from 180–200°C., and is more stable thermally than polyisobutyraldehyde, which it structurally resembles to a degree. There is some evidence, both IR and

degradative, for the presence of some $-(CH_3)_2\overset{\overset{O}{||}}{C}-C-$ units, although the acetal structure is thoroughly predominant. Possibly the carbon–carbon bonds of the former structure provide some thermal stability to the polymer, much as copolymerized ethylene oxide does in the polyformaldehyde chain.

XIII. Diels-Alder Polymers

The **Diels-Alder reaction** has been applied in a number of interesting ways to polymer synthesis (80). The bis-dienophile in most cases has been a **bis-maleimide** from a diamine and maleic anhydride, e.g., *m*-phenylene- or hexamethylenediamine. **The bis-dienes have varied** considerably, and some examples are: the acetal of 2-hydroxymethyl-butadiene (81); 2-vinylbutadiene, which regenerates a 1,3-diene on forming an initial adduct with a dienophile (82); alkylene bis-cyclo-pentadienes (83); benzalazine, which undergoes two 1,3 additions with dienophiles and is not, strictly speaking, a Diels-Alder reaction. Some of these are shown below in brief.

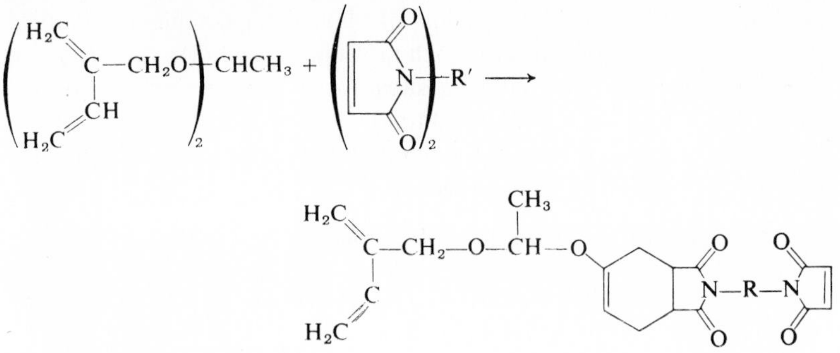

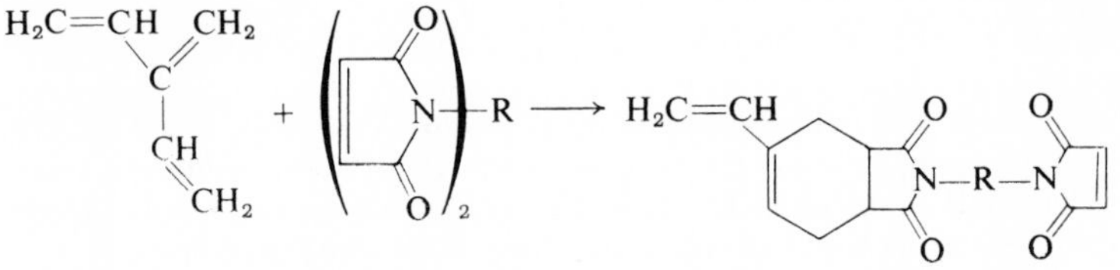

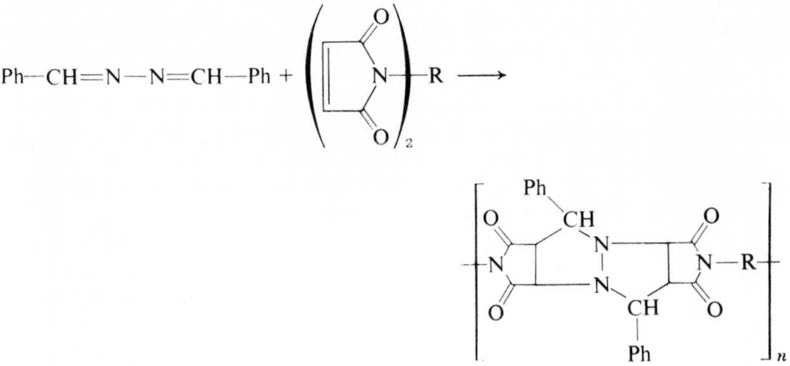

Related to the last reaction is the polyaddition of a bis-acetylene and a bis-sydnone (84), again shown in brief, below.

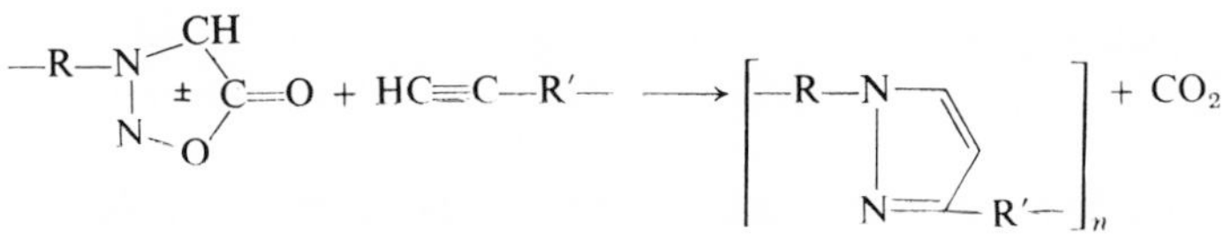

In general, the Diels-Alder polymers have not been of unequivocally high molecular weight so that useful properties could be developed. In fact, most have exhibited solution viscosity numbers of a rather low order. In at least one class of Diels-Alder polyadducts, however, it has been possible to obtain reasonably high inherent viscosities (e.g., 0.7) and to solution cast films which displayed respectable mechanical properties, indicative of a fairly high molecular weight (85, 86). In these instances, the diene was either a substituted 2-pyrone or cyclopentadienone, which, after the initial addition to a bis-maleimide lost carbon dioxide to regenerate the necessary diene for continued addition. This is shown in the following examples.*

405. Preparation of 2,5-Dimethyl-3,4-Diphenylcyclopentadienone (87)

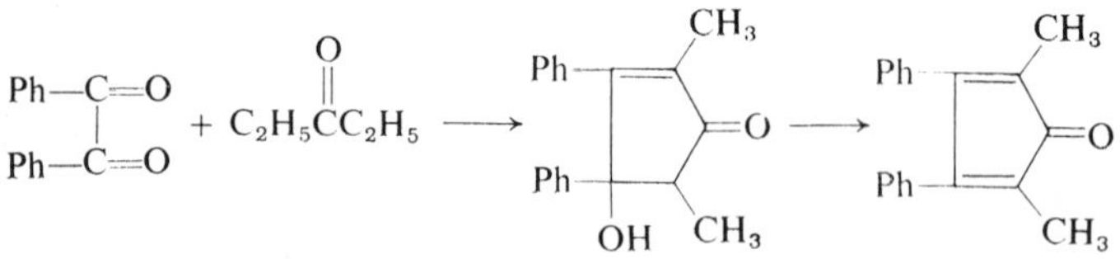

To 250 ml. of 0.5% absolute ethanolic potassium hydroxide in a 1 l. three-necked flask equipped with a stirrer and condenser with drying tube are added 21.0 g. benzil (0.1 mole) and 17.2 g. diethyl ketone (0.2 mole). The mixture is allowed to stand at room temperature until all the benzil has reacted. This will require about 48 hr., and can be determined by adding a few drops of the reaction mixture to water; the characteristic crystals of benzil are easily recognized when the latter is still present. When benzil is no longer in evidence, the mixture is poured into 500 ml. of water and the intermediate cyclopentenolone is filtered and allowed to air dry. It melts at 150° C. when pure. It is mixed with 40 ml. of acetic anhydride in a stirred flask and a drop of sulfuric acid is added. The temperature rises 10–15°C. After an hour, the dienone is precipitated by water, filtered, and recrystallized from ethanol; m.p. 180–181°C. (dec.). 2,5-Dimethyl-3,4-diphenylcyclopentadienone is obtained, above, as the colorless, carbonyl-bridged dimer:

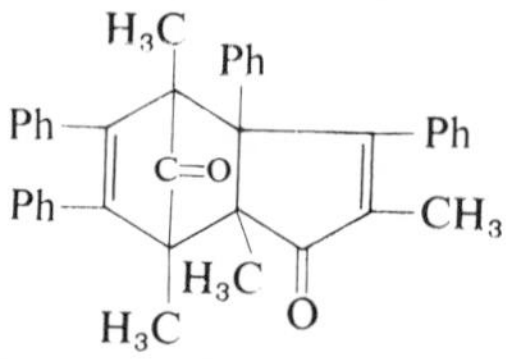

* We wish to thank Professor John Stille for the detailed preparations 405–409.

The latter dissociates to the red monomer on heating. The dimer functions in polymerization by such a reversion.

406. Preparation of the Bis-maleimide of Methylene Bis(aniline) [Methylene Bis(4-aminobenzene)] (88,89)

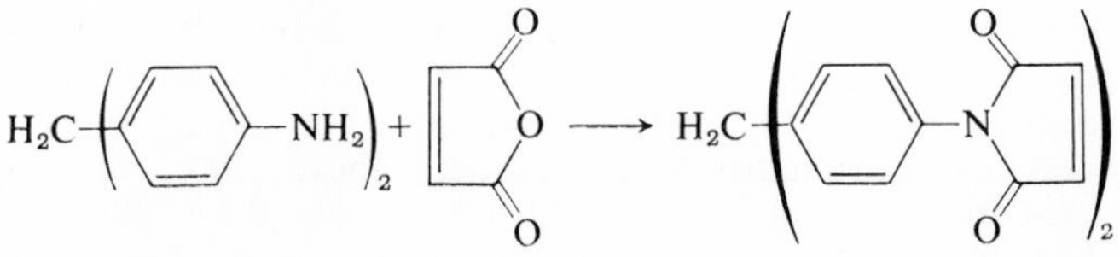

In a three-necked 1 l. flask with stirrer, condenser and drying tube, thermometer, and dropping funnel is placed 200 ml. dry chloroform and 39.2 g. maleic anhydride (0.4 mole). The solution is cooled to 15°C. and a solution of 39.6 g. methylene bis(aniline) (0.2 mole) in 200 ml. dry chloroform is added dropwise; the temperature of the reaction is maintained at 15–20°C. and stirring is continued one hour after addition is complete. The solid bis(maleamic acid) is filtered, washed with chloroform, and sucked dry on the filter.

The above product is placed in a 500 ml. three-necked flask equipped with stirrer, condenser, and thermometer; 100 g. glacial acetic acid and 10 g. fused sodium acetate are added and the mixture is stirred and heated until a clear-yellow solution results (about 90–95°C.) and the heat removed. An exothermic reaction sets in briefly, after which the mixture is allowed to cool to room temperature. It is then poured slowly into a vigorously stirred slurry of ice and water (about a kilogram total), and the resulting precipitate filtered, washed with water till neutral, and dried over phosphorous pentoxide in vacuum. The solid is repeatedly recrystallized from toluene and twice from methyl ethyl ketone, to give about 12 g. of purified bis(maleimide), m.p. 158°C.

407. Polyadduct of 2,5-Dimethyl-3,4-Diphenylcyclopentadienone and Methylene Bis(4-maleimidobenzene) (90)

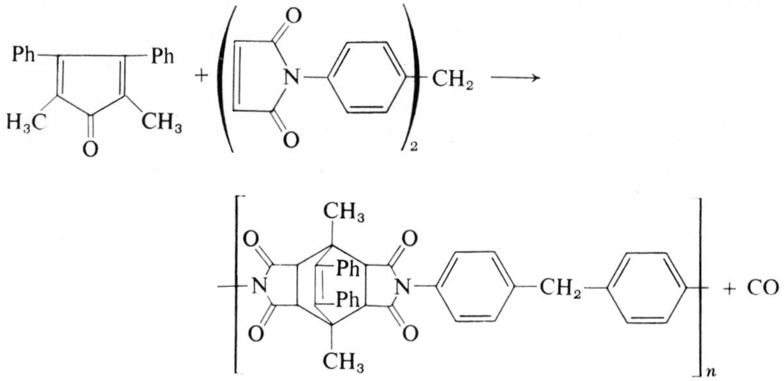

A mixture of 27.6 g. (0.10 mole, calculated as monomer) 2,5-dimethyl-3,4-diphenylcyclopentadienone dimer and 35.8 g. (0.10 mole) of methylene bis(4-maleimidobenzene) is stirred and heated to reflux in 100 ml. of α-chloronaphthalene (about 260°C.). The reaction is carried out in a 250 ml. three-necked flask equipped with stirrer, nitrogen inlet, and condenser. The flask is purged with nitrogen originally and a nitrogen blanket is maintained during reaction. The mixture can be diluted further, but the molecular weight of the product is less the lower the concentration. After 30 min. at reflux, the mixture is cooled and poured into excess methanol. The precipitated polymer is filtered, washed several times in a blender with excess methanol and dried for 15 hr. at 80°C. in vacuum. The polymer is obtained in slightly less than quantitative yield. It softens above 300°C., and shows a reduced viscosity of about 0.6 in dimethylformamide (0.4 g./100 ml., 25°C.) from which films can be cast. Tough specimens can also be compression molded which have tensile strength/elongation values of about 10,000 p.s.i. and 18%, respectively. The T_g is above 300°C.

408. Preparation of 4,6-Diphenyl-2-Pyrone (91)

$$\text{Ph—C(=O)—CH}_2\text{CO}_2\text{C}_2\text{H}_5 \longrightarrow$$

In a three-necked 500 ml. flask, ethyl benzoylacetate (60 g.) is dissolved in 60 g. concentrated sulfuric acid and allowed to stand at room temperature with continual stirring. Occasional cooling may be necessary to keep the reaction at room temperature, initially. Some gas is evolved. The reaction mixture should be protected from atmospheric moisture. Finally, a deep-green viscous or semisolid mass is formed, and no gas evolution is evidenced on vigorous stirring. At this time, which may take two weeks, the mixture is poured into ice water to give a yellow, crystalline precipitate which is contaminated with an oil (believed to be primarily acetophenone). The organic material is separated from the aqueous acid by filtering or by dissolving in chloroform, washing and drying that solution, and evaporating the solvent. The solid is freed from the oil by triturating with cold methanol, and then recrystallized at least twice from ethanol. Only 12–15 g. of slightly yellow crystals are obtained, m.p. 138–139°C.

409. Polyadduct of 4,6-Diphenyl-2-pyrone and Methylene Bis(4-maleimidobenzene) (85)*

In a 50 ml. three-necked flask equipped with a stirrer and inlet and outlet for nitrogen is mixed 5.16 g. 4,6-diphenyl-2-pyrone (0.02 mole), 7.16 g. (0.02 mole) methylene bis(4-maleimidobenzene), and 25 ml. s-tetrachloroethane. The mixture is stirred, a nitrogen blanket is maintained, and the temperature brought to 146°C. where it is held for 16 hr. The polymer can be precipitated wholly or in part in methanol, washed thoroughly in methanol, and dried in

* We are indebted to Dr. S. W. Chow, Union Carbide, for his helpful comments on this preparation.

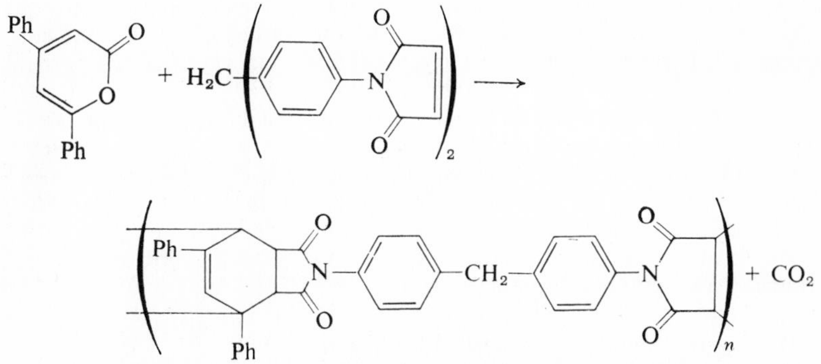

vacuum at 90°C. Alternatively, films can be directly cast from the solution. A polymer with a reduced viscosity of 0.44 (in DMF, 0.2 g./100 ml., 25°C.) will form films with about 10,000 p.s.i. tensile strength and 20% elongation.

XIV. Polymerization of Isonitriles*

Millich and co-workers have recently reported the **polymerization of α-phenylethyl isonitrile,** over a powdered glass catalyst to give a high polymer with the unusual structure

$$(\text{—CH—})$$
$$\text{N}{=}\text{C—CH}_3$$
$$\text{C}_6\text{H}_5$$

Caution: Isocyanides are very toxic and have vile odors. Ethyl isocyanide has been known to explode.

410. Synthesis of α-Phenylethyl Formamide (*N*-Formyl-α-phenylethyl Amine) (92)

$$\text{C}_6\text{H}_5\text{COCH}_3 + \text{HCONH}_2 + \text{HCOOH} \longrightarrow \text{C}_6\text{H}_5\text{CH—NHCHO}$$
$$\text{CH}_3$$

The synthesis is essentially that of Ingersoll and co-workers (93) and that found in *Organic Reactions* (94). A 2 l., three-necked, round-bottom flask is fitted with a thermometer, a gas bleeder tube and short, wide reflux condenser. The condenser is fitted with a distilling head which is connected to a take-off condenser and a pressure-equalizing dropping funnel. The funnel allows additions to be made down the reflux condenser. In the reaction flask is placed 240 g. (2 moles) acetophenone, 270 g. (6 moles) formamide and 25 ml. formic acid. Reflux is maintained at 175–185°C. by turning off the water to the vertical condenser, and distilling water as needed to keep the temperature

* Acknowledgment is made to the donors of The Petroleum Research Fund, administered by the American Chemical Society, for support of the research that led to the synthesis of this class of polymers.

up. Formic acid is added from the dropping funnel in 25 ml. portions until a 325 ml. total has been added. By adding the formic acid down the condenser, ammonium carbonate is removed from the walls of the vertical condenser. After approximately 40 hr. of reflux only a 3°C. temperature drop occurs with further reflux over several hours, and no more carbonate is deposited on the condenser. After cooling somewhat the vertical condenser is replaced with the distilling head and inclined condenser. Vacuum distillation yields a distinct cut at 189–192°C./26 mm. Yield: 244 g. (1.6 moles); 80% based on acetophenone. Upon standing, the water-white to pale-yellow liquid forms a crystalline solid of melting point 37–42°C. IR spectrum is typical of a substituted formamide.

411. Synthesis of d,l-α-Phenylethyl Isocyanide (95,96)

$$\begin{array}{c} CH{=}O \\ | \\ HN \\ | \\ Ph{-}CH \\ \backslash \\ CH_3 \end{array} \ + \ POCl_3 \ \xrightarrow[CH_2Cl_2]{Et_3N \ (excess)} \ \left[\begin{array}{c} OPOCl_2 \\ / \\ C \\ / \ \backslash \\ N \quad H \\ | \\ Ph{-}CH \\ \backslash \\ CH_3 \end{array} \right] \longrightarrow$$

$$Ph{-}\underset{\underset{CH_3}{|}}{CH}{-}\overset{+}{N}{\equiv}\overset{-}{C}: \ + \ 2Et_3NHCl \ + \ [Cl{-}PO_2]$$

The synthesis is essentially that of Ugi and co-workers (95,96). A 2 l., three-necked flask is fitted with a reflux condenser (vented through a drying tube), a mechanical stirrer, and a pressure-equalizing dropping funnel. The flask is surrounded by an ice-bath, and 77 g. (0.5 mole) of freshly distilled phosphorous oxychloride (boiling point 100–103°C.) is placed in the dropping funnel. In the reaction flask 68 g. (0.45 mole) of α-phenylethyl formamide is dissolved in 300 ml. of dry triethylamine and 750 ml. of dry methylene chloride. The phosphorous oxychloride is added dropwise to the vigorously stirred solution during a period of 15 min. Stirring at room temperature is done for 45 min. Cold water (700 ml.) is added while stirring is continued. The flask contents are poured into a 5 l. separatory funnel and the methylene chloride phase is drawn off. After washing the aqueous phase twice with 100 ml. methylene chloride, the combined organic phases are placed in a separatory funnel and shaken with 100 ml. of concentrated ammonium hydroxide. The organic phase is drawn off into a separatory funnel and extracted with 500 ml. ice water. The organic phase is drawn off and mixed with 5 g. anhydrous calcium chloride, and the organic phases are combined in a 3 l., three-necked distillation flask. The methylene chloride is distilled off at reduced pressure, keeping the pot at room temperature or below. A vacuum pump is used as the temperature rises above 25°C. and distillation is performed through a vacuum insulated 28 cm. packed Allyn column. (A Claisen head does not separate well enough.) After discarding a forecut there is collected 37 g. (63% yield) at 54°C./0.6 mm. of water-white, α-phenylethyl isocyanide. An IR spectrum shows no amide bands and has a strong band at 2150 cm.$^{-1}$ (4.7 μ). UV:

e(max., 257 $m\mu$) = 234; n_D^{31} = 1.5041; density = 0.952 g./ml. at 32°C. The product is stored in an amber bottle in a refrigerator.

Other synthetic methods for the preparation of isocyanides have been reviewed recently (95).

412. Polymerization of α-Phenylethyl Isocyanide (92)

$n = 250-700$

Powdered Glass Catalyst Preparation. Powdered glass, approximately 200 mesh (Fischer Scientific Company) is washed with benzene, dried, soaked overnight in sulfuric acid–dichromate solution, washed clear with water, then washed alternately on a frit with 5N sodium hydroxide, distilled water, and 6N sulfuric acid; the last wash is acidic which is sucked down on the filter thoroughly. The acid powdered glass is spread out on a petri dish and dried at 50 ± 2°C. at 1 ± 0.5 mm. Hg for 4–16 hr. Usually the weight loss is slow after 4 hr. Approximately 20 g. of powdered glass is conveniently handled in a batch. The powdered glass preparation contains approximately 0.02 g. of coating per g. of powdered glass. Titration indicates acid coating is present as a concentration of 80% by weight. The acid powdered glass is white, free of visible debris and with some tendency to form lumps. It is neither cakey nor a freely flowing powder. It is stored in a desiccator, but may show complete loss of activity after one month's storage.

Polymerization. In a 100 ml. round-bottom flask, in any atmosphere, 2.0 g. of acid powdered glass is covered with 10 ml. n-heptane. A magnetic stirrer is turned on and 3.0 ml. of α-phenylethyl isocyanide is added to the reaction flask. A red-brown color occurs immediately. A vertical condenser is fitted into the flask, and oxygen is passed through anhydrous calcium chloride, a flask of n-heptane (to saturate the gas), and then by a fine tipped bubbler into the reaction mixture. The reaction flask is heated 20–40 hr. at 50°C. with stirring and oxygen bubbling. The powdered glass should now be coated with red-brown curds of polymer, and the solution is red-brown.

The n-heptane is decanted through coarse filter paper, leaving behind the powdered glass–polymer matrix in the flask. Dissolution of the polymer may require 25–50 ml. of benzene to produce a viscosity which will flow through the filter paper. Gravity filtration and not suction filtration must be used. The filter paper is washed with benzene until free of nearly all color; the latter may require cutting up the paper, washing with benzene and putting through fresh filter paper. The combined benzene phase at room temperature is reduced in volume to approximately 25–50 ml., which is then added to a ten-fold excess of vigorously stirred methanol, to precipitate the polymer. The precipitate is collected on a Büchner funnel, air dried somewhat, dissolved in approximately 30 ml. of benzene and lyophilized at 0.5–1.0 mm. Hg vacuum. Under the best conditions the yield is quantitative.

The fluffy solid appears yellow due to tail-end absorption in the visible spectral region of a band which peaks at 242 $m\mu$ ($e = 2000$ in chloroform). The polymer is soluble in aromatic hydrocarbons, and some haloalkanes, from which a clear, dark-red film may be formed by evaporation. Number-average molecular weights (determined by dynamic membrane osmometry) of around 50,000, with a weight-average to number-average molecular weight ratio of 1.6, may be produced by the above method, although, the weight-average molecular weight (determined by light-scattering) may range from 25,000 to over 1,000,000 depending upon the age of the catalyst, the amount of oxygen, and other altered preparative conditions. The polymer samples are stable to normal storage conditions but show a degradation of molecular weight upon the application of heat or exposure to light.

REFERENCES

1. G. B. Butler and R. J. Angelo, *J. Am. Chem. Soc.*, **79**, 3128 (1957).
2. C. S. Marvel and R. D. Vest, *J. Am. Chem. Soc.*, **79**, 5771 (1957).
3. J. F. Jones, *J. Polymer Sci.*, **33**, 15 (1958).
4. J. F. Walker, *Formaldehyde*, Reinhold, New York, 1953, Chapter 2.
5. H. Staudinger and A. Gaule, *Ber.*, **49**, 1897 (1916).
6. H. Staudinger and R. Signer, *Helv. Chim. Acta.*, **11**, 1847–1851 (1958).
7. A. K. Schneider, U.S. Pat. 2,795,571 (June 11, 1957).
8. R. N. MacDonald, U.S. Pat. 2,768,994 (October 30, 1956).
9. F. M. Berardinelli, T. J. Dolce, and C. Walling, *J. Appl. Polymer Sci.*, **9**, 1419 (1965).
10. C. D. Kennedy, W. R. Sorenson, and G. G. McClaflin, *Polymer Preprints*, p. 665, 150th Am. Chem. Soc. Meeting, Atlantic City, September, 1965.
11. W. C. Fernelius, K. Tarada, and B. E. Bryant, *Inorg. Syn.*, **6**, 147 (1960).
12. S. Okamura, E. Kobayashi, M. Takeda, K. Tumikawa, and T. Higashimura, *J. Polymer Sci. C*, **4**, 827 (1963).
13. D. B. Miller, *Am. Chem. Soc. Polymer Preprints*, **6**, 613 (1965).
14. S. Okamura, K. Hayashi, and Y. Kitanishi, *J. Polymer Sci.*, **58**, 925 (1962).
15. H. Rao and D. S. Ballantine, *ibid.*, *A*, **3**, 2579 (1965).
16. E. Gipstein, E. Wellisch, and O. J. Sweeting, *J. Polymer Sci. B*, **1**, 237 (1963).
17. J. B. Lando and V. J. Stannett, *J. Polymer Sci. B*, **2**, 375 (1965).
18. J. Lal, *J. Org. Chem.*, **26**, 971 (1961).
19. R. C. Schulz, G. Wegner, and W. Kern, *J. Polymer Sci.*, in press.
20. O. Vogl, *J. Polymer Sci. A*, **2**, 4591 (1964).
21. O. Vogl, *J. Polymer Sci. A*, **2**, 4607 (1964).
22. I. Rosen and C. L. Sturm, *J. Polymer Sci. A*, **3**, 3741 (1965).
23. I. Rosen, C. L. Sturm, G. H. McCain, R. M. Wilhjelm, and D. E. Hudgin, *J. Polymer Sci. A*, **3**, 1545 (1965).
24. W. J. Middleton, E. G. Howard, and W. H. Sharkey, *J. Org. Chem.*, **30**, 1375 (1965).
25. A. Schonberg and A. Stephenson, *Ber.*, **66 B**, 567 (1933).
26. A. L. Barney, J. M. Bruce, Jr., J. N. Coker, H. W. Jacobson, and W. H. Sharkey, *J. Polymer Sci. A*, **4**, 2617 (1966).
27. W. Sweeny, *J. Appl. Polymer Sci.*, **7**, 1983 (1963).
28. V. E. Shashoua, W. Sweeny, and R. F. Tietz, *J. Am. Chem. Soc.*, **82**, 866 (1960).
29. C. King, *J. Am. Chem. Soc.*, **86**, 437 (1964).

30. T. W. Campbell, J. J. Monagle, and V. S. Foldi, *J. Am. Chem. Soc.*, **84**, 3673 (1962).
31. J. J. Monagle, T. W. Campbell, and H. F. McShane, *J. Am. Chem. Soc.*, **84**, 4288 (1962).
32. T. W. Campbell and K. C. Smeltz, *J. Org. Chem.*, **28**, 2069 (1963).
33. T. W. Campbell, U.S. Pat. 2,941,966 (June 21, 1960).
34. W. B. McCormack, U.S. Pat. 2,663,736; 2,663,739.
35. W. B. McCormack, *Org. Syn.*, **43**, 73 (1963).
36. C. E. H. Bawn and A. Ledwith, *Chem. Ind.*, **1957**, 1180.
37. G. D. Buckley and N. H. Ray, *J. Chem. Soc.*, **1952**, 3701.
38. A. Nasini et al., *J. Polymer Sci.*, **34**, 106 (1959).
39. C. E. H. Bawn, A. Ledwith, and P. Matthies, *J. Polymer Sci.*, **34**, 93 (1959).
40. A. Ledwith, *Chem. Ind.*, **1956**, 1310.
41. G. Saini et al., *Gazz. Chim. Ital.*, **87**, 342 (1957); also, *Intern. Cong. Pure Appl. Chem.*, *XVI, Paris 1957*. Handbook Vol. II, p. 184.
42. W. Sweeny, private communication.
43. W. Kantor and R. C. Osthoff, *J. Am. Chem. Soc.*, **75**, 931 (1953).
44. C. E. H. Bawn, S. Ledwith, and P. Matthies, *J. Polymer Sci.*, **33**, 21 (1958).
45. M. Szwarc, *J. Polymer Sci.*, **6**, 319 (1951).
46. M. Szwarc, *J. Chem. Phys.*, **16**, 128 (1948).
47. F. S. Fawcett, U.S. Pat. 2,757,146 (July 31, 1956).
48. H. E. Winberg, F. S. Fawcett, W. E. Mochel, and C. W. Theobald, *J. Am. Chem. Soc.*, **82**, 1428 (1960).
49. T. E. Young, British Pat. 807,196 (January 7, 1959).
50. W. F. Gorham, *Polymer Preprints*, **6**, 73, Am. Chem. Soc. Meeting, Detroit, April, 1965.
51. H. G. Gilch and W. L. Wheelwright, *J. Polymer Sci. A-1*, **4**, 1337 (1966).
52. H. Gilch, *Angew. Chem., Intern. Ed.*, **4**, 598 (1965); *J. Polymer Sci. A-1*, **4**, 43 (1966).
53. H. Gilch, *J. Polymer Sci. A-1*, **4**, 1351 (1966).
54. L. A. Auspos, L. A. R. Hall, J. K. Hubbard, W. Kirk, Jr., J. R. Schaefgen, and S. B. Speck, *J. Polymer Sci.*, **15**, 9 (1955).
55. L. A. Auspos, C. W. Burnam, L. A. R. Hall, J. K. Hubbard, W. Kirk, Jr., J. R. Schaefgen, and S. B. Speck, *J. Polymer Sci.*, **15**, 19 (1955).
56. J. R. Schaefgen, *J. Polymer Sci.*, **15**, 203 (1955).
57. J. von Braun and W. Leistner, *Ber.*, **59B**, 2323–9 (1926).
58. W. F. Gorham, *Polymer Preprints*, **6**, 73, Am. Chem. Soc. Meeting, Detroit, April, 1965.
59. H. E. Winberg and F. S. Fawcett, *Org. Syn.*, Vol. 42, V. Boekelheide, Ed., John Wiley, New York, 1962, p. 83.
60. D. F. Pollart, U.S. Pat. 3,149,175 (to Union Carbide) (September 15, 1964).
61. W. L. Gorham, British Pat. 883,940 (December 6, 1961).
62. A. W. Anderson and N. G. Merckling, U.S. Pat. 2,721,189 (October 1, 1955).
63. A. W. Anderson, N. G. Merckling, and P. H. Settlage, German Pat. 1,037,103 (August 21, 1958).
64. W. L. Truett, D. R. Johnson, I. M. Robinson, and B. A. Montague, *J. Am. Chem. Soc.*, **82**, 2337 (1960).
65. E. E. Magat, B. F. Faris, J. E. Reith, and L. F. Salisbury, *J. Am. Chem. Soc.*, **73**, 1028 (1952).

66. E. E. Magat, L. B. Chandler, B. F. Faris, J. E. Reith, and L. F. Salisbury, *J. Am. Chem. Soc.*, **73**, 1031 (1951).
67. E. E. Magat and L. F. Salisbury, *J. Am. Chem. Soc.*, **73**, 1035 (1951).
68. E. E. Magat, *J. Am. Chem. Soc.*, **73**, 1367 (1951).
69. W. H. Hunter and M. J. Morse, *J. Am. Chem. Soc.*, **55**, 3701 (1933).
70. G. Staffin and C. C. Price, *Rubber World*, **139**, 408 (1958).
71. A. S. Hay, H. S. Blanchard, G. F. Endres, and J. W. Eustance, *J. Am. Chem. Soc.*, **81**, 6335 (1959).
72. A. S. Hay, *J. Org. Chem.*, **25**, 1275 (1960).
73. A. S. Hay, *J. Org. Chem.*, **25**, 637 (1960).
74. G. Natta, G. Mazzanti, G. Pregaglia, M. Binaghi, and M. Peraldo, *J. Am. Chem. Soc.*, **82**, 4742 (1960).
75. G. Natta, G. Mazzanti, G. F. Pregaglia, M. Binaghi, and M. Cambini, *Makromol. Chem.*, **51**, 148 (1962).
76. G. Natta, G. Mazzanti, G. F. Pregaglia, and M. Binaghi, *Makromol. Chem.*, **44–46**, 537 (1961).
77. G. Natta, G. Mazzanti, G. Pregaglia, and M. Binaghi, Belgian Pat. 623,181 (to Montecatini) (April 3, 1963).
78. W. E. Hanford and J. C. Sauer, in *Organic Reactions*, Vol. III, R. Adams, Ed., Wiley, New York, 1947, p. 135 ff.
79. E. U. Elam, *Org. Chem. Bull.*, **36**, 1 (1964).
80. J. K. Stille, *Advan. Polymer Sci.*, **3**, 48 (1961).
81. W. J. Bailey, J. Economy, and M. E. Hermes, *Polymer Preprints*, 138th National Am. Chem. Soc. Meeting, New York, 1960, p. 1.
82. W. J. Bailey and J. Economy, Abstr. Papers, 126th National Am. Chem. Soc. Meeting, New York, September, 1954, p. 195.
83. J. K. Stille and L. Plummer, *J. Org. Chem.*, **26**, 4026 (1961).
84. J. K. Stille and M. A. Bedford, *J. Polymer Sci. B*, **4**, 329 (1966).
85. S. W. Chow, U.S. Pat. 3,074,915 (to Union Carbide Corp.) (January 22, 1963).
86. E. A. Kraiman, U.S. Pat. 2,890,206 (to Union Carbide Corp.) (June 9, 1959).
87. C. F. H. Allen and J. A. Van Allen, *J. Am. Chem. Soc.*, **72**, 5166 (1950); F. W. Gray, *J. Chem. Soc.*, **95**, 2131 (1905).
88. N. E. Searle, U.S. Pat. 2,444,536 (to du Pont), July 6, 1948.
89. P. Kovacic and R. W. Hein, *J. Am. Chem. Soc.*, **81**, 1187 (1959).
90. E. A. Kraiman, U.S. Pat. 2,890,206 (to Union Carbide) (June 9, 1959).
91. F. Arndt and B. Eistert, *Ber.*, **58**, 2318 (1925).
92. F. Millich and R. G. Sinclair, submitted for publication; also, *Polymer Preprints*, **6** (2), 736 (1965).
93. A. W. Ingersoll et al., *J. Am. Chem. Soc.*, **58**, 1808 (1936).
94. M. L. Moore, *Organic Reactions*, **5**, 1949, pp. 316–20.
95. I. Ugi et al., *Angew. Chem.*, **77**, 492 (1965).
96. I. Ugi and R. Meyr, *Angew. Chem.*, **70**, 702 (1958).

CHAPTER 7

Crosslinked Synthetic Resins

The term "resin" had its original usage in connection with certain naturally occurring materials, obtained in most cases from coniferous trees, which found use as hard, protective coatings when solutions of these materials in organic solvents were allowed to dry in air. The most widely used natural resin is rosin (or colophony). "Resin" was then applied to any of the synthetic materials which were developed to supplement or replace the natural products, and eventually to most of the early synthetic materials which were products of organic chemistry, but were without the strictly definable structure and typical properties of crystalline organic solids. The concepts of modern polymer chemistry were as yet undeveloped, and the growth of the synthetic materials parallel to the usage of the natural materials kept the term "resin" in continual application to a wider spectrum of products. Today, "resin" covers a multitude of polymer types, including the classical phenol-formaldehyde condensates and the relatively recent epoxy resins, vinyl polymers such as polystyrene and poly(methyl methacrylate), and condensation polymers of the polyamide or polyester class. Most of the application of the term "resin" is to those linear or crosslinked (or crosslinkable) polymers that are used in molding, casting, or extruding operations and in surface coatings; and, to most crosslinked (or crosslinkable) polymers, no matter what the end use (as in adhesives, textile finishes, etc.). Thus, poly(methyl methacrylate) and various polyamides, both essentially linear polymers, are termed molding resins when directed to a molding end use. However, polyamides would not be termed resins by the synthetic fiber industry in their usage of the material.

While almost any polymer may find itself classed as a resin at one time or another, and while many of the polymers prepared in other sections of this book may be resins to some readers, we have arbitrarily chosen to limit the designation to certain well-known classes of wholly synthetic condensation polymers which are usually characterized by a high degree of crosslinking. In most of the world of polymer chemistry, they will be found to have the term "resin" in their descriptive title, as

445

urea–formaldehyde resins, epoxy resins, alkyd resins, etc. They will also be found together under the general designation of thermoset resins, indicating that they are brought to a final crosslinked condition and neither dissolve nor melt on heating. Several reference works are available on the synthetic and natural resins generally and may be consulted for further information (1–5,7–9).

I. Crosslinked Polyesters

Polyesters (1a,10) which have been rendered insoluble and infusible by crosslinking are commercially important types of polymeric materials. Crosslinking may be accomplished in several ways. One of these is to start with an unsaturated polyester made by conventional esterification of a glycol with an unsaturate such as maleic acid. The double bonds in the polyester can be used, then, as sites for copolymerization with vinyl monomers, of which styrene is typical and the most widely used. The resulting polymer is something of a hybrid, therefore, of condensation and vinyl type polymers.

$$\left[R-O-\overset{\overset{\textstyle O}{\|}}{C}-CH=CH-\overset{\overset{\textstyle O}{\|}}{C}-O \right]_n + Ph-CH=CH_2 \longrightarrow$$

$$\left[R-O-\overset{\overset{\textstyle O}{\|}}{C}-\underset{\underset{\textstyle Ph}{|}}{\underset{\textstyle CH-CH_2}{|}}{\overset{\overset{\textstyle -CH-Ph}{|}}{\overset{\textstyle CH_2}{|}}}CH-CH-\overset{\overset{\textstyle O}{\|}}{C}-O \right]_n$$

The final product is complex in structure* and can be only generally indicated by equations such as this. Usually, the linear unsaturated polyester is prepared and mixed with the vinyl monomer to give a viscous solution which is treated with a free radical catalyst to initiate the crosslinking polymerization step. The latter step is generally carried out after the polymer solution has been placed in the casting, laminating, or other operational process from which the desired product is to be obtained.

The possible **combinations of unsaturated polyester and vinyl monomer** are very great. Copolyesters of various diols or mixtures of saturated, unsaturated, and aromatic acids (11) permit a wide range of properties to be obtained with the use of any one vinyl monomer. However, the most widely used unsaturated acids are maleic and fumaric (12). Tetra-

---

* In this chapter, the subscript n is often omitted, since the indicated structures may not be true repeat units.

hydrophthalic and endomethylenetetrahydrophthalic acids are diene adducts of maleic acid which also find use (13). Ethylene-, propylene-, and diethylene glycols are widely used in the ester polymerization. In addition to styrene, diallyl phthalate is useful as the vinyl component, but others, such as triallyl cyanurate and diallyl diglycol carbonate, can be used which may be better suited to particular processing applications.

413. Preparation of a Polyester Resin Based on Poly(oxydiethylene maleate) and Styrene (14)

$$HOCH_2CH_2OCH_2CH_2OH + HC\!=\!\!=\!CH$$

$$\left[\text{-}OCH_2CH_2OCH_2CH_2O\text{---}\overset{\overset{\displaystyle O}{\|}}{C}\text{---}CH\!=\!\!=\!CH\text{---}\overset{\overset{\displaystyle O}{\|}}{C}\text{-}\right]$$
(I)

$$(I) + CH_2\!=\!CH\text{---}Ph \longrightarrow \left[\text{-}OCH_2CH_2OCH_2CH_2O\text{---}\overset{\overset{\displaystyle O}{\|}}{C}\text{---}\overset{|}{CH}\text{---}\overset{|}{CH}\text{---}\overset{\overset{\displaystyle O}{\|}}{C}\text{-}\right]$$

A 1 l. four-necked flask is equipped with a stirrer, siphon, nitrogen inlet, and thermometer, all reaching below the surface of the solution and a side arm with condenser set for distillation (Fig. 7.1). In the flask is placed 233.4 g. (2.2 moles) diethylene glycol, which is heated to 80°C. by means of a Glas-Col heater while nitrogen is passed through in a slow stream, and stirring is begun. Then, 196.1 g. (2.0 moles) maleic anhydride is added. The temperature is raised to 150°C. over 1 hr., then to 190°C. over 4 hr. An exothermic reaction occurs at about 100°C. and the heat should be removed until the reaction subsides. The temperature is maintained at 190°C. for 1 hr., and a vacuum of 100–200 mm. is applied. The temperature is then lowered to, and maintained at, 170°C. until the acid number of a sample of the polyester removed through the siphon is 50 or less. This requires about 1 hr. The acid number is determined as described in Chapter 3, Preparation 94, using 75 ml. acetone as solvent. The vacuum is removed and the reaction product permitted to cool to 100°C. under nitrogen. About 0.02 g. hydroquinone or p-t-butylcatechol is added as an inhibitor. At 100°C. the liquid, slightly yellow polyester, is poured with good stirring into a sufficient quantity of styrene at 25°C. to give a 70% solution of the polyester. The solution is relatively stable at room temperature when stored under nitrogen in a brown bottle.

Copolymerization of the solution can be effected by adding 4.0 g. benzoyl peroxide to 200 g. of the polyester–styrene mixture. This mixture forms a hard, tough solid in about 2 hr. at room temperature. Castings can be obtained if the mixture is poured into a suitable mold or container and allowed to set up.

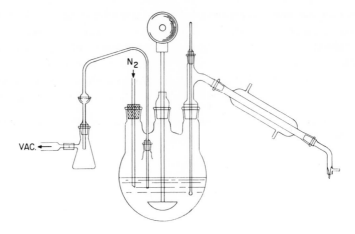

Figure 7.1

414. Preparation of a Polyester Resin Based on Poly(ethylene-oxydiethylene maleate-phthalate-adipate) and Styrene (14)

In the same apparatus as described in the preceding preparation, but using a 2 l. reaction flask, are placed 170 g. (2.75 moles) ethylene glycol and 292 g. (2.75 moles) diethylene glycol. The temperature is raised to 80°C. and 343 g. (3.5 moles) maleic anhydride, 111 g. (0.75 mole) phthalic anhydride, and 109 g. (0.75 mole) adipic acid are added. The temperature is raised to 150°C. over 1 hr., then increased at the rate of 10°C./hr. to 210°C. It is maintained at this level until the acid number (see Preparation 413) of a sample of the polyester is 60 or less. A vacuum of about 100 mm. is applied and the temperature dropped to 180°C. When a sample of polyester has an acid number of 20–30, the product is allowed to cool to room temperature under nitrogen and a trace of t-butylcatechol is added as an inhibitor.

A solution of the polyester is made in styrene containing a trace of inhibitor in the proportion of 100 g. polyester to 43 g. styrene. A casting can be made in the following way. One-half g. of a 6% commercial solution of cobalt naphthenate is added to 100 g. of the polyester–styrene varnish and carefully mixed to avoid the formation of a large number of air bubbles. Then, 1.5 g. of a 60% solution of methyl ethyl ketone hydroperoxide in dimethyl phthalate (Lupersol DDM) is dispersed carefully and thoroughly into the solution. The solution will cure in a mold at room temperature in about 2 hr. to give a hard, tough casting.

The term "**alkyd**," a blend of the first part of the word alcohol and the last of acid, is generally applied to the **polyesters from reaction of alcohols and acids** where the total functionality is capable of causing crosslinking directly (14a). Such a combination would be glycerol with phthalic anhydride, a reaction product sometimes termed a **glyptal resin**. As is evident, no additional crosslinking agent is needed. The functionality of the reactants assures crosslinking when the reaction has been carried sufficiently far.

Fundamental studies of the unmodified **glycerol–phthalic anhydride reaction** have been made by Kienle (15), who found that gelation can occur at 75% esterification. Intraesterification and anhydride formation occur to a small extent along with the primary reaction of interesterification.

415. Preparation of Poly(glyceryl phthalate) (15)

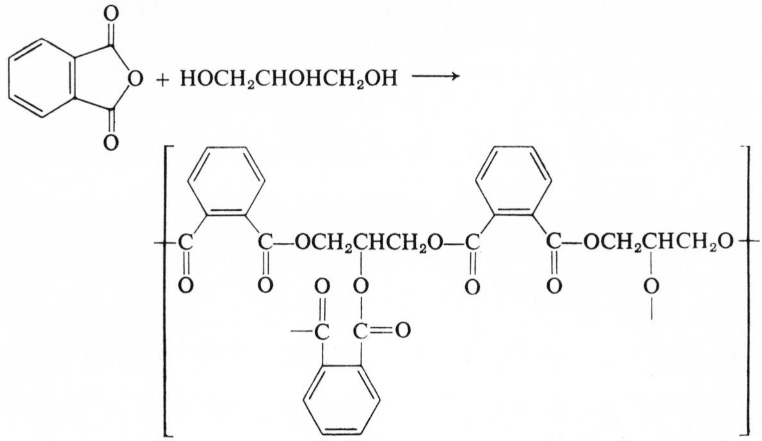

In a 600 ml. beaker immersed in a silicone oil or Wood's metal bath, and equipped with a thermometer and stirrer are placed 148.1 g. (1.0 mole) phthalic anhydride and 61.4 g. (0.67 mole) glycerol. The mixture is stirred and the temperature raised to 200°C., where it is maintained for $1\frac{1}{2}$ hr. The acid value should be about 127–132, determined in acetone (Preparation 413). At this point, the product is still soluble in acetic acid, acetone, and others. Continued heating at 200°C. for about 15 min. causes the mixture to set to an immobile gel.

The possible **combinations of glycerol with dibasic acids other than phthalic or in combination with phthalic** is evident. In most cases, the acids used are limited primarily to phthalic, or phthalic plus a limited quantity of acids such as adipic or sebacic. Maleic anhydride also may be substituted wholly, or in part, for phthalic anhydride. In some cases, it is possible to include rosin with the maleic-containing polymerizates. Reaction of the dienic abietic acid and other unsaturated portions of the rosin with maleic anhydride in a Diels-Alder reaction leads to products with different and desirable properties. Pentaerythritol also has been used in place of glycerol.

A widely used modification of the basic polymerization technique is the addition of an air-drying unsaturated fatty acid or oil to the glycerol–phthalic anhydride such that the addend becomes incorporated in the polyester. Such polymers are soluble in the hydrocarbon or ester solvents used in the paint and varnish industry. These drying oil-modified alkyds have been extremely important in surface coating uses.

The following is an example of an **oil-modified alkyd resin.** Free fatty acids are used as the modifying agent, hence the term **Fatty Acid Process** (11). The unsaturated acids are esterified by the glycerol and become part of the poly(glyceryl phthalate) molecule. Structural formulas for such polymers can only be representative of typical groupings, rather than an accurate delineation of molecular structure.

416. Preparation of a Drying Oil-Modified Poly(glyceryl phthalate) Alkyd by the Fatty Acid Process (16)

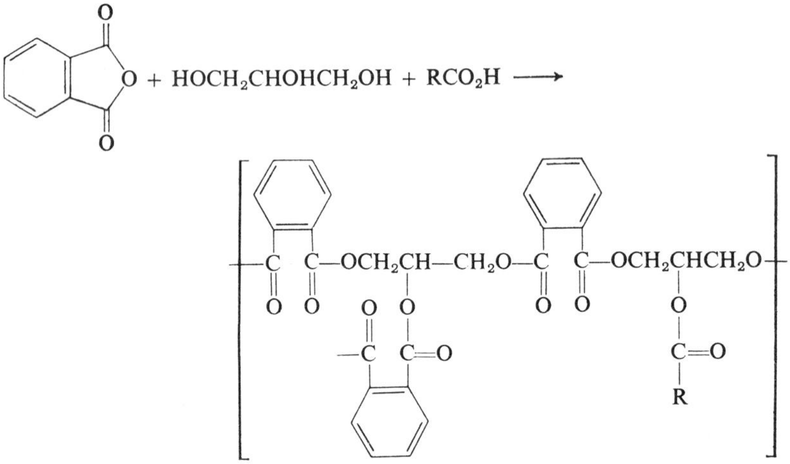

where $R = CH_3(CH_2)_4CH{=}CHCH_2CH{=}CH(CH_2)_7{-}$, and related unsaturates.

In a 1 l. beaker immersed in a silicone oil bath and equipped with a stirrer is placed 206 g. phthalic anhydride. An excess of anhydride is used to compensate for an anticipated 15% loss by sublimation. The anhydride is melted by raising the bath temperature to 130–135°C. and 200 g. linseed oil fatty acids is added. The mixture is stirred and heated at 135–140°C. until miscible. Then 92 g. of glycerol is added to the solution and the reaction heated at a rate of about 1°C./min. until a temperature of 240°C. is reached. This temperature is maintained for 10–15 min. Water is evolved during heating and some phthalic anhydride may sublime; for this reason, the reaction should be run in a hood. The product, when cooled, is a clear solid which is soluble in butyl acetate/toluene (75/25 volume). A 50% solution of the resin in this solvent mixture can be cast onto a glass plate, smoothed out with a doctor knife or glass rod, and heated at 150°C. for 2 hr. A hard, tough, crosslinked coating results. If cobalt naphthenate drier (0.2 g. per 100 ml. of resin solution) is added, a film can be air-dired at room temperature.

The fatty acid may be replaced in certain formulations by the fatty oil from which it is derived, obviating the need for freeing the acid from its glyceryl ester. Such a variation is called the **Alcoholysis Process** (4) **or** the **Fatty Oil Process.** It involves, first, an ester exchange reaction between glycerol and the triglyceride fatty oil, giving mono- and diglycerides of the fatty acid component of the original fatty oil. The remaining hydroxyls of the glycerides formed are further esterified with a polybasic acid such as phthalic acid.

417. Preparation of a Drying Oil-Modified Poly(glyceryl phthalate) by the Fatty Oil or Alcoholysis Process (17)

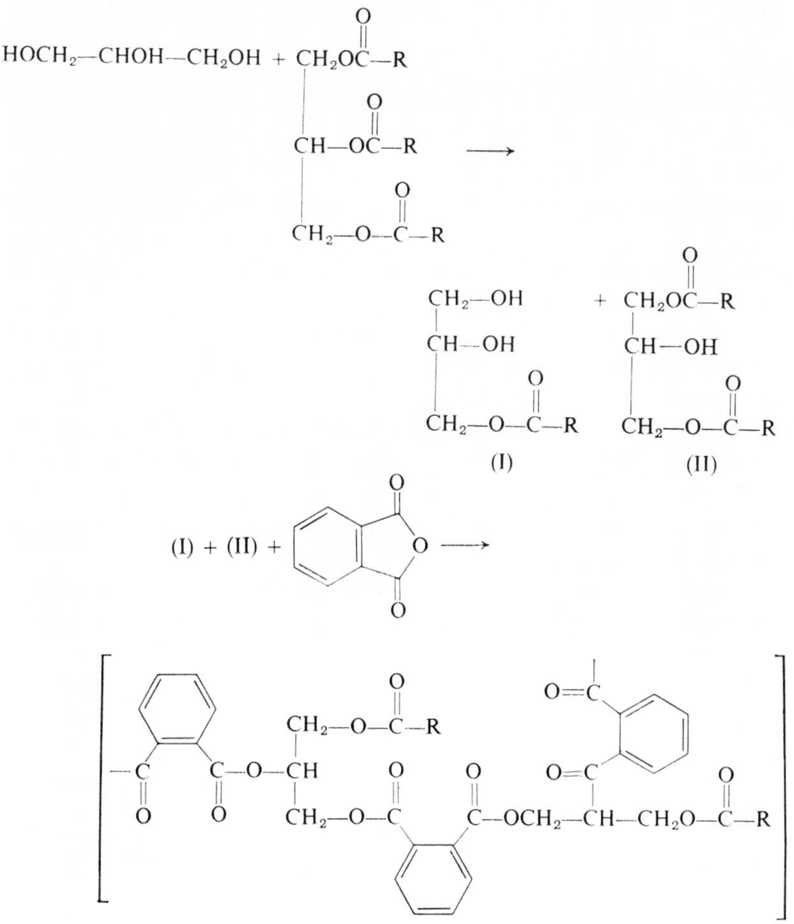

$$HOCH_2-CHOH-CH_2OH \;+\; \begin{matrix} CH_2O\overset{\displaystyle O}{\overset{\|}{C}}-R \\ CH-O\overset{\displaystyle O}{\overset{\|}{C}}-R \\ CH_2-O-\overset{\displaystyle O}{\overset{\|}{C}}-R \end{matrix} \longrightarrow$$

$$\underset{(I)}{\begin{matrix} CH_2-OH \\ CH-OH \\ CH_2-O-\overset{O}{\overset{\|}{C}}-R \end{matrix}} \;+\; \underset{(II)}{\begin{matrix} CH_2O\overset{O}{\overset{\|}{C}}-R \\ CH-OH \\ CH_2-O-\overset{O}{\overset{\|}{C}}-R \end{matrix}}$$

$$(I) + (II) + \text{[phthalic anhydride]} \longrightarrow$$

A 500 ml. resin kettle is equipped with stirrer, thermometer, dropping funnel, reflux condenser, and nitrogen inlet reaching to the bottom of the vessel. To the reactor, which has been flushed with nitrogen, is charged 118.4 g. of linseed oil. The oil is then heated under nitrogen to 235°C. and, after first adding 0.5 g. lead oxide, 25.6 g. of glycerol is added slowly from the dropping funnel over a period of about 20 min. with vigorous agitation. In about 30 min., the glycerol and linseed oil become miscible. Fifty-four g. of phthalic anhydride is then added all at once, preferably molten so that air is not introduced. The dropping funnel is replaced by a siphon for sampling. The mixture is heated and stirred at 250°C. until an acid number of 5 or less is reached. (See Chapter 3, Preparation 94; acetone is used as a solvent in this case.) Nitrogen flow is fairly rapid during this part of the reaction. The final product is a pale-yellow, viscous liquid, soluble in aromatic hydrocarbons, butyl acetate, and acetone.

A 50% solution of the resin in benzene, to which is added 1.5% of a cobalt naphthenate drier, forms a tough lacquer when cast as a thin coating on a metal surface and dried at room temperature. A white enamel can be made from a mixture of 100 g. of the resin, 150 g. lithopone, 50 g. zinc oxide, 55 g. turpentine, and 1 g. cobalt naphthenate drier.

II. Allyl Resins

Allyl resins are formed by the polymerization of allyl esters of di- and higher carboxylic acids; diallyl phthalate is the most widely employed ester in this technology, but others are diallyl isophthalate, triallyl cyanurate and diethylene glycol bis(allyl carbonate) (17a). The monomer is usually polymerized to a limited degree of conversion to give a relatively low molecular weight thermoplastic solid containing a large amount of residual unsaturation. On being mixed with a free radical catalyst and raised to an elevated temperature, polymerization occurs through the remaining allyl groups to give a crosslinked resin. They are noted generally for good heat and chemical stability and excellent electrical properties. The diethylene glycol bis(allyl carbonate) resin is especially significant for outstanding optical clarity, akin to poly-(methyl methacrylate), but with greater surface hardness than the latter.

The well recognized phenomenon of degradative chain transfer in the polymerization of allyl esters prevents extensive chain growth in the case of monoesters; but, with di- or higher allyl esters network formation is ultimately possible, despite what must be the relatively short length of individual chains. The structure of the thermoplastic prepolymer undoubtedly involves much branching. There is evidence that in the case of diallyl phthalate, at least, cyclization also occurs to a significant extent, delaying the onset of gel formation (18). In the equations of the next example, an oversimplified structure is shown for convenient illustration.

418. Preparation of an Allyl Resin from Diallyl Phthalate (19)

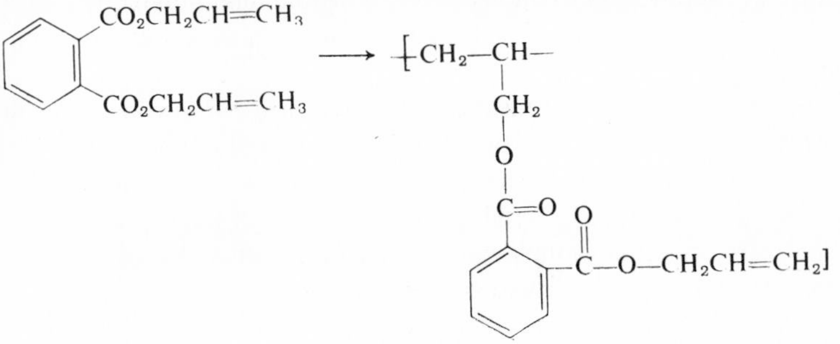

To a 2 l. three-necked flask equipped with stirrer, thermometer, and condenser are added 886 g. of diallyl phthalate, 65 g. of isopropanol, and 7.5 g. of 50% hydrogen peroxide. The mixture is stirred and heated to reflux, which should correspond to a pot temperature of 104–108°C. The reaction should remain essentially homogeneous. After 10 hr., the solution is cooled to 25°C. and poured with stirring into 6 l. of isopropanol cooled to 0°C. to precipitate the solid polymer. The entire polymer–precipitant mixture is held at 0°C. for an hour before separating the polymer by filtration, washing with cold isopropanol on the filter, and drying in vacuum at 45°C. The conversion of monomer to polymer is about 25%. The polymer softens on a melting point block in the range 80–105°C. The degree of unsaturation is indicated by an iodine number of around 55. The polymer is soluble in methyl ethyl ketone, ethyl acetate and benzene. If the dry, powdered polymer is mixed with 2% by weight of *tert*-butyl perbenzoate and heated in a mold at 175°C. for 15 min. at 6000 p.s.i. pressure, a clear thermoset resin of high hardness and stiffness is formed, having a heat deflection temperature of 155°C. (at 264 p.s.i. fiber stress).

Diethylene glycol bis(allyl carbonate) (20),

$$O(CH_2CH_2-O-\overset{\overset{\displaystyle O}{\|}}{C}-O-CH_2CH=CH_2)_2$$

can be polymerized to clear sheets by dissolving 3% by weight of dibenzoyl peroxide in the monomer and heating in a mold at a cycle determined by the thickness of the sheet to be cast; i.e., the thicker the sheet, the slower the temperature rise used and the longer the time cycle required. A $\frac{1}{8}$ in. sheet can be cast in an open mold under nitrogen by using the following cycle: from room temperature to 75°C. in 5 hr.; to 80°C. in 3 hr.; to 87°C. in 4 hr.; a postcure at 115°C. for 2 hr. The objective is to bring about heat evolution at a uniform rate throughout polymerization.

III. Resins from the Reaction of Formaldehyde with Phenols

Formaldehyde condenses readily with phenols (2,4,6,21–25) primarily in the ortho and para positions, **to give,** eventually, **crosslinked polymers having aromatic rings linked together by methylene or oxydimethylene bridges.** The reaction is usually carried out only to such a point that a soluble, meltable intermediate condensate is formed which can be formed readily. It is converted to an insoluble, infusible final polymeric product by a later treatment, usually heat plus additional catalyst or formaldehyde.

The intermediate condensation products are of low or moderate molecular weight and may be of one of two types. The first is often called a "**resol**," and is formed by the reaction of excess formaldehyde with phenol, about 1.5:1 mole ratio, in the presence of base. It contains hydroxymethyl groups which can condense further on heating. A typical resol may be indicated by the structure:

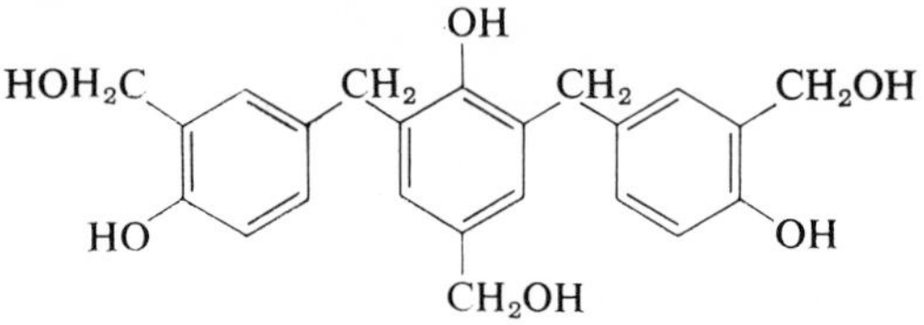

Some of the links between rings may be —CH_2OCH_2—. The resol-type products are mixtures of much more complex structures than that above.

The second type of intermediate is called a "**novolak**." It arises from the reaction of less than equivalent amounts of formaldehyde with phenol, about 1:0.8 mole ratio, in an acid catalyzed reaction. There are then essentially no hydroxymethyl groups present for further condensation, and the structure may be represented by:

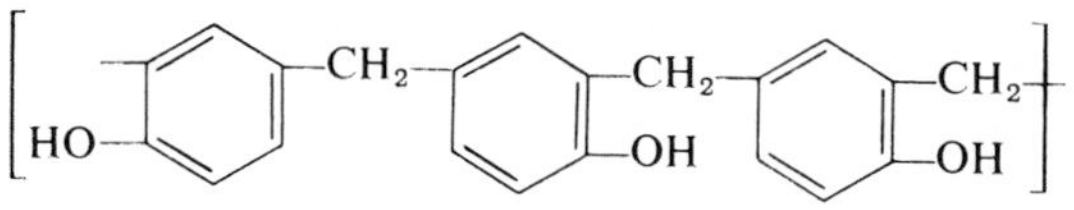

The novolaks may have molecular weights up to 1200–1500. The resols are lower molecular weight, about 300–700. Novolaks do not condense further without the addition of a catalyst and more formaldehyde. Hexamethylenetetramine is frequently used as a catalyst; it may also take part in the condensation, by providing formaldehyde by hydrolysis, or in formation of dibenzylamine bridges:

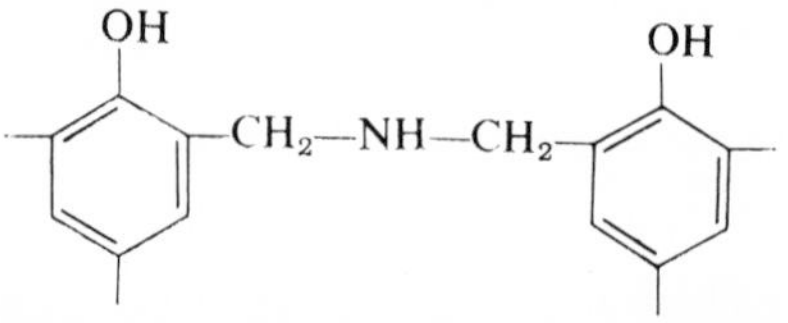

For the following, and similar resin preparations, use of a resin kettle rather than a round-bottom flask is recommended for greater ease of product removal.

419. Preparation of a Resol from Formaldehyde and Phenol (22)

A 500 ml. resin kettle is equipped with a reflux condenser, stirrer, thermometer, and siphoning tube leading to a collecting trap for the removal of samples for testing. To the reaction vessel is added 94 g. (1 mole) of distilled phenol, 123 g. of aqueous formaldehyde, 37% by weight (1.5 moles formaldehyde), and 4.7 g. barium hydroxide octahydrate. The reaction is stirred and heated in an oil bath at 70°C. for 2 hr. Two layers form if stirring is stopped. Sufficient 10% sulfuric acid is added to bring the pH to 6–7. Vacuum is then applied by means of a water aspirator (pressure regulated at about 30–50 mm.) and water is removed through the condenser, which is now set for distillation. The temperature is not permitted to exceed 70°C. Samples (1–2 ml.) are withdrawn every 15 min. through the vacuum siphon take-off and tested for gel time; by working with a spatula on a hot plate at 160°C., gel time is taken as the time required for the resin to set up to a rubbery infusible solid. A portion of each sample removed from the reaction mixture should be cooled to room temperature and its brittleness noted. The dehydration should be stopped when the gel time is less than 10 sec., or the resin is brittle and nontacky at room temperature. This product has been termed "**A stage**" **resin.** Further heating forms a resin which softens with heat but doesn't melt, and is no longer soluble. It is referred to as "**B stage**" **resin.** The final product from continued heating, "**C stage**" **resin,** is hard, insoluble and infusible. Resin at the first stage can be mixed with wood flour, lime, and pigments, and used as a molding powder for conversion to the final stage C by means of heat. Much industrial use is made of the "A" stage resin in laminates, adhesives, and varnishes.

To observe the eventual hardening to the "C stage" resin, the resin prepared above should be removed at the A stage and heated in test tubes or small beakers at 100°C.

420. Preparation of a Novolak from Formaldehyde and Phenol (22)

A 500 ml. resin kettle is equipped as described in the preceding preparation and charged with 130 g. phenol (1.38 moles), 13 ml. water, 92.4 g. 37% aqueous formaldehyde (1.14 moles), and 1 g. oxalic acid dihydrate. The mixture is stirred and refluxed for 30 min. An additional 1 g. of oxalic acid dihydrate is then added, and refluxing is continued for another hour. At this point, 400 ml. water is added and the mixture cooled. The resin is permitted to settle for 30 min. and the upper layer of water decanted or withdrawn through the siphon. Heating is then begun with the condenser set for vacuum distillation. Water is distilled at 50–100 mm. pressure until the pot temperature reaches 120°C., or until a sample of the resin is brittle at room temperature. The resulting novolak resin is soluble in alcohol. About 140 g. of resin is obtained. It can be used in the following preparation.

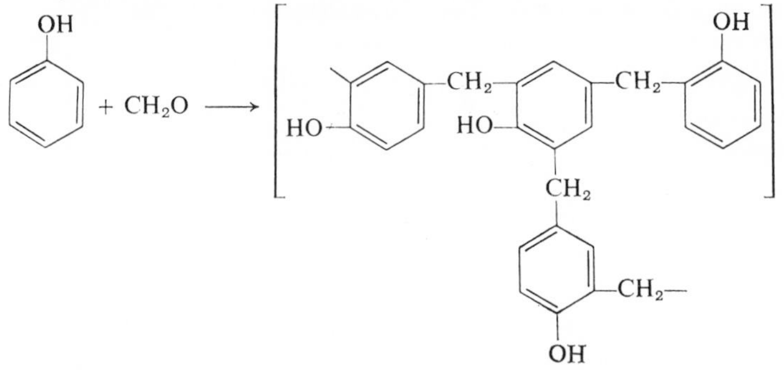

421. Preparation of a Molding Powder from a Novolak Resin (26)

A mixture of 46 g. of finely ground novolak (Preparation 420), 44.6 g. of dry wood flour filler (80–100 mesh), 6.7 g. hexamethylenetetramine, 2.0 g. magnesium oxide, and 1.0 g. magnesium or calcium stearate is blended by tumbling in a jar or a ball mill. The blended material can then be placed in a mold and heated under 2000 p.s.i. at 160°C. for 5 min. A hard, cured solid results.

422. Preparation of a Cast Phenolic Resin (26)

In a 1 l. resin kettle equipped with a stirrer, condenser, thermometer, and vacuum siphon for sampling, is placed 100 g. phenol (1.06 moles), 203 g. of 37% aqueous formaldehyde (2.5 moles), and 3.0 g. of 20% aqueous sodium hydroxide. The reaction is stirred and heated to 70–80°C. by means of an oil bath for about 3 hr. The reaction mixture is then concentrated at 30 mm. pressure until a pot temperature of 65°C. is reached. Then, 6.5 g. lactic acid is added, followed by 15 g. glycerol. The removal of water is then continued at 30 mm. until a sample of the resin withdrawn through the vacuum siphon forms a ball that will just barely yield to pressure between the fingers when a drop is placed in 11–13°C. water. This may require that a pot temperature of about 85°C. be reached. Samples of this finished resin, a viscous liquid, may then be poured while hot into test tubes or beakers and heated at 80°C. for 4–8 days to give hard castings which are clear if sufficient water was removed from the resin during preparation.

Although formaldehyde condenses preferentially at the ortho and para positions of phenol, it is not possible to prepare only linear, soluble high polymers from formaldehyde and a phenol with either an ortho or para position blocked. Some condensation apparently takes place at open meta positions, since *o*- and *p*-cresol will eventually give an infusible, thermoset material, although times involved are very long (4). However, other **para-substituted phenols,** such as *p-t*-butylphenol and *p*-phenylphenol, are used to **give oil soluble condensates with formaldehyde** which are useful in varnish applications. Linear polymers of relatively low molecular weight have also been prepared and studied, using **formaldehyde** and *o*- and *p*-chlorophenol (27,28). These polymers are too brittle to give useful products, however.

IV. Reaction of Formaldehyde with Urea and Melamine

Formaldehyde and **urea** react under alkaline conditions to give isolatable **mono- and dimethylolureas** (2,4,6,29).

$$H_2N-\overset{\overset{\displaystyle O}{\|}}{C}-NHCH_2OH \qquad\qquad HOCH_2NH-\overset{\overset{\displaystyle O}{\|}}{C}-NHCH_2OH$$

Such compounds are precursors in the formation of **crosslinked urea-formaldehyde resins.** The mechanism of the polymerization is still not known with certainty; one suggestion is that of Marvel (30), wherein urea is considered as an aminoacid amide. Thus, the two —NH$_2$ groups are not identical; one is considered an amino, the other an amide, —NH$_2$. The amide —NH$_2$ is thought to react with formaldehyde to give the monomethylolurea which trimerizes with loss of water. Further reaction occurs with the —CONH$_2$ of the trimer with formaldehyde to produce a crosslinked material. The stoichiometry of the mechanism requires a urea:formaldehyde ratio of 1:1.5, which is about what is generally used in commercial resin production.

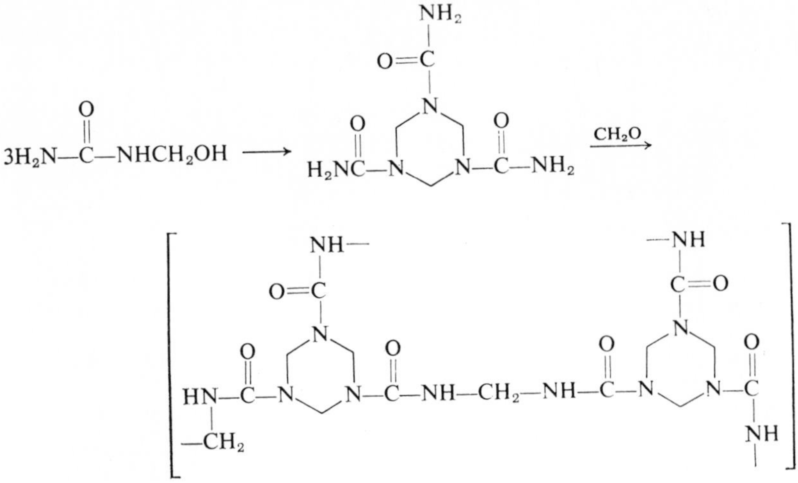

Cyclic units are not a requisite for ultimate crosslinking, however. Later evidence has indicated that a noncyclic methylene urea having linear and branched segments is the correct structure (31) with few or no rings present.

$$
\left[
\begin{array}{l}
\quad\quad\quad \overset{O}{\overset{\|}{}} \quad\quad\quad\quad \overset{O}{\overset{\|}{}} \\
-H_2CNHC-NH-CH_2-N-C-NH- \\
\quad\quad\quad\quad\quad\quad\quad\quad | \quad | \\
\quad\quad\quad\quad\quad\quad\quad\quad O \quad CH_2 \\
\quad\quad\quad\quad\quad\quad\quad\quad \| \quad | \\
\quad\quad\quad\quad\quad\quad -NHC-N \\
\quad\quad\quad\quad\quad\quad\quad\quad\quad | \\
\quad\quad\quad\quad\quad\quad\quad\quad\quad CH_2 \\
\quad\quad\quad\quad\quad\quad\quad\quad\quad | \\
\quad\quad\quad\quad\quad\quad NH-C-N-CH_2- \\
\quad\quad\quad\quad\quad\quad\quad\quad\quad \| \quad | \\
\quad\quad\quad\quad\quad\quad\quad\quad\quad O \quad CH_2 \\
\quad\quad\quad\quad\quad\quad\quad\quad\quad\quad\quad |
\end{array}
\right]
$$

The commercial preparation of urea–formaldehyde resins usually involves the formation of soluble methylol–urea derivatives with basic catalysts. This intermediate condensate is then compounded with various fillers, pigments, and an accelerator. The latter is either an acidic material or one capable of functioning as an acid at a high temperature. The product so obtained can then be placed in a mold and heated to effect the final thermosetting, crosslinking (4) reaction. Urea–formaldehyde condensates can also be used as additives for wet strength in papers and as finishes for fibers to impart crease resistance, and as adhesives.

423. Preparation of a Urea–Formaldehyde Resin (32)

To a 500 ml., three-necked flask equipped with a stirrer and reflux condenser is charged 130 g. of 37% aqueous formaldehyde (1.6 moles) which is brought to a pH of about 7.5 by the addition of 10% sodium hydroxide solution. Then, 60 g. (1.0 mole) urea is added and the mixture gently refluxed and stirred for 2 hr. The mixture is then concentrated to 70% solids by distillation of 40 ml. of water under water aspirator pressure. The resulting syrup, after acidifying with acetic acid, can be heated further at 100°C. for several hours to effect gelation.

424. Preparation of a Urea–Formaldehyde Adhesive (32)

To prepare a plywood adhesive, 100 g. of the unacidified concentrated syrup prepared as in Preparation 423, can be mixed with 28 g. furfuryl alcohol, 16 g. wood flour (80–100 mesh), 1 g. calcium phosphate, and 0.35 g. triethanolamine by stirring, while raising the temperature to 90°C. over ½ hr. This temperature is held for 15 min., then the mixture is cooled slowly to room temperature. The mixture will set to a solid at room temperature if mixed with 2 g. of ammonium chloride and 3 ml. water in a beaker. The ammonium chloride and water function as a hardening catalyst, providing a working life for the adhesive of about 6 hr. Before addition of the catalyst, the adhesive resin is stable for weeks.

425. Preparation of a Urea–Formaldehyde Molding Powder

The resin solution prepared in Preparation 423 may be used without concentrating in the preparation of a molding powder. Fifty g. of the resin solution is mixed with 40 g. of alpha flock cellulose and 0.5 g. zinc stearate in a dough mixer or by hand in a metal beaker or dish until all the lumps are broken up. The mix is dried in a circulating air oven for 2–4 hr. at 70°C. and is ground in a mechanical mill or by hand in a mortar to a powder. The material can then be pressed in a mold or laboratory press at 145°C. for 2–3 min. at 2000 p.s.i. to give solid pieces.

The methylolurea groupings in the soluble first stage of the urea-formaldehyde reaction reduce the compatibility of the product with many nonpolar organic solvents and oils. **Solubility** in such solvents can be achieved by carrying out the initial reaction in the presence of an alcohol. The **methylol groups are partially etherified**, and the solubility of the product depends on the chain length of the alcohol used. Methanol for instance, gives an etherified intermediate which is still water soluble. Butanol will produce a toluene-soluble product. Etherification of the methylols reduces the likelihood of gelation at moderate temperatures.

426. Preparation of a Urea–Formaldehyde Resin Modified with Butanol (33)

$$NH_2CONH_2 + CH_2O \longrightarrow -\overset{|}{N}CH_2OH \xrightarrow{\text{BuOH}} -\underset{|}{N}-CH_2OBu(n)$$

$$-NCH_2OBu(n) \longrightarrow \text{crosslinked polymer} + n-\text{BuOH} + H_2O$$

In a 1 l. three-necked flask equipped with reflux condenser, thermometer, and stirrer are placed 243 g. of 37% aqueous formaldehyde (3.0 moles formaldehyde) and 4–6 g. of concentrated ammonium hydroxide to bring the pH to 7.5–8.5. Sixty g. (1.0 mole) urea is added with stirring and the mixture heated to 100°C. over a 1 hr. period by means of a Glas-Col mantle. This temperature is maintained for $\frac{1}{2}$ hr. One hundred forty-eight g. (2.0 moles) n-butanol is added, followed by enough phosphoric acid to bring the pH to 5.5. The reaction is heated and stirred for $\frac{1}{2}$ hr. at 100°C. The resin is freed of water by heating at 60–75°C. under a water aspirator pressure of 100–200 mm. The hot resin is pourable, but becomes tacky at room temperature. The resin can be dissolved in butanol or toluene to give a 50–60% solution. When this solution is flowed onto glass or metal plates which are then heated for $\frac{1}{2}$ hr. in an oven at 150°C., a hard, clear coating results.

Melamine reacts with **formaldehyde** in much the same way as urea, forming compounds of varying degrees of N-methylol substitution depending on the mole ratio of reactants.

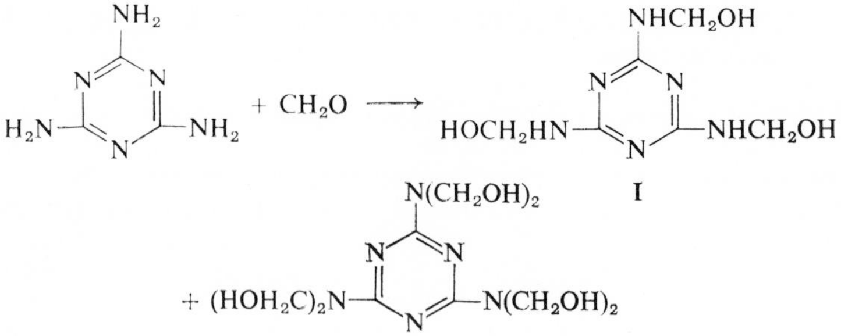

I

II

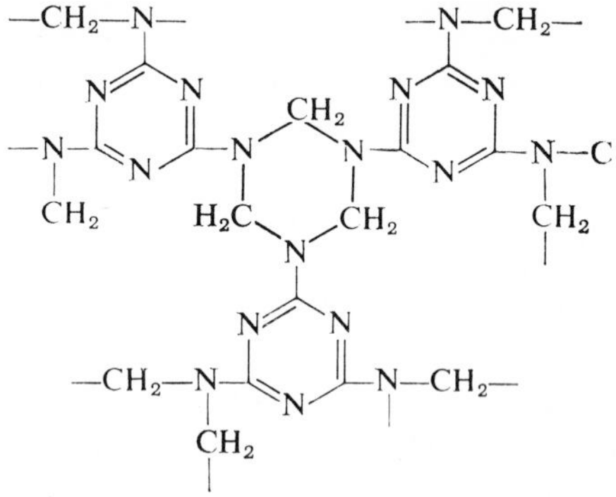

III

The tri- and hexamethylol compounds (I and II) are readily prepared and isolated, and may be polymerized to crosslinked products. The structure of the final polymer is presumably that obtained from elimination of water between *N*-methylol groups and remaining —NH— groups. From the hexamethylol melamine, reaction may be through interetherification of methylol groups, or elimination of some formaldehyde followed by the first described condensation. As in the case of the urea-formaldehyde reaction, it is possible that cyclic structures may also be formed in the melamine reaction (III).

In practice, the initial reaction is carried to a soluble syrup, which can be mixed with fillers or used as such in molding or casting under conditions of heating, to give hard, insoluble, infusible products.

427. Preparation and Polymerization of Hexamethylol Melamine (34)

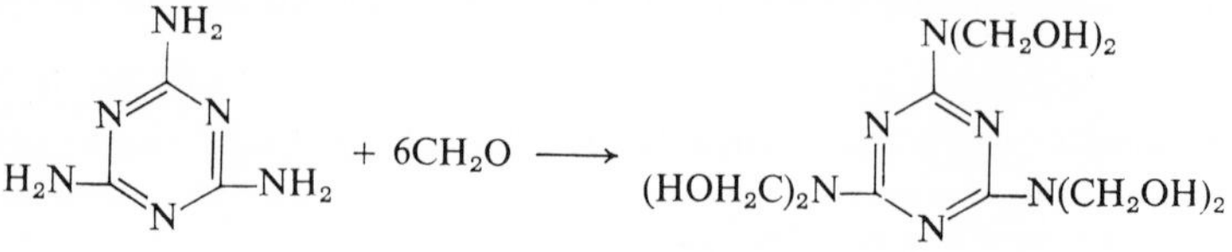

In a 500 ml., three-necked flask equipped with stirrer and condenser are placed 37.8 g. (0.3 mole) melamine and 195 g. of 37% aqueous formaldehyde (2.4 moles) which has been made slightly basic (pH 7.5) with dilute sodium hydroxide. The mixture is stirred and heated on the steam bath until a solution results. Heating is continued for 10 min.; then the reaction is cooled. A solid separates which is filtered, washed well with ethanol, and dried at 50°C. The melting point is about 150°C. The clear melt resolidifies on further heating to a clear, hard, insoluble product.

428. Preparation of a Melamine–Formaldehyde Molding Powder (34)

In a 1 l. resin kettle equipped with condenser and stirrer are placed 126 g. (1.0 mole) melamine and 365 g. (4.5 moles) of 37% neutralized aqueous formaldehyde. The mixture is stirred and heated at reflux for 40 min. Dilution of a sample of the solution with an equal volume of water should give a precipitate of resin. The undiluted solution is cooled to room temperature and 235 g. of the reaction mixture is kneaded with 50 g. of alpha flock and 0.5 g. zinc stearate in a dough mixer, if available, or by hand in a metal beaker or dish, making sure any lumps are broken up. The mass is then dried in a circulating air oven for 2–4 hr. at 70–80°C. It is ground to a uniform powder in mechanical mill or by hand in a mortar to give a solid, which, if pressed in a mold or laboratory press at 145°C. for 2–3 min. at 2000 p.s.i., gives a hard, lustrous, water-insensitive material.

429. Preparation of a Melamine–Formaldehyde Casting Resin

The method of the preceding preparation is used to condense 126 g. (1.0 mole) of melamine and 243 g. (3.0 moles) of 37% aqueous formaldehyde. At the end of the 40 min. reflux period, the solution is concentrated to about 70% solids by distilling about 60 ml. of water at water aspirator pressure. As a softening agent, 20 g. of glycerine is stirred into the resin. The resulting syrup can be solidified in a mold, or in a beaker, by gradually raising the temperature to 150°C. to give a clear, hard product.

430. Preparation of Melamine–Formaldehyde Resin Modified with Butanol (34)

Fifty g. of the hexamethylolmelamine (Preparation 427) is added to 80 g. of n-butanol and 0.5 g. concentrated hydrochloric acid in 250 ml. flask equipped with a condenser. The reaction mixture is heated to reflux for 15 min. A clear solution is obtained which forms a hard, clear coating when a portion of it is evaporated to dryness on a surface, then heated at 150°C. for 30 min.

Ion exchange resins can be **prepared by condensing formaldehyde with a phenol, a urea or a melamine** in such a way as to introduce ionic sites in the final resin (35–38). This can be achieved by **using an ionic coreactant** which enters into the polymer structure, by using a phenol carrying an ionic substituent, or by after treatment of the resin (e.g., sulfonation). Ion exchange resins are fundamentally of two types: (a) those having **basic groups capable of exchanging anions,** and (b) those having **acidic groups capable of exchanging cations.** The types of reactions are shown below, with the exchangeable ion boxed:

$$(a) \sim\!\!N + HCl \longrightarrow \sim\!\!NH^+ \boxed{{}^-Cl}$$

$$(b) \sim\!\!CH_2-SO_3Na \longrightarrow \sim\!\!CH_2-SO_3^- \boxed{Na^+}$$

In the first type, various basic nitrogen-containing compounds can be used as coreactants. Among these are dimethylamine, guanidine, 2-aminopyridine, diethanolamine, and tetraethylenepentamine. To introduce anionic groups, sodium bisulfite, *p*-hydroxybenzene sulfonic acid, glycine, taurine, and others have been used.

The crosslinked resins from copolymerization of styrene with divinylbenzene can be sulfonated (38a) or chloromethylated and aminated to give important ion exchange resins having sulfonic acid or amine (primarily tertiary) groups as exchange sites for cations and anions, respectively.

V. Epoxy Resins

Epoxy resins (6,39–41) are most commonly **prepared by the base-induced condensation of a polyhydroxy compound,** usually a bisphenol, **with,** in most cases, **epichlorohydrin** to give as an intermediate a low molecular weight, essentially linear polymer, having terminal epoxide groups and pendant hydroxyls. An excess of epichlorohydrin in the reaction accounts for the termination of chains with epoxy groups. The following reactions are believed to occur in the one-step operation leading to the fusible prepolymer:

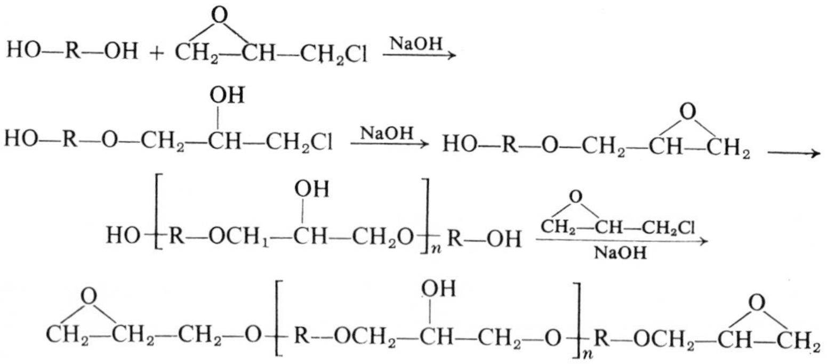

$$HO-R-OH + \overset{O}{\overset{\frown}{CH_2-CH}}-CH_2Cl \xrightarrow{NaOH}$$

$$HO-R-O-CH_2-\underset{\underset{OH}{|}}{CH}-CH_2Cl \xrightarrow{NaOH} HO-R-O-CH_2-\overset{O}{\overset{\frown}{CH-CH_2}} \longrightarrow$$

$$HO\left[R-OCH_1-\underset{\underset{OH}{|}}{CH}-CH_2O\right]_n R-OH \xrightarrow[NaOH]{\overset{O}{\overset{\frown}{CH_2-CH-CH_2Cl}}}$$

$$\overset{O}{\overset{\frown}{CH_2-CH_2}}-CH_2-O\left[R-OCH_2-\underset{\underset{OH}{|}}{CH}-CH_2-O\right]_n R-OCH_2-\overset{O}{\overset{\frown}{CH-CH_2}}$$

I

The value of n in the polyether formula above can vary from 0 to 20, and the intermediate resin (I) can range from a liquid to a high melting (150°C.) solid, accordingly. The final crosslinking, to give an infusible, insoluble, hard product, can be carried out in a variety of ways, which usually involve either ring-opening of the terminal epoxides and/or esterification of the chain hydroxyls. Among the more widely used cross-linking, or curing, agents are amines and dicarboxylic acids or their anhydrides (42). The reactions are presumed to be of the addition type in the case of the primary amines.

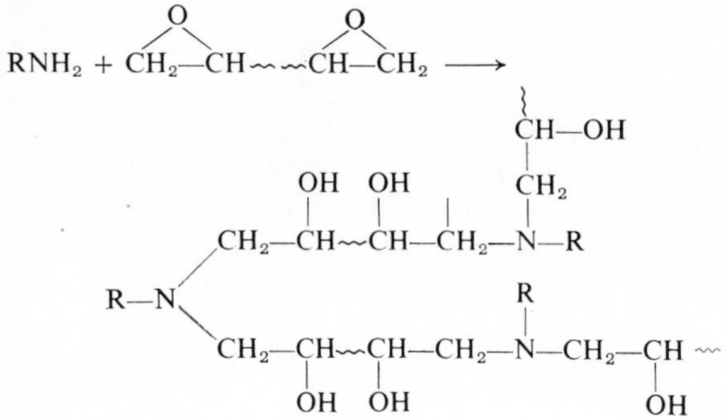

$$[\text{where } R = -C_6H_4C(CH_3)_2C_6H_{4-}]$$

The tertiary amines are believed to operate by a catalytic ring-opening polymerization mechanism involving epoxy groups rather than a simple addition reaction, which is unavailable to the R_3N compounds. Secondary amines function in the same way after an initial single step addition reaction.

Tertiary amines are more generally used in conjunction with anhydrides, wherein they catalyze reactions of the latter with the epoxide function.

Anhydrides of dibasic acids react first with a chain —OH. The free carboxyl can then esterify an —OH of another chain (path A) or open a terminal epoxide (path B):

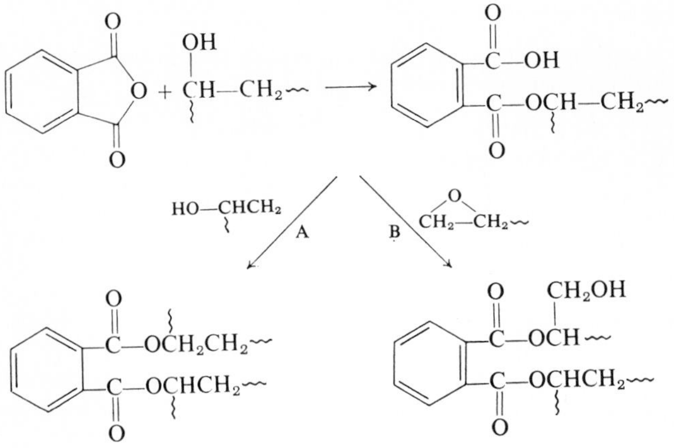

The epoxy resins are very stable to heat and have little tendency to crosslink before a curing agent has been added. After compounding with a suitable curing agent, the epoxy resin is then used in its soluble, fusible state for a variety of applications (adhesives, surface coatings, potting of electrical assemblies, laminates, foams, etc.). Curing to the final hard resin is effected either by the application of heat or, more slowly, at ambient temperatures.

A number of other curable di- and higher epoxides have been made available commercially, and are useful in many cases as the sole epoxy component of a formulation or can be used in conjunction with epoxies based on bisphenol A. Examples are vinyl cyclohexanedioxide, dicyclo-pentadienedioxide, and the diepoxy ester

R = CH_3 or H

The latter is evidently obtained by epoxidation of the Tischenko condensate of the cyclic aldehyde from reaction of acrolein with isoprene or butadiene. All of these epoxides (41a) have specific advantages either in final product properties (e.g., higher heat deflection temperatures) or in handling characteristics (e.g., low viscosity in the case of diepoxy ester). Sometimes monoepoxides such as butyl glycidyl ether have found use as a reactive diluent to lower the viscosity of bisphenol A epoxides; a decrease of some properties generally occurs, however (42a). Relatively low molecular weight emulsion polybutadienes, (e.g., 2,000–6,000), have been epoxidized with peracetic acid to give poly-epoxides with residual unsaturation plus hydroxyl and acetoxy groups; flexible resins can be obtained by proper curing.

431. Preparation of Epoxy Resins from 2,2-Bis(4-hydroxyphenyl)-Propane (Bisphenol A) and Epichlorohydrin (43,44)

Resins of the formula I can be prepared in a variety of average molecular weights. The following examples are typical of the conditions used and products obtained. The latter are designated below by the arbitrary assignment of letters to permit ease of later reference.

Resin A: Molecular Weight 370. In a 2 l. resin kettle equipped with stirrer, thermometer, condenser, and dropping funnel is placed a mixture of 228 g. (1 mole) of bisphenol A, 925 g. (10 moles) epichlorohydrin, and 5 ml. of water. A total of 82 g. (2.05 moles) solid sodium hydroxide is added in portions. First, 13 g. of the base is added and the mixture is heated with stirring. The heating is stopped when the temperature reaches 80°C., and the Glass-Col heating mantle replaced by an ice water bath so that the temperature does not exceed 100°C. When the reaction temperature falls to 95°C., another 13 g. of sodium hydroxide is added. Temperature control is exercised as above. The remainder of the sodium hydroxide is added in 13–14 g. increments. After the final addition of base, no cooling is applied. When the exothermic reaction subsides, the excess epichlorohydrin is distilled at a pressure of about 50 mm. with a pot temperature not exceeding 150°C. The residue is then cooled to about 70°C. and 50 ml. benzene is added to precipitate the salt present. The salt is removed by vacuum filtration and washed with benzene (50 ml.). The benzene solutions are combined and the benzene distilled. When the pot temperature reaches 125°C. a vacuum of about 25 mm. is applied and the distillation continued until a pot temperature of 170°C. is reached. The resulting clear, highly viscous liquid epoxy resin has an average molecular weight of about 370, as determined ebullioscopically in ethylene dichloride. It has a softening point of about 9°C. by the Durrans' mercury method (see Chapter 2).

The epoxide content is determined by heating 1 g. of resin at reflux for 20 min. with 25 ml. of a standardized solution prepared from 16 ml. concentrated hydrochloric acid diluted with pyridine to 1 l. After cooling, the excess hydrochloric acid is back-titrated with $0.1N$ sodium hydroxide in methanol to a phenolphthalein endpoint. One HCl is considered equivalent to one epoxide group. For the resin prepared above, the epoxy content per 100 g. is about 0.5, which corresponds to 1.85 epoxy groups per molecule for a molecular weight of 370. The epoxide equivalent weight (the grams of resin containing 1 g. mole of epoxide) is, therefore, 200. In general:

Epoxy Content = number of epoxy groups per 100 g. of resin

Epoxy Equivalent Weight = grams resin per epoxy group = 100/epoxy content

Thus, Resin A corresponds closely to the epoxy resin product (I) in the preparative equation, where $n = 0$, which has a calculated molecular weight of 340, an epoxy functionality of 2.0, and an epoxide equivalent weight of 170. In resin derived from diols, there shall be between 1 and 2 epoxides per molecule, if the experiment is run correctly.

Resin B: Molecular Weight 900. In a 1 l. resin kettle equipped as in procedure for Resin A, with added provision for a siphon, are placed 228 g. (1 mole) bisphenol A and 75 g. (1.88 moles) sodium hydroxide as a 10% aqueous solution, and the mixture heated to 45°C. Then, 145 g. (1.57 moles) epichlorohydrin is added rapidly with stirring. The mixture is then heated to a temperature of about 95°C. where it is maintained for 80 min. The mixture separates into two phases. The aqueous layer can be siphoned from the taffy-like product. The latter is washed with hot water with stirring while molten until the wash water is neutral to litmus. The resin is then removed while hot and is dried by heating in an air oven at 130°C. The solid product has a softening point (Durrans' mercury method) of about 69°C., and molecular weight (ebullioscopic in ethylene dichloride) of about 900. The epoxy content per 100 g. is about 0.2, hence an epoxy functionality of 1.8 groups per molecule. The epoxide equivalent weight is, therefore, 500. The resin corresponds approximately to formula I, where $n = 2$; the calculated molecular weight is 908.

Resin C: Molecular Weight 1400. The procedure for Resin B is followed except that 54.8 g. (1.37 moles) of sodium hydroxide (10% solution) and 113 g. (1.22 moles) epichlorohydrin are used. The product is a brittle solid with a softening point (Durrans' mercury method) of about 98°C., and an ebullioscopic (ethylene dichloride) molecular weight of about 1400. The epoxy content per 100 g. is about 0.1. Thus, there are 1.44 epoxide groups per molecule and the epoxide equivalent weight is 970. The resin corresponds approximately to I with $n = 3.7$.

Resin D: Molecular Weight 2900. One hundred g. of Resin C (0.071 mole, containing 0.103 mole epoxy groups) in 250 ml. beaker is heated with stirring to 150°C. by means of an oil bath. Then 5 g. (0.022 mole) bisphenol A is added and the mixture heated to 200°C. over a 2 hr. period. The resulting resin has a softening point of about 130°C. (Durrans' mercury method) and a molecular weight (as in the preceding examples) of about 2900. There are approximately 0.05 epoxy groups per 100 g., hence, 1.45 epoxy groups per molecule, and epoxide equivalent weight of 2000. The resin is approximately represented by I where $n = 9$.

432. The Curing of Epoxy Resins

The method of choice in curing an epoxy resin is determined by a combination of factors. The end use of the resin, whether as a casting or potting material, a surface coating, an adhesive, etc., fixes certain limitations on cure temperature and time. The effect of curing agents on color, or stability to heat, light or moisture of the final form of the product is critical also. Moreover, the strength, heat deflection temperature and hardness of the end product often depends on the type of curing agent and the quantity used. The following examples demonstrate only a few of the **types of curing agents** that have been used for the epoxies and only some of the variations of technique in using them. Resins used in the following examples are those prepared above.

A. With a Tertiary Amine (45,46). A surface coating can be made from a solution of 10 g. Resin C and 1 g. of benzyldimethylamine in 5 ml. each of xylene and methyl cellosolve acetate. The solution is flowed onto a glass plate. The solvent is evaporated in air and the plate heated at 100°C. for $\frac{1}{2}$ hr. A hard film coating results.

B. With a Secondary Amine (43). To 142 g. of diethylamine in a 1 l. resin kettle equipped with stirrer, condenser, and thermometer is added 125 g. of Resin A in 125 g. of dioxane, with stirring. A slightly exothermic reaction occurs. The mixture is then heated to reflux (55–60°C.) for 3 hr. The resulting mixture is poured into 750 ml. water in a 2 l. beaker and the sticky product washed repeatedly with water by stirring and decantation to remove excess amine and dioxane. The resin is then dissolved in 500 ml. diethyl ether, and the solution extracted with 500 ml. portions of water until the washings are neutral to litmus. The etheral solution is dried over Drierite and the ether removed by distillation on the steam bath. The product (about 92 g.) is a very viscous liquid at room temperature, but fluid at 60°C.

The resin is still soluble in methyl ethyl ketone and chloroform. The large amount of diethylamine used provides for a one-to-one reaction of amine with epoxy groups, and no crosslinking is, therefore, possible. If, however, 50 g. of Resin A is mixed with 2.5 g. of diethylamine and kept at room temperature for 60 hr. followed by 65°C. for 24 hr., a solid, insoluble product is obtained. In this case, each amine group, present in low quantity, effects the catalytic polymerization of several epoxides, with crosslinking as the result. If now 50 g. of Resin A is mixed with 7.5 g. of the soluble resin prepared above from Resin A and excess of diethylamine, the mixture will cure to a hard, clear solid in 1–2 hr. at 60°C. The combined amine groups in the amine-modified Resin A serve to crosslink the mixture through the epoxides of the added Resin A.

C. With an Acid (47). A solution is prepared in a 50 ml. Erlenmeyer flask by dissolving 10 g. of Resin C in 12 ml. of ethyl ketone, to which is then added 1 g. oxalic acid dihydrate. The mixture is gently warmed on the steam bath to assist in dissolving the acid. The solution is cast on a glass plate with aid of a doctor knife and the solvent allowed to evaporate at room temperature. The glass plate is then heated in an oven at 150°C. for 30 min. to an hour to give a cured coating of considerable hardness.

D. With an Anhydride (48,49). Fifty g. of Resin B is placed in a 200 ml. tall-form beaker in an oil bath. The resin is heated to 120°C. Fifteen g. of molten phthalic anhydride is added and stirred into the resin. Part of the phthalic anhydride will precipitate if the resin is cooled at this point to 60°C. or below, but reheating will dissolve it. The beaker is covered with a glass plate and the resin–phthalic anhydride mixture is held at 120°C. for 1 hr., at which point it is still soluble in acetone and chloroform. Heating at 170–180°C. will effect the final cure and produce a clear, hard, insoluble resin in one to two hours.

If 0.5 g. N,N'-dimethylaniline is added to the reaction immediately after or along with the phthalic anhydride, the resin will cure in about 1 hr. at 120°C. Tertiary amines function as accelerators for anhydride curing of epoxy resins.

The condensation of bisphenol A with epichlorohydrin can be carried out with equimolar amounts of each reactant to give a thermoplastic solid polymer of sufficient molecular weight to have good mechanical properties and thus practical utility in its linear state. The chemical repeat unit of the polymer has a secondary hydroxyl, and the polymer can be modified chemically through reaction at that point (e.g., acetylation) and thus modified in its physical properties (50).

433. Preparation of a Poly(hydroxy ether) from Bisphenol A and Epichlorohydrin (51)

To a 2 l. three-necked flask equipped with a stirrer, thermometer, and condenser is added 228.3 g. (1.0 mole) 2,2-bis(p-hydroxyphenyl)propane (recrystallized from toluene), 92.5 g. (1.0 mole) epichlorohydrin (distilled, heart cut), 256 g. ethanol, 40.0 g. (1.0 mole) sodium hydroxide, and 160 ml. water. The caustic should be added first as a standard solution containing 1 mole of base. The bisphenol A is added second and the alcohol and epichlorohydrin in that order after solution of the bisphenol. The mixture is stirred at room temperature for 6 hr., when 6.0 g. (0.15 mole) sodium hydroxide in 24 ml. water added. The mixture is then heated to reflux, which should occur at a pot temperature of around 80°C. Chlorobenzene (distilled) is added in portions: 60 ml. after 30 min. of reflux, 30 ml. after 45 min., and another 30 ml. after a total of 60 min. at reflux. Refluxing is continued for 4 hr., when 9.4 g. (0.1 mole) of phenol in 60 ml. chlorobenzene is added. Reflux is continued for 2 hr. The mixture is cooled and the aqueous phase is separated by decantation and the chlorobenzene–polyether phase is washed 3 times with 400 ml. portions of water. Then, 400 ml. chloroform is added to dilute the chlorobenzene–polyether and this solution is acidified by adding with stirring a solution of 20 ml. of 87% phosphoric acid in 100 ml. water. The organic phase is then washed 8 times with 400 ml. portions of water. The polymer solution is precipitated by pouring it into 2 l. of isopropanol with stirring. The precipitated polyhydroxyether is filtered, washed well with isopropanol, and dried in vacuum at 65° for 24 hr. or more. The inherent viscosity is about 0.6 (0.2 g./100 ml. in tetrahydrofuran at 25°C.). The polymer is amorphous and is soluble in chlorinated solvents. Tough films can be cast from methylene chloride, or melt-pressed above 160°C. The polymer is amorphous and has a glass temperature of about 100°C.

The crosslinking reaction of diepoxides with polycarboxylic acids can be utilized to make surface coatings valuable as enamels for appliances, among other things. A typical vinyl copolymer is made in solution wherein one of the comonomers is acrylic acid. Bisphenol A diglycidyl ether is added to the copolymer solution followed by application of the solution to a surface and a heat curing step. The result is a crosslinked coating whose properties (e.g., metal adhesion, hardness, and heat, grease, and detergent resistance) reflect the original vinyl copolymer constituency and the epoxy crosslinking agent. Such a resin is derived, therefore, from vinyl and epoxy technology.

434. Preparation of Poly(styrene-co-methyl acrylate-co-acrylic acid) (72/20/8 wt. %), Crosslinked by Reaction with Bisphenol A Diglycidyl Ether (52)

A 500 ml. three-necked flask is equipped with condenser, dropping funnel with pressure equalizing sidearm, nitrogen inlet, and stirrer. It is flushed with

$$CH_2=CHPh + CH_2=CHCO_2CH_3 + CH_2=CHCO_2H \longrightarrow$$

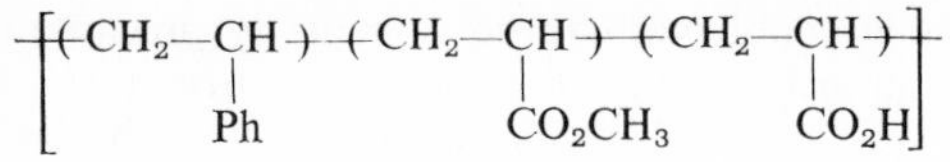

$$\left[(CH_2-CH)-(CH_2-CH)-(CH_2-CH) \atop \underset{Ph}{|} \quad \underset{CO_2CH_3}{|} \quad \underset{CO_2H}{|} \right]$$

I

$$I + \left(\underset{CH_2-CH-CH-CH_2-O-}{\overset{O}{\triangle}} \hspace{-0.5em} \left\langle \rule{0pt}{1.2em} \right\rangle \right)_2 CH(CH_3)_2 \longrightarrow$$

$$\left[(CH_2-CH)-(CH_2-CH)-(CH_2-CH) \atop \underset{Ph}{|} \quad \underset{CO_2CH_3}{|} \quad \underset{C=O}{|} \right]$$

$$\begin{array}{c} | \\ O \\ | \\ CH-CH_2OH \\ | \\ CH_2 \\ | \\ O \\ | \\ Ph \\ | \\ CH_3-C-CH_3 \\ | \\ Ph \\ | \\ O \\ | \\ CH_2 \\ | \\ CH-CH_2OH \\ | \\ O \\ | \\ C=O \\ | \end{array}$$

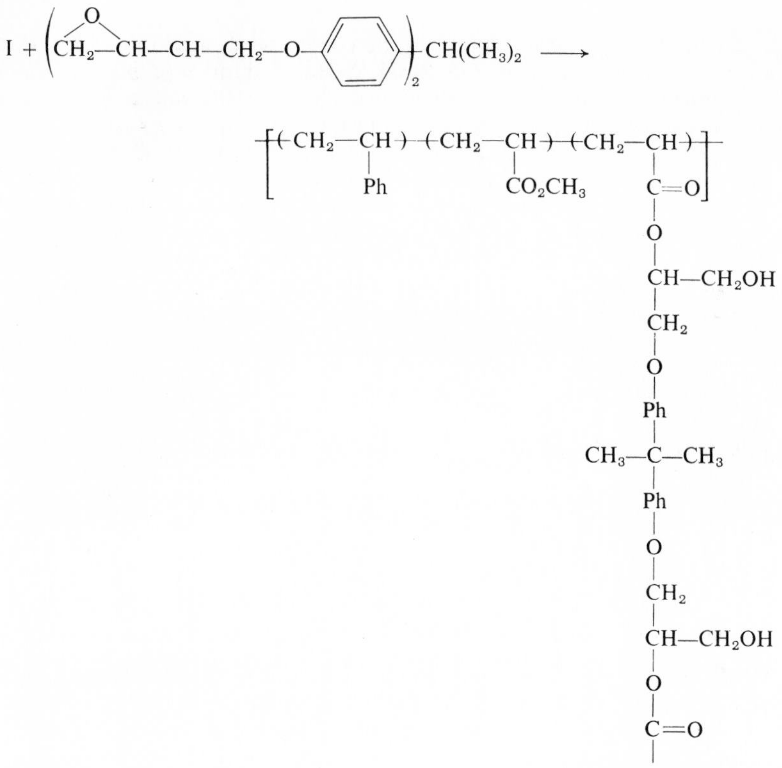

nitrogen and 250 ml. distilled xylene is added. Four separate monomer–initiator batches are prepared; each one contains 18 g. styrene, 5 g. methyl acrylate, 0.5 g. azoisobutyronitrile, and amounts of acrylic acid in successive batches of 1.28 g., 1.76 g., 2.24 g., and 2.72 g., respectively. The xylene is brought to reflux under a light stream of nitrogen so that essentially no volatiles escape the condenser, and the 4 monomer–initiator batches are added in succession at a constant rate over a period of 20 min. each. The objective attained by this technique is to provide a homogeneous distribution of acrylic acid in the copolymer; it is essential for satisfactory curing that each copolymer molecule have as nearly as possible the same average number of carboxyl groups.

When addition of the last batch of monomers is completed, refluxing is continued for another hour; the solution is then allowed to cool. A portion of the copolymer can be isolated by precipitation into methanol followed by reprecipitation and methanol washing and drying in the usual way. The weight average molecular weight can be fairly well estimated from the intrinsic viscosity in methyl ethyl ketone by the following relationship, determined for the copolymer esterified by reaction with diazomethane:

$$[\eta] = 1.59 \times 10^{-3} M_w^{0.42}$$

To the cooled xylene solution of the copolymer is stirred in 18.7 g. of a bisphenol A diglycidyl ether (see Resin A, described earlier in this Section, or a commercial product). This should give approximately equimolar amounts of carboxyl and epoxy, though not all of the former needs to, or appears to, react with an epoxy group to give good final film properties. As a catalyst to the crosslinking reaction, 0.75 g. of benzyldimethylamine or triethylenediamine is added. The solution can be cast onto metal plates, the xylene evaporated in a forced air oven at 100°C., and the film cured for about 30 min. at 150°C. to give a hard, chemical and heat resistant coating. If desired, the polymer solution can be pigmented by dispersing TiO_2 or other materials in it.

REFERENCES

1. R. E. Burk, H. E. Thompson, A. J. Weith, and I. Williams, *Polymerization*, Reinhold, New York, 1937.
1a. J. R. Lawrence, *Polyester Resins*, Reinhold, New York, 1960; W. Funke, *Advan. Polymer Sci.*, **4**, 157 (1965).
2. C. Ellis, *The Chemistry of Synthetic Resins*, Reinhold, New York, 1935.
3. R. Houwink, Ed., *Elastomers and Plastomers*, Elsevier, New York, 1949.
4. R. S. Morrell and H. M. Langton, Eds., *Synthetic Resins and Allied Plastics*, 3rd ed., Oxford University Press, London, 1951.
5. E. Ott, H. M. Spurlin, and M. W. Grafflin, *Cellulose and Cellulose Derivatives*, 2nd ed., Interscience, New York, 1954.
6. C. E. Schildknecht, Ed., *Polymer Processes*, Interscience, New York, 1956.
7. W. Schlack, Ed., *A Manual of Plastics and Resins*, Chemical Publishing, Brooklyn, 1950.
8. H. R. Simonds, A. J. Weith, and M. H. Bigelow, *Handbook of Plastics*, D. Van Nostrand, New York, 1949.
9. H. R. Simonds, *Source Book of the New Plastics*, Reinhold, New York, **1**, 1959; **2**, 1961.
10. Bjorksten Research Laboratories, Inc., *Polyesters and Their Applications*, Reinhold, New York, 1956.
11. E. F. Carlston, G. B. Johnson, F. G. Lum, D. G. Huggins, and K. T. Park, *Ind. Eng. Chem.*, **51**, 253 (1959).
12. C. Ellis, U.S. Pat. 2,195,362 (March 26, 1940).
13. G. S. Weith, U.S. Pat. 2,475,731 (July 12, 1949).
14. *Composition and Utilization of Polyesters*, National Aniline Division, Allied Chemical and Dye Corporation, 1954.
14a. T. C. Patton, *Alkyd Resin Technology*, Interscience, New York, 1962.
15. R. H. Kienle, P. A. Van Der Meulen, and F. E. Petke, *J. Am. Chem. Soc.*, **61**, 2258 (1939).

16. E. S. Dawson, U.S. Pat. 1,888,849 (November 22, 1932).
17. British Pat. 359,365 (October 22, 1931); British Pat. 316,914 (August 6, 1929).
17a. H. Raech, Jr., *Allylic Resins and Monomers*, Reinhold, New York, 1965.
18. W. Simpson and T. Holt, *J. Polymer Sci.*, **18**, 335 (1955).
19. C. A. Heiberger, U.S. Pat. 3,096,310 (to FMC Corp.) (July 2, 1963).
20. W. R. Dial, W. E. Bessinger, B. J. DeWitt, and F. Strain, *Ind. Eng. Chem.*, **47**, 2447 (1955).
21. T. S. Carswell, *Phenoplasts: Their Structure, Properties, and Chemical Technology*, Interscience, New York, 1947.
22. Office of Tech. Serv., U.S. Dept. of Commerce, Washington, D.C. (P.B. Report 25,642) (1945).
23. D. F. Gould, *Phenolic Resins*, Reinhold, New York, 1959.
24. R. W. Martin, *The Chemistry of Phenolic Resins*, Wiley, New York, 1956.
25. N. J. L. Megson, *Phenolic Resin Chemistry*, Academic Press, New York, 1958.
26. O. Pantke, U.S. Pat. 1,909,786 (May 16, 1933).
27. W. J. Burke and S. H. Ruetman, *J. Polymer Sci.*, **32**, 221 (1958).
28. W. J. Burke, S. H. Ruetman, and H. P. Higginbottom, *Linear Phenol-Formaldehyde Polymers*, ASTIA Report AD 202, 138 (August, 1958); *J. Polymer Sci.*, **38**, 513 (1959).
29. J. F. Blais, *Amino Resins*, Reinhold, New York, 1959.
30. C. S. Marvel, J. R. Elliott, F. E. Boettner, and H. Yuska, *J. Am. Chem. Soc.*, **68**, 1681 (1946).
31. J. I. de Jong and J. de Jonge, *Rec. trav. chim.*, **72**, 1027 (1953).
32. W. G. Simons, U.S. Pat. 2,518,388 (August 8, 1950).
33. T. S. Hodgins and A. G. Hovey, U.S. Pat. 2,226,518 (December 24, 1940).
34. G. Widmer and W. Fisch, U.S. Pat. 2,328,592 (September 7, 1943).
35. R. Kunin, *Ion Exchange Resins*, 2nd ed., Wiley, New York, 1958.
36. H. M. Day, U.S. Pat. 2,477,328 (July 26, 1949).
37. H. Wasseneger and K. Jaeger, U.S. Pat. 2,204,539 (June 11, 1940).
38. R. C. Swain, U.S. Pat. 2,285,750 (June 9, 1942).
38a. W. C. Bauman, J. R. Skidmore, and R. H. Camum, *Ind. Eng. Chem.*, **40**, 1350 (1948); F. Helfferich, *Advan. Polymer Sci.*, **1**, 329 (1959).
39. Technical Bulletins on epoxy resins, Shell Chemical Corp.
40. H. Lee and K. Neville, *Epoxy Resins: Their Applications and Technology*, McGraw-Hill, New York, 1957.
41. *Reports on the Progress of Applied Chemistry*, Vol. XLII, Society of Chemical Industry, London, 1957, p. 462.
41a. *Chem. Week*, **March 21**, 1964, p. 39.
42. S. H. Christie, III, *Modern Plastics*, **42** (12) 134 (1965); Y. Tanaka and H. Kakiuchi, *J. Polymer Sci.*, A, **2**, 3405 (1964); *J. Appl. Polymer Sci*, **7**, 1063 (1963).
42a. F. E. Pschorr and E. N. Dorman, *Preprints Fifteenth Conf. Soc. Plast. Eng.*, V, Paper 78, 1–9 (1959).
43. E. C. Shokal, H. A. Newey, and T. F. Bradley, U.S. Pat. 2,643,329 (June 23, 1953).
44. Q. T. Wiles and D. W. Elam, U.S. Pat. 2,681,901 (June 22, 1954).
45. H. A. Newey and E. C. Shokal, U.S. Pat. 2,553,718 (May 22, 1951).
46. E. C. Shokal and A. C. Mueller, U.S. Pat. 2,548,447 (April 10, 1951).
47. T. F. Bradley, U.S. Pat. 2,500,449 (March 14, 1950).
48. P. Castan, U.S. Pat. 2,324,483 (July 20, 1943).

49. E. C. Dearborn, R. M. Fuoss, A. K. MacKenzie, and R. G. Shepherd, *Ind. Eng. Chem.*, **45**, 2715 (1953).
50. N. H. Reinking, A. E. Barnabeo, and W. F. Hale, *J. Appl. Polymer Sci.*, **7**, 2135 (1963), ff.
51. J. Wynstra, N. H. Reinking, and A. E. Barnabeo, French Pat. 1,309,401 (to Union Carbide) (October 8, 1962).
52. J. D. Murdock and G. H. Segall, *Offic. Dig. Federation Soc. Paint Technol.*, **33**, 709 (1961).

Author Index

Numbers in parentheses are reference numbers and indicate that the author's work is referred to although his name is not mentioned in the text. Numbers in *italics* show the pages on which the complete references are listed.

A

Abe, Y., 230(74), *334*
Abramo, S. V., 170(132), *201*
Adams, H. E., 319(278), *340*
Addor, R. W., 261, *336*, *337*
Aelion, R., 80(12), 81(12), 105(11), *199*
Akutsu, S., 272(190), *337*
Alcolac Chemical Corp., 238(95), *335*
Alderman, V. U., 253(135), *336*
Alderson, T., 359(35), 360(35), *396*
Aldrich, P. H., 183(144), *202*
Alexander, P., 90(28), 123(28), 126(28), *199*
Allcock, H. R., 391(101), 392, *398*
Allegra, G., 291(233), 326(296,298), *339*
–341
Allen, C. F. H., 436(87), *444*
Allen, P. W., 43(19), 44(19), 50(19), *65*,
213(42), *333*
Allen, S. J., 82(14), 83(14), 85(17), 86
(23), *199*
Allied Chemical and Dye Corp., 447
(14), 448(14), *470*
Amberg, J. O., 373(72), *397*
American Cyanamid Co., 248(118), *336*
American Society Testing Materials, 45
(45), 50(45), 60(78,81,83), *66*, *67*
Amerongen, G. J. van, 310(266), 320
(266), *340*
Amos, J. L., 221(52), *334*
Anderson, A. W., 287(223,224), 289
(223–225), 290(223–225), *338*, 427(62,
63), *443*
Anderson, H. V., 253(134), *336*
Anderson, J. K., 135(89), 136(89), *200*
Ang, F., 297(243), *339*
Angelo, R. J., 208(27), *333*, 399(1), *442*

Arbuzov, A. Y., 364(46), *396*
Ardis, A. E., 286(220,221), 308(220),
338
Arndt, F., 438(91), *444*
Arnold, F. E., 173, 174(136), 175(136),
202
Arnold, H. R., 132(85), *200*
Arnold, H. W., 264(163), *337*
Arnon, U., 352–354(32), *396*
Asahina, M., 230(73), *334*
Astbury, W. T., 352(25), *395*
Aufdermarsh, C. A., Jr., 324(290), *340*
Auspos, L. A., 420(54–55), *443*
Averill, S. T., 286(221), *338*

B

Badische Anilin und Soda Fabrik, 224
(56), *334*
Baggett, J. M., 369(58–61), 370(58–61),
396, *397*
Bailey, D. L., 253(138), *336*
Bailey, F. E., Jr., 368(53,54), *396*
Bailey, J. T., 213(45), *334*
Bailey, W. J., 45(30), *65*, 307(258), *339*,
435(81,82), *444*
Baker, W. P., Jr., 328(303), 329(303,
305), *341*
Baldwin, D. E., 253(137), *336*
Baldwin, R. L., 43(24), *65*
Ballantine, D. S., 404(15), *442*
Ballman, R. L., 61(84), *67*
Bamford, C. H., 204(1), 216(1), 303(1),
332, 352(31), 353(31), 357, *396*
Barb, W. G., 204(1), 212(35), 216(1),
303(1), *332*, *333*
Barbagallo, A., 19(10), *65*
Barclay, R., Jr., 128(75), 129(78), *200*

473

Subject Index*

A

ABS resins, 221
Acenaphthylene, 267
Acetone, copolymer with dimethyl-
    ketene, 432
Acetophenone, 439
N-Acetylcaprolactam, 344
Acetylene polymers, 304
Acetylenes, addition to, 186
N-Acetyl pyrrolidone, 347
Acid chloride, polymeric, 246
Acid number, determination, 155
Acidolysis, polyesters from, 148, 150
Acrolein, 250
Acrylamide, 102, 248
Acrylate esters, glass temperature of
    polymers, 248
    polymerization, 248
Acrylic acid, 469
N-Acyllactams, 344, 347
Acrylonitrile, anionic polymerization,
    283
  emulsion polymerization, 236
  polymerization of, in emulsion, 236
    in slurry, 235
  reaction with poly(vinyl alcohol), 243
Acryloyl chloride, crosslinking by, 256
  polymers of, 246
Addition polymers, 203
Adhesive, from phenol–formaldehyde
    condensation, 458
Adipic acid, 74, 90, 154, 448
Adipic acid dihydrazide, 121
Adipoyl chloride, 138
β-Alanine, 103
Alcoholysis process, in alkyd techno-
    logy, 451
Aldehyde–hydrazide condensation,
    polymers from, 121
"Alfin" catalyst, 305

Alkali metals, reaction with aluminum
    alkyls, 345
Alkyd resins, 448
Alkylene polysulfides, 185
Allene, 328
Allyl bromide, 296
Allyl chloride, 296, 350
Allyl resins, 452
Allylsodium–sodium isopropoxide
    catalyst, preparation of, 305
Alternating copolymers, 209
Aluminum alkyls, effect of type on
    stereoregulation, 291
Aluminum bromide, 433
Aluminum chloride, 273, 322, 364
Aluminum sulfate octadecahydrate, 271
Aluminum triethyl, 290, 298, 311, 312,
    321, 328, 345, 383, 410, 433, 434
Aluminum triisobutyl, 290, 291, 309,
    319, 320, 329, 331
Amide interchange reactions, 89
Amines, tetrafunctional, 103, 174, 176,
    177
Aminoacid, polymerization of, 80, 82
α-Amino acids, 352
α-Aminoisobutyric acid, 355
Aminolysis, of a bisurethane, 110
  of diesters, 83
5-Aminopentylchloroformate, 124
11-Aminoundecanoic, 81
Ammonia, liquid, 275
Ammonium persulfate, 249, 259
n-Amyl methacrylate, 255
Amylsodium, 306
Anhydrosulfites, 359
Aniline, in N-phenyltriazole formation,
    172
Anionic polymerization, 102, 401, 405,
    407, 409, 432, 434
  general, 206, 274

*I am grateful to my daughter, Patty Sorenson, who provided a high level of as-
sistance in work on the index for a low level of pay.